THE AUDUBON ILLUSTRATED
HANDBOOK OF AMERICAN
BIRDS

THE
Audubon
ILLUSTRATED HANDBOOK OF
American
BIRDS

EDGAR M. REILLY, Jr.

OLIN SEWALL PETTINGILL, Jr.
Editor in Chief

Drawings by ALBERT EARL GILBERT

SPONSORED BY THE NATIONAL AUDUBON SOCIETY

McGRAW-HILL BOOK COMPANY

NEW YORK · TORONTO · LONDON · SYDNEY · JOHANNESBURG

*To all conservationists and
community planners, who work
unremittingly to preserve
natural areas for all wildlife
as well as for humanity.*

TABLE OF CONTENTS

COLOR PLATES

FOREWORD

The Bureau of Outdoor Recreation tells us that 8,196,000 people in the United States are already watching birds, and I have no doubt that the number is growing steadily. Why not the same surge of interest in other wild creatures? The answer is simple: birds have the winning combination of qualities.

Birds are numerous and various, readily available and observable. They are pleasing in color and form, graceful in movements, inoffensive in habits, and incapable of inflicting serious physical harm. They are ever alert with sensory responses similar to man's and therefore understandable. In their feats of locomotion, navigation, migration, and survival in every earthly environment, they excite one's thinking and stir one's search for knowledge.

To meet the rising demand for more information about birds, books by the score have appeared on the market in the past few years. Some help to identify different species and indicate where they may be found; others provide instructions on how to attract birds around the home and garden; and still others deal with the migration of birds, the general biology of birds, special groups of birds, and even particular species. Yet, despite the dire need, no book like this one has ever been published.

Here, at long last, is the first single volume to cover comprehensively all the birds regularly occurring in the conterminous United States, Hawaii, Alaska, and Canada and to give, in addition, appropriate attention to all the known stragglers and the most recently introduced species. Nearly 875 species are included.

Although this handsome volume is titled *The Audubon Illustrated Handbook of American Birds,* I like to think of it as more than a handbook. It is a compendium of information. Between these two covers Dr. Reilly, after the most prodigious research, has brought together in concise form, for quick reference, those essential facts about different birds that all of us want to know, whether our interest in birds happens to be casual, recreational, or professional. What does each species look like? How does it sound? Where does it live? When can it be seen? What are the highlights of its nesting biology? What does it eat? Where can we read still more about it? The answers are here. To find them, all one need do is refer to the species in the index and turn to the appropriate page.

I must give a few words of caution, lest one consulting this book expect something it does not offer. It is not intended as a guide to identification, although it will help substantially in settling questions about the physical appearance and vocal attributes of different species. Nor does it reveal everything about every species, for the simple reason that everything is not known. Dr. Reilly has taken great care to point up, rather than cover up, the various gaps in our knowledge, thereby providing all of us with an incentive to help fill them. Ornithology is still a fact-finding science, and ornithologists welcome new colleagues with the interest and inclination to seek more information.

The years ahead will see the publication of many more books enlightening us on various aspects of bird life. Meanwhile *The Audubon Illustrated Handbook of American Birds* will remain our most useful reference. It is the book to which we shall turn when we want some item of information about a species or a group of species, stated precisely, with brevity, and, above all, with authority.

OLIN SEWALL PETTINGILL, JR.
Director, Laboratory of Ornithology
Cornell University

INTRODUCTION

The Audubon Illustrated Handbook of American Birds provides a species-by-species account of every American bird commonly found north of Mexico, in addition to Hawaiian species, stragglers, and birds only recently introduced to the region. In all, nearly 875 species are described. Although the photographs and drawings will be of some use for identification purposes, the book is intended not as a field guide but rather as a useful desk reference for the amateur or professional bird student, the volume to turn to after consulting the regional field guides and before studying highly specialized sources for extremely detailed information.

Organized according to families of birds, the handbook follows the sequence established by the fifth edition of the *Check-list of North American Birds,* published in 1957 by the American Ornithologists' Union at Baltimore, Maryland. The *Check-list,* with subsequent corrections and additions appearing in professional journals, also serves as the authority for nearly all the scientific names and the majority of the common names used, and significant variations have been noted in the discussions of the families or species concerned.

Although the *Check-list* includes only one "official" common name for each species, the different vernacular names used by popular field guides are noted parenthetically in this handbook. No attempt has been made to list the many common names used in various areas of the country, for such a listing would be endless. Some widespread species have more than fifty common names, many of them very strange; in parts of Appalachia, for example, the Whip-poor-will is called a "salamander." Common names, moreover, frequently are confusing. The Common Teal of Eurasia, for instance, is rare in America, where the most common species is the Green-winged Teal, and both species have the same amount of green on their wings; the best solution is to call the Eurasian species the Eurasian Common Teal. In the case of Hawaiian birds—which are not included in the fifth edition of the *Check-list* but almost certainly will be covered in the sixth edition—common names in this handbook, with few exceptions, are those used by Roger Tory

Peterson in the second edition of *A Field Guide to Western Birds,* published in 1961 by Houghton Mifflin, Boston.

Another source of confusion in the identification of birds is pronounced geographic variation over the breeding ranges of widespread species. Working with museum specimens, ornithologists have shown that most bird species can be separated into lesser groups on the basis of variations in size or color and other minute differences, with the groups usually assigned to geographic areas separated by mountain ranges, deserts, and large bodies of water. These distinctive populations, known as subspecies, have been given separate scientific names by addition of a third word to their binomial names. Thus there are designations such as the Northern Yellowthroat, *Geothlypis trichas brachydactyla;* the Maryland Yellowthroat, *Geothlypis trichas trichas;* the Florida Yellowthroat, *Geothlypis trichas ignota;* and so on. With the fifth edition of the *Check-list,* ornithologists decided that subspecies should no longer be assigned vernacular names, and so all these subspecies are now identified simply as the Yellowthroat rather than Northern or Maryland Yellowthroat.

For the most part, subspecific designations are beyond the scope of this book, especially when you consider that some bird species, such as the Song Sparrow, include more than thirty subspecies. More importantly, very few subspecies are distinctive enough to be separated in the field; it takes museum measurements to identify most of them. Where it is necessary to refer to subspecies in this book, the trinomial, or three-word, scientific name has been used. But generally the trinomial is not used for ordinary sight reports, and subspecies need not concern the nonprofessional.

Within the text most species accounts contain several categories of information, labeled in boldface type: Appearance, Voice, Range and status, Habitat, Seasonal movements, Biology, and Suggested reading. It would be useful to comment on some of the factors that have determined the handling of information within these categories.

Appearance. A single illustration rarely shows more than one aspect of a bird's plumage, and black-and-white photographs, of course, do not show color. Nor is every species in the book illustrated. Thorough, detailed verbal description is therefore an important part of each account, with such description intended to be as clear and useful as possible.

Consider, for example, the size of a bird. From a practical point of view, size is relative. An observer would hardly attempt to estimate the precise lengths of twigs scattered at unknown and varying distances on the ground, but he might be more successful in guessing which ones were longer or shorter than one foot, especially if a foot rule were lying near the twigs. By the same token, it is usually futile to attempt to estimate the precise size in inches of a bird glimpsed in the wild. But if the observer is fairly familiar with the Robin and Crow, he can usually tell whether a strange bird is Robin-sized or Crow-sized. Thus, when the size range of a bird is stated in inches as part of its description, a comment on its size in relation to a common and well-known species is often included as well.

Impressions of color may be just as untrustworthy. Very few people can accurately identify as many as twenty colors without recourse to standard color samples placed immediately adjacent to the unlabeled colors. By contrived adjustments of all the variable factors of lighting, visual distance, and visual acuity, moreover, a single sample of drab brown could be made to appear almost any color of the rainbow.

Plumage color can best be described in terms of a few standard colors commonly found among birds. Descriptions in this book are based primarily on the color standards shown between pages 4 and 5 in volume 1 of the *Handbook of North American Birds,* edited by Ralph S. Palmer (Yale University Press, New Haven, Conn., 1962). It must be remembered that some color variations are due to the texture of the feathers. The finer structure of feather surfaces may result in colors that are glossy, metallic, iridescent, or brighter or softer than the standard colors. For example, almost all the blues in the bird world are determined by feather structure rather than pigment; a dark blue plumage results from structural blue masking some dark pigment in the feathers. Thus an Indigo Bunting looks gray on a cloudy day or on a rainy day, when the structure of its feathers is obscured by water.

Molting, the regular seasonal loss and replacement of feathers, must also be considered in a description of a bird's appearance. Many species have quite different summer and winter plumages, and some birds may wear special plumes or crests for short periods in spring or early summer (though not in all cases only during the courtship period). But since the nomenclature and sequence of molts are presently a subject of debate among professional ornithologists, it would be best to dispense with the confusing details in this matter and merely point out that the change from one plumage to another usually is gradual and does not always follow the same pattern, even within a single species. In addition, feathers may be lost through accident or sickness and replaced out of season. And there are some color and pattern changes when feather tips are worn off and differently colored areas on the feathers are exposed.

All these things taken together explain why some birds cannot be readily identified, even with the aid of the best available field guides and the finest field glasses—and why one puzzled bird watcher could describe a Scarlet Tanager in autumn as "green and red plaid." Thus, wherever possible, descriptions in this book emphasize the characters that help separate a species from those it resembles most closely.

Voice. No living man has heard the songs and calls of every North American bird or probably even all the species that breed in the smallest state in the union. Some bird notes, moreover, are too high or too low to register through the ears of most humans, and many people are unable to hear high notes within the normal human hearing range. Verbal description of a birdsong is, at best, a rather crude mnemonic device providing vague clues to pitch, cadence, and quality. In the vast literature on birds, no two authorities really agree either on the words to use for a song or on the precise definition of other qualities of the sound. Musical notations and sound graphs probably are the most accurate means of representing songs, but they seldom help to identify the sounds when first heard. For the average bird watcher, the best course is to identify the bird positively by means other than song and then assign his own mnemonic labels to the notes.

Birdsong recordings now available at most music stores are marvelously accurate, yet it is astonishing how much is missing. Even the Cornell University Laboratory of Ornithology, which owns one of the most complete bird-sound libraries in existence, lacks recordings of a surprisingly large number of North American species and may have on file less than 30 percent of the common sounds produced by all these species. The Song Sparrow, for instance, varies greatly in plumage throughout its large range and has at least as many song variations as subspecies, but not even all the variations in the songs and calls of the eastern subspecies have been recorded. It can only be hoped that descriptions in this volume will be helpful enough to allow the reader to formulate his own translations of birdsongs for future use. A simple system that might prove helpful to some is contained in *A Guide to Bird Songs,* by A. A. Saunders (Doubleday, New York, 1951.)

Range and status. Even before the advent of man, the range and status of bird species were changing constantly as a result of competition with other species and/or climatic change. Many species became extinct, some greatly expanded their ranges or increased their populations, some invaded new territories and were eliminated from old ones, and others acquired new habits or habitats. In recent centuries, the rate of change has accelerated. Through his agricultural practices, draining of marshes, lumbering of forests, waste disposal methods, and other activities, man has so altered habitats that few wild animal species have the same range or status as they had just fifty years ago. As a result, field guides and other works dealing with animal ranges become obsolete in this category almost as soon as they are published.

Since birds are so highly mobile, it is reasonable to expect that, given enough time, most North American species will have occurred at least once in most states and provinces. Each year the bird journals record accidental appearances of many species in states where they had not been recorded previously. Similarly, each decade records the expansion or retraction of the ranges of many species. Thus it must be assumed that any descriptions of range should be interpreted as once-upon-a-time factors and that high-population, aggressive bird species are likely to be increasing their ranges while rare, more timid species may tend to be crowded into smaller and smaller ranges.

In this volume, delineation of a range—as it is presently understood—begins with the northern edge, from west to east, and goes on to the southern boundary, also from west to east. But, for the reasons noted above, a positive degree of accuracy cannot be achieved. It must also be remembered that within a general range, each species will be restricted to its favorite habitats in the various seasons, except when it is under climatic or other stress.

Status is even more difficult to describe precisely.

Birds fluctuate in number from habitat to habitat, from season to season, and from year to year. According to the rules of individual serendipity, apparent abundance may also vary from observer to observer.

The words used to describe abundance not only are very general in meaning but may be applied in several different ways. "Common," for example, may be used to relate the abundance of one species to that of another species or to indicate its position on a scale listing all species in order of abundance. Kirtland's Warbler might be considered common at the center of its breeding range, but in migration outside this area, even in autumn after the annual increase in population, it could only be called one of the rarest of American warblers. The meaning of "common" as applied by the full-time fieldman, moreover, would differ from the meaning implied by the average birder who keeps to the more comfortable trails during occasional days off when the weather is agreeable.

The best gauge of status would be an actual census, particularly one taken during the breeding period throughout much of the bird's range and in all the kinds of habitat frequented by the species. But such a census requires a rather rare proficiency and a great deal of time. Each year one issue of *Audubon Field Notes,* a bimonthly journal published by the National Audubon Society, is devoted to breeding bird censuses taken in various areas and habitats throughout North America. The reader will find it worthwhile to refer to back issues of *Audubon Field Notes* for accounts of breeding bird and winter bird censuses of some area similar to and close to his home.

As a rule, the adjective "common" has been used in this book when a fairly active amateur birder could see five to twenty individuals of the species in suitable habitat in any one day of the season under discussion. If more than twenty could be seen under similar conditions, the species might be described as abundant. A count under five would then indicate a rather rare species, and only one or two sightings would mean that the bird was definitely rare. "Accidental stragglers" are species that appear in an area very irregularly, perhaps only once or twice each decade. In the compilation of the A.O.U. *Check-list's* geographical list of stragglers, only specimen records were used, since sight records generally are unreliable; it is more prudent to disregard all sight records than to use only a few, implying that the remainder are suspect.

Status may also involve designation of a species as either a migrant or a permanent resident, considerations that are covered in the discussion of seasonal movements. Again, these are not hard-and-fast categories. A species may properly be regarded as a permanent resident of an area if it is observed there throughout the year, even if no individual remains in the area for as much as one season. The Snowy Owl, for instance, is a permanent resident to the northernmost limits of its arctic breeding range even in the most severe winter; but in response to a lowered food supply, the population thins out as a result of sporadic dispersal southward out of the regular range. Other species may be regarded as erratics because of continual temporal and/or geographic shifting of their breeding or wintering range. Some species are altitudinal migrants, moving between mountaintops and valleys with the changing seasons. With other species the winter range varies according to the severity of the weather. Many water birds, for example, remain as far north as they can find open water in which to feed and obtain shelter. And some species might be overlooked as regular winter residents simply because man seldom invades the more desolate areas in winter.

Habitat. Every bird species has its favored haunts and habitat, but few are restricted to a single habitat: although the Common Crow prefers open lands to forests, it is adaptable enough to cross dense forests frequently and to take shelter in them when the need arises. Some birds change their habitat with the seasons. Nonmigratory mountain-dwelling species nest and raise their young in open alpine meadows at high altitudes, yet when the meadows are swept by wind and snow in winter, the birds descend to the protection of forests on lower mountain slopes. Migratory birds that nest in ·northern spruce forests may spend the winter in tropical areas, where there are no spruces or conifers at all. For most species, migrating between summer and winter ranges presents problems, such as finding suitable food, for species that feed in the tops of spruces on their breeding grounds may have to become ground foragers in areas crossed during migration.

Many behavior patterns of birds are extremely rigid. Migration times and habitat preferences may be so fixed in a species that temporary destruction of a habitat can lead to decimation even when suitable food substitutes are available. Birds capable of long, sustained flight often have such rigid patterns of behavior that, in the face of immediate disaster, they seldom make more than weak attempts to reach other, safe areas and almost never return to sanctuaries where they feasted just a few days before.

Habitat has been defined in terms of dominant plant cover. Actually, in forests many species may depend more on certain shrubs or other plants than on the dominant tree species. But though such plants may grow only in a certain type of forest, not all such forests will contain this undergrowth, and so one cannot always expect to find a bird associated with a particular forest type.

When a species population is very high, it may occupy habitats that it would not normally exploit; conversely, when the population is low, much of the optimum habitat will remain unoccupied. Far too little is known about the minimum-to-optimum habitat requirements of the great majority of species. Data now being gathered in bits and pieces by amateur and professional ornithologists, and made available to others in various publications, are certain to be of tremendous future help in areas such as the conservation of many endangered species.

Seasonal movements. The swallows of Capistrano are not really always on schedule, for the seasonal movements of birds are subject to the vagaries of climate and food supply. Even so, local bird clubs covering relatively small areas are able to keep meticulous records each year which, after a decade or two, enable them to make surprisingly accurate statements about each species, such as: "Arrives most years Apr. 5–10, but has been recorded as early as Mar. 21 in 1956 and not until Apr. 27 in 1964."

But if records cover the entire United States and Canada, they must be more general. When the schedule for spring migration is stated, say, as mid-March to mid-May, it is assumed that the reader understands that the species most likely will be in the southern part of its migration range in the early part of the period and quite close to its breeding range in the later part.

There are exceptions, however. The Robin migrates through Maryland, but it also breeds and winters there. From March to early June, any Robin in Maryland may be a migrant, an early breeder, or a late winterer. Birds that remain farthest north in winter, moreover, *may* travel the shortest distance to their breeding grounds, while a series of leapfrog movements carries those that wintered farthest south the greatest distance to the northernmost breeding areas. We simply do not know if most species migrate in this fashion or if they tend to move in blocs, with those that winter farthest north also nesting farthest north.

Biology. Text discussions of biology begin with descriptions of mating behavior, provided it is known. If it is essentially identical for all members of a family, details of mating behavior are not repeated for every species.

With one exception, the Marbled Murrelet, the nest of every species of American bird has been positively identified. Descriptions here are based on typical nests built by the species, but common variations on the usual construction and materials also are noted. It must be emphasized, however, that a nest can be positively identified only when the bird has actually been observed constructing it.

Eggs are much more variable in form and color than the average person realizes. When we describe something as "egg-shaped," we usually think in terms of the egg of the domestic chicken, yet even the graded eggs sold in modern supermarkets have discernible differences in shape. By the same token, the eggs of any species of wild bird vary considerably in shape, size, color, and markings. While various attempts have been made to measure and describe these differences accurately, no such effort has yet been successful. Thus descriptions of color and markings in this book are intended only to indicate the general range of variations, and it is quite possible that readers may occasionally discover eggs of almost any species that do not fit the description given.

Incubation periods also are quite variable. To be scientifically precise, incubation periods should be stated in terms of hours and minutes of constant temperature at the incubating temperature of the parent bird. Such data should also include lists of variations resulting from factors such as size and climatic differences, or from the fact that eggs are not incubated constantly in the wild.

Unfortunately, many existing data on incubation periods are completely erroneous. As a result, much of the information on incubation is queried in the text, largely because early methods of measuring incubation periods often were faulty. For example, some birds do not begin to incubate until the complete clutch has been laid, while other species start incubating the moment they have deposited the first egg. Unaware of these differences, early fieldworkers often simply measured the time from the date the first egg was laid until the first chick hatched, and assumed this was the incubation period.

It is possible for the investigator to overcome this difficulty by marking individual eggs and counting the time until they hatch, but there is a risk that the adult bird will desert the nest or throw out the marked eggs. The safest, simplest method is to record the interval between the laying and hatching of the last egg in the nest. Even this procedure requires a great deal of painstaking effort, since the count is worthless if not all the eggs hatch, if even one egg is destroyed, or if only one clutch is observed. The difficulties are further multiplied with extremely rare species and with birds that nest in remote areas of the world. And the sheer mechanical problems are almost insurmountable in the case of any bird that lays more than one egg in a burrow or deep cavity: notice, for instance, how few accurate periods can be presented for the woodpeckers.

Additional errors resulted from attempts by some of the early ornithologists to compute incubation periods in various ways, without specifying how they obtained their data. Although such errors are constantly being eliminated from the literature, a modern author may unwittingly perpetuate misinformation by consulting inadequate references or failing to check the latest literature on each species. The serious amateur may still contribute to our knowledge of birds by carefully measuring incubation periods of even the common species and publishing his findings as short notes, especially if they differ from existing published figures.

Age at first flight is another category subject to misinterpretation and error. Gallinaceous birds, for example, leave the nest soon after hatching; their age at first flight cannot be measured accurately unless the individual young are clearly marked and followed constantly. Natural enemies and other disturbances may force nestlings to leave the nest several days early, and under this stress they may actually fly short distances. But normally the young do not leave the nest until they are physiologically and psychologically most ready. Since the age at first flight is important to the survival of birds, scientists naturally are eager to acquire accurate data.

Information on the feeding habits of birds can be fairly accurately determined in a number of ways. Obviously, the feeding bird can be observed directly, but this method is satisfactory only under the best conditions. Positively identified droppings can also be examined, although decomposition may hinder proper identification of food remains. The best method is to examine the stomach contents of a freshly killed or preserved specimen. Even so, it is surprising how many stomachs seem to be empty or contain material that is all but unidentifiable.

As a result, information on feeding habits often is incomplete. For many of the rarer species, we can only make guesses based on our knowledge of closely related, more common species. Moreover, birds frequently vary their diets in the face of sudden shortages of their favorite food. Or they may temporarily alter their feeding habits in order to take advantage of sudden increases in the availability of foods that are normally rare. Many birds, on the other hand, apparently would rather starve than change their diets even temporarily. Thus, it is obvious from the entries in this book that more data are needed on feeding habits of even the common species.

Suggested reading. Throughout the text, suggestions for further reading represent a highly selective list. Strictly technical references are not included. Titles that contain technical matter are cited only if they are readable and understandable to the nonprofessional. Longer references covering the life history of the species in some detail are given whenever possible, rather than short articles covering only minor phases of the bird's natural history. Unfortunately, however, for many species the sum total of our knowledge exists only in the form of brief scattered notes contributed by many observers; in these instances no single article has been noted.

One of the better sources of additional information on American birds is the work of Arthur Cleveland Bent. In the period from 1919 to 1953 his twenty-two volumes of *Life Histories of North American Birds* were published by the United States National Museum. Since his death in 1954, an additional title was published from his manuscript, and the National Museum has since made arrangements to complete the series in at least two more books. Although the small printings of the original bulletins have long since been exhausted, Dover Publications (New York) has reprinted the entire series to date, using the original printing plates and pagination. All these titles are available in reasonably priced paperback editions.

Wherever Bent's species account is sufficiently complete, it has been listed as suggested reading. Where no such listing appears, reference to his volumes may still be useful; remember, however, that corrections and a great many new data may have been published elsewhere in the years since Bent wrote his accounts.

In order to keep abreast of current developments in bird study, the naturalist and the amateur bird watcher should also be familiar with the major North American ornithological journals and the publications of provincial, state, and regional bird clubs and associations. Not all the articles in the journals are written by professionals, and many are written in nontechnical language. In addition to reporting many new data on range changes and life histories, these publications keep the student informed of any advances in bird study and the types of research currently being conducted.

The following list is designed to help the reader become familiar with some of the journals, especially those cited as suggested reading, and to provide a selection of some of the available field guides and general reference works on American birds.

JOURNALS OF NATIONAL ORNITHOLOGICAL SOCIETIES

The Auk: A quarterly journal published by the American Ornithologists' Union at the University of Kansas, Lawrence, Kansas.

The Wilson Bulletin: Published quarterly by the Wilson Ornithological Society at West Virginia University, Morgantown, West Virginia.

The Condor: Issued bimonthly by the Cooper Ornithological Society at the Museum of Vertebrate Zoology, Berkeley, California.

NATIONAL MAGAZINES OF MORE POPULAR APPEAL

Audubon: A bimonthly publication of the National Audubon Society, 1130 Fifth Ave., New York.

Natural History: Ten issues each year, published by the American Museum of Natural History, Central Park West at 79th St., New York.

FIELD GUIDES

Peterson, Roger Tory, *A Field Guide to the Birds*, Houghton Mifflin, Boston, 1947.

———, *A Field Guide to Western Birds*, Houghton Mifflin, Boston, 1961.

Pettingill, Olin Sewall, Jr., *A Guide to Bird Finding East of the Mississippi*, Oxford University Press, New York, 1951.

———, *A Guide to Bird Finding West of the Mississippi*, Oxford University Press, New York, 1953.

Pough, Richard H., *Audubon Land Bird Guide*, Doubleday, Garden City, N.Y., 1946.

———, *Audubon Water Bird Guide*, Doubleday, Garden City, N.Y., 1951.

———, *Audubon Western Bird Guide*, Doubleday, Garden City, N.Y., 1957.

Robbins, C. S., B. Bruun, and H. S. Zim, *Birds of North America*, Golden Press, New York, 1966.

GENERAL REFERENCES

Palmer, Ralph S. (editor), *Handbook of North American Birds,* Yale University Press, New Haven, Conn., 1962.

Peterson, Roger Tory, and James Fisher, *The World of Birds,* Doubleday, Garden City, N.Y., 1965.

Pettingill, Olin Sewall, Jr. (editor), *The Bird Watcher's America,* McGraw-Hill, New York, 1965.

Thomson, Sir A. Landsborough, *A New Dictionary of Birds,* McGraw-Hill, New York, 1964.

Welty, Joel Carl, *The Life of Birds,* W. B. Saunders, Philadelphia, 1962.

Albert Earl Gilbert, whose drawings enhance so many of the pages in this book, would like to acknowledge the assistance of some of his predecessors in the field of bird art. His rendering of the Hawaii Oo is based on a drawing by D. M. Reid-Henry, and his Ivory-billed Woodpecker is based on life sketches by George M. Sutton. His Labrador Duck, Slender-billed Shearwater, and Passenger Pigeon are based to some extent on drawings by L. A. Fuertes. Both Mr. Gilbert and I gratefully acknowledge the generous assistance of George M. Sutton, who examined all of Mr. Gilbert's drawings and made many helpful suggestions.

For their assistance in producing this book, special thanks are due Olin Sewall Pettingill, Jr., who patiently edited both text and pictures, and Roland C. Clement of the National Audubon Society, who also read the text. In addition, I must thank my wife Alice, not only for her patience but also for her help in reading both typescript and galley proofs, and my two sons and daughter, who maintained a very reasonable silence and forbearance while work was in progress. And for showing me, while a child, the joys of nature—particularly birds—I thank my mother, May Anna Reilly, and my aunt, Mrs. Belle V. Roeder.

EDGAR M. REILLY, JR.
Curator of Zoology
New York State Museum

THE AUDUBON ILLUSTRATED
HANDBOOK OF AMERICAN
BIRDS

The Common Loon nests on freshwater lakes and ponds but usually winters on salt water.

THE LOONS (GAVIIDAE)

Loons are large (26–37½ in.), strictly aquatic birds of the n. half of the N. Hemisphere. These, and the somewhat similar but unrelated grebes, have existed since the Eocene (about 60 million years ago) with little change in range or form. There are 4 species: Common Loon, Yellow-billed Loon, Arctic Loon, Red-throated Loon. Loons are swift, skillful divers and swimmers. When diving, they may go as deep as 30 ft. and remain submerged for as long as 60 seconds; there are a few records of up to 90 seconds. Being heavy, with relatively small wings, they require considerable space for taking off and alighting. On land they maneuver only with difficulty. In the air their flight is rapid and direct, with bill pointed forward, neck fully extended, and feet held backward flatly, giving the bird a "humpbacked" appearance. All species feed primarily on fish, plus other aquatic vertebrates and invertebrates. The sexes are alike. Pairs are solitary in the breeding season. Nests are near the water in order that incubating birds may slide into it quickly. There are usually 2 eggs; young leave the nest soon after hatching.

COMMON LOON (Great Northern Diver) (*Gavia immer*)

Appearance: Nearly the size (28–36 in.) of a goose. Adults have distinctive pattern in spring and summer; in fall and winter, young and adults are mostly unpatterned gray above. The stout, pointed bill and short neck are characteristic.

Voice: In the breeding season, a loud, high-pitched "laugh" with a quavering tone; also a 2-syllable, mournful cry. Almost silent in other seasons.

Range and status: Breeds from Iceland, Greenland, and Alaska south to n. New England, n. Mich., N.Dak., and n. Calif. Winters from Maine, the Great Lakes, and s. Alaska south, sometimes on inland lakes, but mainly along both ocean coasts to Fla. and Baja Calif., also along the Gulf Coast to s. Tex. and from Scandinavia to Spain and the Azores. The commonest loon, a status not always implied in a name.

Habitat: Primarily a freshwater inhabitant in summer, occupying n. spruce-country lakes that are relatively undisturbed. In the winter usually on salt water, where it may be seen in rough seas offshore (but not far at sea) or in protected harbors and inlets.

Seasonal movements: These loons reach their nesting grounds as soon as the lakes are free of ice and leave them shortly before the winter freeze-up. They migrate by day or night, singly or in loose groups, at considerable height. During the winter they occasionally congregate in large numbers.

Biology: Nest: Always within 2–3 ft. of water, occasionally on a muskrat house; usually concealed and

1

consisting of a large mass of sticks, grasses, reeds, and debris. Eggs: Dark olive-brown, spotted with black. Incubation: About 29 days, by both sexes. Both parents assist in rearing the chicks. When 10–13 days of age, the young birds are proficient in diving and swimming. Age at 1st flight: 10–11 weeks. Food: Mainly fish; also crustaceans, mollusks, insects, and some aquatic plants.

Suggested reading: S. T. Olson and W. H. Marshall, *The Common Loon in Minnesota*, Minn. Mus. Nat. Hist. (Univ. of Minn.) Occ. Papers, no. 5, 1952.

YELLOW-BILLED LOON (White-billed Northern Diver, White-billed Diver) (*Gavia adamsii*)

Appearance: Very similar to Common Loon in all plumages, but differs in color and shape of bill; somewhat larger (30–36½ in.). The bill is ivory or yellowish in the Yellow-billed, pale blue-gray to black in the Common Loon. Shape of bill probably a better field character; Yellow-billed has straight upper edge and angled lower edge, giving the whole bill an upturned appearance. Bill of Common Loon appears straight.

Voice: Resembles Common Loon's, but louder and harsher; in flight an occasional monotonous *ha-ha-ha-ha-ha-ha-ha*.

Range and status: Summer records from n. Finland east across n. Siberia to n. Alaska and arctic Canada, east to the Melville Peninsula. Actual breeding records in our area are scattered. Winters from open water in breeding area south to Japan, s. Alaska, and coasts of Scandinavia.

Habitat: Freshwater lakes and rivers of far-n. tundras in summer, moving to adjacent coastal waters in winter.

Yellow-billed Loon

The Arctic Loon's simple nest (above) *often is little more than a depression in the grass. The Red-throated Loon's nest* (below) *is a more elaborate structure of mud and vegetation.*

Seasonal movements: More sedentary than Common Loon, few individuals moving out of arctic waters in winter; hardly more than a straggler to temperate coastal areas.

Biology: Nest: Resembles that of Common Loon; sometimes merely a flattened place on a hummock. Eggs: 2, resembling those of Common Loon. General biology like that of Common Loon so far as known.

Suggested reading: Alfred M. Bailey, *Birds of Arctic Alaska*, Col. Mus. Nat. Hist. Popular Series, no. 8, pp. 133–138, 1948.

ARCTIC LOON (Pacific Loon, Black-throated Diver) (*Gavia arctica*)

Appearance: Smaller (23–29 in.) than Common Loon. Winter and 1st-year birds difficult to distinguish from small Common Loons; more slender bill, head, and neck and generally smaller size are probably best characters.

Voice: More varied than that of Common Loon; during breeding season, "deep growls, playful barks," and "a plaintive *ah-hah-wee*, the last syllable high, penetrating, and mournful" (Sutton). A high yelp when disturbed.

Range and status: Breeds around the world in the arctic tundra regions south to Scotland, n. Germany, Russia south to about 55° N. latitude, n. Mongolia, ne. China, se. Siberia, s. Alaska, Yuk., Mack., and s. Hudson Bay; absent from Lab., Greenland, and Iceland. Winters south to the Mediterranean, India, Japan, and northwesternmost Mexico; absent (except strays) from w. Atlantic region.

Habitat: Freshwater lakes of tundra regions in summer, generally on larger and deeper lakes than preferred by Red-throated Loon. Almost completely confined to salt water in winter.

Seasonal movements: Highly migratory, although some birds may simply move to coastal waters near breeding range. Populations in Canada must move westward to the Pacific before going south, as the species is no more than a straggler inland and along the Atlantic Coast.

Biology: Nest: On a bank or small island adjacent to a lake; usually less elaborate than those of larger loons, sometimes a mere depression in grass. Eggs: Highly variable in color and shape, even within a single clutch; ground color varies from greenish olive to dark brown, with more or less black spotting and blotching. Incubation: 28–30 days, apparently by both sexes. Young are tended by both sexes and accompany their parents to salt water at end of summer prior to molt and migration. Age at 1st flight: About 60 days. Food: As in Common Loon. On Southampton I., Arctic Loon feeds only on salt water, flying regularly from nesting lake to coastal areas to feed and to bring back fish for young (Sutton).

Suggested reading: George M. Sutton, *The Birds of Southampton Island*, Mem. Carnegie Mus., no. 12, part 2, pp. 13–18, 1932.

RED-THROATED LOON (Red-throated Diver) (*Gavia stellata*)

Appearance: Smallest (24–27 in.) of our loons. In spring and summer, unlike other loons in color; head light gray, throat patch dark red, upperparts dark grayish brown without visible pattern. Winter and 1st-year birds paler than other loons; gray above, thickly speckled with white. Slender upturned bill gives head a distinctive appearance in any plumage. Can take off into flight more directly than other loons.

Voice: Varied; low quacks, henlike clucks, deep groans, and wild, high wails.

Range and status: The most widely distributed loon. Breeds around the world in tundra areas, from Greenland and Iceland, Scotland and Scandinavia east across n. Siberia to Kamchatka, Alaska, and n. Canada south to James Bay, s. Lab. and se. Que. Winters from the s. edge of breeding range south to the Mediterranean, Japan, n. Mexico, and s. Fla.

Habitat: Breeds in n. tundras and barren n. coasts, preferring smaller lakes than Arctic Loon. Primarily coastal in winter, but not uncommonly found on Great Lakes and other large bodies of fresh water.

Seasonal movements: Highly migratory, tending to winter farther south than other species of loons.

Biology: Nest: Variable; sometimes a large mound of mud and wet vegetation, used for more than 1 breeding season. Sometimes nests may be associated in loose colonies, whereas other loons are usually solitary nesters. Eggs: Variable in ground color from olive-green to dark brown; black markings usually sparse. Incubation: By both sexes; 29 days, possibly less. Young tended and fed by both sexes; family groups remain together when moving to salt water at onset of migration. Age at 1st flight unknown; probably about 60 days. Food: Similar to that of Common Loon, but no plants so far as known.

Suggested reading: George M. Sutton, *The Birds of Southampton Island*, Mem. Carnegie Mus., no. 12, part 2, pp. 19–24, 1932.

Like all its relatives, the Red-necked Grebe is an adept swimmer and diver.

THE GREBES (PODICIPEDIDAE)

Grebes are small- to large-sized (9–24 in.) water birds, cosmopolitan in distribution except for the polar regions and some oceanic islands. There are 20 species, of which 6 are found in N. America: Red-necked Grebe, Horned Grebe, Eared Grebe, Least Grebe, Western Grebe, Pied-billed Grebe. Adept swimmers and divers, grebes are almost helpless on land. Their feet are lobe-webbed and well to the rear of the body. They ordinarily float high on the water, but they are able to force the air from their bodies and plumage and sink slowly in the water until only their heads remain above the surface. Like the loons, they need long takeoff and "landing" water surfaces; sudden, early freezes in late fall trap and kill many grebes unable to get airborne from the reduced water surface. Their dives may last as long as 80 seconds, some

reaching depths of 30 ft. Owing to their short, weak wings and almost nonexistent tail, their flight is rather poor. Their food is primarily fish and other aquatic animals, with some water vegetation; all grebes eat some of their own feathers and feed them to the young. These birds are mainly solitary or only slightly gregarious, though 3 of the N. American species are colonial. Both sexes participate in nest building, incubation, and care of young. The nest is made of floating vegetation in shallow water, sometimes drifting to deeper waters. There are 3–9 eggs, and the adults cover them with nesting material when leaving the nest. Young leave the nest right after hatching and are often ferried about on the backs or under the wings of the adults.

RED-NECKED GREBE (Holboell's Grebe) (*Podiceps grisegena*)

Appearance: In size (17–22 in.) and general shape like a long, stiff-necked, short-crested merganser. Bill long, strong, sharply pointed; yellowish. In summer, large white cheek patches and henna-red front of neck are distinctive; in winter, red of neck replaced with gray,

and all that remains of the cheek patch is a sickle-shaped area running from the throat up the angle of the jaws. Silhouette showing size, neck, prominent bill, and slight crest is usually enough for identification.

Voice: Except for an occasional *teck-teck*, silent in fall and winter; in other seasons sounds more equine than avian. Calls by both sexes in spring described as a repeated braylike *konk*, often becoming a duet ending in a tremulous whinnying. Varied calls during courtship and breeding are donkeylike or piglike and have been described as "ungodly."

Range and status: Breeds from Alaska (except the Aleutians and the n. part), c. Yuk., sw. Ont. to ne. Wash., n. Idaho, n. Mont., n. N.Dak., and c. Minn. Winters along seacoasts from Aleutians to s. Calif. and from N.B. and N.S. to e.-c. Fla. In migration through the Great Lakes and St. Lawrence River Valley. Also occurs in Europe (mainly c. and e.) and Asia (mainly e.; some c. and w.). Not a common species; may be locally common in winter along the coasts.

Habitat: In summer, quiet inland waters, usually with some emergent vegetation. In winter mostly marine waters, sometimes well away from land. During migration found in all types of water habitat.

Seasonal movements: Northward movements start as early as Feb., and northernmost breeding areas are usually reached by early June; southward migration begins in July; migrants often congregate in great numbers on larger bodies of water on the way to the coasts.

Biology: Solitary nester as a rule; sometimes in loose colonies. Nest: Floating, anchored in and made of aquatic vegetation. Eggs: 3–6, usually 4–5; whitish or pale bluish or buffy when first laid, turning brown later. Incubation: 22–23 days by both sexes, but some variation. Young are fed aquatic insect larvae at first, then increasingly larger fish. It is not known at what age the young become independent of parents; some recorded not to have flown at age of more than 2 months even though adept swimmers.

Suggested reading: J. Munro, "Studies of Waterfowl in the Cariboo Region, British Columbia," *Condor*, vol. 39, pp. 163–173, 1937.

HORNED GREBE (*Podiceps auritus*)

Appearance: Silhouette similar to that of Red-necked Grebe, but smaller (12½–15 in.), with bill much less prominent and neck shorter. In summer dark-capped with dark cheek patches and back, reddish neck and flanks (white breast seldom shows on swimming birds), and with prominent "horns" of bright buff on sides of head. In winter gray above, white below, with large, prominent white cheek patches.

Voice: Low conversational rolls, with occasional sharper calls during nonbreeding seasons; during courtship and nesting seasons a trill with a variety of other notes ranging from high squeals through mournful gurgles to harsh croaks.

Range and status: Nests in Yukon Valley of Alaska and from n. Yuk., nw. Mack., and n. Man. south to ne. Wash., c. Idaho, n. Mont., N.Dak., and c. Minn.; formerly, now only casually, farther south and east. Winters coastally from the Aleutians to s. Calif. and from N.S. to s. Tex. Migrates through the valleys of the Frazer, Oregon,

Mississippi, and Ohio Rivers. Also occurs in Europe and Asia; breeds from the Baltic region through c. and s. Siberia to the Pacific, and winters in the w. Mediterranean, in the Black and Caspian Seas, and along the coasts of China and Japan. Less shy than other grebes and, although not a strong flier, often seen flying and shot in error by duck hunters.

Habitat: In breeding season, ponds and marshes with open water, or protected areas of larger ponds, lakes, and slow-flowing rivers. Other seasons, on any inland waters; nearshore marine waters, particularly in winter, very rarely far offshore.

Seasonal movements: Migration overland at night or along shores by day. Starts northward in Feb.–Mar., reaching more northerly parts of range by June; southward journey starts in July and is often completed by mid-Sept.

Biology: Solitary nester; rarely more than 1 pair to a pond. Nest: Of reeds and aquatic plants, floating; more or less exposed, in emergent aquatic plants and sometimes anchored to them. Receding water levels may leave nest on land. Eggs: 3–6, generally 4–5, whitish becoming buffy or brownish. Incubation: 24–25 days, perhaps as long as 28. Hatchlings are able to swim and can dive weakly; age when independent of parents unknown.

Horned Grebe

Food: 99% smaller aquatic animals; feathers often make up 50% of stomach contents. Usually feeds in water at depths of 5–25 ft.

Suggested reading: J. Munro, *Studies of Waterfowl in British Columbia: The Grebes,* Occ. Papers Brit. Col. Provin. Mus., no. 3, pp. 1–71, Dec., 1941.

EARED GREBE (Black-necked Grebe) (*Podiceps caspicus*)

Appearance: Generally like the Horned Grebe in size (12½–13½ in.) and coloration, but somewhat smaller. Its bill gives definite impression of being upturned. In its summer plumage it has a single prominent, sharp crest; its "ears" are a large patch of buffy feathers encompassing the eyes and extending over the cheeks to the back of the head. The rest of the head, the neck, and the back are blackish; the flanks are reddish brown; and the breast, not usually seen in swimming birds, is white. In winter the crestless bird is darker gray above, lighter below, with a V patch of very light gray on the side of the head.

Voice: A squeaky, penetrating *pu-weep* call, seldom heard except during breeding season; various other wheezy, rippling, whistling notes, usually 2 or 3 in each call and with rising inflection, have been ascribed to the bird.

Range and status: Breeds and winters in both Americas, Africa, and Eurasia, but range is not continuous and often local. In N. America only very rarely straggles east of the Mississippi; breeds from s.-c. B.C., c. Alta., s. Sask., and s. Man. south to nw. Baja Calif., c. Ariz., c. and se. N.Mex., and c. Tex.; winters in Pacific marine waters from Victoria I., B.C., to Guatemala and inland from c. Calif., Nev., Utah, c. N.Mex., and c. Tex. to Guatemala. Fairly common; sometimes seen in huge flocks during migration and in winter.

Habitat: Sometimes breeds on small, shallow, reedy ponds and lakes but more commonly on similar coves and bays of larger freshwater lakes. It winters close inshore on marine waters and open freshwater ponds and lakes.

Seasonal movements: Migrational movements largely nocturnal; in spring it has left marine waters even in B.C. by Apr.; inland migration flocks of up to 20,000 birds have been reported at some localities. Fall migration starts in Aug., with largest movements in Oct. and a few lingerers to Nov.

Biology: Gregarious; a colonial nester, with isolated nesting pairs discovered only rarely. The pairs indulge in elaborate courtship displays on water, including breast-to-breast frothy splashing dances and races. Nest: Of reeds and algae in emergent aquatic vegetation; many early nests complete with eggs may be deserted for no apparent reason and others started and completed. Eggs: 1–6, most often 3–4, whitish, greenish, or buffy-tinted.

When adults are incubating, nest may settle in water so eggs are at least partially submerged. Incubation: 20–22 days. Newly hatched young are able to swim and are cared for by parents until they become independent at an unknown age. Food: All stages of both land and aquatic insects and other invertebrates make up about 90% or more of food eaten; small fish and amphibians also consumed. Percentage of feathers found in stomachs apparently not so great as in other grebes.

Suggested reading: N. M. McAllister, "Courtship, Hostile Behavior, Nest Establishment, and Egg Laying in the Eared Grebe," *Auk,* vol. 75, pp. 290–311, 1958.

LEAST GREBE (*Podiceps dominicus*)

Resident species of New World tropics; breeds from s.-c. Mexico, s. Tex., and the W. Indies to n. Chile and c. Argentina. Casual to accidental in s. Calif., Ariz., and La. Similar to the Pied-billed, but smaller (9–10½ in.), predominantly gray instead of brown, and bill slenderer; the bright orange eye, usually visible over some distance, is a good field mark.

WESTERN GREBE (Swan Grebe) (*Aechmophorus occidentalis*)

Appearance: A large (22–29 in.) grebe with a long, slender neck and a long, thin, slightly upturned bill. Drooping head, neck, and feet in flight give bird a peculiar broken-back appearance. Upperparts grade from an almost black back to a dark gray tail; rest of plumage is white. The eyes are scarlet; bill and feet vary from yellowish in breeding season to olive and darker in the other seasons. Plumage is much the same color throughout the year, except that the white is duller and the dividing line between the white and grays is not so sharp in winter.

Voice: A variety of loud, shrill 3-part calls rising on the last syllable; often 1- or 2-note calls as *kree* or *kree-kree;* some notes may have a thin or a raspy quality. Other calls and notes have been described as like a steam-kettle whistle, a loud double-toned whistle or raspy *crick-crick,* ratchetlike growls, and purrs.

Range and status: A common grebe of the w. U.S. Breeds on inland fresh waters from c. B.C., Alta., s. Sask., and sw. Man.; south, west of the Cascades, to s.-c. Calif., n. Ariz., sw. and ne. Colo., w. Nebr., and ne. S.Dak. It is a regular breeder in probably less than half this total range and has been a regular local breeder in sw. Minn. In winter it is found along the Pacific Coast from se. Alaska south to the Mexican state of Nayarit and including the Gulf of Calif.; inland it winters in the s. ⅔ of the Central Valley of Calif., on Lake Tahoe in Nev., on open-water lakes of n.-c. Wash., and along the sw. edge of the Mexican plateau.

The Western Grebe anchors its islandlike nest to projecting rocks or vegetation.

Habitat: Aquatic, in both fresh and salt water, preferring extensive open areas edged with rushes, tules, or cattails. In marine environment usually found in sheltered bays and coves.

Seasonal movements: Migrates overland at night; partial daylight movements along coasts. Travels in large flocks, beginning northward movements in late Mar. and completing spring migration in early May. Moves south in smaller groups; noticeable large flocks usually seen in mid-Sept., but they are not reported off Mexico until late Oct.; by Dec. they are well distributed over the wintering range.

Biology: Prebreeding display of this species is famous. Before reaching the breeding area, hundreds at a time will indulge in the "racing" display wherein, propelled by feet alone, they attain such speed that their bodies become almost erect, with only the feet foaming the water's surface. The wings during this race are held rather rigidly, projecting but slightly; the head is held almost horizontally ahead, with the neck in a stiff, exaggerated S-shaped curve. The birds call continually while racing in flocks, adding this din to the water noises, which resemble the roaring of wind. A colonial species; some colonies have thousands of pairs. Nest: Built in water of dry or soggy plant material anchored to vegetation or soil or rocks projecting from the bottom. Eggs: 3–4; larger numbers reported in literature are probably from more than 1 female. Incubation: 22–23 days. It is not known at what age the chicks become independent of the adults. Food: 70–80% small fish; other items are insects, crustaceans, mollusks, amphibians, and marine worms, as well as a good percentage of feathers and some small stones.

Suggested reading: G. E. Lawrence, "The Diving and Feeding Activity of the Western Grebe on the Breeding Grounds," *Condor,* vol. 52, pp. 3–16, 1950.

*In contrast to its relatives, the Pied-billed Grebe
has a short, chickenlike bill.*

PIED-BILLED GREBE (*Podilymbus podiceps*)

Appearance: A small (12–15 in.), brownish grebe
with a short, rather conical bill. In summer it has a black
chin, a black throat patch, and a black ring around the
light-colored bill. In winter the black marks on chin and
throat are replaced by whitish, and the front of the neck
is reddish brown. Juveniles are similar to adults in winter
but have a whitish, brown-streaked cheek patch.

Voice: A loud, long, far-carrying cacophony beggar-
ing description, generally ending in a series of *wup-wup*
calls suggestive of our cuckoos' notes. This grebe sometimes restricts itself to 1 mournful note. Such notes may
be uttered only by the male; the female utters a repetitive soft *up-up-up* call to her chicks.

Range and status: The most far-ranging of Ameri-
can grebes. Breeds from s.-c. B.C., Alta., Sask., Man.,
Ont., sw. Que., and the Maritime Provinces south to c.
Chile and s.-c. Argentina, including the Greater Antilles.
In winter it is more or less regular from sw. B.C., Utah, s.
N.Mex., c. Tex., the Gulf Coast, and the se. U.S. to the s.
limits of its breeding range. Moderately common.

Habitat: Mainly ponds and marshes with open
water and emergent vegetation in breeding season; also
marshy inlets and bays on larger bodies of water. Uses
brackish and saltwater habitats more commonly in winter.

Seasonal movements: Migration nocturnal; general
flow in spring from Mar.–mid-Apr. and in fall from
Aug.–Nov.

Biology: Mating displays much less spectacular than
in other grebe species. Nest: A floating structure of drier
aquatic vegetation anchored to reeds or bushes; solitary
structures in small ponds, 15–30 ft. apart on larger
ponds. Eggs: 2–10, 4–7 most commonly; bluish white or
greenish white when fresh-laid, later becoming buffy or
dark brown. Incubation: About 23 days. Young are
probably more or less independent of parents 3 weeks
after hatching. Food: Small fish, crayfish, and insects
(about 1:1:2 ratio), with feathers taking up about half
the stomach contents.

Suggested reading: R. H. Chabreck, "Breeding
Habits of the Pied-billed Grebe in an Impounded Coastal
Marsh in Louisiana," *Auk*, vol. 80, pp. 447–452, 1963.

THE ALBATROSSES (DIOMEDEIDAE)

Albatrosses are medium to large (28–53 in.) gull-like, volant marine birds breeding on small offshore islands and islets and on oceanic islands of the S. Hemisphere and throughout the Pacific Ocean. About 14 species are known, and 6 have been recorded in our area: the Short-tailed, Black-footed, Laysan, Black-browed, White-capped, and Yellow-nosed Albatrosses. No species is of regular occurrence in the N. Atlantic Ocean, and only rarely do individuals cross the tropics and doldrum areas. Their mode of flying is perfectly adapted to regions of strong, steady winds; they are past masters at taking advantage of any strong horizontal breeze, but they would be almost helpless in the tropical belts where most air currents are mainly mild vertical drafts. The Wandering Albatross (*Diomedea exulans*), the largest species, has a wingspan of 10–12 ft.; its wings are only about 9 in. wide; and its length from tip of bill to tip of tail is about 4 ft. The ratio of length of wing to width is greater than for any other group of birds (18:1 in 1 species).

The nostrils are enclosed in tubes, and special glands near the nose eliminate salt from the body, enabling the birds to subsist on salt water. The tail is relatively short, and in flight the webbed feet frequently serve as rudders or brakes. The feet are webbed, and the hind toe is very short; the bill is hooked. Food consists primarily of fish and other sea animals. Usually only 1 egg is laid, on the ground or on hollow-topped hillocks. Incubation takes 30–70 days. The young may be 3–4 months old before their 1st flight, and the birds may be 7 years old or more before they breed. Coleridge, in his *Rime of the Ancient Mariner*, created the false legend that sailors believe the slaying of an albatross might result in bad luck. For an interesting account, which includes an analysis of the flight of the albatrosses, read W. Jameson, *The Wandering Albatross*, Wm. Morrow & Co., New York, 1959. The book is mainly about a species not in our range, but much of the information applies to all albatrosses.

SHORT-TAILED ALBATROSS (*Diomedea albatrus*)

A very rare (almost extinct) white-bodied albatross of the N. Pacific, which formerly ranged from the Bering Strait to coastal s. China and the shores of Baja Calif. Now breeds certainly only on Torishima I. of the Izu Is., Japan.

BLACK-FOOTED ALBATROSS (Black Gooney) (*Diomedea nigripes*)

Appearance: Uniformly dark gray, sometimes blackish, all over except for whitish feathers near bill and, on a few individuals, light gray under the tail. Wingspan is 7 ft.

Voice: Silent when alone at sea; noisy in groups, making groaning noises, squeals, loud snappings of bill, and medium-pitched, rather harsh notes.

Range and status: Breeds mainly on w. Hawaiian Is. (Leeward chain), but also other islands in about the same latitude nearly to Japan, and ranges over the N. Pacific Ocean north of the equator. There are about 50,000 breeding pairs and perhaps fewer than 200,000 individuals scattered over this vast area.

The Black-footed Albatross engages in elaborate displays on its breeding territory.

The slender wings of the Laysan Albatross span nearly 7 feet.

Habitat: Strictly pelagic, seldom close to shore. Largest concentrations at confluences of cold and warm oceanic currents.

Seasonal movements: Nonbreeders dispersed over N. Pacific. Breeding adults arrive at nesting islands in Oct. and Nov., leave in July and Aug.

Biology: May not start breeding until 9 years old. Display on nesting territory a posturing, bill-fencing dance. Colonial nester. Nests: Hollows scraped in soil. Egg: Dull chalky white. Incubation: 63–67 days. Chick makes 1st flight 5–5½ months after hatching and leaves island about 2 weeks later. Both sexes share incubation and "nursery" duties. Food: Animal matter of all kinds, including refuse from ships; fatty and oily items preferred. Flying fish, rockfish, sea urchins, and amphipods among stomach contents examined.

Suggested reading: L. Miller, "Observations on the Black-footed Albatross," *Condor*, vol. 42, pp. 229–238, 1940.

LAYSAN ALBATROSS (White Gooney) (*Diomedea immutabilis*)

Appearance: Plumage of head, neck, and body white to yellowish; wings and tail blackish gray to brownish; bill light gray or yellowish; feet pinkish. Wingspread nearly 7 ft.

Voice: Similar to Black-footed, but lower-pitched and less strident.

Range and status: Nearly 5 times as numerous as the Black-footed. Present breeding restricted to leeward Hawaiian Is., from Niihua I. to Kure I. Sea range does not extend so far south, nor apparently does it come so close to the mainland, as that of the Black-footed Albatross.

Habitat: Pelagic; greatest concentrations where colder currents rise to surface. Nests on oceanic islands well above tide lines, among sparse vegetation.

Seasonal movements: Similar to those of the Black-footed, but arrives at and departs from breeding islands 1–2 weeks later.

Biology: Probably does not start breeding until after 7th year. In "courtship" dances its movements are at a slower beat than those of Black-footed Albatross. Indications point to lifelong mating. Colonial nester. Nest: A hollow scraped in the ground, with debris tucked in around the brooding adult to form a ridge. Egg:

The Black-browed Albatross builds a cuplike nest of mud and vegetation.

Yellow-nosed Albatross

Roughened; dull white. Incubation: 62–67 days. Age at which young become independent is unknown, but close to that of the Black-footed. Food: Mainly squid; probably other animal matter, including refuse from whaling operations.

Suggested reading: D. W. Rice and K. W. Kenyon, "Breeding Cycles and Behavior of the Laysan and Black-footed Albatrosses," *Auk,* vol. 79, pp. 517–567, 1962.

BLACK-BROWED ALBATROSS (*Diomedea melanophris*)

A blackish-winged white albatross, the most common in the seas from the shores of Antarctica to the Tropic of Capricorn. Underside of wings is white with a heavy black border. To those who cruise south of the Tropic of Capricorn, this is the most common long-pinioned, graceful aeronaut, follower of ships at sea. Besides garbage cast overboard, this bird eats a great variety of animal food. Stragglers have been taken off Greenland, Spitsbergen, and in the North Sea; it is possible that some of these were escaped pets, carried into the N. Atlantic by homeward-bound European sailors.

WHITE-CAPPED ALBATROSS (*Diomedea cauta*)

A dark-mantled white albatross, with underside of wings white except for a narrow dark leading edge. Breeds on islands near Australia and New Zealand and ranges over most of the seas south of the Tropic of Capricorn. Taken once off Wash. (mouth of Quillayute River).

YELLOW-NOSED ALBATROSS (Molly or Mollymawk) (*Diomedea chlororhynchos*)

A slender, dark-billed albatross with the upper central plate of the bill a distinct yellow. One of the dark-mantled white albatrosses found in the seas south of the Tropic of Capricorn from the s. S. Atlantic to off se. Australia. Wingspan is 6–7 ft. Taken or reported from the Gulf of St. Lawrence, the Bay of Fundy, sw. Maine, and off Freeport, Long I., N.Y.

PETRELS, SHEARWATERS, AND FULMARS (PROCELLARIIDAE)

Like their relatives the albatrosses, the petrels, shear-waters, and fulmars are gull-like marine birds. They are found in all oceans and are more widespread than the albatrosses, probably because their method of flight makes them less dependent on vagaries of the winds. Their nostrils are in a single septum-divided tube. The smallest member of this family is about the size of a Starling, while the largest is up to 3 ft. long, with a wingspan of 4–5 ft. In flight they flap and soar, usually close to the water's surface. There are about 60 species, of which 24 come within the sphere of this book (4 are Hawaiian). Food and food-gathering habits divide the family into 4 main groups: Fulmars and large petrels, which are scavengers and pirates; shearwaters and smaller petrels, which are adapted to capture fish under-water; gadfly petrels, which eat small floating cephalo-pods; and the prions, which strain small animal life from the seawater through "sieves" at the edges of their bills. Many species nest in burrows which they excavate; others nest in natural holes or crevices of rocks; others nest on rocky ledges; some nest on the ground. On land, most of the petrels do not stand erect on their toes, as do the robins and most other birds, but rest their weight on both toes and lower legs, giving the impression that they are definitely weak-legged. Plumage colors are white, grays, black, and browns; the sexes look alike. Most species breed in colonies, and many are also gregarious at other seasons. All petrels lay but 1 white or whitish egg, and both sexes incubate and care for the young.

CAPE PETREL (Pintado Petrel, Cape Pigeon) (*Daption capense*)

A medium-sized (15–16 in.) petrel of the S. Hemisphere that ranges to the equator along w. Africa and w. S. America. Plumage dark above with irregular whitish patches; entire head dark; whitish below. Straggles into the N. Hemisphere, where it has been recorded from Calif. and Maine (once each).

FULMAR (Northern Fulmar, Fulmar Petrel) (*Fulmarus glacialis*)

Appearance: A large (17–20 in.) petrel, similar to the gulls, but stockier and heavier-billed. Two main color phases: the "white," in which the mantle, wings, and lower back are light to medium gray and the rest of the plumage white; and the dark phase, in which the entire plumage is a medium gray. There are mixtures of these phases. The tubed nostrils and heavier hook on the bill help separate the Fulmar from gulls.
Voice: Described as a "hoarse whirring cackle" and squabbling grunts and grumbles.
Range and status: N. Hemisphere, ranging from ice-free waters to Japan and s. Calif. in the Pacific and Nfld. and n. France in the Atlantic. Nests on rocky cliffs or tops of isles, islets, and exposed coasts of Kuriles, Aleutians, e.

Tubed nostrils and a prominent hook at the tip of its sturdy bill distinguish the Fulmar from any of the gulls.

Franklin District of Canada, Greenland, Iceland, Spitsbergen, Franz Josef Land, Norway, and Great Britain. Becoming more abundant, especially in the Atlantic, since it has found the waste around commercial fisheries to be a copious source of rich food. Breeding colonies in Britain have more than doubled in recent years. The Fulmar is a straggler in the e. U.S., down the St. Lawrence Valley to Lake Ontario and coastally to N.J.

Habitat: Marine; formerly along southerly edge of cold arctic waters. Now spreading southward into warmer subarctic seas.

Seasonal movements: May only be described as dispersal from breeding areas over feeding range. A commonly used feeding locality is the Newfoundland Banks. Fulmars move farther south in winter than in summer, but difference not too great as nonbreeders may wander anywhere.

Biology: May be 7 years old or more before breeding. Colonial; some colonies estimated to contain 100,000 pairs! Nest: Sometimes a slight hollow in the ground or none. Egg: The coarse-grained white egg may be stained with reddish spots. Incubation: 55–57 days. Birds defend nests by ejecting foul-smelling food (adults) and oil (young) at intruders. Young able to fly off on their own after 42–56 days. Food: Fish, offal, almost all aquatic animals small enough to swallow or kill and dismember.

Suggested reading: James Fisher, *The Fulmar*, Collins, London, 1952, 496 pp.

BLACK-TAILED SHEARWATER (Great Gray Shearwater) (*Adamastor cinereus*)

A large (18 in.), chunky, heavy-billed shearwater; head and upperparts medium gray and underparts whitish. Ranges from the Antarctic to the Tropic of Capricorn; once taken off Monterey, Calif.

CORY'S SHEARWATER (Mediterranean Shearwater, Cinereous Shearwater, Cape Verde Shearwater) (*Calonectris diomedea*)

A brownish gray, large (16–18 in.) shearwater with white undersides, dark tail, and yellow bill. Found in the Mediterranean and off sw. Europe and nw. Africa. Its sea range extends across the Atlantic to offshore waters from the Newfoundland Banks to Cape Hatteras, but rare this far west, especially to north and south. Appears regularly but not commonly at sea off sw. Africa. A straggler inland in Europe and in British waters. One of the more common shearwaters off Long I., N.Y., in summer.

PINK-FOOTED SHEARWATER (*Puffinus creatopus*)

One of the larger (19–20 in.) shearwaters, dark brownish gray above and white below, with black-tipped pink

Although it is an agile flier, the Black-tailed Shearwater moves awkwardly on land.

bill and pink feet. It is silent most of the time at sea except for a high-pitched squeal when squabbling over food. It makes mewing, guttural, and cooing sounds at its breeding islands off the coast of Chile. At sea it ranges along the Pacific Coast of the Americas from se. Alaska to c. Chile. It has not been recorded from the c. Pacific, and apparently restricts its wandering to the width of the larger coastal currents. It is a rare but regular visitant off the coasts of the w. U.S. and Canada in spring and autumn. Breeds at the age of about 5 years, the egg being laid in Dec. in burrows 3–5 ft. long. Food is principally small fish, crustaceans, and squid.

PALE-FOOTED SHEARWATER (*Puffinus carneipes*)

This is considered by some ornithologists to be a geographic variation of the Pink-footed; if this is the case, the two would both be called Flesh-footed Shearwater (*Puffinus carneipes*). However, this form breeds on islands off sw. Australia and off n. and nw. New Zealand. It differs from the Pink-footed only in general appearance, as its plumage is uniformly dark brownish gray. Ranges westward from its breeding grounds to the s. tip of India and nearly to the coast of Africa north of Madagascar. It has been recorded off e. Japan and also off Calif. It may be that the species (or both species) follows the ocean currents clockwise around the Pacific, taking advantage of the rich food supplies at the edges of such ocean rivers.

Suggested reading: J. Warham, "The Nesting of the Shearwater," *Auk*, vol. 75, pp. 1–14, 1958.

GREATER SHEARWATER (Great Shearwater)
(*Puffinus gravis*)

Appearance: About the same size (18–20 in.) as Cory's Shearwater; medium brown above with blackish tail and cap and dark bill; a white crescent on the rump and whitish underneath.

Voice: Harsh screams while at sea, particularly when fighting over food. On the breeding grounds, loud bleating, screeching, braying noises, also twittering and gurgling notes. At night, when colony is most active, an ear-pressing vocal cacophony.

Range, status, habitat, and seasonal movements: Breeds only on Gough, Nightingale, and Inaccessible Is. in the S. Atlantic, and apparently circles both the N. and S. Atlantic Oceans, but unrecorded along African shores from the Canaries to the Cape Verde Is. and in the Gulf of Guinea. Enters the w. Mediterranean but not the Caribbean and only once recorded from the Gulf of Mexico. Prefers cooler water than the similar Cory's Shearwater, and so the two species are very rarely found together. Where warm and cool currents converge, Greater Shearwater ranges over the cooler water. From dates of observations it travels over Atlantic Ocean in a figure-8 pattern, following winds and currents to S. Africa and then to n. S. America, then following the cool edge of the Gulf Stream to w. Europe and then back to S. America to the Falkland Is. and to the breeding islands. As many as 400 individuals have been counted off Long I., N.Y., at a single time.

Biology: Lays egg in chamber at end of 3-ft. burrow about mid-May. Incubation: 53–57 days. Very active at night, especially on breeding grounds. Parents may leave islands shortly before young, but by mid-May all have started their peregrination. Food: Mainly surface fish, squid, and refuse from fishing boats.

Many Wedge-tailed Shearwaters breed on the western islands of Hawaii.

The wide-ranging Red-billed Tropicbird is occasionally sighted off the coasts of California and Washington. It lays its single egg in natural crannies on rocky cliffs.

The Brown Booby, widespread over tropical and subtropical oceans, is sometimes seen off California and along the Gulf and Atlantic Coasts from Texas to Maine.

Suggested reading: G. J. Broekhuysen, "Observations on the Greater Shearwater in the Breeding Season," *British Birds*, vol. 41, pp. 338–341, 1949.

WEDGE-TAILED SHEARWATER (*Puffinus pacificus*)

An all-gray shearwater with yellowish feet, black-tipped pink bill, and wedge-shaped tail. Not quite so large (17–19 in.) as Greater Shearwater. Breeds on islands in the warmer waters off New Zealand and Australia and in the Indian and Pacific Oceans. Breeds on Wake I., the smaller islands of Hawaii, islets off Oahu, and the Revilla Gigedo Is. off w. Mexico. Does not stray too far from breeding islands, but occasionally noted in warmer waters off s. Calif. Breeds in burrows. Eats mainly squid.

GRAY-BACKED SHEARWATER (New Zealand Shearwater, Buller's Shearwater) (*Puffinus bulleri*)

A rather rare species with dark gray back and cap and white underparts. Breeds on islets off North I., New Zealand, and occurs at sea off Japan, w. U.S., and Chile.

SOOTY SHEARWATER (*Puffinus griseus*)

Appearance: About the same size (19–20 in.) and coloration as Wedge-tailed Shearwater, except that the bill and feet are blackish, the undersides of the wings are light gray, almost white, and the tail is not wedge-shaped.

Voice: Strident screams and calls at sea; groans, growls, and cackles at nesting islands; crooning notes in burrows.

Range, status, habitat, and seasonal movements: The most far-ranging of the "cool current" shearwaters circling the Atlantic, Pacific, and Antarctic Oceans. Breeds on islands and islets off s. S. America, New Zealand, and se. Australia. Unrecorded in warm equatorial waters, which it certainly must cross to reach the N. Pacific and the N. Atlantic. As it breeds on many islands in both the E. and W. Hemispheres, the timetable of its seasonal wanderings is difficult to ascertain; birds circling the Antarctic area during summer in S. Hemisphere are probably adolescents. Sooty Shearwater occurs in N. Hemisphere usually from July to late Sept.; in the 1st part of this period, it is more common on the w. shores of N. Hemisphere oceans, and in the latter part on the e. shores. As many as 100,000 have been recorded off coast of Calif. in a single day during migration.

Biology: Especially nocturnal during breeding season, Nov.–mid-May. Egg laid in terminal chambered burrow, sometime after mid-Nov. Incubation: About 56 days. Young leave burrows for 1st flight when 86–106 days old, after exercising wings nightly just outside burrow. Food: Squid, small fish, and crustaceans, which they capture at water's surface or by shallow dives.

Suggested reading: L. E. Richdale, "Biology of the Sooty Shearwater," *Proc. Zool. Soc. London,* vol. 141, pp. 1–117, 1963.

SLENDER-BILLED SHEARWATER (Muttonbird, Whalebird) (*Puffinus tenuirostris*)

Smaller (16 in.) than the Sooty, but similar to it, except that the undersides of the wings are brownish gray like the rest of its plumage. Breeds on islands and islets off Tasmania and se. Australia and circles the Pacific in a clockwise direction, reaching Japan, the Kuriles, the Aleutians, Bering Strait, the Pacific Coast of America south to s. Baja Calif. and thence to New Zealand. Colonial breeder in burrows 18 in. to 6 ft. long, dug at night. First breed at 5–7 years for females, 6–8 years for males. Egg laid in late Nov. and hatches in 52–55 days. Young are 88–108 days old at 1st flight. Food mainly crustaceans, small fish, and squid.

Slender-billed Shearwater

The Manx Shearwater is seen occasionally along our northern Atlantic and southern Pacific coasts.

MANX SHEARWATER (Common Shearwater, Black-vented Shearwater) (*Puffinus puffinus*)

A medium-sized (12–15 in.) shearwater with blackish upperparts, bill, and tail; undersides (including lining of wings) white, sometimes mottled with blackish at throat and lower belly. Feet and legs are pinkish. Feathers under tail (coverts) are white in the Atlantic forms and blackish in the Pacific forms. Breeds in burrows on small islands off Iceland, the British Isles, the Azores, Madeira, the Canaries, in the Mediterranean and Aegean Seas, and on islands off n. and w.-c. Baja Calif. Ranges throughout the e. N. Atlantic, west to Nfld. and Canadian Maritime Provinces; in the Pacific it wanders along the American coast north to c. Calif., 1 straggler reaching B.C. In winter it is also found along the e. coast of S. America from e. Brazil to Argentina. Food is small fish, squid, and crustaceans.

   Suggested reading: R. M. Lockley, *Shearwaters*, J. M. Dent & Sons, London, 1942 (mainly concerning this species but excellent about shearwaters generally).

NEWELL'S SHEARWATER (*Puffinus newelli*)

May be only a subspecies of Manx Shearwater; upperparts blacker, underparts whiter and more extensive than on Manx. Almost extinct; formerly bred on most of the Hawaiian Is., but now probably only in scattered remote unknown localities somewhere in Hawaii.

TOWNSEND'S SHEARWATER (*Puffinus auricularis*)

Like Newell's, probably a subspecies of Manx Shearwater. Breeds on Revilla Gigedo Is. off w. Mexico, ranging north to s. Baja Calif. and south to Clipperton I.

BLACK SHEARWATER (Christmas Island Shearwater) (*Puffinus nativitatis*)

A medium-sized (14 in.) shearwater, blackish above and dark brown below, with dark bill, feet, and legs. Breeds on islands of the tropical Pacific from Wake I. and the Hawaiian Is. southeastward to the Austral Is. and the Tuamotu Archipelago. Its sea range is not much more extensive; it has not been recorded from N. America. Its 1 egg is laid on the bare sand in the shelter of some plant growth; the breeding season seems to be much extended and may last through most of the year.

LITTLE SHEARWATER (Allied Shearwater) (*Puffinus assimilis*)

A small (10 in.) shearwater, similar to Audubon's Shearwater, of the e. N. Atlantic and the cooler temperate seas north of Antarctica. Recorded twice from e. N. America.

AUDUBON'S SHEARWATER (Dusky Shearwater) (*Puffinus lherminieri*)

About the same size (12 in.) as the Little Shearwater, but a bird of the tropical and subtropical seas, not prone to wander too far from its breeding places. Breeds on islands in the Pacific from the Bonins and islets off the Celebes southeast to Tuamotu Archipelago and in the Galápagos Is.; also on small islands in the Caribbean Sea, the Lesser Antilles, the Bahamas, and the Bermudas; and on islands in the w. Indian Ocean. A colonial breeder; lays its egg in rock crevices or under thick vegetation. At sea the species travels in very small flocks or singly. Food is primarily small fish and squid. Rats accidentally introduced on the breeding islands by man severely limit the population.

BLACK-CAPPED PETREL (Capped Petrel) (*Pterodroma hasitata*)

About the size (14–18 in.) of Manx Shearwater, with medium gray to blackish upperparts, including a dark grayish cap and white rump and underparts; bill and feet dark, legs pinkish. Formerly a common species of the e. Greater Antilles and n. Lesser Antilles. Owing to hurricanes, it has been recorded inland in e. N. America: Ont., Ky., Ohio, N.Y., Fla., Va., Conn., and N.H., and also in England. Many ornithologists believe that this is but a subspecies of a much wider-ranging species which includes the Bermuda Petrel and others.

A Little Shearwater and chick were photographed by removal of the top of their nest burrow.

BERMUDA PETREL (Cahow) (*Pterodroma cahow*)

Lazarus-like, this species (probably only a subspecies of the Black-capped Petrel), long believed extinct, was dramatically "raised" from "extinction" by the discovery of a small breeding colony on a tiny Bermudian islet. It was formerly so abundant that early mariners and colonists in the Bermudas used it as an important food resource. It was so easy to capture and kill at its nesting burrows that man and his cohorts, the rat and domestic cat, abused their privileges. Its cap is blacker than that of the so-called Black-capped Petrel, but otherwise it is very similar (size about 16 in.). The habit of being most active about land during the night protected it from early rediscovery, and we can but hope that it will be possible to protect the remnant.

Suggested reading: R. C. Murphy and L. S. Mowbray, "New Light on the Cahow, *Pterodroma cahow*," *Auk*, vol. 68, pp. 266–280, 1951.

SCALED PETREL (Mottled Petrel) (*Pterodroma inexpectata*)

A medium-sized (14 in.) petrel with gray upperparts; the underparts are white with a broad gray belly band. Breeds on islands off New Zealand and cruises the seas off Antarctica from se. Australia to s. S. America. Lives up to its specific scientific name (*inexpectata*) by showing up as a straggler in Alaska (4 records), Ore., N.Y., and the Galápagos Is.

TRINDADE PETREL (South Trinidad Petrel) (*Pterodroma arminjoniana*)

About the size (ca. 15 in.) of the Scaled Petrel; grayish brown above, white below. Breeds on Trindade I. (off Brazil; not "South Trinidad I."; it is Trindade I. on almost all modern maps) and on islands east of Madagascar. A gadfly petrel, on our list by courtesy of a hurricane that blew one all the way to Caroline Center, N.Y.

COOK'S PETREL (*Pterodroma cookii*)

A small (10½ in.) gadfly petrel of the s. and se. Pacific, recorded once in the Aleutians and once off Baja Calif. Similar to the Scaled Petrel, but without the gray belly band.

DARK-RUMPED PETREL (*Pterodroma phaeopygia*)

A very rare species endemic on the main islands of Hawaii. Nests in burrows dug under tree roots, etc., at elevations of 1,000–5,000 ft. About the same size (13–17 in.) as Black-capped Petrel and much like it, except that the lighter cap and white forehead give it the appearance of being a white-headed bird. The natives collected this species from its burrows for food without reducing the population too much, but the introduced mongoose eliminated it effectively from its former haunts. It may still nest on remote mountains of Kauai I., as the mongoose has not become established there. It apparently did not wander very far from its nesting islands. Possibly this species is but another subspecies of the Black-capped Petrel.

STOUT-BILLED GADFLY PETREL (Bonin Island Petrel) (*Pterodroma leucoptera*)

Smaller (13 in.) than Dark-rumped Petrel. Forehead a mixture of gray and white feathers, rest of upperparts dark gray to blackish; underparts white. Bill and feet black, legs pinkish. Breeds on islands off New Zealand, the New Hebrides, Fiji, on Bonin I., the w. Hawaiian Is., and Masafuera I. off w. Chile. Nests in burrows in large colonies on Midway and Laysan Is. Very rare on the main islands of Hawaii. Apparently remains rather close to home islands during nonbreeding periods.

BULWER'S PETREL (*Bulweria bulwerii*)

A small (11 in.) gadfly petrel breeding on islands in the Pacific area from coast of China to the w. Hawaiian Is. and the Marquesas and in the Atlantic on Madeira, the Salvages, Canary, and Cape Verde Is. Plumage is entirely dark brown, but a little lighter on the undersides; bill black, feet and legs dark brown. Its principal food is small floating organisms. It has difficulty surviving on islands where the rat has become established.

The White-faced Storm-petrel is rarely seen over American waters.

THE STORM-PETRELS (HYDROBATIDAE)

The storm-petrels are the smallest of the marine birds, of sparrow to robin size (5½–10 in.). There are 18 species, of which 12 have occurred in N. America. They range over the world's oceans, nesting in burrows or rock crevices of marine islands and islets. All species are colonial. Plumages are various shades of brown or gray with black and/or white. The nostrils are joined in a single tube at the top center of the strongly hooked bill. The feet are webbed; and since the legs are weak, the birds cannot stand erect on land. Their flight is fluttering, and they frequently hover close to the water surface in even the highest seas. Their habit of pattering their feet on the surface while they hover is the reason for the name "petrel," which means "little Peter," after the saint who managed to walk on water. The storm-petrels are almost certainly the original "petrels," so named by the fishermen of France, since the larger petrels of the preceding family do not "walk" on the water. In high winds and the accompanying high seas, the birds keep to the lee side of the waves and any large object at sea, so they "suddenly" appear alongside ships at sea during storms; this accounts for the name "storm-petrel." They are also called "Mother Carey's chickens." Early mariners naturally associated the birds with danger, which the tiny creatures seemed to ride out with ease. Nests are hollows or burrows in the ground or natural hollows in rocks. Usually only a single white egg is laid; very rarely, perhaps only accidentally, are 2 found in a nest. Both parents share duties of raising the family. Food consists of small fish, crustaceans, and other animals, as well as floating refuse. In this book all species of this family will be referred to as storm-petrels.

WHITE-FACED STORM-PETREL (Frigate Petrel)
(*Pelagodroma marina*)

A medium-sized (7½–8 in.) storm-petrel of the subantarctic regions, the Indian Ocean, and the e. Atlantic. It has been taken twice in our waters, once off Nantucket I., Mass., and once off Long I., N.Y. It has a gray cap and back, black tail and wing tips, and white underparts; the webbing between the black toes is yellow.

FORK-TAILED STORM-PETREL (Fork-tailed Petrel)
(*Oceanodroma furcata*)

Appearance: A medium-sized (8 in.) storm-petrel, light to medium gray above and white below, with a distinctly forked tail, a dark area around the eye, and with blackish bill, feet, and legs.

Voice: Makes soft twittering noises while flying near breeding grounds and barely audible squeaks from burrows when disturbed.

Range, status, habitat, and seasonal movements: Breeds on islands and islets in an arc about the N. Pacific Ocean from the Kuriles north of Japan to islands off n. Calif.; at sea it ranges south to the Bonin Is. and c. Calif. and north into the Bering Sea. It is not a rare species. Inhabits the colder waters, and is often found in the icebound Arctic near small openings in the ice. Found singly or in flocks of up to 500 birds on the open seas. During the nonbreeding seasons it disperses farther from land, but it is not known to follow definite routes or directions.

Biology: Nocturnal on the nesting islands, where it burrows in a variety of situations or in deep holes in the rocks. Some plant material may be used to line the

An expert flier, the Leach's Storm-petrel ranges far out to sea.

nesting chamber. The 1 egg may be laid from late June to mid-July and may have a ring of small dark spots around the larger end. Incubation period not known. It is a rather feeble swimmer and relies on stiff breezes to aid takeoff from water. Much remains to be learned about this species. Food is small fish, crustaceans, and floating oil; young *may* be fed on regurgitated oil.

LEACH'S STORM-PETREL (Leach's Petrel) (*Oceanodroma leucorhoa*)

Appearance: An average-sized (8 in.) storm-petrel with a forked tail. Plumage blackish brown except for a lighter bar on upper wings and, particularly in the Atlantic populations, a distinct white upper and lower "rump" patch. The white may be entirely absent in some populations in the Pacific area. Rapid, light flight; gliding, hovering, rapid changes of direction.

Voice: A distinct ticking, becoming more rapid and ending in a slurred trill, made during flight and in burrows. In burrows various rolling, whirring, crooning notes ending in a chuckle; also squeals and harsh screams.

Range and status: An abundant and widespread species in the N. Hemisphere just entering the S. Hemisphere in the Atlantic off Brazil and S. Africa. Breeding on islands and offshore islets in the Pacific from the Ryukyus through the Kuriles and the Aleutians, down the w. coast of N. America to s. Baja Calif. and in the Atlantic from Mass. to s. Lab., Iceland, the Faeroes, and the Hebrides. Its sea range reaches south to Sumatra, Java, and New Guinea, the Galápagos, and into the Caribbean Sea. Its center of abundance is off Nfld.

Habitat: Frequents parts of sea where cold currents rise to the surface, nourishing a plentiful supply of plankton; widespread in tropical seas in winter.

Seasonal movements: Arrives in numbers at breeding islands in late Apr. Apparently more or less general dispersal from these places, as some individuals certainly remain wherever there is open water.

Biology: At least 2 years old at 1st breeding. Colonial, nesting in burrows at least 3 ft. long. Some burrows have several lateral chambers, each occupied by 1 pair. The male digs the burrow. Nocturnal; on land, airborne birds often collide with each other in the dark. Banding returns indicate that the birds may mate for life. Incubation: 41–42 days; eyes do not open until 15 days after chick hatches. The young gain weight until deserted by parents at about the 40th day, then lose weight before 1st flight when 63–70 days old. Does not dive; swims well but not often. Continually in motion on wing. At breeding islands, cats, dogs, and gulls capture many petrels as they return from sea. Food: Fish, crustaceans, refuse from ships, and oily substances. Follows whales to dine on remnants of the mammals' meals. Many of the crustaceans found in their stomachs are of species that reach the ocean's surface only at night.

Suggested reading: W. A. O. Gross, "The Life History Cycle of Leach's Petrel on the Outer Sea Islands of the Bay of Fundy," *Auk*, vol. 52, pp. 382–399, 1935.

ASHY STORM-PETREL (Ashy Petrel) (*Oceanodroma homochroa*)

A medium-sized (8 in.) storm-petrel; dark gray except for lighter gray lines on upper and lower wings. The tail is forked; bills, legs, and feet are black. Nests in chambers at the ends of burrows on islands off the coast of Calif. from the Farallon Is. to the Coronado Is. off n. Baja Calif. It is a rare, little-known species that has been recorded from the mainland of Calif. only once.

GUADALUPE STORM-PETREL (Guadalupe Petrel) (*Oceanodroma macrodactyla*)

About the size (8 in.) of Leach's Storm-petrel; blackish above and brownish below, with forked tail. Formerly bred on Guadalupe I. off n. Baja Calif. Probably extinct.

SOOTY STORM-PETREL (Tristram's Petrel) (*Oceanodroma markhami*)

A large (10 in.) sooty-brown storm-petrel with deeply forked tail. Breeds from islands off Japan east to Midway and Laysan Is. of Hawaii. Rare, even in breeding areas, but a form of this species ranges the seas off Peru and Chile.

HARCOURT'S STORM-PETREL (Madeiran Petrel, Harcourt's Petrel, Hawaiian Storm-petrel) (*Oceanodroma castro*)

A medium-sized (9 in.) white-rumped blackish brown storm-petrel with a shallowly forked tail. Breeds on islands of the e. Atlantic from the Azores to St. Helena, on the Galápagos and Hawaiian Is., and also probably on islands off e. Honshu, Japan. Has straggled or been storm-borne on 5 occasions to inland N. America (as far as Mo.). It is not common in Hawaii but has been reported throughout the islands.

GALÁPAGOS STORM-PETREL (Galápagos Petrel) (*Oceanodroma tethys*)

A small (7 in.) brownish black storm-petrel with slightly forked tail and white rump patch. Breeds on the Galápagos Is. and islands off the coast of Peru and ranges north to Baja Calif. and south to n. Chile.

BLACK STORM-PETREL (Black Petrel) (*Oceanodroma melania*)

A medium-sized (9 in.) fork-tailed storm-petrel, blackish except for paler marks on upper wings. Breeds on islands off the n. half of Baja Calif. in both the Pacific Ocean and the Gulf of Calif. It ranges along the shores of the e. Pacific from c. Calif. to n. Peru. This species breeds in burrows that may be usurped from other birds. It follows ships regularly and has been seen in waters off Calif. in flocks as large as several hundred.

The Black Storm-petrel nests in natural crannies or in burrows abandoned by other birds.

Least Storm-petrel

LEAST STORM-PETREL (Least Petrel) (*Halocyptena microsoma*)

The smallest (5½–6 in.) storm-petrel. Similar in range and coloration to the Black Storm-petrel, but has a wedge-shaped tail. Its marine range does not extend past n. Baja Calif. Little is known about the habits of this rare species.

Wilson's Storm-petrels appear to walk on water as they flutter near the surface.

WILSON'S STORM-PETREL (Wilson's Petrel)
(*Oceanites oceanicus*)

Reputedly the original "Mother Carey's chicken" of sailors. A small (7 in.) white-rumped, square-tailed blackish storm-petrel with bright yellow webbing between its toes. Breeds from the shores of Antarctica to islands of s. S. America and islands in the sw. Indian Ocean. Its marine range covers the Atlantic, Indian, and S. Pacific Oceans; it has straggled to Japan, Calif., the interior of the e. U.S., Europe, the w. Mediterranean, and into the Red Sea. It is the most abundant storm-petrel, and some claim that it is the most abundant bird species in the world. Large flocks gather around fishing vessels on moonlit nights, so that a dozen or more may be killed by the swing of a pole. Fishermen believe that killing one brings bad luck. Despite its abundance, much has yet to be learned about the food and other habits of this species.

    Suggested reading: S. A. Eliot, Jr., "Banding Wilson's Petrel," *Bird-banding*, vol. 4, pp. 45–49, 1933.

WHITE-BELLIED STORM-PETREL (White-bellied Petrel) (*Fregetta grallaria*)

A medium-sized (7½–8½ in.) species with black wings, tail, head, and neck; the back is gray, and the underparts and rump are white. Ranges the s. temperate seas between Australia and S. America and between S. America and the sw. Indian Ocean. A reported capture of 7 birds off St. Marks, Fla., by hook and line may be an adulterated fish story.

The White-tailed Tropicbird's spectacular tail accounts for about half its length.

THE TROPICBIRDS (PHAËTHONTIDAE)

The tropicbirds are marine birds not much larger than the Domestic Pigeon; they look larger than pigeons, however, because of the bigger head, the longer wing, and the greatly elongated central tail feathers (the birds are 16–20 in. without elongated tail feathers). These birds are found throughout most of the tropical and subtropical seas. There are 3 species, all of which have occurred in our area: Red-billed Tropicbird, White-tailed Tropicbird, Red-tailed Tropicbird. Their plumage is white with some black. They fly with rapid wingbeats and almost no gliding; it is startling to observe the butterflylike flight when one circles a ship far out at sea.

Their feet are webbed; the bill is long, pointed, and decurved. As in the petrels, the feet are weak and the birds push themselves about the ground on their bellies. Only fully adult birds have the elongated central tail feathers, called "streamers." A small, poorly developed bare-skinned pouch at the throat indicates relationships with pelicans, boobies, frigatebirds, and cormorants. Food, which consists of small fish and other sea animals, is obtained by diving, often from great heights. No nest is built; the single egg is laid on bare rock or in crevices or holes on tiny islands and offshore islets. Both parents share the incubation and nursery duties.

RED-BILLED TROPICBIRD (*Phaëthon aethereus*)

Appearance: Large (36–42 in. including streamers, 18–20 in. without) white tropicbird with black barring on back, black wing tips, and black streak starting just behind the red bill and running through the eyes to the back of the head. The legs are gray and the feet black.

Voice: Strident rattling or clicking noises made in flight or when birds are disturbed at nesting sites. It is

because of the shrill, trilling whistle that mariners refer to the larger tropicbirds as "bosun birds," as it resembles the tone of whistles blown by boatswains aboard naval vessels.

Range, status, habitat, and seasonal movements: Nests on islands in, and ranges through, tropical waters of the Pacific, the s. Caribbean Sea, the Lesser Antilles, the c. Atlantic Ocean, and the nw. Indian Ocean into the Red Sea and Persian Gulf. In our area it has strayed from breeding islands off Baja Calif. into s. Calif., Ariz., and coastal Wash. Common. Nomadic at sea, with no apparent regular schedule.

Biology: Flocks indulge in aerial displays prior to breeding. The buffy to reddish brown egg, spotted and blotched with darker colors, is laid in a natural cliff cavity or under a protective overhanging rock. Apparently breeds at any time of year. Nothing seems to be known of the incubation period or the age at which the young make 1st flight. Found scattered over the oceans after breeding, alone or in pairs; approaches ships at sea and circles them once or twice before proceeding on its way. Eats fish and squid, although its food habits are little known.

WHITE-TAILED TROPICBIRD (*Phaëthon lepturus*)

A small (28–32 in. with streamers, 15–16 in. without) tropicbird. Similar to the Red-billed in color, but in adults the black on the back is in streaks and patches, not barred, and the black through the eye curves downward behind the eye. The bill is usually yellow. Its range is more extensive than that of the Red-billed, as it breeds on islands in the tropical waters of the Caribbean and e. Atlantic, the n. S. Atlantic, the Indian Ocean, and the c. and w. Pacific. It has straggled along the shores of the Gulf of Mexico and the e. coast of the U.S. and Canada. More is known about this species' biology than any other. Its egg is whitish, densely spotted with browns or dark reds. An egg in an incubator hatched in 28 days, and 1 chick was able to fly when 62 days old. Food is mainly fish, cephalopods, and small crustaceans.

RED-TAILED TROPICBIRD (*Phaëthon rubricauda*)

Between the 2 other species in size (18–36 in.); white with a black crescent over the eye, and black on wings and flanks. The streamers are bright red. Ranges through the tropical waters of the Indian and Pacific Oceans from Madagascar and the islands south of Japan to the w. Hawaiian Is. and the Galápagos Is., straggling to the waters off Baja Calif.

The White Pelican flies with its head tucked back and its feet trailing behind.

THE PELICANS (PELECANIDAE)

Pelicans are large (50–72 in.) aquatic birds with a big pouch of naked skin running the length of the lower bill. There are 8 species, 2 of which fall within the scope of this work: White Pelican and Brown Pelican. All 4 toes are joined by webbing, and the birds are competent swimmers. Their dives (Brown Pelican only) for food from medium height above water cannot be described as graceful, but they certainly are effective and splashy. The long, hooked bill on the outstretched neck is well below the water's surface before the big splash of the body. Food is also taken from a swimming position on the water. The birds are awkward on land, waddling laboriously. In the air they become almost graceful, like a large passenger airliner. The head is held well back, with the bill apparently resting on the breast; they soar and turn in flight on wings that span almost 10 ft., flapping powerfully, if ponderously, on takeoff and as needed. Food consists of fish and sometimes other aquatic animals. Pelicans are gregarious and nest in colonies. The sexes are alike. Nests are made of sticks in trees or of grasses, reeds, and mud on the ground. The eggs, 1–6, are white; parents share the family duties.

WHITE PELICAN (*Pelecanus erythrorhynchos*)

Appearance: A large (50–65 in.), heavy-bodied white bird with black-tipped wings, large yellow or orange bill and pouch, and reddish orange feet.

Voice: Silent except on breeding grounds, and even there the grunts and croaking notes are barely audible.

Range and status: Restricted to N. America, mainly west of the Mississippi. Formerly bred from c. B.C. and the Prairie Provinces of Canada to s. Calif., n. Utah, c. Colo., and n. Iowa; now scattered in pockets within that range, with main area in the Prairie Provinces and smaller pockets in e. Wash., s. and n. Calif., w. Nev., s. Idaho, n. Utah, Mont., Wyo., the Dakotas, w. Minn., and coastal Tex. Winters in the Central Valley of Calif., along the Pacific Coast to Guatemala, along the shores of the Gulf of Mexico, and through most of Fla. There are many stragglers into the e. U.S. and Canada, and one has reached Cuba and another the Bahamas.

Habitat: Sizable freshwater lakes and ponds in breeding seasons; in addition, found in shallow marine and brackish waters, especially in winter.

Seasonal movements: Overland, even across deserts and mountains. Spring movement in March–May; a gradual dispersal from nesting colonies in fall, with largest movements Sept.–Oct.

Biology: Feeds from surface of water. Nests: May be depression in the ground or a mound of dirt and debris as much as a foot high and a yard wide. Eggs: 1–6; usually 2. Incubation: 36 days. Young insert head

The Brown Pelican, a strictly marine bird, seldom ventures far from the seacoast.

and bill into parent's throat for partially digested fish. The 1st flight is taken when the birds are about 2 months old. Man is the main enemy; misguided fishermen often kill them on sight.

Suggested reading: J. B. Low, L. Kay, and D. I. Rasmussen, "Recent Observations on the White Pelican on Gunnison Island, Great Salt Lake, Utah," *Auk,* vol. 65, pp. 345–356, 1950.

BROWN PELICAN (*Pelecanus occidentalis*)

Appearance: Somewhat smaller (42–54 in.) than the White Pelican, with brown around the lower part of the neck, extending up the back of the neck to the rear of the head and up the front of the neck to the throat, leaving a V of light color from the yellowish crown to the white point at the side of the lower throat; the brown is lacking in immature birds. The rest of the plumage is grayish to blackish, somewhat lighter underneath. The pouch is dark gray; the bill is yellowish, and the lower bill has a reddish tip.

Voice: Grunting noise of adults infrequent; young noisy with grunts and high screams. Birds of all ages snap and pop their large bills.

Range and status: Breeds on islands and along coastal lagoons in the Pacific from c. Calif. to s.-c. Chile, and on the Galápagos Is.; the coastal se. U.S. from N.C. to Tex.; and in the Caribbean islands, the Greater Antilles, and n. Lesser Antilles. Ranges north to coastal Wash. and straggles to the interior U.S. Common where protected within regular range.

Habitat: Strictly marine, preferring clear, shallow waters.

Seasonal movements: Mainly dispersal and return after breeding, with some individuals and groups rather sedentary.

Biology: Starts breeding at age of 2 years. Nests: May be hollows in ground; mounds of mixed debris, soil, and guano, or of available stick and reedlike material woven into branches of shrubs and low trees. Eggs: 2–3; 3 more commonly. Incubation: Not certain; about 4 weeks. The young are about 9 weeks old at 1st flight. Food: Coarse fish generally, obtained by diving. Sometimes acts as a scavenger, eating almost any animal matter small enough to gulp. Man is chief enemy.

Suggested reading: F. M. Chapman, *Camps and Cruises of an Ornithologist,* D. Appleton, N.Y., 1908, pp. 83–112.

The Blue-faced Booby has the bare neck and face typical of pelican relatives.

GANNETS AND BOOBIES (SULIDAE)

These large (26–40 in.) seabirds range through the temperate and tropical seas of the world, except for the cooler temperate regions of the N. Pacific. Of the 9 species, 5 appear in our region: Blue-faced Booby, Blue-footed Booby, Brown Booby, Red-footed Booby, and Gannet. They are excellent swimmers and fliers; their flight is by strong, rapid wingbeats and short glides. They dive from the air into the sea after their food and often pursue it for some distance beneath the surface. The bare-skinned throat patch, indicating relationship with the pelicans, is small. In the nestlings the pouch is proportionately larger. Plumage is largely white in the adults; the larger feathers of the wings are dark, sometimes black; the tails are usually dark-colored. The immature birds are mostly dark-plumaged, though some are white. All 4 toes are connected by webbing, as in all pelicans and related birds. The long, pointed bill is conical-shaped, slightly decurved at the tip. Fish and squid are the major food items. The sexes are alike. These are gregarious birds and nest in colonies. The 1–3 eggs are chalky bluish white. Parents share nest building, incubation, and feeding of young.

BLUE-FACED BOOBY (Masked Booby) (*Sula dactylatra*)

A large (26–34 in.) booby of more tropical seas, absent from the e. Atlantic and c. Indian Oceans. Adults white except for black mask, black flight feathers of wings, and dark tail. Immature birds are brownish gray with white breast and belly. Has straggled to the Gulf Coast and the Carolinas in the U.S.

BLUE-FOOTED BOOBY (*Sula nebouxii*)

A medium-sized (30–33 in.) booby ranging from the Gulf of Calif. along the Pacific Coast to the Galápagos and n. Peru. White with blackish brown back, wings, and tail; bluish gray bill and feet. Younger birds are browner with darker head and hind neck. Has straggled to Wash. and inland in s. Calif.

BROWN BOOBY (*Sula leucogaster*)

An average-sized (26–29 in.) booby, widespread in all tropical and subtropical oceans; this equatorial range is interrupted in the e. Pacific by the lack of islands from the Hawaiian Is. and the Tuamotu Archipelago to Revilla Gigedo and Galápagos Is., with another gap off the mouth of the Amazon River. Adults are brown-plumaged except for the white breast and belly and the contiguous patch of white under the wings. The bill and feet are yellowish. Immature birds are grayish brown all over. From its breeding islands in the Gulf of Calif., and from the Gulf of Mexico-Caribbean area, it has straggled into Calif. and along the coasts of s. and e. U.S. from Tex. to Maine and to Bermuda. It is possibly a rare but regular visitor to the Gulf Coast and has apparently bred on the Dry Tortugas off the Florida Keys.

RED-FOOTED BOOBY (*Sula sula*)

A small (26–29½ in.) white booby with black flight feathers. The feet are reddish orange or red, and there is

Gannets nest in dense colonies on inaccessible cliffs along the seacoast.

a patch of similar color at the widest part of the bill; the small throat patch is dark. A second phase, with plumage completely brown except for white undertail feathers, resembles the immatures. In both phases the tail is white, although the brown phase may have a brownish tail. Distribution is rather scattered in the tropical seas. It has straggled to the Gulf Coast of the U.S.

Suggested reading: J. Verner, "Nesting Activities of the Red-footed Booby in British Honduras," *Auk*, vol. 78, pp. 573–594, 1961.

GANNET (*Morus bassanus*)

Appearance: Largest (35–40 in.) member of the family. Adults are mainly white-plumaged; the head and neck are light tawny, the wing tips black. The white tail is a sharp-pointed wedge. Immatures are medium gray, sometimes flecked with white, and the flight feathers are black.

Voice: Purportedly silent at sea; at breeding places utters a loud throaty bark.

Range and status: Breeds on offshore islands and inaccessible sea cliffs in cool temperate N. Atlantic Ocean from Gaspé Peninsula, Que., N.S., and Nfld. to Iceland and the British Isles. Another subspecies, considered a separate species by some authorities, breeds off S. Africa, New Zealand, and se. Australia. The n. form ranges south along the coasts to Fla., the Gulf Coast, and nw. Africa, also into the Mediterranean and North Sea. Straggles inland, especially in the ne. U.S.

Habitat: Courses the coastal waters, mostly out of sight of land except during breeding season. Breeding places must have high rocky ledges or cliffs so that birds can take flight immediately by launching directly into midair.

Seasonal movements: Almost continually at sea for 1st 3 years. Moves southward Sept.–Nov., northward Mar.–late May.

Biology: At least 3 years old at 1st breeding. Displays prior to and during breeding season include curtsies and bows and bill-touching greeting ceremony. Nests: In densely packed colonies; built of variety of sea-drifting objects, some entirely of seaweeds. More than 1 egg in a nest may be the result of more than 1 female's activity. Incubation: 43–45 days in captivity. Young first fly when 95–107 days old. Food: Mainly fish that school and some squid.

Suggested reading: Bryan Nelson, "Bass Rock Gannets," *Natural History*, vol. 73, pp. 32–41, 1964.

THE CORMORANTS (PHALACROCORACIDAE)

Cormorants are moderate- to large-sized (19–40 in.) aquatic birds related to the pelicans and boobies. They are found in aquatic habitats throughout the world, except the Arctic and Antarctic regions, the coolest temperate areas, and the islands of the sw. Pacific. There are 30 species, 6 of which are found in our region: Great Cormorant, Double-crested Cormorant, Olivaceous Cormorant, Brandt's Cormorant, Pelagic Cormorant, Red-faced Cormorant. Cormorants are adroit swimmers and divers. They fly with steady wingbeats, very seldom far above the water's surface. They can adjust their buoyancy so that they are able to swim in the water with varying amounts of the body showing. A large flock swimming with only their heads and long necks protruding from the water reminds one of the emergent branches of a drowned forest. The plumages are predominantly black and browns, occasionally some white; bright colors occur in the bills, feet, and exposed skin. The immatures are mainly browns and white. The bill is long and hooked; the legs are short and close to the rear of the body as an adaptation to more efficient swimming. Food, caught by dives from the water surface (never launched from flight), is primarily fish, crustaceans, and amphibians. The sexes are very much alike. The nests are of sticks, seaweed, etc., on the ground or in trees or shrubs. The 2–4 eggs are usually of pastel blues or greens, rather chalky, marked with brown in 1 species. Both parents share incubation and feeding of the young, which are born naked and then acquire down. The young feed from the gullet of the adult by inserting the head in the mouth of the parent.

GREAT CORMORANT (*Phalacrocorax carbo*)

Great Cormorant

Appearance: A large (32–40 in.) cormorant. Breeding adults have a white throat and cheeks; the rest of the head, the neck, shoulders, and underparts are metallic green-black; thin white plumes, lost after the breeding period, are present among the longer feathers at the back of the neck. Back wings and tail are bronzy gray with darker edging on the smaller feathers. This species has a white patch on the thighs, lacking in Double-crested Cormorant. The bill is gray, the bare skin at the base of the bill is yellow, and the pouch is yellow spotted with black. Immature birds are brown with white underparts and are a lighter brown from the bill down the front of the neck to the breast.

Voice: At nesting colonies the adults, silent elsewhere, make a variety of throaty gurgling noises and querulous barks. The young make trilling or staccato peeping sounds.

Range, status, habitat, and seasonal movements: In Europe resident mainly on marine littoral, and breeds on inland bodies of water in se. Europe and Asia; resident in Africa from Nile Valley of Egypt through lake regions to all of s. Africa, and in New Zealand and Australia (except the desert interior). In America breeds in colonies about the Gulf of St. Lawrence, including Nfld., and winters from this region to Long I., N.Y., casually along the coast to Ga.; has straggled inland to W. Va., Pa., Ont., N.Y., Vt., and Maine. In n. parts of range it has a short migration, at least to more open and ice-free marine waters, and in Asia to India, se. Asia, and Sumatra.

Biology: 3–5 years old at 1st breeding. Nest: Interlaced twigs and sticks in trees near water, sometimes in dense colonies. Eggs: 3–4. Incubation: 29–31 days. Young independent at 12–13 weeks. Food: Fish and crustaceans caught during dives, which usually last 20–30 seconds but may last 71 seconds.

Suggested reading: D. L. Serventy, "Notes on Cormorants," *Emu*, vol. 38, pp. 357–371, 1939.

DOUBLE-CRESTED CORMORANT (*Phalacrocorax auritus*)

Appearance: Smaller (29–36 in.) than the Great Cormorant, without white in the adult plumage; in the immature the white is mainly on lower throat and breast. The "double crest," worn for a short period during the breeding season, comes from long, upcurled crown feathers at each side of the head.

Voice: Only at breeding and roosting places, hoarse grunts and an alarm note resembling the call of a bullfrog. Also low repetitive staccato notes, clicking and gurgling noises, and "whooping cough" notes.

Range and status: Restricted to N. America, where it breeds in colonies along the coasts from the Aleutians to s. Baja Calif., and from Nfld. to Fla., Cuba, and the Bahamas. Inland it breeds from s. Wash. to s. Calif. and from the c. Prairie Provinces of Canada to n. Utah, Nebr., and the Great Lakes region, casually farther south. Inland breeders move to marine waters and s. areas in winter. Where the birds are unmolested by man, they become quite common.

Habitat: Almost any body of water, fresh or salt, where fish abound. For breeding, rocky islands and islets or cliffs facing water or stands of trees near water are needed.

Seasonal movements: Some populations are resident. Inland populations migrate down the Mississippi and St. Lawrence river systems. Spring movements governed to some extent by weather; arrival at nesting sites usually in May–June. Fall migration starts in Aug., and birds are concentrated in wintering waters by early Dec.

Biology: Starts breeding at 3 years. Nest: In colonies near water; of a variety of sticks and debris lined

The Double-crested Cormorant loses its crests soon after the onset of the nesting season.

with finer materials; built in mounds on ground or in trees. Eggs: 2–7, usually 3–4, pale bluish becoming stained. Incubation: 24–25 days. The young are able to take flight from water when 7 weeks old and can dive at an earlier age, but do not become fully independent of parents until 10 weeks old. Food: A great variety of fish makes up over 90% of stomach contents; amphibians, crustaceans, and other animals are also consumed.

Suggested reading: G. A. Bartholomew, Jr., "The Fishing Activities of the Double-crested Cormorants on San Francisco Bay," *Condor,* vol. 44, pp. 13–21, 1942.

OLIVACEOUS CORMORANT (Neotropic Cormorant) (*Phalacrocorax olivaceus*)

A small (23–29 in.), dark, sleek-headed cormorant resident from the coasts of Tex. and the tropical regions of Mexico to s. S. America and in Cuba. Has straggled as far north as Colo., Kans., and Ill.

BRANDT'S CORMORANT (*Phalacrocorax penicillatus*)

Appearance: Fairly large (35 in.), dark, sleek-headed cormorant with a rather slender bill and short tail. The pouch is bluish with a grayish buff feather patch at its base.

Voice: Described as a low grating growl, croak, or gargle during squabbles over perches and territory. Also a penetrating, high, clear *kauk* repeated 3 or more times.

Range, status, habitat, and seasonal movements: Abundant along the Pacific Coast from Vancouver I., B.C., to s. Baja Calif. and into the Gulf of Calif. Strictly marine, it never strays inland or far from the more shallow ocean waters. Nests in large colonies on islands within its range and disperses only a little more widely in nonbreeding seasons.

Biology: Some start breeding when only 2 years old. Nest: Of marine vegetation procured by diving: always on the ground. Eggs: 3–6, commonly 4, pale blue. Incubation: Unknown. Little is known of growth and development of the young. Food: Fish and some crustaceans.

Suggested reading: L. Williams, "Display and Sexual Behavior of the Brandt Cormorant," *Condor,* vol. 44, pp. 85–104, 1942.

PELAGIC CORMORANT (*Phalacrocorax pelagicus*)

Appearance: A small (25–29 in.), dark, slender-billed, red-faced cormorant with 2 crests, 1 above the eyes and 1 at rear of head. Crests help separate it from the larger Brandt's Cormorant, with which it associates, but it is difficult to separate in the field from the rarer, less widespread Red-faced Cormorant.

Voice: Very little information; said to hiss when disturbed and to groan like someone in pain.

Range, status, habitat, and seasonal movements: Breeds in colonies on islands and offshore islets in n. Japan, the Sea of Okhotsk, the Bering Sea, the Arctic Ocean off ne. Siberia and nw. Alaska, the Aleutians, and along the N. American coast from the Alaska Peninsula to northernmost Baja Calif. Apparently not so common as the Brandt's Cormorant. Retreats from more n. areas in winter, at which time it may be found along coasts of China and Korea and to w.-c. Baja Calif. It has been recorded once from Hawaii. It is strictly marine, there being no inland records. It reaches ne. Siberia as early as May and leaves in Oct.

Biology: 2 years old at 1st breeding. Nest: Of seaweeds, grasses, and rubbish on remote precipitous islands and cliffs. Eggs: 4–6. Incubation: 1 report, unsubstantiated, of 26 days. Food: Besides fish and crustaceans, it also eats marine worms. This species has been taken in fishnets set at 20 fathoms (120 ft.), and reportedly uses both wings and feet for underwater propulsion after food.

RED-FACED CORMORANT (*Phalacrocorax urile*)

A larger (30 in.) edition of the Pelagic Cormorant, difficult to separate from the latter in the field. Breeds in the Aleutians, Pribilofs, and islands off the Alaska Peninsula; winters in the same area south to the Kuriles.

THE ANHINGAS (ANHINGIDAE)

These are essentially moderate-sized (34–36 in.) cormorants with long snakelike necks and long, sharp-pointed bills. There are 2 very similar species (4 according to some ornithologists) found in the tropics throughout the world, where they frequent slow-moving, sheltered waters, mainly fresh but also brackish and marine. Only 1 species occurs in our area. Anhingas enter the water only in search of food. They swim with all but the head and neck submerged, looking much like a snake in the water, hence the name Snakebird. These birds climb out of water before taking flight; they flap and soar. There are more than the usual number of vertebrae in the neck. Unlike the cormorants, anhingas spear their food underwater. Upon emerging from the water, they spend long periods on a perch with wings spread to dry in the sun. They are gregarious and are colonial nesters; the males build nests of sticks brought by the females to the site in a bush or on the ground or rocks. The females are larger and browner than the males. There are 3–6 eggs in a set. The young are born naked, and down appears later. Family duties are shared by male and female.

ANHINGA (Snakebird, Water Turkey) (*Anhinga anhinga*)

Appearance: Medium-sized (34–36 in.) birds. In the water, the snakelike appearance of the head and neck is unique among birds, while in the air the relatively long tail, fanned out, gives it the name Water Turkey. Glossy black head, neck, and body, with long brownish, black-barred tail; back and wings are spangled and streaked with silvery white, making a beautiful pattern when spread for drying in the sun. The bill is yellow, the pouch dark yellowish. The long neck is always distinctive. Female is browner than male.

Voice: Rapid whirring clicking or chattering; sometimes a repetitive *cruk-cruk-cruck*.

Range and status: Breeds from the tropical lowlands of Mexico, s. and e. Tex., se. Okla., southeasternmost Mo., s. Ala., s. Ga., and the e. Carolinas south to Ecuador, Colombia, e. Paraguay, and most of Brazil; also resident in Cuba. Retreats to the Gulf Coast, Fla., and s. S.C. in winter. Has straggled as far north as Ariz., Nebr., Ont., Ohio, and Va.

Habitat: As described under family; rare in marine waters of Fla. but common in cypress swamps.

Seasonal movements: N. breeders arrive at breeding areas in Mar.–Apr. and leave by Oct.; otherwise no pronounced regular movements.

Biology: At least 2 years old at 1st breeding. Males display while perched in trees at nesting grounds. Nesting activities described under family. Breeds throughout the year in s. Fla. Eggs: 2–5, usually 3–4; pale, chalky, bluish green. Incubation: Probably 25–28 days. Food: Largely so-called rough fish, but also aquatic insects, amphibians, snakes, and crustaceans.

Suggested reading: T. T. Allen, "Notes on the Breeding Behavior of the Anhinga," *Wils. Bull.*, vol. 73, pp. 115–125, 1961.

Because of its long, sinuous neck, the Anhinga is sometimes known as the Snakebird.

The Magnificent Frigatebird's fully inflated throat pouch is 7 to 8 inches in diameter.

THE FRIGATEBIRDS (FREGATIDAE)

Frigatebirds are medium- to large-sized (31–45 in.) marine birds ranging around the world in tropical and subtropical oceans. There are 5 species, 3 of which fall within the scope of this book: Magnificent Frigatebird, Lesser Frigatebird, and Least Frigatebird. A throat pouch and just enough webbing between all the toes show that they are related to the pelicans and boobies. Only by accident do they "land" in the water, over which they fly so easily and gracefully on scimitar-shaped wings. The identifying features of all frigatebirds are the long, pointed wings, the deeply forked tail, and complete swallowlike mastery of the air. In the breeding season the pouch of the male, just noticeable before, is inflated into a large scarlet balloon sometimes 7–8 in. in diameter. The bill is long and strongly hooked. Frigatebirds obtain their food by forcing other seabirds to drop their prey in midair, catching it before it falls to the sea or land; they are also capable of snatching floating animals or fish from the surface of the sea. The wingspan is greater in proportion to their weight than that of any other bird, and the flight muscles are more specialized for the aerial environment. The males are entirely black, with a bright red pouch. The females are larger, with a black head, and the rest of the plumage is dark brown except for a white breast; females lack the red throat pouch. The young are like the females except that the head and neck are entirely white. Frigatebirds lay 1 white egg in a nest of twigs in a tree or on the ground. Both parents share all the family-raising chores. The young are born naked, and their development parallels that of young pelicans.

MAGNIFICENT FRIGATEBIRD (Man-o'-war-bird)
(*Fregata magnificens*)

Appearance: Largest (37–45 in.) of the frigatebirds. Plumage generally as described under family, but underside of wings is uninterrupted black or dark brown. In the air, this large dark bird, with long, narrow, pointed wings and deeply forked tail, reminds one of a gigantic Barn Swallow. Flies or soars with head drawn back in the manner of pelicans.

Voice: A harsh rasping noise uttered by fighting males; at nesting colonies nasal cackling, high whining, and peeping sounds; also considerable bill snapping and rattling.

Range and status: In the Pacific breeds on islands off Mexico, south to Ecuador, and on the Galápagos Is., ranging along the coasts to n. Calif. Also breeds on offshore islands in the s. Gulf of Mexico and the Caribbean Sea (including the Greater and Lesser Antilles), and on the Bahamas, ranging along the coastline of the Gulf of Mexico and north to S.C.; breeds on islands off ne. and e. Brazil, and on the Cape Verde Is. off nw. Africa. Such a competent aerialist survives being blown great distances by violent storms and has been captured off the mouth of the Columbia River, in Kans., Iowa, Wis., Que., N.S., Nfld., Britain, France, and points between. A common sight within its regular range, especially near nesting islands.

Habitat: Marine coasts in tropics; the bird usually stays within sight of land. Follows large rivers inland and regularly crosses the Panamanian Isthmus.

Seasonal movements: Only dispersal from nesting places and scattering by hurricanes and other storms. Returns to perches and roosts on land at nightfall.

Biology: Males with ballooning throat pouches are considered a sign of probable breeding. Nesting occurs in different periods in each colony or close group of colonies; thus, during any month of the year some individuals are nesting somewhere. The 1 egg is laid in a nest, seemingly too small for the bird, constructed of twigs, reeds, seaweed, and grasses and situated 5–15 ft. off the ground in low trees or shrubs, sometimes on the ground or in grass tussocks. Incubation: Unknown, but possibly about 40 days, as with other species. The young are fully feathered when 20 weeks old but still unable to fly. There is still much to learn about the species' way of life. Food: A great many fish captured from surface of water while bird flys at great speed; others are pirated from boobies, pelicans, etc. Other food items include squid, jellyfish, offal, young turtles, and occasionally nestling seabirds snatched from their nesting sites.

LESSER FRIGATEBIRD (Great Frigatebird) (*Fregata minor*)

Smaller (34–40 in.) than Magnificent Frigatebird and distinguishable from it by brownish bar on wings. Breeds on islands in the tropical Indian, Pacific, and S. Atlantic Oceans. One subspecies breeds on the Hawaiian Is. and is seen there quite commonly. Habits, habitats, and biology are much the same as those of Magnificent Frigatebird.

LEAST FRIGATEBIRD (Lesser Frigatebird) (*Fregata ariel*)

The smallest (ca. 31 in.) of the frigatebirds and easily separated from the other species by the white patch on each side of the abdomen. Breeds on tropical islands in the Indian, w. Pacific, and S. Atlantic Oceans; has been photographed once at Deer Isle, Maine. Since this species and *F. minor* have both been called the Lesser Frigatebird, the scientific name must be used to prevent confusion.

HERONS, EGRETS, AND BITTERNS
(ARDEIDAE)

These small to large (11–56 in.) birds are found throughout the world, except the arctic regions and some oceanic islands, usually near or associated with water. There are arguments about the number of species in this family, 1 authority listing 100 and another 58; 16 are found in the area covered by this book. They are long-necked, long-legged birds found near water, particularly during the breeding seasons. The toes are unwebbed, but nearly all species are able to surface on and take off from deep water. The wings are broad and rounded; flight is usually by steady, rather slow flapping. In flight, the neck is held in a compressed S shape, with the head well back on the shoulders. Pairs of powder-down feather patches are present in all species; these are feathers that decompose at the ends into minute water-resistant dust, and are most useful, when spread through the plumage, to any animal exposed to the elements. Herons and egrets have 3 pairs of powder-down patches, and bitterns only 2 pairs. In herons and egrets the outer toe is longer than the inner, and in bitterns the reverse holds true. They all have special plumage adornments of some kind during the breeding seasons and indulge in courtship displays, some of which are quite elaborate. Most species feed by stalking aquatic animals in quiet water and spearing or seizing them with the long, pointed bill. Typically, members of the family stand with straightened legs and hold the neck in an S-shaped curve. Fish constitute the major food item; mollusks, crustaceans, insects, amphibians, reptiles, rodents, and nestlings of other birds are also often eaten. The sexes are alike in most species; both incubate and care for the young. They nest as isolated pairs or in small to large colonies. The 3–7 eggs are usually unspotted. The young are fed by regurgitation; they usually remain in the nest for some time before they are able to fly.

GREAT WHITE HERON (*Ardea occidentalis*)

This species illustrates 1 reason why there is no agreement among ornithologists as to the correct number of species in the family. Many believe that it is but a color phase of the Great Blue Heron, just as there are gray and red phases in the Screech Owl. It looks exactly like a white-plumaged Great Blue Heron and breeds freely with that species. Breeds in the Florida Keys, in Cuba, and along coast of Yucatan Peninsula; formerly on Jamaica and up the w. coast of Fla. There are casual records from the rest of Fla., and stragglers north even to Pa., but some of these records could pertain to albino Great Blue Herons. Details of habits and biology like those of the Great Blue.

GREAT BLUE HERON (*Ardea herodias*)

Appearance: Our largest heron, standing about 4 ft. high and often seeming taller; has a typical heron stance. The head is whitish with black plumes originating just above the eyes and projecting out behind the head. There are browns and black and white in the rest of the plumage, but overall effect is grayish blue.

Voice: Generally silent, but sometimes utters a low croaking noise.

Range and status: Breeds from se. Alaska and s. Canada south to s. Mexico, Cuba, and Jamaica; winters from se. Alaska and the c. U.S. to nw. S. America and the W. Indies. Many varieties or subspecies in this area, each formerly known under a separate common name. Remarkably common for a large water bird.

Habitat: Found in both freshwater and saltwater situations where shallows enable it to stalk its prey. Trees usually required for nesting purposes, and many varieties prove suitable.

Seasonal movements: At close of nesting season the birds disperse in all directions, and at this time the range is extended farther north. Many individuals, especially in the s. part of the range, are resident, as are some subspecies. Those that breed in the n. parts start for breeding grounds in Feb., and the movement is over by early May. Fall migration depends on weather but usually runs from mid-Sept. to late Oct.

Biology: Not known certainly at what age the bird starts breeding. Nests: New ones are flimsy platforms of sticks high in a tree, although in some places they may be mounds on the ground; through additions of new

Great White Heron

material each year of use, old nests may become quite massive. Solitary nesting is unusual; often several nests in 1 tree. Eggs: 3–7, usually 4, pale bluish green or pale olive. Incubation: Not exactly known, but given as about 28 days. The young probably do not leave nest until about 60 days old. Food: Fish, amphibians, snakes, small mammals, crustaceans, leeches, and insects.

Suggested reading: W. P. and B. D. Cottrille, *Great Blue Heron: Behavior at the Nest,* Misc. Publ. Mus. Zool. Univ. Mich., no. 102, pp. 1–15, 1958.

GRAY HERON (*Ardea cinerea*)

Slightly smaller than Great Blue Heron and similar, but lacks the reddish brown of neck and flanks. Found throughout Africa and Eurasia except deserts and n. Siberia. Reaches Iceland casually and has straggled several times to Greenland. The Old World counterpart of our Great Blue Heron.

GREEN HERON (*Butorides virescens*)

Appearance: Except for the Least Bittern, the smallest (18–22 in.) of our herons. The shaggy cap is greenish black, the wings are a dusky green, and the back is a dark, glossy grayish green; but the reddish brown cheeks, neck, and breast, and the white throat streak overpower the greens and give one the impression that this is a brown, not a green, heron. The legs are yellow or orange. The immature resembles an American Bittern without the black "sideburns," and it lacks the white spots on the back, which are conspicuous in the immatures of both of our night herons.

Voice: Low grunting and clucking noises, but the clear, high *keow* note uttered in flight is more familiar.

Range and status: Breeds from sw. Wash., s. Nev., c. Ariz., Tex., Nebr., c. Minn., the Great Lakes region, coastal Maine, and N.B. south to Panama and the W. Indies. Winters from coastal Calif., s. Ariz., s. Tex., and Fla. south to Colombia and n. Venezuela. Has straggled to Man., N.S., and Nfld. Common in the e. U.S. and locally common in the w. states.

Habitat: Found in almost any freshwater or saltwater environment; able to build nest in a great variety of situations.

Seasonal movements: Begins northward migration in late Mar. or early Apr. and generally completes it by May; fall movements Aug.–Nov. Scatters over wide area after nesting period.

Biology: Some breed in 1st year. Nest, not necessarily near water, built of twigs lined with finer twigs and grasses; new nests are flimsy, becoming more solid with passing years. It is either a solitary nester or nests in small groups. Eggs: 3–6, most often 4–5, pale greenish or bluish green. Incubation: 19–21 days. Young start flying when 21–23 days old. Young swim well and readily.

The Great Blue Heron, our largest bird species, stands nearly 4 feet high.

Food: Small fish, reptiles, amphibians, crustaceans, leeches, spiders, insects, and mollusks.

Suggested reading: A. J. Meyeriecks, *Comparative Behavior of Four Species of North American Herons*, Publ. Nuttall Ornith. Club, no. 2, pp. 3–83, 1960.

LITTLE BLUE HERON (*Florida caerulea*)

Appearance: A small (25–29 in.) heron. Head and neck purplish brown, rest of plumage bluish gray; legs dark. A slender-necked bird. The immatures are white-plumaged but may be separated from the egrets by the dark bluish bill and the completely dark legs and feet.

Voice: A strident, quarreling note; also a harsh croak and a repeated rough *gerr-gerr-gerr*. Usually silent.

Range and status: Breeds from the lowlands of Mexico, e. Tex., c. Okla., se. Mo., c. Ala., s. Ga., and Conn. south through the W. Indies and C. America to Peru, Brazil, and Uruguay. In winter it extends its range in Mexico to s. Baja Calif. and s. Sonora, but in the U.S. it withdraws to the Gulf Coast and coastal S.C. and Fla. Postbreeding dispersal spreads it over the e. U.S. to Nebr., Iowa, Mich., s. Ont., and s. Que. It has straggled to Sask., Lab., and Nfld. It is a common heron in its breeding and wintering areas.

Habitat: Mainly an inland species, but occurs in saltwater sites. Prefers ponds, marshes, small lakes, wet meadows.

Seasonal movements: Many breeding birds of Tex. and La. winter in C. America with pronounced flight in Oct.; reach La. and Tex. in Feb.–Mar. and Va. in Apr. Postbreeding dispersal often spectacular in numbers and in area covered.

Biology: A few breed in their 1st year. Twigs and sticks from area of nesting site are used to build the nest, which is placed in low trees 3–15 ft. above the water or ground. Eggs: 3–6, usually 4–5, pale bluish green. Incubation: 22–24 days (in Ark.). Young are able to fly when about 1 month old. Food: Small fish and other aquatic animals; lives on insects when water dries up; only rarely feeds in salt water.

Suggested reading: B. Meanley, "A Nesting Study of the Little Blue Heron in Eastern Arkansas," *Wils. Bull.*, vol. 67, pp. 84–99, 1955.

CATTLE EGRET (*Ardeola ibis*)

Appearance: An all-white medium-sized (19–21 in.), comparatively short-necked and short-legged heron. The legs and feet are blackish, becoming magenta to brownish in breeding season; the rather stout bill is yellowish. Prior to and during the breeding season the

Its head still tufted with down, an immature Green Heron stalks through streamside vegetation.

The Cattle Egret feeds on insects disturbed by grazing cattle and other animals.

adults wear rather long, light tawny plumes from the forehead to the back and on the breast; the bill becomes a dull scarlet with a bright yellow tip.

Voice: Usually quite silent. Occasionally a low, deep croak; some guttural and gargling noises. The young hiss loudly when disturbed.

Range, status, habitat, and seasonal movements: Formerly restricted to tropical and subtropical Europe, Africa, Asia, Madagascar, Ceylon, the Philippines, and Indonesia; now established naturally in Australia, nw. S. America, the Greater Antilles, Fla., and locally along the Gulf Coast to Tex. and along the Atlantic Coast to N.J. It has found conditions in the New World ideal and is spreading rapidly; only recently it has been found breeding in s. Ont. and reported landing on a ship at sea off the w. coast of Mexico. It was first reported on this side of the Atlantic sometime between 1877 and 1882 in Surinam; its spread in the Americas has apparently been from this general area. First appeared in the U.S. at Clewiston, Fla., in 1941 or 1942; first breeding evidence, in Fla., was obtained in 1953. A gregarious species; when first colonizing an area, it mixes with other heron species, even nesting at the edges of their colonies. Less fearful of humans than are other herons, and for this reason would appear to be very common where established. As the common name indicates, it is found associated with cattle, wild and domestic, and may be found with most varieties of large hoofed mammals in open fields, forests, and jungles. It is more independent of water than are other herons. The approach of winter causes a southward movement, more pronounced in the more northerly parts of its range. Birds from the U.S. apparently migrate to C. America and the W. Indies.

Biology: Nest of sticks and twigs from nearby vegetation. Eggs: 3–6, but not enough data from N. America to establish range and average; light blue. Incubation: 28 days. Young start to fly when about 40 days old. Food: Follows hoofed animals about to glean insects stirred up by the feet. Insects by far the largest food item, also small mammals; in some areas small fish, a few ticks, spiders, and earthworms.

Suggested reading: A. Sprunt, Jr., *The Spread of the Cattle Egret,* Smithsonian Report for 1954, pp. 259–276, 1955. D. W. Rice, "Dynamics of Range Expansion of Cattle Egrets in Florida," *Auk,* vol. 73, pp. 259–266, 1956.

REDDISH EGRET (*Dichromanassa rufescens*)

A moderate-sized (27–32 in.) heron breeding coastally in Mexico, Guatemala, Tex., Cuba, Hispaniola, and the Bahamas. Winters in s. Fla. and n. Venezuela. Rare, formerly more widespread; has straggled to Calif., Ariz., Colo., La., Ill., and S.C. Somewhat like the Little Blue Heron; there is a white-phase adult (rare). The dark phase has a lighter reddish brown head and neck than the Little Blue, and both phases have a pinkish or yellowish *black-tipped* bill.

Suggested reading: R. P. Allen, "The Reddish Egret: Bird of Colors and Contrast," *Aud. Mag.*, vol. 56, pp. 252–255, 1954; and vol. 57, pp. 24–27, 1955.

COMMON EGRET (Great Egret, American Egret) (*Casmerodius albus*)

Appearance: Smaller (37–41 in.) than the Great White Heron, from which it also differs by having blackish legs and feet; its plumes grow from the back, not the head.

Voice: A loud, low-pitched croak and, during displays and nesting seasons, a series of cuckoolike notes and a loud, nasal *frawnk* of alarm.

Range and status: Breeds from the Balkans and c. Asia south to s. Africa, Madagascar, India, Indonesia, Australia, and New Zealand, and from e. Ore., se. Minn., Lake Erie, and s. N.J. to s. Chile and s. Argentina. Has bred recently on Long I., N.Y. In winter it retreats south of n.-c. Africa, n. India, c. China, and Korea, and in America to Calif., s. Ariz., c. N.Mex., c. Tex., the Gulf Coast, Fla., and N.C. on the Atlantic Coast. Postbreeding dispersal takes it farther north in the U.S. and into se. Canada. Not nearly so abundant as prior to plume-hunting days, but recovering somewhat.

Habitat: Fairly open, shallow freshwater, saltwater, or brackish-water situations in swamps, ponds, and lakes or along rivers and protected coasts. Nests in nearby forests or shrubby growth.

Seasonal movements: Recent range expansion and alterations have obscured any migration schedules; the species is resident over most of its range and moves southward rather leisurely at winter's approach.

Biology: May not reach maturity until the 3rd year. Nest: Of dead sticks and branches found on ground or floating on water. Eggs: 1–4, usually 3–4, pale bluish green. Incubation: Probably 23–24 days. 1st flight when about 6 weeks old. Food: All sorts of aquatic animals and some small mammals and snakes; surprisingly little is known of this species' food preferences.

Suggested reading: A. C. Bent, *Life Histories of North American Marsh Birds,* Dover, N.Y. (reprint of U.S. Nat. Mus. Bull. 135, 1927), 1963, pp. 133–146.

SNOWY EGRET (*Egretta thula*)

Appearance: A white egret smaller (22–26 in.) than the Common Egret, with blackish legs, yellow feet, and a

Wading rapidly through shallow water, a Snowy Egret shows its distinctive yellow feet.

dark-colored bill; its breeding-season plumes are curlier and grow from both the head and back.

Voice: Much noisier than other herons during display and nesting periods. Calls at these times a grating *aah-aah* and a harsh *a-wah-wah-wah*.

Range, status, habitat, and seasonal movements: Restricted to the New World, where its range is very similar to that of the Common Egret, although it is generally rarer and retreats somewhat farther south in winter. It is slowly recovering from the depredations of the plume hunters, but active extension of range and wide postbreeding dispersal in more recent years have prevented any accurate appraisal of migration dates and routes. Found in same general habitat as Common Egret. It would be a serious omission to discuss the recovery of this species from near extinction to present range extension without mentioning the great work of the then infant National Audubon Society. Private sanctuaries were purchased and protected by dedicated wardens, several of whom lost their lives protecting these birds.

Biology: First serious depredation, then careful protection may be the reasons why we have so few data on the biology of this bird. Nest: Singly or in colonies; made of slender twigs on the ground or in trees as high as 30 ft. Eggs: 3–4(?), pale bluish green. Incubation: 18(?) days. Age at 1st flight is unknown. Food: Aquatic animals; some seeds of aquatic plants, but more information needed. Has been reported feeding by hovering over water surface like a petrel and snatching unidentified food from just below the surface.

Suggested reading: A. J. Meyeriecks, *Comparative Behavior of Four Species of North American Herons*, Publ. Nuttall Ornith. Club, no. 2, pp. 125–140, 1960.

LITTLE EGRET (*Egretta garzetta*)

An all-white egret of the warm temperate to tropical regions of the E. Hemisphere. Much like the Snowy Egret, but plumes straighter and feet never wholly yellow. Has been taken in Nfld. and Trinidad.

REEF HERON (*Demigretta sacra*)

A small (23 in.) egret with 2 color phases: all white, and grayish brown with a white throat. Found along the coasts of the w. Pacific from Japan to Malaya, Australia, and New Zealand; taken once in Hawaii.

LOUISIANA HERON (Tricolored Heron) (*Hydranassa tricolor*)

Appearance: One of the smaller (24–28 in.) herons with long head and back plumes. Principal colors of the adults are reddish brown, white, and bluish gray; the front of the long neck is striped with reddish brown and

Like all its kin, the Louisiana Heron engages in elaborate courtship displays.

white, the rest of the neck is bluish gray. The belly and flanks are white, the back reddish brown, and the wings bluish gray. Immature birds lack the plumes, and the gray on the neck is replaced with reddish brown. Neck appears longer and thinner than those of most other herons.

Voice: Strident croaks and low groans. Other sounds made at breeding grounds.

Range, status, habitat, and seasonal movements: Resident along the coasts of s. N. America and n. S. America (from Baja Calif. and s. Sonora to Ecuador and from s. N.J. to ne. Brazil) and in the Bahamas and Greater Antilles. Moves farther inland during postbreeding dispersal to Calif., Okla., and Ark., also to the interior of Mexico and C. America. Except for the Reddish Egret, more addicted to marine coastal areas, especially for breeding, than our other herons. Found in a great variety of aquatic coastal environments and does not eschew freshwater or brackish-water habitats. Returns to the coasts and moves southward along the Atlantic Coast in Nov.; returns to n. coastal areas in Mar. Has straggled as far away as Ore., Nebr., Ind., N.Y., and N.B.

Biology: Colonial nester; uses same types of materials as other herons. Eggs: 3–7, usually 3–4, pale bluish green. Incubation: 21(?) days. Other data on young lacking. Food: Aquatic animals of all sorts, but a large proportion of small marine fish; many grasshoppers consumed.

Suggested reading: R. S. Palmer (ed.), *Handbook of North American Birds*, Yale Univ. Press, New Haven, 1962, vol. 1, pp. 464–472.

BLACK-CROWNED NIGHT HERON (*Nycticorax nycticorax*)

Appearance: A stocky, medium-sized (23–26 in.) heron with a stocky bill, a greenish black cap and mantle, gray wings, and a white forehead and underparts. There are 2 long, limp white plumes from the rear of the head. The eyes are yellow in the young, becoming orange, and then scarlet in the adults. The immatures are brown-and-white-streaked, much like the American Bittern, but lack the black mark on the side of the head and the white throat; the young Green Heron has no white streaking on its back.

Voice: A hoarse, throaty *quock* most often heard after dark; repeated rapidly as an alarm note.

Range and status: Breeds from s. Europe, s.-c. Asia, and Japan to Africa, Madagascar, Ceylon, Java, and the Philippines; disperses over most of Europe. In the New World from Ore., e. Wash., s. Idaho, se. Wyo., s. Sask., sw. Man., c. Minn., s. Wis., s. Mich., s. Ont., and s. Que. south to s. S. America. Apparently missing from most of Brazil. In winter withdraws from more northerly parts of its range. Nocturnal habits may account for its being considered rare in much of its range.

Habitat: Occupies almost any aquatic environment from salt to fresh; even breeds in some city parks.

Seasonal movements: Covers great distances; arrives in spring Mar.–May, departs in fall Sept.–Nov. In winter may remain in much of its breeding range if water is ice-free.

Biology: Usually mature at 2–3 years. Not strictly nocturnal, as implied by the name. Colonial nester; nest of coarse twigs, reeds, and branches lined with finer materials; on ground or as high as 130 ft. in tree. Eggs: 1–5, usually 3–5, pale bluish green. Incubation: 24–26 days, but some question. Young able to fly at about 6 weeks of age. Food: Same as other herons. Active at night. It is an excellent fisherman and swimmer and has been seen alighting on water to seize prey.

Suggested reading: G. K. Noble, M. Wurm, and A. Schmidt, "Social Behavior of the Black-crowned Night Heron," *Auk*, vol. 55, pp. 7–40, 1938.

YELLOW-CROWNED NIGHT HERON (*Nyctanassa violacea*)

In size and build, much like the Black-crowned Night Heron, but head black with a white cap and cheek

The Black-crowned Night Heron sets out at dusk to hunt for fish and other prey.

patches; the white head plumes become yellowish from spring to fall. Body plumage is bluish gray; feathers of the back and wing are blackish edged with light gray, giving a scaled effect. This species also has back plumes extending beyond the tail. Immature birds are brown and buffy-streaked, very difficult to separate in the field from immature Black-crowned Night Heron. In the U.S. it breeds in the lower Mississippi, Ohio, Red, and Arkansas river basins and coastally from Conn. (casually in Mass.) to Tex. It is resident throughout C. America and the W. Indies and along the coasts of Mexico and S. America from Ecuador to se. Brazil. In the U.S. it winters along the Gulf Coast and through Fla. Less gregarious than our other night heron, and perhaps less nocturnal in habits. One of the differences is that this species' major food item is crustaceans, with other aquatic animals being of minor importance.

Suggested reading: M. M. Nice, "Herons with Golden Crowns," *The Watcher at the Nest*, Macmillan, N.Y., 1939, chap. 17, pp. 128–134.

LEAST BITTERN (*Ixobrychus exilis*)

Appearance: Our smallest (11–14½ in.) heron comes in 2 color phases. The more common light phase has a greenish black cap and mantle, with the neck shading from a dark brownish red at the back to whitish in front and at the throat, the rest of the underparts being buffy; the wings shade from buffy at the shoulders to brownish red and black at the tips. In the dark phase, brownish red replaces all the lighter colors of the other phase except the throat, which is dark buff. The female is more subdued in color; the greenish black and brownish red are replaced with dull browns, and the whole is streaked with white and light buff. Because of its size, habits, and habitat, this species often goes unnoticed in an area.

Voice: Male's in spring resembles that of a dove or frog, a low throaty series of *coo*'s and *tut*'s to which the female may answer with a shorter *uk-uk-uk*. It also makes a cackling sound when disturbed.

Range and status: The secretiveness of the birds and difficulty of observation result in a map measled with scattered breeding records. In general it breeds throughout much of the U.S. and in se. Canada south through Mexico, C. America, and the Greater Antilles to most of tropical and subtropical S. America east of the Andes. It is rarer in the w. U.S. and upland areas generally. In winter it moves south of s. Calif., s. Tex., and c. Fla.

Habitat: Many freshwater situations supporting rather dense aquatic plant cover, particularly reeds, sedges, cattails, etc.

Seasonal movements: Supposedly weak fliers; those nesting in the U.S. winter as far south as the Bahamas, Greater Antilles, Panama, and Colombia.

Biology: Not colonial. Few accurate data available.

The nest, built in dense stands of aquatic vegetation, is made of twigs and both dry and living plant materials. Eggs: 2–7, usually 4–5, pale bluish or greenish. Incubation: 17–19(?) days. Young are able to leave nest at 5 days, and generally all have done so at 10–11 days; it is not known at what age 1st flight occurs. Food: Small fish, amphibians, insects, leeches, crustaceans, and sometimes small mammals.

Suggested reading: M. W. Weller, "Breeding Biology of the Least Bittern," *Wils. Bull.*, vol. 73, pp. 11–35, 1961.

AMERICAN BITTERN (*Botaurus lentiginosus*)

Appearance: An average-sized (24–34 in.) heron, brown-and-buff-streaked on back and brown-and-whitish-

Yellow-crowned Night Heron

Its heavily streaked breast helps camouflage the American Bittern among reeds and cattails.

streaked below, with a white throat and black sideburns. To escape notice by enemies, it remains motionless with bill thrust skyward, making a difficult target against the reedy background of its chosen habitat.

Voice: In spring its deep reverberating ventriloquial *pump-er-lunk* has earned it such nicknames as "stake-driver" and "thunder-pumper." It also utters a guttural *kok-kok-kok* and a nasal *haink*.

Range and status: Breeds from c. B.C., s.-c. Mack., the n. Prairie Provinces, n. Ont., c. Que., and Nfld. to the s. U.S. (there are some large gaps in this general range); winters from sw. B.C., n. Nev., n. Utah, s. Okla., Ark., c. Ohio, n. Ga., and c. Md. to w. El Salvador, w. Honduras, and Cuba; straggles to Panama and Puerto Rico. A fairly common heron, judging by the frequency with which its pumping sound is heard. It has straggled to Great Britain

and the Canary Is. It was first made known to science from a specimen taken in England!

Habitat: Rare in other than freshwater swamps, marshes, and bogs.

Seasonal movements: Spring migration from Mar.–mid-Apr. and in fall from Sept.–Oct., occasionally lingering longer into winter.

Biology: Not colonial. Nest: Of available vegetation on ground in marshes or grassy meadows; sometimes floating. Eggs: 2–6, commonly 3–5, buffy brown to brownish olive. Incubation: About 24 days. Young remain in nest about 2 weeks; age at 1st flight unknown. Food: Fish, amphibians, reptiles, small rodents, crustaceans, mollusks, and insects.

Suggested reading: H. Mousley, "Home Life of the American Bittern," *Wils. Bull.*, vol. 51, pp. 83–85, 1939.

THE STORKS (CICONIIDAE)

Storks are large (30–60 in.), long-necked, long-legged, long-billed birds, ranging through the tropics and subtropics of the W. Hemisphere and throughout the E. Hemisphere, except for the Arctic, the s. third of Australia, and some oceanic islands. The face and sometimes the head and neck are bare. The pointed bills may be straight, curved up, or curved down. The sexes are alike. Of the 17 species, only 1, the Wood Stork, occurs in our area. They are strong fliers; a flapping flight is most common, but some species soar considerably. In flight the neck is extended. Except for grunts, hisses, and bill clacking, they are most often silent. Food is almost completely animal matter, including carrion. Nests are platforms of twigs and sticks in trees, on cliffs, or on buildings. They lay 3–6 white eggs; both sexes incubate and care for the young, which are born naked and later acquire down.

WOOD STORK (Wood Ibis) (*Mycteria americana*)

Appearance: Large (35–45 in.) birds with bare black neck and head, blackish legs, and pinkish feet; the stout, rather cone-shaped blackish bill is decurved. Plumage is white, except for the black tail and flight feathers at the tips of wings. In flight the bird is unmistakable because of the stark black-and-white pattern and the stiffly extended head, neck, and legs.

Voice The adults make buzzy hisses; also much clacking with their bills. The young make a loud, high, nasal *nyah-nyah-nyah*, raising a constant din in the nesting colonies.

Range and status: Resident wherever it now breeds in most of peninsular Fla., Cuba, Dominican Republic, the s. tip of the Mexican plateau, coastal Mexico from Sinaloa and Vera Cruz southward, coastal C. America, n. Colombia, se. Ecuador, and from ne. Venezuela, Guyana, and n. Brazil to e.-c. Argentina. It formerly bred along the coasts of the U.S. from S.C. to Tex. Postbreeding dispersal takes it more or less regularly to s. Baja Calif., s. Calif., c. Ariz., and southernmost Nev.; also to c. Tex., c. Ark., w. Tenn., c. Ga., and e. Va. It has straggled as far as n. Calif., sw. Mont., Nebr., Mich, Ont., Maine, and N.B. Now much reduced in numbers; destruction of its favored habitat by droughts and drainage constitutes a danger.

Habitat: Mainly freshwater areas, wooded swamps, and, for feeding, any shallow fresh water.

Seasonal movements: Extensive postbreeding dispersal, with individuals often straying as much as 100 miles or more from breeding areas. Nesting failures resulting from inadequate food supply lead to even wider dispersals by idle adults.

Biology: Colonies, now few and mostly small, formerly contained several thousand pairs each. Breeds in winter and spring. Nest: A flimsy platform of sticks with some lining of finer materials, built from a few feet above the water to the tops of the tallest trees. Eggs: 3–4, finely granulated. Incubation: 28–32 days. Young, if undisturbed, remain in nest 50–55 days before beginning 1st flights, but do not leave nest finally until 75 days old. Food: Mainly small fish, any other aquatic animals and insects, and some vegetable matter.

Suggested reading: A. Sprunt IV and M. P. Kahl, Jr., "Mysterious Mycteria: Our American Stork," *Aud. Mag.*, vol. 62, pp. 206–209, 234, 252, 1960.

The Wood Stork, also called the Wood Ibis, is the only true stork found in the United States.

IBISES AND SPOONBILLS
(THRESKIORNITHIDAE)

These are medium to large (19–42 in.), long-legged, long-necked, chiefly aquatic birds ranging in the Americas from s. U.S. to s. S. America and from n.-c. Eurasia to s. Africa, Madagascar, India, Ceylon, Indonesia, and Australia. There are 28 species, 5 of which occur in our area. The toes are partly webbed, and all species can swim. There is variation in the amounts of bare skin in the head region; on some birds the entire head and neck are featherless. They are strong fliers and alternate between flapping and gliding. Like their close relatives the storks, they fly with extended head and neck. Sometimes the legs are extended behind, but at other times they dangle beneath like unwanted appendages. The long bill is curved downward at tip and pointed (ibises), or flattened and broadened at tip (spoonbills). Food varies from species to species; insects, crustaceans, fish, amphibians, reptiles, and some grain and other vegetable products are eaten. The sexes are alike or similar, and both take part in all family duties. Most species are gregarious and are usually colonial nesters. Nests are made of sticks, twigs, grasses, etc., on the ground or in trees, not always near water. Eggs are white, usually 2–5 in a clutch; the young have downy coats at hatching.

The Glossy Ibis uses its long, decurved bill to probe for food in shallow water.

GLOSSY IBIS (*Plegadis falcinellus*)

Appearance: Smallest (19–26 in.) member of the family. The bare skin is confined to the areas between the eyes and the typical ibis bill. Plumage is predominantly a chestnut color with varying amounts of metallic gloss; there is a band of bronzy green on the wings. Toward the w. part of its range the population acquires an edging of white about the bare skin of the face; these birds are referred to as White-faced Ibises.

Voice: Rarely heard grunts and guttural notes; sometimes bleating and cooing notes.

Range and status: Breeding is in discrete areas: Calif., Nev., and Utah; w., s.-c., and ne. Mexico, s. Tex., and sw. La.; peninsular Fla.; w. Cuba; Hispaniola; Puerto Rico; s.-c. S. America; the lake region of e. Africa; se. Europe; sw. Asia; India and Burma; Madagascar; and se. Australia. In isolated colonies in c. Europe, S. Africa, coastal China, Ore., Colo., Nebr., Kans., Minn., s. Fla., and along the Atlantic Coast of the U.S. from S.C. to Long I., N.Y. In winter withdraws southward to tropical and subtropical regions. Extensive postbreeding dispersal, especially in w. and c. U.S., Europe, and Africa. The species straggles considerably, even to se. Canada, Iceland, n. Europe, and New Zealand. Probably the most common of the ibises.

Habitat: A variety of freshwater, brackish-water, or saltwater situations. Prefers reedy or grassy pools surrounded by trees or brush.

Seasonal movements: Postbreeding dispersal mainly,

On a perch near the nest, an immature Little Blue Heron begs its slate-colored parent for a meal of partially digested fish and other aquatic animals.

The Scarlet Ibis is most abundant near its breeding colonies in Trinidad, Venezuela, and Surinam but seems to have been successfully introduced in southern Florida.

The Roseate Spoonbill's distinctive bill and vibrant color make it unmistakable in any setting.

plus winter withdrawal. The non-white-faced population may actually be a recent invader (prior to 1880) from the Old World as a result of increased dispersal activity.

Biology: Usually associated with other waders at feeding and nesting grounds. Nests on ground or in low trees. Eggs: 3–4. Young fly when about 7 weeks old. Food, generally obtained by probing, consists of crayfish, insects, amphibians, worms, mollusks, and some fish.

Suggested reading: D. E. Baynard, "Home Life of the Glossy Ibis," *Wils. Bull.*, vol. 25, pp. 103–118, 1913.

WHITE IBIS (*Eudocimus albus*)

Essentially a white-plumaged Glossy Ibis with scarlet face, bill, legs, and feet and with black-tipped wings. Resident along coasts of Mexico, C. America, nw. S. America, the Greater Antilles (except Puerto Rico), and se. U.S. from Tex. to S.C. Has straggled to Calif., Colo., S.Dak. Mo., Vt., Que., and N.S. Immature bird differs from immature Glossy Ibis in having a white breast and belly.

SCARLET IBIS (*Eudocimus ruber*)

An all-scarlet ibis with black wing tips. In its adult plumage it cannot be mistaken for any other bird species, but immature bird is difficult to separate from the young White Ibis. It ranges from Venezuela to ne. Brazil and is found regularly in s. Brazil. There are 3 definitely known breeding colonies, 1 each in Trinidad, Venezuela, and Surinam. Stragglers have been in Tex. (at least 4 occasions), La., Fla., Honduras, and Jamaica. Some reports may have been of birds escaped from a zoo, but the species now appears to have been established in Fla. by egg transplantation in 1960.

Suggested reading: Paul A. Zahl, *Coro-coro*, Bobbs-Merrill, N.Y., 1954, 264 pp.

WHITE SPOONBILL (*Platalea leucorodia*)

A medium-sized (ca. 34 in.) white-plumaged, spoon-billed member of the ibis family, ranging through s. and c. Europe, n. and ne. Africa, and c. Asia to Japan, India, and Ceylon. It straggles farther north in Europe and has been taken once in Greenland.

ROSEATE SPOONBILL (*Ajaia ajaja*)

Appearance: A moderately large (30–34 in.) spoon-billed member of the family. Adult plumage preponderantly pinkish with a ruby slash on the wing from the bend to the back, a white neck, red legs and feet; the skin of the almost completely bare head and the bill are greenish. The tail is almost orange. Plumage of immature birds is entirely white, tinged slightly with pink; the head is feathered except for the area around and in front of the eyes. The bill is yellowish, and the legs and feet are dark yellowish.

Voice: An inquisitive, low, rapid, monotonous *huh-huh-huh;* sometimes low, soft grunting noises and clucking.

Range, status, habitat, and seasonal movements: A resident species from w. and s.-c. Mexico, s. Tex., sw. La., and s. Fla. to Ecuador and c. Argentina; also c. Chile, Cuba, Hispaniola, and the s. Bahamas. It has straggled as far north as Calif., Utah, Colo., Nebr., Ind., and Pa. Population declining in recent years because of swamp-draining activities but is numerous on dry coastal islands, mangrove-covered coasts, and wooded swamps. Considerable postbreeding dispersal; birds move into more northerly breeding areas in Apr.–May and depart from Sept.–Oct. Fla. birds apparently spend some time in Cuba.

Biology: Does not breed until 3rd year. Nests in colonies. Constructs a bulky nest of sticks and twigs lined with leaves and grasses, in low trees 5–15 ft. above the ground or water. Much display prior to and during nesting. Eggs: 1–4, usually 2–3, spotted and blotched with browns. Incubation: Probably 23–24 days. Young are practicing flight at 7–8 weeks after hatching. Food: Fish; also some crustaceans, insects, mollusks, slugs, and vegetable matter. The nestlings insert their bills into the parent's throat to obtain their food.

Suggested reading: R. P. Allen, *The Roseate Spoonbill,* Nat. Aud. Soc. Research Report, no. 2, 142 pp., 1942. R. P. Allen, *The Flame Birds,* Dodd, Mead, N.Y., 1947, 233 pp.

American Flamingos feed by straining small animals from mud in shallow water.

THE FLAMINGOS (PHOENICOPTERIDAE)

Flamingos constitute a peculiar, distinctive group of birds, thought by some ornithologists to be related to the herons, storks, and ibises and by others to be related to the ducks, geese, and swans. They hardly need description, as all 6 species are large pinkish birds with very long attenuated necks and legs and a unique stumpy, angled bill. From the tip of the bill to the tip of the tail they range from 3–4 ft.; the legs make them look longer; some stand 6½ ft. high. There is only 1 species in our area. Contrary to popular belief, they are not strictly tropical birds; 2 species are resident in the high Andes of S. America, where they have been seen incubating their eggs during snowstorms. Most species do occur in the tropical zone around the world. In flight they look like shallow pink arcs moving through the skies on black-tipped wings, as their extended necks and legs have a tendency to droop somewhat. Despite their appearance, they are excellent swimmers. They feed on a variety of crustaceans, mollusks, and other animals, in addition to algae and seeds of aquatic plants. As they wade through the almost bare tidelands or mudflats, they strain their food from the mud of shallow waters by swinging their special bills upside down in arcs at the ends of their long necks. They sometimes feed with head, neck, and feet under the water. They are gregarious and colonial nesters, building truncated cones of mud as nests, on which they lay 1–2 white eggs. The sexes are alike and share incubation and family feeding duties.

AMERICAN FLAMINGO (*Phoenicopterus ruber*)

Appearance: Largest (to 50 in.) of the flamingos and unmistakable. All flight feathers are black, so the outstretched wing has a black tip and trailing edge. The tip of the bill is black, grading from orange to yellow near the eye.

Voice: In flight gabbles like ducks and geese and makes gooselike honks (*not* like any native American geese).

Range, status, habitat, and seasonal movements: Now restricted to n. Yucatan, Cuba, Hispaniola, the Bahamas, the Galápagos Is., and n. S. America from ne. Colombia to the Amazon Delta. Wanders very rarely to s. Fla. Some believe that this is the same species as the European Flamingo of the Mediterranean region, nw. and e. Africa, sw. Asia, and India, and refer to it, thus constituted, as the Greater Flamingo. It has straggled to Kans., S.C., and the Lesser Antilles. Zoos now know which diets help captive flamingos maintain the beautiful pink color, so even pink individuals observed in the wild may be escaped captives; whitish individuals almost certainly are. It prefers large, shallow, hypersaline flats. American Flamingos leave the breeding areas for long periods, probably because food supply has become depleted, at which time they scatter to nearby coasts and islands. Man's activities, such as gathering salt, flying low over nesting colonies, and introducing mongooses and rats to nesting islands, have greatly reduced the number of colonies and birds.

Biology: Nest and eggs are described under family. Incubation: Estimated as 28–32 days. The young can leave the nest and swim 3–4 hours after hatching; they are able to fly when about 75–78 days old. Food as described under family.

Suggested reading: Leslie Brown, *The Mystery of the Flamingos*, Country Life, Ltd., London, 1959 (not about the American Flamingo, but interesting and pertinent). R. P. Allen, *The Flamingos*, Nat. Aud. Soc. Research Report, no. 5, 285 pp., 1956.

SWANS, GEESE, AND DUCKS (ANATIDAE)

These small to large (11–66 in.) water birds are world-wide in distribution except for the polar regions. There are about 145 species; 66 occur in N. America. They are good swimmers and fliers, although there are some flightless species. The 3 front toes are joined by webbing. In many species the sexes are alike. They nest in a variety of places: on the ground, on rocky ledges, in holes in the ground or in trees, or on the branches of trees. They lay 2–16 eggs, usually of pale colors. Incubation and care of the young are undertaken by both sexes or by the female. The young leave the nest shortly after hatching. During the breeding season or shortly after, most species undergo a complete molt; the males of many species then acquire a somber, femalelike feathering known as the eclipse plumage. The female usually does not start her molt until after the nesting season, somewhat later than the male. Both sexes lose all flight feathers in this molt and are unable to fly until these are replaced; since they are able to escape their enemies by swimming, they are not in great danger during this period. The adults regain their wing feathers about the time the young are learning to fly.

Anatomy and coincident habits divide the Anatidae into 10 major groups known as subfamilies, 7 of which are found in America: the swans (Cygninae), the geese (Anserinae), the tree ducks (Dendrocygninae), the dabbling or surface-feeding ducks (Anatinae), the diving ducks (Aythyinae), the ruddy and masked ducks (Oxyurinae), and the mergansers (Merginae). There is still some disagreement about the classification of this family, but the one used here is that followed by nearly all field guides and general references.

Swans are large (45–66 in.), long-necked, heavy-bodied members of the waterfowl family, with large feet and short legs. The neck is a little longer than the body. These birds are found in the subarctic and temperate zones of the N. Hemisphere, in s. S. America, and in Australia and Tasmania. Adults of species native to the S. Hemisphere have black in the plumage; the Black Swan of Australia is all black except for white flight feathers in the wing. There are 7 species; of the 5 n. forms, 4 occur in N. America. They are powerful fliers; the neck is fully extended while the birds are in flight; flocks usually form shallow V's or long oblique lines. All species feed almost exclusively on vegetation, primarily aquatic, which they obtain by tipping the body forward and extending the head and neck underwater to pluck the bottom vegetation. Swans dive under the surface only in emergencies. They nest on the ground. The 2–12 eggs are whitish, creamy, or pale green. Both male and female incubate and care for the young; they are noted for their fierce defense of the family.

Geese are moderately large (20–42 in.) waterfowl found in the temperate and subarctic regions of the world, rarely in the subtropics (India, Ethiopia, Hawaii). Their necks are long, but never so long as the body. Their legs are not so stocky as those of the swans; compared with swans, they have lighter, slimmer bodies. Their plumages usually contain some combination of browns, grays, black, and white. They are excellent fliers; their flight patterns are spectacular V's or crisscrossing wavy lines in the sky. They swim well and dive much more than the swans, but plunge beneath the surface mainly in play or escape activities. The birds obtain food, almost entirely plant materials, by grazing on land more often than tipping in water. There are about 20 species, 10 of which are found in America. They are gregarious, nesting in large colonies. The nest, of plant matter lined with down, is constructed on some hillock or in a hollow in the ground. The 1–10 eggs are white, whitish, or creamy. Incubation, by both sexes, continues for 22–30 days; both parents share in care of the young.

The medium-sized (16–26 in.) tree ducks are of pantropic distribution (found in the tropical zone around the world). "Whistling duck" is a more descriptive name than "tree duck," as all species make a rather unducklike whistle and not all of them perch regularly in trees. Of the 8 species, 3 have been recorded in America. Anatomically, tree ducks appear to be midway between the dabbling ducks and the geese. Their stance is gooselike; the legs and necks are rather long. They are gregarious, but not true colonial nesters. Their nests may be on the ground or in trees. The eggs, 8–20 in a clutch, are white. Incubation, performed by both parents (in some species mostly by the male), takes 28–32 days. The males probably also share the duties of rearing the young. Flight is slow and appears labored. Tree ducks are not expert swimmers, but they dive well and often. Food is varied, but largely vegetable. They graze considerably and are considered pests in rice fields.

The small to large (11–34 in.) surface-feeding or dabbling ducks are the most familiar species. Distribution is cosmopolitan except for the polar regions. There are about 70 known species, and 19 occur in America. Dabbling ducks are generally shorter-legged and shorter-necked than geese or tree ducks. The major observable differences between these ducks and diving ducks are that the dabblers have a small unlobed hind toe and that they obtain their food, mainly plants, by tipping or dabbling—tipping the body forward in the water and extending only the head, neck, and forepart of the body underwater. Swans, geese, and tree ducks also use this method of feeding. The males of all American species molt, usually in June, into an eclipse plumage. Members of this subfamily hybridize quite freely in captivity and occasionally in the wild. In getting airborne they spring almost directly upward from the water. The courtship displays and actions of most of them are interesting and sometimes complex.

The small to medium-sized (12–27 in.) diving ducks include many familiar species. They are cosmopolitan, except for Antarctica. There are about 31 species, with 22 recorded in America. They are often referred to as bay and sea ducks, as most of the common marine ducks belong to this subfamily; however, many species of diving ducks are most often found in a freshwater habitat. These ducks dive beneath the water's surface, often quite deep, after their food, which consists primarily of plant life. Many species eat mollusks and other animal life. The lobed hind toe, a primary difference between these ducks and the dabblers, is an aid to their underwater swimming. Their feet are closer to the rear of the body than are those of the dabblers. In taking off from the water, they patter along the surface some distance before becoming airborne. The males of only a few species acquire an eclipse plumage, and none of the American species has bright-colored speculums on the wings. Courtship performances are often spectacular. Hybridization is also fairly common among members of this subfamily. Females bear the sole responsibility for incubating the eggs and raising the young, although the males may remain near the nests until the eggs are about to hatch. The females of most species occasionally lay their eggs in the nest of another duck, not always one of their own species. The young are able to dive shortly after hatching.

The small (13–18 in.), chunky ruddy and masked ducks are more aquatic in habits than other subfamilies and rather grebelike in behavior. They are not found in polar regions or in most of Asia. There are 9 species, but only 2 occur in America: the Ruddy Duck and the Masked Duck. Their stiff, usually short tails are held erect in the water, at least in the case of the drakes. These short-winged, heavy-bodied ducks require some distance for taking off from water, and their flight is labored and buzzy. They are excellent divers and, like the grebes, can sink slowly beneath the surface without a ripple or a sound. Their feet are even closer to the rear of their bodies than are those of the diving ducks, and, partly because of this, they are almost helpless on land. The sexes are not alike. They have no eclipse plumage, but they have a summer and a contrasting winter plumage. Their eggs are larger in proportion to their size than those of any other duck. The drakes do not help incubate, but they remain near the nest and assist in caring for the young. The diet is mostly vegetarian, but 1 species eats as much as 25% animal matter. These ducks are not vociferous, but during the courting periods some squeaking and clucking noises are made.

Mergansers and smews are small to medium-sized (15–28 in.) fish-eating ducks. The 6 species are found in Eurasia and the Americas, occasionally reaching Africa; a 7th species, now believed extinct, was found in Auckland Is. off New Zealand. Their long, thin, tapering bills, serrated on the edges, effectively hold slippery prey. Most species are crested, and the males assume a complete or partial eclipse plumage in midsummer. These birds fly strongly, with the head, neck, body, and tail held stiffly in a line. They swim and dive well and are able to pursue their prey underwater, but they are awkward on land. The females incubate the eggs, but the males remain nearby and help rear the young. There is some nest parasitism; several females may lay their eggs in another's nest. Small numbers of mollusks, crustaceans, and insects are eaten, but fish constitute the main diet of all species. Game fish form a very small part of their meals.

MUTE SWAN (*Cygnus olor*)

Appearance: A typically large (57–60 in.) white-plumaged swan separated from all others in our area by the knob at the base of the upper bill. The bill is a very light "pinkish" scarlet-orange with black tip and base. The male is larger than the female.

Voice: As the common name implies, mainly silent; adults snort and make hissing noises, and the young peep. The noise of the wings during flight is very noticeable.

Range and status: Breeds in the British Isles, n.-c. Europe, and n.-c. Asia; winters south to n. Africa, the Near East, nw. India, and Korea; straggles to Japan. It has been successfully introduced in e. N. America at Long I., N.Y., and has strayed from this area to R.I., N.J., W.Va., and Ohio. In Europe it is the common swan in the wild, in parks, and on country estates.

Habitat: Shallow, sheltered bays, estuaries, lakes, ponds, and marshes. More common in winter on marine waters.

Seasonal movements: In the wild state it moves to ice-free waters, marine or fresh. There is no mass migration, but birds congregate in flocks of more than 100 in winter.

Biology: Even in semidomestication, the defense of its nest is strong and determined. It is capable of killing or maiming some of the larger predators. Nest: A huge structure of reeds, stems, roots, and coarser aquatic vegetation well above the regular water level in swampy places near a pond, lake, or backwater; lined with feathers and down. The incubating adult has the top of the head and part of the neck stained by plant materials and mud from its feeding activities, a common occurrence among birds of similar feeding habits, known as "adventitious coloring." Eggs: 5–12, more often 5–7; pale gray or pale blue-green. Incubation: 35–38 days. The brownish gray young remain in the nest but 1 day and are able to fly in about 60(?) days. Food: Aquatic vegetation. Ducks often attend flocks of swans to feed on the leftover plants freed from the bottom.

Suggested reading: D. A. Bannerman, *Birds of the British Isles,* Oliver and Boyd, Edinburgh, 1957, vol. 6, pp. 179–191. B. E. Berglund and others, "Ecological Studies of the Mute Swan in Southern Sweden," *Acta Vertebratica,* vol. 2, pp. 163–288, 1963.

WHOOPER SWAN (Whooping Swan) (*Olor cygnus*)

Smaller [56–58(?) in.] than the Mute Swan. The bill from the base to the nostrils is bright lemon-yellow, and the remainder is black; plumage is white. It holds its neck more erect while swimming than does the Mute Swan. Breeds in Iceland and n. Eurasia, wintering south to s. Europe, China, Korea, and Japan. Formerly bred in Greenland. It has been taken once in Alaska (St. Paul I.) and in Maine (Alexander Township, Washington Co.). In flight it utters a low, soft *hoo-hoo-hoo,* repeated many times; it also makes noises said to resemble "a double bugle note."

WHISTLING SWAN (*Olor columbianus*)

Appearance: The smallest (50–54 in.) of our swans, with the bill entirely black or with a small patch of yellow just in front of the eye. The bill of the young is marbled with pinkish, and their plumage is a light blackish brown.

Voice: A flock flying overhead sounds like a high-pitched, musical flock of Canada Geese. Individual calls

The Mute Swan is readily distinguished by the knob at the base of its bill.

Whistling Swans, the most common wild swans in North America, migrate in large flocks.

consist of 3 double-noted *whoop*'s in succession, the middle *whoop* being slightly longer and louder.

Range and status: Breeds in arctic N. America from n. Alaska, Victoria I., and Baffin I. south to the Alaska Peninsula, c. Mack., Southampton I., and the Belcher Is. Winters coastally from the Aleutians to northernmost Baja Calif. and from Del. to Tex., very rarely in the Great Lakes region. The commonest wild swan in N. America. Casual in Mexico; accidental in Cuba, Bermuda, Puerto Rico, and Siberia.

Habitat: Shallow waters, where it may reach growing vegetation at the bottom without diving; feeds in marine waters more than does the Mute Swan; breeds near fresh waters.

Seasonal movements: In migration it occurs on large inland bodies of water, even in the Great Basin. Spring migration begins in early Mar. and continues into May; fall movements last from Sept.–Nov.

Biology: Nest: A bulky mass of debris, grasses, and mosses gathered into a heap with a shallow depression in the top; on islets off the shores of shallow lakes or flooded tundra. Eggs: 2–7, usually 4–5, dull white. Incubation: 35–40(?) days. The young leave the nest shortly after hatching, and 50–60 days pass before they are able to fly.

They are about 5 years old before they assume the full-white plumage of the adult. Food: Primarily aquatic plants, but also grasses, sedges, etc. Wild celery, eelgrass, and foxtail grass are favorite winter foods in the Chesapeake Bay area. Like Canada Geese, Whistling Swans fly across the sky in long skeins, shallow V's, or wedge-shaped flocks.

Suggested reading: R. E. Stewart and J. H. Manning, "Distribution and Ecology of Whistling Swans in the Chesapeake Bay Region," *Auk*, vol. 75, pp. 202–212, 1958.

TRUMPETER SWAN (*Olor buccinator*)

Appearance: The largest (62–66 in.) of our swans, with a solid black bill.

Voice: A short *beep* not unlike an old-fashioned automobile horn, low, vibrant, and far-carrying.

Range and status: Now breeds from se. Alaska, c. B.C., and w. Alta. to e. Idaho, sw. Mont., and nw. Wyo., with artificially established colonies in Ore. and Nev. Formerly bred from c. Alaska and Mack. across to James Bay and south to s. B.C., Nebr., Iowa, Mo., and Ind. In winter it is now restricted to ice-free fresh waters of se.

Alaska, B.C., and nw. Wash. Its former winter range included much of the Missouri and Mississippi Valleys south to the Gulf Coast from Tex. to Ala. It has made some return from the verge of extinction but is still in danger, as suitable nesting places are being reduced by drought and the advance of civilization.

Habitat: Prefers the wilder, lonelier regions, where it frequents shallow bodies of water; in winter often found near waterfalls and rapids, where motion keeps waters free of ice.

Seasonal movements: Its migration is simply a retreat before the ice of winter, although there is a gathering into large flocks preceding and during this movement.

Biology: It has been accorded full protection at breeding areas in Mont. and Wyo. so that the population in these places is probably at the saturation point. Data from these places have filled in gaps in our knowledge of the life history of this bird. Nest: Of grasses, reeds, and feathers, on slight elevations or hummocks near water. The nests are seldom closer to each other than ½ mile; geese and other swans are driven from the area, but ducks and smaller water birds are tolerated. Eggs: 2–10, usually 5–8, creamy white and rough-shelled. Incubation: 36–40 days. The young in Wyo. were unable to fly well until they were at least 100 days old. Their plumage is not entirely white until the 3rd year. Food: Favors wild celery and other freshwater plants; also eats grain, grasses, insects, snails, and small vertebrates.

Suggested reading: W. S. Banko, "The Trumpeter Swan," *N. American Fauna*, no. 63, 224 pp., 1960.

CANADA GOOSE (*Branta canadensis*)

Appearance: Medium- to large-sized (22–40 in.) goose. Brown body; black head, neck, tail, bill, and feet; white cheek patches, throat, and underrump. The V-shaped flying formations are well known.

Voice: Varies in the species as much as size: from a buglelike honk to almost a cackle.

Range and status: The advance of civilization in America has seriously disrupted the former breeding range, even eliminating most of some subspecies, including that of the largest form of the n. Great Plains region. Now it is being reestablished by man in some of its former haunts. At present it breeds from n. N. America (including s. Baffin I. and w. Greenland) south to c. Calif., Mont., and se. Canada, with some colonies south of this line. In winter it reaches the s. U.S. and ne. Mexico; some flocks winter from Kamchatka to c. Japan. This species is still one of the more abundant in America; flocks in migration or on wintering grounds may number 50,000 or more. It has been successfully introduced in New Zealand, easily adjusting to the reversed seasons.

Habitat: Almost any situation where water is shallow enough to allow easy feeding from surface and where growth of plants is sufficient. Also, in deeper waters near

Although the female alone incubates the eggs, the male Canada Goose usually remains nearby.

open fields and plains where grasses and other vegetation furnish ample food. Nesting territories range from marine coastal through tundra, prairie to woodlands, and semi-deserts.

Seasonal movements: May be found throughout the year when waters do not freeze over; more northerly nesters are among the earliest migrants and the most notable both by day and night. The sounds of a high-flying migrating flock at night may be haunting, nostalgic, or as musical as a Stravinsky ballet score, or all of these at once.

Biology: They may mate for life. Nest: In a variety of situations, not always close to water; may be a hollow in the ground or a mound of grasses, reeds, and other vegetation, lined with feathers. Eggs: 4–10, usually 5–6, dull white or creamy white. Incubation: 28–30 days by the goose alone, although the gander remains close-by. The young leave the nest shortly after hatching, and swim rapidly and dive readily to avoid enemies; not able to fly until more than 50 days old. Food: A great variety of aquatic plants, grain, grasses, and the sprouting shoots of grain; also occasional small vertebrates and invertebrates, such as frogs, toads, fish, worms, crustaceans, and mollusks.

Suggested reading: H. Hanson and R. H. Smith, *Canada Geese of the Mississippi Flyway*, Bull. Ill. Nat. Hist. Survey, no. 25, pp. 67–210, 1950.

BRANT (Brent Goose) (*Branta bernicla*)

Appearance: Small- to medium-sized (20–24 in.) goose with a rather short neck. The head, neck, chest, and bill are black; adults have a partial white necklace on the upper neck. The rest of the upperparts are dark slaty or brownish, and in the American subspecies the underparts are white with some light gray markings on the forward part. In the Eurasian form only the undertail feathers are white; the rest of the underparts are dark like the back. A swift flier and, on the water, constantly bobbing and turning. It does not fly in V formations as a rule.

Voice: A low, long, throaty honking roll; also hissing and grunting noises. Noise of babbling flock carries long distances.

Range and status: Breeds in the high Arctic of e. N. America and Europe from Prince Patrick I., King William I., and Boothia Peninsula to n. Greenland, Franz Josef I., and Novaya Zemlya; winters along the Pacific Coast from B.C. to Baja Calif. and along the Atlantic Coast from Mass. to N.C., occasionally farther north and south, off Iceland, the North Sea shores, and the coasts of w. Europe to nw. Africa. Numbers apparently dependent, in winter, on crop of eelgrass; only a small percentage of the once vast flocks was able to survive a dieback of this aquatic plant by eating seaweeds.

Habitat: Almost completely marine; although some-times nesting near fresh waters, it is never far from the sea.

Seasonal movements: Not so early as the Canada Goose; northward movements begin in Mar., and it has usually reached the breeding grounds by early June. It starts arriving at the wintering areas in Sept. and completes the movement in late Dec.

Biology: Nest: Sometimes in loose colonies, often a down-lined hollow or low mound of grasses, lichens, and mosses. Eggs: 1–7, usually 3–5, dull white. Incubation: 23–25 days, by female alone. The young leave the nest 1–2 days after hatching. The male remains near the incubating female, helps defend the eggs, and also helps rear the young. It is not known at what age the young become independent of the adults. Food: On breeding grounds, grass, mosses, leaves of arctic plants, and algae; on wintering grounds, eelgrass and sea lettuce. Occasionally small invertebrates are eaten.

Suggested reading: T. W. Barry, "Observations of a Nesting Colony of American Brant," *Auk*, vol. 73, pp. 193–202, 1956. A. S. Einarsen, *Black Brant: Sea Goose of the Pacific Coast*, Univ. Wash. Press, Seattle, 1965, 142 pp.

BLACK BRANT (Pacific Brent Goose) (*Branta nigricans*)

Similar in size, habits, and biology to the Brant, and believed by some to be merely a race of that species. It differs in having a much more prominent white patch on the neck of the adults. Also the forward part of the

Black Brant

The extremely rare Hawaiian Goose survives on a few remote mountain slopes.

undersides is much darker, making the bird seem blacker. It breeds on arctic coasts and islands from the Taimyr Peninsula of Siberia to ne. Mack., Banks I., and Victoria I.; winters along the coasts of the N. Pacific south to Formosa and Baja Calif.

BARNACLE GOOSE (*Branta leucopsis*)

Medium-sized (24–27 in.); similar to the Brant in general coloration, habits, and appearance, except that the face, cheeks, and upper throat are white and there are no white marks on the neck. Breeds in e. Greenland, Spitsbergen, and s. Novaya Zemlya, and winters in n. Europe. It has straggled to the coasts of N. America from Lab. to N.C. and inland to Ohio and Vt.

HAWAIIAN GOOSE (Nene) (*Branta sandwichensis*)

Appearance: Similar to a small (22–24 in.) Canada Goose, but with a buffy cheek patch extending to cover the entire front and sides of the neck, and with blackish streaks on the neck and throat. Webbing between the toes is much reduced, and the legs are stockier.

Voice: According to Peterson, a high-pitched *chuck, chuck, chuck-ah-yaw, ah-yaw, chuck, chuck, chuck.*

Range and status: Rare on the island of Hawaii; straggles to Maui I.; formerly more widely spread in the Hawaiian Is. In great danger of extinction; needs more effective protection from man and from predators introduced by man. Early records show that the species was rather abundant at least until 1823, and from then on it is a story of continual decline in population. By 1900 it was considered rare; in 1939 it was estimated that only about 50 birds survived in the wild. A program involving propagation in captivity and the establishment of ecologically suited sanctuaries in Hawaii has increased the Nene's number somewhat. It is still in great danger.

Habitat: Mostly in uplands among old, vegetation-covered lava flows where water is scarce and usually of temporary occurrence.

Seasonal movements: These birds are good fliers; they apparently flew from island to island in Hawaii. General consensus is that this goose is closely related to the migratory Canada Goose.

Biology: Little information on nests in the wild. From birds raised in captivity, we know the following.

Eggs: 5–8 creamy white. Incubation: 30 days. From various sources the Hawaiian Goose has been found to feed on 31 different plants, including grasses, leaves, and berries; in captivity it needs abundant grazing range. Its greatest enemies are swine, dogs, mongooses, and, of course, man.

Suggested reading: P. H. Baldwin, "The Hawaiian Goose: Its Distribution and Reduction in Numbers," *Condor,* vol. 47, pp. 27–37, 1945.

EMPEROR GOOSE (*Philacte canagica*)

Appearance: A medium-sized (26–28 in.) goose, bluish gray with a white head and hind neck and a black throat. Feathers of body and wings have dark edges, giving a scaly effect; immature birds lack the white and black on head and neck, which are blue-gray spotted with white.

Voice: A harsh *kla-ha, kla-ha.*

Range and status: Breeds on the coasts of ne. Siberia and nw. Alaska (St. Lawrence I. and from the mouth of the Kuskokwin River to Point Barrow). Winters mainly in the Aleutians, but south to Hawaii and Calif. Not common; rare south to Ore. and only casual in Calif.

Habitat: Never farther than 10 miles from the sea at nesting time, and in tundra areas. Marine coasts in winter, but at this season in Calif. found on fresh water.

Seasonal movements: Moves south to open waters about the Aleutian Is. with advance of ice and returns as water opens.

Biology: Apparently mates for life. Nests: feather- and down-lined hollows on marshy islets or among driftwood on beaches; mosses and grasses may also be used in lining. Not a colonial nester. Eggs: 3–8, white. Incubation: About 24(?) days. Age at 1st flight unknown. After eggs are hatched, the male joins the female to help care for young, which leave nest a day or so afterward. Food: Mainly shellfish and seaweeds; on tundra, grasses and berries.

Suggested reading: A. M. Bailey, "Haunts of the Emperor Goose," *Natural History,* vol. 23, pp. 172–181, 1923.

WHITE-FRONTED GOOSE (*Anser albifrons*)

Appearance: Medium-large (26–34 in.), brownish gray with yellow or orange feet and the forepart of the face white. The immatures lack the white face but have a light-colored bill, which helps separate them from the very similar immature Blue Goose.

Voice: The bird is sometimes called laughing goose because of repeated high-pitched, liquid *kah-lah-a-luk,* often referred to as "tootling."

Range and status: Breeds in the arctic tundra from nw. Siberia east to n. Keewatin and on the coasts of c. Greenland. In the nonbreeding seasons it ranges south to

France, Italy, Greece, the Middle East, n. India, China, Japan, c. Mexico, and the w. and c. Gulf Coast; casually along the Atlantic Coast to the Carolinas. Fairly common in the w. U.S.; casual in the e. U.S. and accidental in Hawaii.

Habitat: Coastal marine waters, fresh waters, tundra, prairies, and fields.

Seasonal movements: Migrates through the Great Basin and the Great Plains. Large flocks string across the sky at great heights, cackling as they go. Heaviest fall flights are in late Sept. or early Oct.; in spring northward movement starts in Mar., but largest flights are in Apr.

White-fronted Goose

Biology: Nest: Usually completed by mid-May, in grassy edges of lakes and ponds or in wet fields; of grasses and sedges lined with down. Eggs: 4–7, usually 5–6, cream-colored. Incubation: 22–23 days by female alone. The young are reported as able to fly when about 5 weeks old—a short period for geese. Food: Nuts, grain, berries, leaves, and grasses; occasionally aquatic insects.

Suggested reading: H. Boyd, "Mortality and Fertility of the White-fronted Goose," *Bird Study*, vol. 4, pp. 80–91, 1957.

BEAN GOOSE (*Anser fabalis*)

Medium- to large-sized (28–36 in.), with a dark brown head fading to lighter brown on the body; the dark wing and tail feathers are edged with white; feathers under the tail are white. The bill is blackish with a small pinkish orange band near the tip in 1 subspecies, ranging to pinkish or pale orange with black markings in other

The Snow Goose (above) and Blue Goose (below) are so closely related that some ornithologists consider them to be a single species.

forms. The legs are pink in some forms and orange in others. Bean Goose breeds in e.-c. Greenland, Iceland, Spitsbergen, and the tundra and forested areas of n. Eurasia, wintering south to the Mediterranean, the Near East, India, China, and n. Japan. It has strayed to the Pribilofs and St. Lawrence I., Alaska.

SNOW GOOSE (*Chen hyperborea*)

Appearance: Medium-sized (25–31 in.); white, with black flight feathers. Bill and legs are pinkish; the edges of the bill are black. The young are grayish above and have blackish bills.

Voice: A loud, high-pitched *gwap*, seldom repeated more than twice; also a buzzy, guttural *zung-ung-ung*, described as "conversational." The young occasionally make a clear whistling note.

Range and status: Arctic coasts from ne. Siberia to n. Greenland, and Baffin I. In winter south to Korea, Japan, n. Baja Calif., Mexico, the Gulf Coast, and the Atlantic Coast from N.J. to the Carolinas. Of the geese in N. America, this is the most abundant species.

Habitat: Breeds in tundra; at other seasons found on ponds, lakes, bays, grasslands, and grainfields.

Seasonal movements: Follows fairly well defined migration routes between breeding and wintering grounds; it does not start spring or fall movements as early as the Canada Goose. Neither does it fly in the V pattern as regularly as the Canada Goose, but travels more often in shallow wavy lines.

Biology: Appears to mate for life. Nest: Down-lined hollow in the tundra, usually in loose colonies. Eggs: 4–8, usually 6, whitish. Incubation: 23–25 days. Age at 1st flight unknown. Food: Mainly waterweeds, grain, grasses, sedges.

Suggested reading: L. Lemieux, "The Breeding Biology of the Greater Snow Goose on Bylot Island, Northwest Territories," *Canadian Field Naturalist*, vol. 73, pp. 117–127, 1959.

BLUE GOOSE (*Chen caerulescens*)

Appearance: Medium-sized (25–30 in.), with white head, throat, and upper neck; back and most of body dark brownish gray. Flight feathers of the wing are black; tail and the feathers underneath it are white. Bill and legs are the same color as those of the Snow Goose. The young lack the white head and have dark bills. Birds intermediate in color between this species and the Snow Goose probably constitute only a color phase of this species.

Voice: Exactly like that of the Snow Goose.

Range and status: Breeds on the tundra of n. Keewatin, Southampton I., and s. Baffin I. in mixed colonies with the Snow Goose; winters with the same species on the Gulf Coast of e. Tex. and La.

Ross' Goose

Voice: A weak cackling or gruntlike *gug*.

Range and status: Breeds in a very small area of the coastal tundra in ne. Mack. and nw. Keewatin, and winters in the Central Valley of Calif. A rare species.

Habitat: Like that of Blue Goose and Snow Goose.

Seasonal movements: Its main migration route is apparently through Alta. to w. Mont. and nw. Wyo., then through Idaho and Ore. to Calif.

Biology: Much to learn. Nest: Down-lined hollow. Eggs: 2–6, usually 4, whitish. Incubation: 24 days in captivity. Food: Probably much the same as that of Blue Goose and Snow Goose.

Suggested reading: P. A. Taverner, "The Nesting of Ross's Goose," *Canadian Field Naturalist*, vol. 54, pp. 127–130, 1940.

BLACK-BELLIED TREE DUCK (Red-billed Whistling Duck) (*Dendrocygna autumnalis*)

A medium-sized (20–22 in.) tree duck with bright pink bill, pale pink legs, black belly, brownish breast and upperparts, gray cheeks and throat, and white-mantled dark wings. It is a resident species from Mexico and s. Tex. south to Ecuador, n. Argentina, and s. Brazil. It has strayed to Calif., Ariz., and the W. Indies.

FULVOUS TREE DUCK (Fulvous Whistling Duck) (*Dendrocygna bicolor*)

Appearance: Smallest (18–21 in.) of the tree ducks in our area. Bill and feet grayish; head, breast, and

Like all tree ducks, the Fulvous Tree Duck stands more erect than other ducks.

Habitat: Like that of the Snow Goose.

Seasonal movements: Travels from its breeding area in flocks with the Snow Goose.

Biology: Since both the Blue and Snow Geese are usually monogamous and have strong family ties, it is not strange that the 2 do not mix more rapidly. Apparently the Blue Goose is becoming more numerous in all breeding colonies of the Snow Goose, and they should be considered phases of a single species. Because of the rules of scientific nomenclature, the 2 forms combined as 1 species would take the scientific name of the Blue Goose. Details of biology are the same in both forms.

Suggested reading: J. D. Soper, "Life History of the Blue Goose," *Proc. Bost. Soc. Nat. Hist.*, vol. 42, pp. 121–225, 1942.

ROSS' GOOSE (*Chen rossii*)

Appearance: Our smallest (20–26 in.) goose, very much like the typical Snow Goose, but without the black edging on the bill. The bill is rough and warty at the base.

underparts fulvous or tawny brown; back and back of neck dark brown. It has a buffy throat patch and a series of whitish slashes underlined with dark brown along the side.

Voice: A whistled *k-weeoo* squeal in flight; also a weak call like that of the Killdeer.

West Indian Tree Duck

Range and status: A surprisingly monotypic species of disjunct pantropic distribution. It ranges through the tropical and subtropical regions of N. and S. America, Africa, India, and Burma. It is not found in the W. Indies. It is resident in Calif., N.Mex., Tex., and s. La. and has strayed north to Minn., Mich., Ohio, Ont., N.Y., and N.S. and has also been recorded in Cuba and Bermuda. It is common and seemingly increasing in numbers and probably extending its range in the U.S.

Habitat: Freshwater marshes and cultivated lands, especially irrigated areas of tropics and subtropics.

Seasonal movements: Prone to wander in postbreeding season, which helps explain its peculiar distribution.

Biology: Nest: Almost entirely of grasses, in reeds or grass near marshes; only very rarely in tree hollows. Eggs: 10–20, usually 12–14, whitish; occasionally several females will lay their eggs in 1 nest. Incubation: 30–32 days. Food: Seed of grasses and weeds; frequently found gleaning in cornfields.

Suggested reading: Brooke Meanley and Anna G. Meanley, "Observations on the Fulvous Tree Duck in Louisiana," *Wils. Bull.*, vol. 71, pp. 33–45, 1959.

WEST INDIAN TREE DUCK (Black-billed Whistling Duck) (*Dendrocygna arborea*)

Largest (22–26 in.) of the tree ducks recorded here. Bill black, feet dark gray; plumage medium brown with buffy throat and white-mottled flanks. This duck is resident in the Bahamas, the Greater Antilles, the Virgin Islands, Barbuda, and Antigua. Was taken once in Bermuda.

SHELD-DUCK (*Tadorna tadorna*)

A large (25–26 in.) dabbling duck with a greenish black head and neck and a white body, circled at the breast with a broad chestnut band. The tail, tips of the wings, and inner feathers are dark with green and purple iridescence. The bill of the male is knobbed, red in both sexes; the feet are pink. It breeds in c. and n.-c. Eurasia, wintering south to nw. and ne. Africa, the Persian Gulf, n. India, c. Thailand, and n. Vietnam; also Formosa and Japan. It has straggled to Iceland and Mass.

RUDDY SHELD-DUCK (*Casarca ferruginea*)

About the same size (25–26 in.) as the Sheld-duck, with a tan-colored head; this color becomes more reddish over the rest of the body. Wing tips and tail are blackish; there is a patch of white on the wings; bill and feet are blackish. The male has a dark ring around its neck. Breeds over a wide expanse of c. Asia extending to se. Europe; an isolated population breeds in nw. Africa and on Sardinia. Winter range much the same as Sheld-duck's, but extends south to s. Nile Valley, s. India, and Ceylon.

The Mallard, one of our most common ducks, is seen even in urban areas.

Has straggled to w. Greenland and Iceland and through most of Europe. Captured once in N.J.

MALLARD (*Anas platyrhynchos*)

Appearance: Medium- to large-sized (16–27 in.) dabbling duck. Adult male has a metallic green head and neck separated from the rich chestnut breast by a narrow white ring; underparts are light gray, and upperparts a darker gray; tail is black and white, with sharply curled feathers above; wings are dark with a band of bright iridescent blue bordered on each side first by a narrow black band and then by a narrow white band. These bands, known as the speculum, are partially visible when the bird is at rest. The female has the same speculum, bordered by white, and is otherwise a mottled brown and darker brown all over, with a somewhat darker cap and eye stripe; it also lacks the curled feathers of the tail. Bill of the male is yellow, that of the female orange; feet of both sexes are orange. The drake in its eclipse plumage, assumed in early summer and lost in early fall, looks much like the hen. Mallard is variable in size and appearance throughout its wide range; some isolated island populations would require special descriptions because of this variation.

Voice: It is the female that makes the loud *quack*, familiar to all, since these ducks are ancestral to most domestic ducks; drake has a higher, softer *quack*.

Range and status: Found throughout most of the temperate N. Hemisphere (except ne. Canada) and into the subarctic of Greenland, Iceland, Eurasia, and nw. N. America. In winter it moves south, sometimes to the subtropics. One of the most common ducks.

Habitat: Almost any body of shallow fresh water. In Greenland and Iceland, and occasionally in winter elsewhere, it is found on shallow, protected marine waters.

Seasonal movements: It remains as far north as it can find open shallow fresh water and returns northward in spring as soon as melting ice permits.

Biology: Nest: Of dead grasses and reeds lined with down, on the ground, not far from water. Eggs: 5–14, usually 8–10, light greenish to whitish. Incubation: 23–29 days, by female alone. Young cared for by female; generally leave nest shortly after hatching. Food: Aquatic vegetation, grains, grasses, sedges, acorns, and berries, with a small percentage of animal food, mainly insects and mollusks.

Suggested reading: G. L. Girard, "The Mallard: Its Management in Western Montana," *Jour. Wildlife Management,* vol. 5, pp. 233–259, 1941.

Like most near relatives of the Mallard, the Laysan Duck (above) and the Black Duck (below) are rather drab in coloration.

HAWAIIAN DUCK (Koloa) (*Anas wyvilliana*)

A small (20 in.) isolated close relative of the Mallard. Plumage of the male looks like a good mixture of the breeding plumages of both sexes of the Mallard, but lacks the white neck ring. The female looks and acts like a female Mallard. It is resident on the islands of Kauai and Oahu in Hawaii and is of casual occurrence on the other islands.

LAYSAN DUCK (Laysan Teal) (*Anas laysanensis*)

Smallest (16 in.) of the Mallard relatives. Darker than the Hawaiian Duck. Both sexes have a white patch about the eyes. Found only on Laysan I., one of the w. islands of Hawaii.

MEXICAN DUCK (New Mexican Duck) (*Anas diazi*)

Medium- to large-sized (21–26 in.) duck found from s. N.Mex. and w. Tex. south through the Mexican plateau. It has strayed to Nebr. and Colo. Both male and female look like female Mallard, except that the Mexican Duck has a more yellowish bill. It may be separated from the Black Duck by its white-edged blue speculum and its lighter coloration. In most respects it is so like the Mallard and Black Duck that many experts feel that all 3 are but 1 widespread, highly variable species.

BLACK DUCK (*Anas rubripes*)

Appearance: Mallard-sized (21–26 in.) and very similar to female Mallard in coloration, but browns are darker, bill is yellower, tail is much darker, and speculum is purple with black edges. Underparts of body look almost black in flight. The sexes are alike.

Voice: Like the Mallard's.

Range and status: Breeds from c. Canada east to n. Lab. and Nfld. and south to the Great Lakes region and e. N.C. Winters from the s. edge of the breeding range to the Gulf Coast and s. Fla. Distribution spotty; common in some areas within range and rare in others. It hybridizes readily with the Mallard, with which it is certainly closely related.

Habitat: Like the Mallard's, any body of shallow fresh water; but it prefers more cover and is found more often than the Mallard in saltwater marshes.

Seasonal movements: Some individuals remain as far north as there is ice-free water, and the northward movement in spring is quite early.

Biology: Nest: Similar to Mallard's, but usually better hidden; sometimes built off ground in an old hawk or crow nest. Eggs: 5–14, usually 8–10, whitish to greenish buff. Incubation: 26–28 days, by female. Male in flightless eclipse plumage while female raises young. Age at which young become independent of adults is unknown. Food: About 75% vegetable matter, primarily aquatic plants and grasses, and the rest animal matter, including mollusks, crustaceans, insects, and small fish.

Suggested reading: B. S. Wright, *High Tide and East Wind,* Stackpole Co., Harrisburg, Pa., 1954, 162 pp.

GADWALL (*Anas strepera*)

Appearance: A medium-sized (19–23 in.) dabbling duck. Male's breeding plumage is grayish, with brownish head and neck, and with black feathers above and below the gray tail. He has a conspicuous black-edged white speculum, a patch of chestnut brown at the bend of the wing, a white belly, yellowish feet, and a dark bill. The female is dull brownish all over except for the white speculum and whitish underparts. The male acquires the femalelike eclipse plumage in early summer.

Voice: The female gives a series of quacks, loud at the start, but falling in pitch and volume. The male makes a single low, rather apologetic *quack* and has a low whistled call.

Range and status: Breeds from Europe, sw. Siberia, nw. Mongolia, Kamchatka, Bering I., s. Alaska, s. B.C., the Prairie Provinces, Que., and Iceland south to sw. Europe, n.-c. Africa, the Balkans, n. Iran, n. Afghanistan, ne. China, Sakhalin I., Calif., n. Ariz., s. Colo., n. Tex., n. Iowa, nw. Pa., and the Atlantic Coast to N.C. Breeds only rarely and locally in e. N. America. Winters in areas of ice-free water south to c. Africa, India, Burma, Thailand, s. China, s. Mexico, the Gulf Coast, and Fla.; coastally it is found as far north as s. Alaska, N.Y., the British Isles, and e. China. It is accidental in Greenland, Bermuda, Cuba, and Jamaica. A shy duck, rare in the East and never very common in the West.

Habitat: Shallow, quiet freshwater lakes, ponds, rivers, and marshes; usually prefers good growth of cover. Very rare in marine or brackish waters.

Seasonal movements: A late spring and early fall migrant; very seldom seen in large flocks.

Biology: This is one dabbler that dives well. Nest: A hollow, lined with down, in dense grasses or under bushes. Eggs: 7–15, usually 10–11, whitish. Incubation: 26–28 days, by female alone. The female raises the family; it is not known at what age the young become independent. Food: Aquatic plants, grasses, grains, nuts, and acorns; sometimes as much as 10% animal matter, such as insects and crustaceans.

Suggested reading: J. M. Gates, "Breeding Behavior of the Gadwall in Northern Utah," *Wils. Bull.*, vol. 74, pp. 43–67, 1962.

The shy, inconspicuous Gadwall frequently is overlooked by bird watchers.

The wide-ranging Pintails are often seen in large flocks in the West.

MOTTLED DUCK (Dusky Duck) (*Anas fulvigula*)

This duck looks like a small (20 in.), pale brownish-mottled Black Duck. The speculum is greenish blue, not purplish. Some authorities consider it yet another sub-species of the Mallard, which it closely resembles in habits and biology. It is resident along the Gulf Coast from Tex. to Miss. and in peninsular Fla.

Suggested reading: S. L. Beckwith and H. J. Hosford, "A Report on the Seasonal Food Habits and Life History Notes of the Florida Duck in the Vicinity of Lake Okeechobee, Glades County, Florida," *Amer. Midland Naturalist,* vol. 57, pp. 461–473, 1957.

PINTAIL (*Anas acuta*)

Appearance: Moderate-sized (20–29 in.) dabbler; the very long, pointed tail of the male in full plumage (excluding the eclipse plumage) accounts for the large range in size. The long, slender neck and the tail are distinctive; the tail of the female is at least longer than those of other brownish-plumaged ducks. The male has grayish back and flanks, black under the tail and on the wing; the head and throat are a rich purplish brown, which extends down the back of the neck; the front of the neck and the undersides are white, with a finger of white extending from the throat into the brown of the head to behind the eye. A patch to the rear of the flanks is also white. The bill and feet are grayish blue.

Voice: Generally silent; female quacks softly, and male makes a 2-toned whistle and some thin, raspy whistling noises.

Range and status: Breeds from the s. parts of the tundra regions of Eurasia and w. and n.-c. N. America south to c. Europe, n. Iran, Mongolia, n. Japan, Calif., Colo., c. Nebr., n. Iowa, and the Great Lakes region; locally in parts of e. Canada and New England. Winters south to n. and e.-c. Africa, India, Burma, Thailand, the Philippines, ne. S. America, and the Greater Antilles; in N. America regularly north to se. Alaska, the Gulf Coast, and Mass. In America it is a most common duck in the West and is extending its regular range eastward.

Habitat: Freshwater lakes, ponds, and marshes in prairies, open areas, and tundra; marine bays and estuaries.

Seasonal movements: A very early spring migrant and sometimes a late fall migrant.

Biology: Nest: A hollow scooped in the ground, sparsely lined with grasses and down; may be more than a mile from water, on a prairie or in a marsh. Eggs: 5–12, most often 6–8, light greenish buff. Incubation: 23–25 days, by the female alone. When the young become independent is unknown. Food: Aquatic plants, grasses, grains, weeds, and some mollusks, crustaceans, and insects.

Suggested reading: J. A. Munro, "Studies of Waterfowl in British Columbia: Pintail," *Canadian Jour. Research*, vol. 22, pp. 60–86, 1944.

BAHAMA DUCK (Bahama Pintail, White-cheeked Pintail) (*Anas bahamensis*)

Medium-sized (18–21 in.) dabbler of the W. Indies and S. America, obviously a close relative of the Pintail; its tail is not quite so long, but other proportions are similar. Bill is red, cheeks and upper throat are white, and speculum is metallic green with buffy borders. The rest of the plumage is light brown. It is casual in Fla. and has appeared in Wis. and Va.

FALCATED TEAL (*Anas falcata*)

Medium-sized (19 in.), big-headed, chunky dabbler. The male is crested, and the head and crest are a metallic-glossed reddish brown and green; the throat is white with a black "necklace." The wings and the feathers above and below the tail are green-black, and the speculum (both sexes) is bluish black. The rest of the plumage is gray barred on white, lighter underneath. The female is brownish. Breeds in e. Siberia and n. Japan, and winters south to Burma, s. China, and Formosa. Casual in Europe and in the Aleutian Is. of Alaska.

EUROPEAN COMMON TEAL (European Teal) (*Anas crecca*)

Small (13–16 in.) dabbler of Eurasia and Africa. Many ornithologists consider this to be the same species as our Green-winged Teal; it differs mainly in having a white streak above the wing while at rest. The European variety is seen rarely, but regularly, along the e. coast of N. America as far south as S.C. Another form is resident in c. and w. Aleutian Is. This is the "Common" Teal of Europe.

GREEN-WINGED TEAL (*Anas carolinensis*)

Appearance: Small (12–16 in.) dabbler; both sexes have a bright, glossy green speculum. The male has a bright, brownish red head with a broad bright green band starting from around the eyes and continuing to the rear of the head; his breast is black-spotted buffy; the feathers under the tail are buffy bordered with black, the belly is white, and the rest of the plumage is grayish. While at rest he shows a black streak just above, and a vertical white stripe before, the wing. The female is brownish gray, lighter below. Bill and feet are grayish. Fast and direct in flight.

Voice: The male makes a short whistling note, seldom repeated, and also a short trilling call; the female quacks rather softly.

Range and status: Breeds in a triangular area of N. America from w.-c. Alaska and nw. Mack. south to s.

Bahama Duck

Calif. and east to Nfld.; now extending its range in the East. Winters from s. B.C. through most of the U.S., where it finds open waters, south to Honduras, the Bahamas, and most of the W. Indies. It has strayed to Japan, Hawaii, Bermuda, Greenland, and Great Britain. It is very rare south of Mexico, the Gulf Coast, and Fla. It is quite a common teal in the West and, locally, in the East.

Habitat: Inland ponds, marshes, lakes, streams, and rivers; also freshwater bays; very rarely brackish water. Preference is for quiet, shallow waters.

Seasonal movements: Remains farther north than many larger ducks. Many migrate considerable distances; usually a fairly early spring and late fall migrant.

Biology: Nest: A hollow in the grass or at the edge of a marsh, neatly lined with down. Eggs: 7–15, usually 10–11, light buffy olive. Incubation: 20–23 days, by female alone. Age at which young are independent is not known; said to be 23 days in the closely related European Common Teal. Food: Plants, chiefly aquatic, but with a small amount of grass, make up about 80% of the total; also insects, mollusks, and maggots on rotting fish.

Suggested reading: J. A. Munro, "Studies of Waterfowl in British Columbia: Green-winged Teal," *Canadian Jour. Research,* series D, vol. 27, pp. 147–178, 1949.

BAIKAL TEAL (*Anas formosa*)

Small (16 in.), stout-looking dabbler that breeds in e. Siberia and winters south to se. China, Formosa, and Japan; casually to India and Burma. It has been captured 4 times in Alaska; records from Calif., Ohio, Iceland, and Europe probably refer to escaped captives. The male has a slight crest, and its head is a variegated pattern of bright green, cream, white, and blackish. The female is brownish. Both have a bright green speculum.

BLUE-WINGED TEAL (*Anas discors*)

Appearance: Small- to medium-sized (14–17 in.) dabbler. Most of the small feathers on the top of the wing (the coverts) are very pale blue; when duck or drake is at rest, some of these show as a horizontal streak above the folded wing. Both male and female have long, bright green speculums. Especially during the courting season, the drake has a large white crescent, convex edge forward, in front of the eyes; this may be indistinct until long after the femalelike eclipse plumage is shed. The male's bill is bluish black, and his head is bluish purple; breast, flanks, and underparts are a dull brownish, the back a darker brown; the feathers above and below the

Relatively insensitive to cold, two Green-winged Teal stand in a freezing pool of water.

Comblike teeth along the edges of the Shoveler's bill strain bits of food from mud and water.

tail are black, with a white patch just forward of the tail. The female is brownish, with a pinkish-edged dusky bill. The legs are yellowish.

Voice: Quack of the female not so strong as that of the Green-winged Teal; the drake has a much-repeated peeping note.

Range and status: Breeds from n.-c. B.C., n. Prairie Provinces, and se. Canada south to e.-c. Calif., Nev., se. Ariz., s. N.Mex., w. and c. Tex., n. Mo., and Tenn., and along the Atlantic to N.C. Winters from the s. edge of the breeding range south to Peru and n. Brazil. It is a common marsh duck, particularly east of the Rockies.

Habitat: Sluggish streams, freshwater ponds, and marshes.

Seasonal movements: An early fall and very late spring migrant. Sometimes seen in large flocks.

Biology: Nest: Near water; a down-lined hollow in grass. Eggs: 6–14, most often 9–11, whitish. Incubation: 21–23 days, by hen alone. Age when young become independent is unknown. Food: Aquatic plants, grasses, rice, and corn; about 30% animal matter, including mollusks, insects, and crustaceans.

Suggested reading: L. J. Bennett, *The Blue-winged Teal*, Collegiate Press, Ames, Iowa, 1938, 144 pp.

CINNAMON TEAL (*Anas cyanoptera*)

Appearance: Same size (14–17 in.) as the Blue-winged Teal, and considered a close relative; it is almost impossible to tell the females of the 2 species apart. The drake is readily distinguished by the rich cinnamon-brown of almost all its plumage, except for the back and wings, which are like those of the male Blue-winged Teal.

Voice: The male makes a soft, squeaky chattering sound, and the female a *quack*.

Range and status: Breeds from sw. Canada and Wyo. south to n. Mexico and w.-c. Tex. Winters from the sw. U.S. through C. America to nw. S. America. Also a resident from c. to s. S. America and the Falkland Is. Has been recorded in the e. U.S. and once in Cuba. Travels most often in small flocks; perhaps because of this habit it is not considered a common duck, but it is not rare.

Habitat: Sluggish streams, irrigation ditches, shallow freshwater ponds, and marshes.

Seasonal movements: Southward movement occurs Sept.–Oct., and the return journey Mar.–Apr.

Biology: Its relationship to the Blue-winged Teal is indicated by the similarity of their biology. Nest: A down-lined hollow, usually in grasses near water. Eggs: 6–13, most often 9–10, whitish or buffy. Incubation: Reported questionably as 25–26 days; by the hen alone. Age of independence unknown. Food: About 80% aquatic plants, weeds, and grasses; animal food includes insects and mollusks.

Suggested reading: A. C. Bent, *Life Histories of North American Wild Fowl*, part 1, Dover, N.Y. (reprint of U.S. Nat. Mus. Bull. 126, 1923), 1962, pp. 122–132.

SHOVELER (*Spatula clypeata*)

Appearance: The broadly spatulate bill of this middle-sized (17–22 in.) dabbler is distinctive among N. American ducks; it is longer than the head. The wings alone are hardly separable from those of the Cinnamon and Blue-winged Teals; indeed many ornithologists consider this species as merely a shovel-billed teal and insist that it should be called *Anas clypeata* and placed next to its closest relatives. The drake in breeding plumage has a metallic green head and neck; breast, underparts, tail, and forepart of the back are white. A broad band of brownish red extends across the belly from flank to flank; the rest of the back and the feathers above and below the tail are blackish or greenish black. The female, except for the bill and larger size, resembles the female Cinnamon Teal, even to the pale blue horizontal line above the wing of the swimming bird. The eye of the male is bright yellow, and that of the hen a dull brown.

Voice: The hen makes a weak *quack* like the teals; the drake infrequently utters a series of guttural notes: *took-took-took.*

European Widgeon

Range and status: Breeds in Eurasia from south of the tundra to about 40° N. and in N. America from w. and n. Alaska, nw. Mack., and c. and se. Canada south, east of the Coast Ranges to s. Calif., N.Mex., Kans., Nebr., and the w. Great Lakes region; locally to n. Ala., the remainder of the Great Lakes area, and along the Atlantic Coast to N.C. Winters south to nw. and c. Africa, India, s. China, Nicaragua, and the W. Indies. Accidental in Hawaii, the Gilbert Is., and Bermuda. In U.S. spreads eastward and becomes more common.

Habitat: Slow, muddy creeks, freshwater marshes, and shallow ponds. Mainly in winter, shallow saltwater bays and tidal flats.

Seasonal movements: Early fall and late spring migrant.

Biology: Nest: A grass-lined hollow, not necessarily near water, which has more and more down added as the season progresses. Eggs: 6–14, usually 10–12, pale buffy olive. Incubation: 22–24 days, by female. Young on hatching look like ordinary ducks, but bill rapidly becomes shovel-shaped as it grows. Not known when young become independent of mother. Food: Aquatic plants and grasses, but also a large amount of vegetable debris strained from ooze at bottom of marshes and ponds; some animal matter from same source, including aquatic insects, fish, and mollusks.

Suggested reading: A. C. Bent, *Life Histories of North American Wild Fowl*, part 1, Dover, N.Y. (reprint of U.S. Nat. Mus. Bull. 126, 1923), 1962, pp. 135–143.

EUROPEAN WIDGEON (*Mareca penelope*)

Widgeons (or wigeons) constitute a group of dabblers between the teals and the Mallard in size. This moderate-sized (17–20 in.) species breeds in Iceland, Scotland, Scandinavia, n. Russia, and across n.-c. Siberia, and winters south to nw. and ne. Africa, Mesopotamia, India, Ceylon, Burma, Thailand, Formosa, and Japan. Drake is grayish with a buff-capped, brownish red head and a brownish rose-colored breast; the bill is bluish gray, and the feathers above and below the grayish tail are black. Female is pinkish brown; cannot be separated from American Widgeon hen except by a patch of black on the underside of the wing where it joins the body (not very prominent, even in flight).

AMERICAN WIDGEON (Baldpate) (*Mareca americana*)

Appearance: Somewhat larger (18–23 in.) than European Widgeon. Male has a gray head with a bright white cap and a band of metallic green running from just before each eye to the rear of the head; breast is pinkish, back and flanks are reddish tan, and belly is whitish. Wings and tail are dark, with a bright green speculum and a large white patch atop each wing. There are black feathers above and below the gray tail; just before these, a white mark extends up from the belly. Female has a grayish head, a brownish back, and a reddish tan breast and flanks; patch on the wing is light gray instead of white. Bills and feet of both sexes are bluish gray.

Voice: Drakes have a 3-part whistled call: *whee-whee-whoo* or *whew-whew-whew;* females, a drawn-out *quack;* sometimes loud with alarm.

Range and status: Breeds through c. Alaska, Yuk., w. and s. Mack., Man., and Wis. south through the interior of B.C., e. Wash., and Ore. to ne. Calif., n. Nev., n. Colo., and n. Nebr. Formerly and locally farther east. Winters from s. Alaska, the c. U.S., and New England to Costa Rica and the W. Indies; casually farther south. Accidental in e. Asia, Hawaii, Greenland, Iceland, and Europe. Not a rare duck.

Habitat: Freshwater marshes, lakes, ponds, and bays; also sometimes on marine and brackish water. Quite common on irrigated lands.

Seasonal movements: Migration protracted; in both fall and spring it starts early and arrives late.

Biology: Nest: Of grasses, weeds, and down, in a hollow on dry ground some distance from water. Eggs: 8–12, commonly 10, whitish. Incubation: 22–24 days, by female alone. Age at which young become independent is unknown. Food: More than 90% vegetable. Often stolen from diving ducks as they emerge from the depths with mouths full of food, which explains why this species is so often found accompanying divers in habitats not seemingly suitable for dabblers. Also consumes some mollusks and insects.

Suggested reading: J. A. Munro, "Studies of Waterfowl in British Columbia: Baldpate," *Canadian Jour. Research*, series D, vol. 27, pp. 289–307, 1949.

WOOD DUCK (*Aix sponsa*)

Appearance: Small- to medium-sized (17–21 in.) dabbler. By many considered the most beautiful native American duck. Large-crested (except during part of eclipse plumage) and chunky-bodied; difficult to confuse with any of its American relatives. Drake's head is iridescent greenish and purplish black with 2 thin white lines, one curving over the eye from the bill to the end of the crest and the other paralleling it but starting behind the eye. Throat is white, with 1 finger extending to just below the eyes and another to the rear of the head. Bill is a variegated pattern of red, black, and white. Breast and neck are a rich brownish red, back is dark and iridescent, and flanks are creamy buff with black-and-white vertical lines separating them from breast. Underparts are whitish. Female has a grayish head, with a white ring around the eye, and a white throat; her back is medium brownish gray, and her breast and flanks are brownish. In eclipse drake maintains the bright colors of the bill and the distinctive white throat pattern; otherwise like the female.

Voice: Loud *ooo-eek* alarm calls, sparrowlike whistles, and squeaks and squeals by the male; a croaking *quack* by the female.

Range and status: Breeds from c. B.C. to c. Calif. and from s. Man., the Great Lakes region, New England, N.B., and s. N.S. to s. Tex., the Gulf Coast, s. Fla., and

The male American Widgeon (left) *is more colorful than the female* (right).

Like most ducks, the Redhead feeds primarily on plant materials.

Cuba. In winter it retreats from the more northerly parts and extends its range south to c. Mexico. Now again a common duck, thanks to timely protective laws and provision of many nesting boxes at suitable sites.

Habitat: Forest-edged ponds, swamps, and rivers; will even occupy those in inhabited areas if encouraged. Thoroughly at home in the woods.

Seasonal movements: Migrations are short, starting early in the fall; northward movements are not quite so early as with other ducks.

Biology: Nest: In natural cavities in trees, lined with down, often as high as 50 ft. above the ground. Eggs: 9–14, usually 10–12, dull or creamy white. Incubation: 30–32 days, by female alone. On hatching, the young possess sharp claws that enable them to climb out of the nesting cavity, from which they simply jump to the ground, regardless of distance. Because of their lightness, very few are hurt, even by a long drop. Young make 1st flight when almost 9 weeks old. Food: Mostly vegetable: tree and shrub seeds, grasses, aquatic plants; some spiders and insects.

Suggested reading: F. Leopold, "A Study of Nesting Wood Ducks in Iowa," *Condor*, vol. 53, pp. 209–220, 1951.

REDHEAD (*Aythya americana*)

Appearance: A medium-sized (18–22 in.) diving duck with grayish back, flanks, wings, and tail, a blackish breast, and a brownish red head. Legs and bill of both sexes are bluish gray; black tip of the bill is separated from the rest of the bill by a narrow whitish line; breast is white. Female is buffy brown with a white breast. In autumn the drake molts into a plumage best described as a mixture of the breeding plumage of both sexes; at this time both hen and drake are flightless.

Voice: Drake makes a guttural rolling *purr* and a hoarse catlike *meow;* female precedes her *quack* with a slight hiss.

Range and status: Breeds in a triangular area from e. B.C. and sw. Mack. south to s. Calif. and from these points east to Minn., Wis., and w. Pa.; formerly, and now locally, farther east. Winters from sw. B.C. and the c. U.S. east to Md., south to s. Baja Calif., c. Mexico, the Gulf Coast, and Fla.; casually farther north and to Cuba and Jamaica. Advance of civilization into breeding areas, drainage of marshes, and hunting pressure in the past have greatly reduced range and numbers; with reintroduction to formerly occupied ranges and better management of hunting, this species has been making some recovery. It is not yet rare.

Habitat: Breeds in freshwater marshes; otherwise lakes, estuaries, shallow sounds.

Seasonal movements: Flies swiftly in large V-shaped flocks during migration, which is usually at its height in Oct. and Mar. Feeding and resting flocks tend to bunch tightly (raft), especially when disturbed.

Biology: Nest: Neatly woven of weeds and lined with down, most often in a marsh not far from deep water. Eggs: 10–18, usually 10–16, buffy. Incubation: 22–23 days. The young are able to fly in about 67 days (56–73 days). Food: 90% aquatic plants; some insects and mollusks.

Suggested reading: M. W. Weller, "Distribution and Migration of the Redhead," *Jour. Wildlife Management*, vol. 28, pp. 64–103, 1964.

COMMON POCHARD (*Aythya ferina*)

Smaller (17–19 in.) than the Redhead, which it resembles closely, except that the grays of the plumage are much lighter. Breeds across Eurasia from the British Isles, s. Scandinavia, and Germany to the Caspian and Lake Baikal regions. Winters south to n. Africa, Iran, India, Burma, s. China, and Japan. Has occurred in the Pribilof Is. of Alaska, the Azores, the Canaries, Madeira, and the Komandorskie Is.

BAER'S POCHARD (*Aythya baeri*)

A rather rare diving duck about the size (19 in.) of the Redhead. Breeds in se. Siberia, and winters in Burma,

China, Korea, and Japan. It has a greenish head, a brownish red breast, whitish undersides crossed by a brown band, and a brownish back. Female has a brown head and breast. It was collected once in 1841 in "Oregon," which then included Wash. and s. B.C.

RING-NECKED DUCK (*Aythya collaris*)

Appearance: Small- to medium-sized (14–18½ in.) diver with a purple-glossed head, black breast, greenish-glossed dark back, grayish flanks, and whitish under-parts. Bill has a black tip, then a narrow white ring; the rest of the bill is grayish. Hunters call this duck the "Ring-bill"; probably a better name than Ring-neck, as the brownish ring separating the breast and neck is discernible only in good light. Female is brownish, with a white ring about the eye and a thin white line leading from this toward the rear of the head; bill is also "ringed." Both sexes have a large, pale blue patch on the wing. Drake enters a partial eclipse plumage in fall, acquiring then a "mixed female" feathering.

Voice: Drake's has been described as a purring or hissing whistle; hen gives a loud *scaup* call.

Range and status: Breeds from s. B.C., the Prairie Provinces of Canada, and the w. Great Lakes region south to Nev., n. Utah, Colo., and Mo.; and from the Maritime Provinces to Maine and N.H.; rarely and locally between these disjunct areas. Winters north along coasts to sw. B.C. and Mass. and from the s. tier and e.-c. states of the U.S. to Panama, the Bahamas, and the Greater Antilles. It is not a rare duck; apparently becoming more common in the East.

Habitat: Wooded lakes and ponds, especially in coniferous forests. In winter also marshes, rivers, bays, and sheltered marine waters.

Seasonal movements: Migrates in small, loose flocks; fall flights from mid-Oct. into Nov.; in spring mid-March–Apr. and May.

Biology: Nest: In wet places at edges of marshes and ponds; constructed of grasses and reeds, lined with down. Eggs: 6–12, usually 8–10, greenish buff. Incubation: 25–29 days. Age at 1st flight: 49–56 days. Food: 80% vegetable, mainly aquatic plants, grasses and sedges; animal food includes insects and mollusks.

Suggested reading: Howard Mendall, *The Ring-necked Duck in the Northeast*, Univ. Maine Bull. 60, no. 16, 1958.

CANVASBACK (*Aythya valisineria*)

Appearance: A medium-large (19–24 in.) diver, very much like the Redhead, but the flanks and back are white or whitish and the bill and head are longer-looking; bill merges with head in a gentle concave curve—not an angle, as in the Redhead. Female has a brownish head and breast, whitish flanks and belly, and light grayish back. Drake has a partial eclipse plumage retain-

Once rare in the East, Ring-necked Ducks have become more abundant in recent years.

The Canvasback's whitish back and smoothly sloping profile are good identification marks.

In winter, large flocks of Greater Scaup congregate in bays and estuaries along both coasts.

ing some of the brighter feathers among those of a femalelike aspect.

Voice: Drake growls and croaks; female quacks.

Range and status: Breeds from c. Alaska, c. Yuk., n.-c. Mack., and se. Man. south to n. Calif., n. Utah, n. Colo., Nebr., and c. Minn. Winters from B.C., nw. Mont., Colo., Tenn., the e. Great Lakes, and e. Mass. south to c. Mexico, the Gulf States, and n. Fla.; casually to Guatemala and Cuba. Formerly quite abundant; numbers fluctuate from year to year according to conditions on breeding grounds, hence hunting is carefully regulated. Still a common duck.

Habitat: Freshwater marshes and potholes in summer; almost any open fresh water or sheltered marine waters in other seasons.

Seasonal movements: Migrating flocks fly in large wedge-shaped formations, sometimes at speeds of over 60 miles per hour. Flocks are usually a little later than the Redheads in fall and start earlier in spring.

Biology: Nest: In swamps, well hidden, usually above high-water line; woven of reeds, grasses, and sedges, and lined with down. Eggs: 7–12, most often 7–10; grayish olive, darker than those of most other ducks. Incubation: 22–23 days. Age at 1st flight: 63–77 days. Food: Over 80% vegetable, mainly aquatic plants; wild celery of the genus *Vallisneria* is a favored item, responsible for the specific name of the duck. Animals eaten are mollusks, insects, and fish.

Suggested reading: H. A. Hochbaum, *The Canvasback on a Prairie Marsh*, Amer. Wildlife Inst., Washington, D.C., 1944, 201 pp.

GREATER SCAUP (*Aythya marila*)

Appearance: Medium-sized (15–21 in.) diver, very much like the Redhead except that the male has a metallic green head with a purplish cast and the female has a dark brown head with a large white feather patch at the base of the blue bill. Often impossible to separate scaups by head color alone. In Greater Scaup the white extends farther out in the wing as a narrowing blurry line; "nail" at tip of bill is much larger in the Greater, but this is useful only when the birds are very close or in the hand. In July drake enters an eclipse plumage, looking quite like the hen but retaining some of the male feathering.

Voice: Not noisy; low whistling and purring notes and occasional loud *scaup*'s, from which the name is derived.

Range and status: Breeds through c. and s.-c. Alaska through Yuk. into w. Mack.; possibly to Keewatin and locally in n. Ont. and n. Que. Also in Iceland and across n. Eurasia south of the tundra from Scandinavia to Kamchatka. Winters from se. Alaska to s. Calif., from the e. Great Lakes region and the Canadian Maritime Provinces to s. Fla. and the Gulf Coast; Great Britain, the shores of the North and Baltic Seas, the n. shores of the Mediterranean, Mesopotamia, and from Korea to s. China and s. Japan. A common duck; not so common as the Lesser Scaup in America.

Habitat: Rivers, lakes, and prairie ponds in summer; also sheltered marine waters in winter.

Seasonal movements: Starts southward at 1st frosts, moving in small compact flocks; spring movements also start fairly early, following close upon the retreating frost line.

Biology: Nest: A slight hollow in the ground, not far from water; lined with grasses and down. Eggs: 8–11, 9 most commonly; shades of olive-buff. Incubation: 25–28 days (some records of as few as 22 days). Age at 1st flight: 5–6 weeks. Food: Half vegetable (aquatic plants and grasses) and half animal (mollusks, insects, and crustaceans).

Suggested reading: J. A. Munro, "Studies of Waterfowl in British Columbia: Greater Scaup Duck, Lesser Scaup Duck," *Canadian Jour. Research*, vol. 19, pp. 113–138, 1941.

LESSER SCAUP (*Aythya affinis*)

Appearance: Slightly smaller (14–19 in.) than the Greater Scaup but so similar in all plumages that it is difficult to separate in field. This species has less white in wing, and a smaller dark "nail" at tip of bill; head is usually glossed purplish instead of greenish and gives appearance of having a slight crest.

Voice: Apparently indistinguishable from that of the Greater Scaup.

Range and status: Breeds from c. Alaska and from the tree limits of Mack. and Keewatin south, east of the Coast Ranges to c. B.C. and Idaho, and east of the Rockies to Colo., Nebr., and Iowa; casually farther east. Winters north along the coasts to B.C. and Conn. and in the interior to s. Ariz., s. N.Mex., c. Tex., Mo., and the s. Great Lakes region. More numerous than the Greater Scaup.

Habitat: Freshwater marshes, ponds, and lakes; in winter, sheltered marine waters.

Seasonal movements: Late fall and late spring migrant; one of the last ducks to leave the breeding grounds in autumn.

Biology: Nest: In hollow near marshes or ponds, well hidden in grasses; lined sparsely with grasses but with considerable down. Eggs: 6–15, commonly 9–12, dark buffy olive. Incubation: 22–23 days. Age at 1st flight: 56–73 days. The long learning period of the young coupled with a late annual molt of the adults probably accounts for the late fall migration. Food: Possibly more of a vegetarian than the Greater Scaup. Aquatic plants and grasses, mollusks, insects, and crustaceans.

Suggested reading: J. A. Munro, "Studies of Waterfowl in British Columbia: Greater Scaup Duck, Lesser Scaup Duck," *Canadian Jour. Research,* vol. 19, pp. 113–138, 1941.

TUFTED DUCK (*Aythya fuligula*)

A small- to medium-sized (ca. 17 in.) diver resembling the Ring-necked Duck, with a long tuft of feathers at back of head. Female lacks the white on the bill and looks like a dark Lesser Scaup female. Breeds south of the tundra in Eurasia to c. Europe and n.-c. Asia. Winters to n. Africa, s. India, Burma, Vietnam, and the c. Philippines. Has been reported from the Pribilof and Aleutian Is. of Alaska and from Greenland and Mass.

COMMON GOLDENEYE (*Bucephala clangula*)

Appearance: Medium-sized (15–21 in.) divers. Drakes have a dark, green-glossed head with a roundish white patch just before and slightly below the golden eyes; neck, breast, flanks, and undersides are white, and the dark gray back is broadly hatched with white at the sides. Female and young have a brownish red head, and a white neck, breast, and undersides; the flanks and a bar across the upper breast are gray, as is the back. White on hen's wings not so prominent as on drake's. In his partial eclipse plumage the drake looks like the female but for a few of his brighter feathers showing through. Feathers of cheek region are long and extend outward and to the rear, giving a long-headed "mumpy" appearance.

Voice: Rather quiet; the male has a harsh *speer-speer* call, the female a hoarse *quack*. During head-tossing courtship the drake makes a double-noted nasal *peenk,* and the female makes whistled *peep*'s.

Range and status: A common breeding duck of the n. coniferous forests of N. America and Eurasia from the tree line south to s. Alaska, s. B.C., ne. Wyo., c. Nebr., n. Minn., n. Mich., s. Que., ne. N.Y., Maine, N.B., and Nfld.; and to c. Europe, sw. and s.-c. Siberia, n. Mongolia, and Kamchatka. Winters from s. edge of breeding area to the s. U.S., the n. shores of the Mediterranean Sea, Mesopotamia, n. India, s.-c. China, Formosa, and Japan.

Habitat: Rivers and lakes; also marine waters in winter.

Seasonal movements: Starts spring migration in Mar.; return journey begins in early Oct.

Biology: Nest: Almost always in tree cavity, sometimes more than a mile from water; down-lined. Scandinavians put up nesting boxes for this species, as we do for the Wood Duck. Eggs: 5–19, commonly 10–12, light grayish green. Incubation: Uncertain; estimates range from 20–30 days, but many authorities agree on about 27 days. Age at 1st flight unknown. Food: Mainly animal; mollusks, crustaceans, fish, and insects make up 75% of diet. Plants seem to be consumed mainly during breeding season.

Suggested reading: B. C. Carter, *The American Goldeneye in Central New Brunswick,* Canadian Wildlife Serv. Wildlife Management Bull., series 2, no. 9, 47 pp., 1958.

BARROW'S GOLDENEYE (*Bucephala islandica*)

Appearance: About the same size (16–20 in.) and general appearance as the Common Goldeneye. Females of the 2 species can be separated only by the shorter bill

Barrow's Goldeneye

of this species; impossible to gauge properly in the field. Drake's head is glossed with purple, and he has a white crescent between eye and bill; top of wings has less white showing while bird swims than in the case of the Common Goldeneye. In spring the bill is reported to turn yellow.

Voice: Harsh croaking; males make mewing calls in mating season.

Range and status: Breeding range in w. N. America is an inverted V starting in se. Alaska and nw. B.C., with 1 arm extending southward to the High Sierras of Calif. and the other southeast to the mountains of Colo. It also breeds in n. Que., Lab., sw. Greenland, and w. Iceland. In winter it ranges along Pacific shores from s. Alaska to c. Calif. and in the Atlantic from the mouth of the St. Lawrence River to Long I., N.Y.; also found in the s. parts of its inland range; only rarely does it move farther south. Has straggled to Europe only 5 times. It is not a common duck, even in the West.

Habitat: Forested lakes and ponds; in winter, coastal marine waters and estuaries.

Seasonal movements: Migrations are short and made as early as weather permits in both spring and fall.

Biology: Nest: In tree hollows or rock crevices, usually near water; lined with down. Eggs: 6–15, most often 10–13, light greenish. Incubation: About 4 weeks. Age at 1st flight unknown. Food: More insects than Common Goldeneye, but still 75% animal food; has been timed feeding on mollusks underwater for as long as 50 seconds.

Suggested reading: M. P. Skinner, "Barrow's Goldeneye in the Yellowstone National Park," *Wils. Bull.*, vol. 49, pp. 3–10, 1937.

BUFFLEHEAD (*Bucephala albeola*)

Appearance: Smallest (12–16 in.) of our diving ducks. Large-looking blackish head, with green-purplish iridescence, has a quarter-circle patch of white above and behind the eye. Back and tail are black; remainder of drake's plumage is white, including a large patch on the upper wing that shows while the duck is swimming. Female has a brownish gray head and back with lighter flanks, whitish beneath, and a small white patch on the lower rear quarter of the head. Drake retains a few of his bright colors in patches amid a femalelike eclipse plumage.

Voice: Drake makes a throaty rolling call and some squeaky notes; hen makes a harsh *quack*.

Range and status: Breeds from s.-c. and e.-c. Alaska, w. Mack., n. Prairie Provinces, and n. Ont. south, east of the Coast Ranges to nw. Calif. and n. Idaho, n. Mont., s. Man., and n.-c. Ont. Winters from the Komandorskie and Aleutian Is., s. Alaska, s. B.C., w. Mont., Colo., Ark., the Great Lakes, Maine, and sw. N.B. south to c. Baja Calif., c. Mexico, the Gulf Coast, and n. Fla.

Has straggled to Japan, Hawaii, Cuba, Puerto Rico, Bermuda, Greenland, and Great Britain. A rather common duck through most of its range.

Habitat: Ponds, lakes, and rivers; in winter mainly inshore marine waters.

Seasonal movements: Late migrant both spring and fall; remains north as long as it finds open water. Usually travels in flocks of 20–50 birds at height of migration.

Biology: Nest: In hollows of trees or deserted woodpecker nesting holes near water; some down lining. Eggs: 6–14, usually 10–12, creamy or pale greenish buff. Incubation: 21–22 days, not certain. Age at 1st flight unknown. Food: Insects, crustaceans, mollusks, and fish constitute 80% of diet; aquatic plants make up the rest.

Suggested reading: J. A. Munro, "Studies of Waterfowl in British Columbia: Bufflehead," *Canadian Jour. Research*, series D, vol. 20, pp. 133–160, 1942.

White lower parts and the white patches on its head distinguish the Bufflehead drake.

OLDSQUAW (*Clangula hyemalis*)

Appearance: A medium-small (14–23 in.) diver; tail is about ⅓ the total length of the drake. This is the only duck species in which drake has 2 distinct bright plumages plus an eclipse plumage each year; female also has different winter and summer plumages. In summer, male has a dull-glossed black head, neck, breast, and tail and a large pale gray patch about the eyes. The black feathers of his back are edged with light brown; underparts and large areas of wings are whitish. Feet are bluish gray; bill is pinkish, with a dark tip, a white edge, and a bluish patch near the base. In eclipse plumage all colors are dulled and the crown becomes whitish. In winter, head, neck, and upper breast are white, with a patch of black below and to the rear of the eye, a grayish area around the eye, and a buffy yellow forecrown. Remainder of breast, tail, most of back, and some wing feathers are black; rest of undersides and wings are white. In all plumages it keeps the distinctive long tail feathers. In summer, female's back and legs are the same as male's, but head and neck are bluish gray with a white eye-ring. A streak of white, starting behind the eye, runs down the neck, broadening near the brownish breast; flanks are brownish gray and underparts light gray. In winter, head and neck are whitish, as are flanks and undersides, although there is a gray patch to the rear and beneath the eye, and there is gray running from the cap down the back of the neck. In all seasons bill is grayish. Immature bird resembles female between her 2 plumages. The bird is continually in motion, and even on calm water a flock looks like a seething white-capped whirlpool.

Voice: Very vocal, continually calling; described as musical buglelike *our-o-u-ah, our-o-u-ah.*

Range and status: Breeds in tundra and tundralike regions of the Arctic from w. Alaska, through n. Canada, Greenland, Iceland, most arctic islands, and n. Eurasia to e. Siberia. Winters along coasts from breeding areas to c. Calif., N.C., n. Europe, Japan, and Korea and casually farther south; also on freshwater lakes inland, such as the Great Lakes and Lake Baikal. A common marine duck; certainly prominent because of its voice and kaleidoscopic actions.

Habitat: Ponds on tundra during summer; seas and large bodies of water, seldom small ponds, during winter.

Seasonal movements: Moves north in Apr., returning in Oct. and Nov.

Biology: Nest: A hollow lined with down, near water. Eggs: 5–11, commonly 7–8, light yellowish olive. Incubation: 23–24 days (possibly 26). Age at 1st flight unknown. Food: Mainly crustaceans, mollusks, insects, and fish, with small amount of grasses and pondweeds. Animal food obtained by diving to recorded depths of up to 80 ft.

Suggested reading: A. C. Bent, *Life Histories of*

The female Oldsquaw lines her shallow nest with soft down plucked from her breast.

North American Wild Fowl, part 2, Dover, N.Y. (reprint of U.S. Nat. Mus. Bull. 130, 1925), 1962, pp. 32–50. D. A. Bannerman, *Birds of the British Isles,* Oliver and Boyd, Edinburgh, 1958, vol. 7, pp. 137–151.

HARLEQUIN DUCK (*Histrionicus histrionicus*)

Appearance: Small- to medium-sized (14½–21 in.) diving duck. Color of drake predominantly a grayed medium blue with brownish red flanks, a large patch of white before the eyes, a small round spot and then a vertical white line behind the eyes, 2 white slashes radiating from the back on the breast, and a white bar followed by smaller white bars showing on the wing while bird is at rest; there is a streak of brownish red on the crown. Legs, feet, and bill are bluish gray in both sexes. Female is a uniform medium brown except for a lighter belly and 3 white spots on the head, 2 before the eyes and 1 behind. The male in eclipse resembles the female but shows some of the white on the wings and has a suggestion of blue in the brown plumage.

Voice: Mouselike squeak (has been called the "sea mouse"), a heavy, hoarse *heh-heh-heh,* and in flight a higher-pitched *oy-oy-oy-oy;* an *ek-ek-ek-ek* by the female.

Range and status: Breeds south of the tundra in e. Siberia, and in n. Mongolia, Manchuria, and the Kurile and Komandorskie Is., and from s.-c. and s. Alaska (including the Aleutians) south and southeast to B.C., the mountains of e.-c. Calif., and Colo.; also from n. Que. and Lab. to c. Que. and Lab. and in se. Baffin I., Greenland, and Iceland. Resident in all but most northerly parts, and ranges casually south in winter to s. Japan, s. Calif., and Md. Casual to accidental in interior elsewhere. Fairly common in the West, rare in the East.

Habitat: Tumbling mountain streams and marine waters not far at sea.

Seasonal movements: Usually very little; moves out to open marine waters or remains near fast-flowing mountain streams.

Biology: Nest: In the East a grass- and down-lined hollow in the ground under bushes, and in the West a similarly lined hollow in a tree or cliffside. Eggs: 6–10, usually 8, light buff. Incubation: About 31 days—not certain. Age at 1st flight unknown. Food: Crustaceans, mollusks, insects, sea urchins, and fish; less than 3% vegetable matter.

Suggested reading: A. C. Bent, *Life Histories of North American Wild Fowl*, part 2, Dover, N.Y. (reprint of U.S. Nat. Mus. Bull. 130, 1925), 1962, pp. 50–62.

LABRADOR DUCK (*Camptorhynchus labradorium*)

Extinct. Medium-sized (20 in.) diving duck with gray body, white head and neck, black necklace, large white area on the wing, and small black cap. Female was completely brown except for extensive white on the wing. Very little is known about this duck. It wintered along the Atlantic Coast from N.S. to N.J., probably to Del., and was taken once at Montreal, Que., and once at Elmira, N.Y. It was believed to have nested along the coast of Lab. It was abundant enough to appear for sale at the Fulton Street Market in New York City, but not regularly, and for how many years is unknown. It was not considered a good "eating" bird, so was not shot intentionally by market hunters. The last bird known to science died Dec. 12, 1878. No one knows what factors caused extinction of this species. There are very few specimens in museums.

STELLER'S EIDER (*Polysticta stelleri*)

Appearance: Eiders are relatively thick-bodied, thick-billed, short-necked diving ducks, and almost exclusively marine. This one is a medium-sized (17–19 in.) diving duck, but a small eider. Drake has a white head with a small grayish crest at the rear, a black throat, and a black eye-ring. Back, tail, undertail feathers, and a neck ring are black; breast and rest of undersides are brownish red; flank and much of the wing feathering visible from the sides are white. Bills and feet of both sexes are blackish. Female is dark brown, with a whitish eye-ring and a white-edged blue wing speculum. The male in eclipse plumage looks like the female except for a

Harlequin Duck

Labrador Duck

large white wing patch, and he retains the slight crest at the rear of the head.

Voice: A humming *koo-roo-uh;* female makes a growling noise.

Range and status: Breeds on arctic coasts and islands of Alaska from Hooper Bay to Demarcation Point, in Siberia from New Siberian Is. to Anadyr Bay, on St. Lawrence I., and on Cape Bathurst in nw. Mack.; recorded in summer from n. Norway and Finland. Winters in Aleutian Is., Kurile Is., the Komandorskie Is., and off the coasts of the Kamchatka Peninsula and Scandinavia. Has been taken in Japan, Greenland, Que., Maine, England, and Germany.

Habitat: Marine shores and offshore waters.

Seasonal movements: Merely moves before pack ice and follows its retreat.

Biology: Nest: Holes in the moss and tundra; lined with down. Eggs: 6–9, pale grayish yellow. Incubation: Unknown, as is age at 1st flight. Food: Crustaceans, mollusks, insects, worms, fish; less than 15% plant food—pondweeds and algae.

Suggested reading: F. McKinney, "The Spring Behavior of Wild Steller Eiders," *Condor,* vol. 67, pp. 273–290, 1965.

COMMON EIDER (*Somateria mollissima*)

Appearance: Our largest (21–27 in.) eider and diving duck. Drake has considerable white on the wings, a white back, and a white head with a black cap and 2 pale green patches on the back of the head; breast is pinkish, and undersides, tail, rump, and flight feathers of the wings are black. Feet grayish green; bill ranges from grayish in European populations to yellowish and orange in American and n. forms. Female is light brown barred with darker browns and blacks; bill grayish throughout range. In eclipse plumage the drake is very dark, with a dark-scaled grayish-looking breast and with a white streak along the side.

Voice: Like Steller's Eider, but louder; female, a rasping *khor-r-r.*

Range and status: Breeds along coasts and offshore islands around n. N. America from the Aleutians and sw. Alaska to Nfld., N.S., and Maine, and north through the Canadian Archipelago and the coasts of all but northernmost Greenland; also in Iceland, Spitsbergen, Franz Josef Land, Novaya Zemlya, n. Russia, Scandinavia, Scotland, the Faeroes, Holland, and n. Ireland; also the coasts of e. Siberia from Chauskaya Bay around East Cape to the base of Kamchatka Peninsula. In winter it remains along the s. edge of the ice pack and ranges south to B.C., Wash., Va., N.C., s. Europe, and s. Kamchatka; very rarely farther south, and only accidentally in the interior of N. America and Europe. The most common and widespread of the eiders.

Habitat: Almost entirely marine.

Seasonal movements: Migration is a comparatively short retreat before the ice of winter and a readvance with the opening of arctic waters.

Steller's Eider

Biology: Nest: A hollow in the tundra or coastal meadows, sometimes in small "colonies"; lined with eiderdown, for which the species is commercially valuable. Eggs: 4–6, medium grayish green. Incubation: 27–28 days. Age at 1st flight unknown. Food: Little plant food; mollusks make up about 80% of stomach contents, with some crustaceans, fish, and echinoderms (starfish and sea urchins).

Suggested reading: A. O. Gross, "Eider Ducks of Kent's Island," *Auk,* vol. 55, pp. 387–400, 1938.

KING EIDER (*Somateria spectabilis*)

Appearance: A large (18–24 in.) diver. At a distance the front half of this duck appears white and the rear half black; breast has a pinkish tinge; crown is grayish, with some pale green on the face and a small black crescent under the eyes. There is a good-sized patch of white on the wing and another on the lower rump; orange bill has a black-edged frontal knob flaring out over the forehead. Female is a somewhat redder brown than the Common Eider hen, and the blackish "scaling" effect on the plumage is less pronounced. The drake in eclipse is blackish except for a whitish spot on the upper back. His orange bill is also duller and no longer quite so enlarged at the forehead. Immature male looks like the drake in eclipse but has a whitish breast.

Voice: Male makes loud, rolling purrs accented on the last purr.

Range and status: Breeds on arctic coasts and islands from nw. Alaska to Hudson and James Bays, n. Lab., and Franklin Territory north to Victoria, Banks, and Ellesmere Is., the e. and w. coasts of Greenland and from n. Russia to East Cape in ne. Siberia. Winters south to Kamchatka, the Aleutians, s. Alaska, Calif. (casually), the Great Lakes, N.J., Nfld., Iceland, the British Isles, and n. Scandinavia; very rarely farther south and only accidentally in the continental interiors. Common.

Habitat: Marine coasts and waters; rarely large lakes.

Seasonal movements: North and south with the solid ice fronts. Large flocks seen migrating along arctic coasts.

Biology: Nest: Tundra; a hollow lined with down. Eggs: 4–7, usually 5–6, olive-buff. Incubation period and age at 1st flight unknown. Food: Mollusks (many mussels), crustaceans, starfish, sea urchins, insects, and a very small percentage of eelgrass and seaweeds.

Suggested reading: D. A. Bannerman, *Birds of the British Isles,* Oliver and Boyd, Edinburgh, 1958, vol. 7, pp. 185–193.

SPECTACLED EIDER (*Lampronetta fischeri*)

Appearance: A medium-sized (20–23 in.) diver with white neck, throat, and upperparts and black underparts; head is pale green, with a large black-edged white area around the eyes. Even the female with her all-brown plumage has "spectacles" of lighter brown. The

Even the female Spectacled Eider has readily discernible spectacles around her eyes.

The handsome male Cinnamon Teal is unmistakable, but the rather drab female is almost indistinguishable from the female Blue-winged Teal.

In breeding plumage the male Wood Duck (right) is one of our most beautiful native species; in eclipse plumage he looks fairly similar to the female (left).

Surf Scoters are fairly common in large lakes and marine bays.

drake in eclipse has bluish black spectacles on a brownish gray head; at this time the rest of his plumage is brownish black with a white wing streak.

Voice: Not described so far.

Range and status: Marine coasts of ne. Siberia from the mouth of the Lena River and New Siberian Is. to East Cape and w. and n. Alaska from the mouth of the Kuskokwim River and St. Lawrence I. to Point Barrow. Winters off the Pribilof and Aleutian Is. and rarely Kodiak I. A favorite food duck of natives; hunting pressure on breeding grounds keeps population low.

Habitat: Arctic marine coasts.

Seasonal movements: No pronounced migration.

Biology: Nest: Like those of other eiders, a down-lined hollow in the tundra. Eggs: 5–9, olive-buff. Incubation and age at 1st flight unknown. Food: Mollusks, crustaceans, insects; 25% plant food—pondweeds, crowberries, sedges, algae (seaweeds).

VELVET SCOTER (*Melanitta fusca*)

A medium-sized (22 in.) diving duck resembling the White-winged Scoter, of which it is possibly a form. Drake differs from male White-winged Scoter in lacking a knob at the base of its bill and in having less white on the wing and about the eye. Female resembles female White-winged Scoter, but is darker. Breeds in n. Eurasia just south of the tundra and winters off n. Europe and in the Black Sea and Caspian Sea areas. It has straggled to Greenland and Iceland.

WHITE-WINGED SCOTER (American Velvet Scoter) (*Melanitta deglandi*)

Appearance: Medium-sized (19–23 in.) diving duck with glossed blackish plumage relieved by a white speculum and a small patch of white about the whitish eye; except for a blackish knob at the base, the bill is orange, lightening to yellow at the tip. Female is dark brownish with whitish underparts and 2 white spots below the eyes, 1 forward and another to the rear; her bill is bluish gray. Both sexes have dusky pink feet and whitish eyes. Immature bird looks like the female. Flight feathers are lost during the fall molt, but there is no eclipse plumage.

Voice: 6–8 low, bell-like whistled notes in flight; sometimes a croak.

Range and status: Breeds from w.-c. Alaska and nw. Mack. southeast, and east of the Rockies to se. Alta., s. Sask., n. N.Dak., and s.-c. Man. Found in summer from n. Ont., s. Lab., and Nfld. south to Mass. Winters on the Great Lakes and from the Gulf of St. Lawrence to S.C. and from the e. Aleutian Is. and s. Alaska to Baja Calif.; casually to c. U.S., only accidentally farther south. Common.

Habitat: Large lakes, marine waters.

Seasonal movements: Spring migration Mar.–mid-May; fall, Aug.–Nov.

Biology: Nest: A hollow scraped in the ground; lined with sticks, leaves, and down. Eggs: 6–14, usually 5–8, pinkish. Incubation: 27–28 days. Age at 1st flight: 63–77 days. Food: Mollusks—mussels, oysters, clams, etc.—are swallowed, shell and all, and crushed in the powerful gizzard; these make up 75% of diet. Crustaceans, insects, and a small amount of plant material make up remainder.

Suggested reading: A. C. Bent, *Life Histories of North American Wild Fowl*, part 2, Dover, N.Y. (reprint of U.S. Nat. Mus. Bull. 130, 1925), 1962, pp. 131–143.

SURF SCOTER (*Melanitta perspicillata*)

Appearance: Medium-sized (17–21 in.) diving duck. Male is black-plumaged, like other scoters, but has a white patch at the rear of the head and another at the forehead; his large, swollen bill is a variegated pattern of white, red, grayish blue, and yellow, and his eyes are white. Both sexes have dusky yellow feet and have no white on the wings. The hen is dark brown, with white patches on the head similar to those of the White-winged Scoter, but with an additional white patch at the rear of the head. Immature bird lacks this added white spot, but otherwise it resembles the female. There is no eclipse plumage, but the birds are flightless during the fall molt.

Voice: Usually silent; low, throaty croaks and occasionally in the mating season a low, clear or bubbling whistle.

Range and status: Breeds from ne. Alaska east to w. half of Mack.; casually farther south, and on islands in James Bay. Also recorded in c. Lab. Reported in summer from localities through Canada and Alaska. Winters along the coasts from the e. Aleutians to Baja Calif. and the Gulf of Calif., and from N.S. to N.C.; rarely Fla. and the Gulf Coast; also in the Great Lakes. Has straggled to the Komandorskie Is., Greenland, Bermuda, Iceland, and Europe. Large concentrations of immatures summer from s. Alaska to Wash. Fairly common.

Habitat: Large lakes, marine bays, and shores; tundra lakes in summer.

Seasonal movements: Spring migration Apr.–May; fall, in Sept.–Oct.

Biology: Nest: A hollow in marshes or under brush near water; lined with leaves, weeds, and down. Eggs: 5–9, pinkish or buffy. Incubation: Unknown, as is age at 1st flight. Food: Mollusks, often obtained by diving in heavy surf, make up 60% of stomach contents; only 10% of food is vegetable. Does not consume so many scallops or oysters as do the White-winged and Common Scoters.

Suggested reading: D. A. Bannerman, *Birds of the British Isles*, Oliver and Boyd, Edinburgh, 1958, vol. 7, pp. 213–215.

COMMON SCOTER (American Scoter, Black Scoter) (*Oidemia nigra*)

Appearance: A moderate-sized (17–21 in.) diving duck with entire plumage blackish and slightly glossy; bill is bright orange with a grayish "lip." European forms have a slight knob at base of bill and only a bit of orange. Feet and legs of both American and European forms are greenish gray. Female is dark brown, with whitish cheeks and throat; her bill is bluish gray. Immature bird resembles the female but is lighter underneath. The eyes of this species are dark. There is no eclipse plumage, but the birds are flightless during the early fall molt.

Voice: Male coos pleasantly; female growls.

Range and status: Breeds in w. and s. Alaska, the Aleutian Is., Iceland, Spitsbergen, n. Scandinavia, n. Russia, and n. Siberia south of the tundra. Winters from the Komandorskie Is. and the Aleutians south to Korea, Japan, and s. Calif.; on the Great Lakes; from Nfld. to S.C. (rarely Fla.), and from n. Europe to the Azores and Canary Is.; very rarely in continental interiors and Mediterranean, Black, and Caspian Seas. Common.

Habitat: Coastal regions and marine waters, large lakes; smaller bodies of fresh water in summer.

Seasonal movements: Fall migration in Oct.; spring, in late Apr.–May.

Biology: Nest: A well-hidden down-lined hollow near water. Eggs: 6–10, most frequently 8, buff or pinkish buff. Incubation: Estimated, doubtfully, as 28–33 days. Age at 1st flight unknown. Food: As with other scoters; less than 10% plant matter. Mollusks preferred; also crustaceans, insects, fish.

Suggested reading: D. A. Bannerman, *Birds of the British Isles*, Oliver and Boyd, Edinburgh, 1958, vol. 7, pp. 194–201.

RUDDY DUCK (*Oxyura jamaicensis*)

Appearance: A small (14–17 in.) duck. The drake in summer is unmistakable: back, flanks, and neck are brownish red; cheeks are white; cap, spiky tail, and flight feathers of wings are blackish. The bill is bright blue, and the underparts are whitish, lightly barred with brownish. In winter the drake resembles the female, but retains its white cheeks. Female has a dark grayish brown cap, neck, upper breast, back, wings, and tail, with a horizontal brown streak running through whitish cheeks. Bill, legs, and feet are grayish, and the under-

A short upturned tail and a rather short neck characterize the Ruddy Duck.

Masked Duck

the whole face; underparts are buffy, with dark spots on flanks; tail and wings are dark, with a large speculum of white on the wings; the back is black-spotted reddish brown. Female is dark buffy, spotted and scaled with dark brown; cap and 2 streaks below the cap are blackish brown; tail and wings as in the male.

HOODED MERGANSER (*Lophodytes cucullatus*)

Appearance: Smallest (16–20 in.) of our mergansers. The large-crested drake has a black head, neck, back, and tail; a large quarter-circle of white starts just below and behind the eye and extends almost to the edge of the crest. Drake's breast and underparts are white, the black and grayish wings have patches of white, and there are 2 fingers of black extending from the back onto the breast just before the finely black-barred reddish buff flanks. His eyes are yellow, feet dusky yellow, and bill blackish. The female has a small crest; back, tail, and white-patched wing are dark gray; upper breast and flanks are medium gray; the rest of the underparts are whitish. Her face is a dusky reddish gray fading to a dusky reddish brown on the crest and the rear of the head; eyes are yellow; bill and feet are a dusky yellow. The drake in eclipse resembles the female.

Voice: Grunting and creaking notes and low chatters of alarm.

Range and status: Breeds from se. Alaska and s. Canada south through all the U.S. except the sw. quarter. Winters from s. B.C., the c. U.S., Pa., N.Y., and

The Hooded Merganser catches fish and other aquatic prey with its long, thin bill.

sides whitish, heavily barred with blackish on the flank and lower breast.

Voice: In courtship, males make a low clucking *chuck-chuck-chuck-churr.*

Range and status: Breeds from c. B.C. and the Prairie Provinces of Canada south to Guatemala, through much of the W. Indies and Bahamas, and in the Andes of Colombia. Winters north to s. B.C., the s.-c. U.S., Pa., and Mass., and south to Costa Rica. It is extending its breeding range eastward into the Great Lakes region, Que., and New England. A fairly common duck.

Habitat: Freshwater ponds, lakes, and marshes; enters marine waters in winter.

Seasonal movements: Moves north in Mar.–Apr. and returns in Sept. Resident in tropical and subtropical parts of range.

Biology: Nest: Among reeds and rushes of marshes; woven of nearby plant material. Eggs: 5–17, usually 6–10, white or creamy. Incubation: 20–21(?) days. Age at 1st flight: 52–66 days. Food: Pondweeds, sedges, grasses, and wild celery form 75% of diet; animal food mainly insects and some shellfish.

Suggested reading: J. B. Low, "Nesting of the Ruddy Duck in Iowa," vol. 58, pp. 506–517, 1941.

MASKED DUCK (*Oxyura dominica*)

A small (13–14 in.) duck resident in the W. Indies and from Costa Rica south to s. Peru and n. Argentina; it has straggled to Tex., Fla., Wis., La., Md., Mass., and Vt. Drake has a brownish red head with a black mask over

A crested female Common Merganser clings to the entrance to her nest hole.

weeds; mainly animal food, including fish, amphibians, crustaceans, and insects.

Suggested reading: P. A. Johnsgard, "The Sexual Behavior and Systematic Position of the Hooded Merganser," *Wils. Bull.*, vol. 73, pp. 227–236, 1961.

COMMON MERGANSER (American Merganser, Goosander) (*Mergus merganser*)

Appearance: A large (21–27 in.) merganser. Drake has a crestless, dark metallic green head and neck, bright red bill, black back, gray tail, orangish feet, and white breast; flanks and undersides in life are often tinged bright pinkish. Female has a rough crest at the rear of her brownish red head and neck, and her white throat is sharply delimited. Her back and tail are medium gray, and flanks are light gray; her gray-and-black wings bear a white speculum, and her undersides are whitish. The male in eclipse plumage resembles the female.

Voice: Low stuttering croaks by the male and a throaty *korr* by the female.

Range and status: Breeds from s. Alaska, s. Yuk., s. Mack., c. Man., n. Ont., c. Que., and Nfld. south in the mountains of c. Calif., Ariz., n. N.Mex., and to S.Dak., the Great Lakes area, c. N.Y., and n. New England; in Iceland, Scotland, c. and n. Europe, and through the forested zone of Russia and Siberia south to n. India, Tibet, and Mongolia. In winter its range extends south to n. Mexico, the w. Gulf Coast, n. Ga., and S.C., and to s. Europe, Mesopotamia, c. India, n. Burma, s. China, Formosa, and Japan. Common and well known.

Habitat: Forested rivers and lakes; in winter openwater lakes, ponds, rivers, and, rarely, sheltered brackish and marine waters.

Seasonal movements: A retreat before ice and re-advance with melting of ice in spring; Feb.–Apr. and Oct.–Nov.

Biology: Nest: Cavity in tree or hollow in embankment; lined with down. Eggs: 6–17, usually 9–12, buffy white. Incubation: 28–31 days. Age at 1st flight unknown. Food: Predominantly fish; some mollusks, crustaceans, insects, and aquatic plants.

Suggested reading: D. A. Bannerman, *Birds of the British Isles*, Oliver and Boyd, Edinburgh, 1958, vol. 7, pp. 216–226.

RED-BREASTED MERGANSER (*Mergus serrator*)

Appearance: Smaller (19–26 in.) than the Common Merganser. Both sexes are ragged-crested and have red bills, eyes, feet, and legs. Drake has a metallic green head, and the front and sides of his neck are white, as are the breast and undersides; breast is crossed by a broad, dark buff band unevenly streaked with dark brown. His back and parts of the wings are black, and there is a white speculum. There are other white patches on the wings, which are otherwise dark gray like the tail;

Mass. to c. Mexico, the Gulf Coast, and Fla.; rarely Cuba. Fairly common.

Habitat: Rivers, lakes, and ponds in woodlands.

Seasonal movements: A retreat before freezing waters; main migration periods Mar.–Apr. and Oct.–Nov.

Biology: A swift, straight-line flier; said to use wings swimming underwater. Nest: In tree hollow. Eggs: 6–18, most often 10; white, almost round. Incubation: About 31(?) days, by female alone. Age at 1st flight unknown. Food: Some vegetable matter, grain, grasses, and pond-

Unlike the Common Merganser, the Red-breasted Merganser always nests on the ground.

the flanks and undertail and overtail feathers are finely barred with blackish. The female and the male in eclipse are like the female Common Merganser, except that their eyes are redder and the white throat grades into the reddish brown head and neck.

Voice: An infrequent harsh croak; female sounds like the female Common Merganser.

Range and status: Breeds north to the tree limit in Alaska and Canada, to s. Baffin I., e. and w. Greenland, Iceland, Ireland, Scotland, and in a broad belt south of the tundra from Scandinavia to Mongolia and Kamchatka; south in N. America to Wash., the c. Prairie Provinces, and the n.-c. and e. U.S. Winters in the coastal regions from se. Alaska to Baja Calif., in the e. U.S., in Europe to n. Africa, and in s. Iran, the coastal regions of Korea and China, and Japan. A common merganser.

Habitat: Rivers and lakes and, mainly in winter, marine waters.

Seasonal movements: Spring migration extends Mar.–Apr.; fall migration, Sept.–Nov.

Biology: Nest: Always on the ground under trees, brush, or driftwood; a down-lined hollow. Eggs: 6–16, most often 8–10, dark greenish buff. Incubation: 26–28 days. Age at 1st flight unknown. Food: Fish; some mollusks, crustaceans, and aquatic insects.

Suggested reading: A. C. Bent, *Life Histories of North American Wild Fowl*, part 1, Dover, N.Y. (reprint of U.S. Nat. Mus. Bull. 126, 1923), 1962, pp. 13–22.

SMEW (*Mergus albellus*)

A small (15–16 in.) whitish, black-and-gray merganser breeding in the forested areas from Scandinavia across Russia and Siberia to Kamchatka. Female has a brownish red cap and nape. It has been questionably reported from N. America in the past; recently pictures were taken of 1 wintering near Niagara Falls, N.Y., and Ont.

THE AMERICAN VULTURES (CATHARTIDAE)

Vultures are medium- to large-sized (23–55 in.) birds of prey only distantly related to the hawks and falcons. (Some authorities insist they do not belong with the falcons and hawks at all, but are related to the storks.) They range from s. Canada to s. S. America. There are 6 species, of which 4 have been recorded from N. America: Turkey Vulture, Black Vulture, California Condor, King Vulture. Their wings are long and relatively broad, well adapted for soaring flight where there are considerable updrafts of air. They fly, characteristically, with wings held in a V, in some species shallower than in others. They are seldom airborne when there are strong horizontal winds. Their food is carrion; rarely do they feed on living animals, and then only on young or otherwise helpless creatures. Their bare heads are usually dark or red-colored; plumages are predominantly grays, black, and white. Their legs and feet are not so large and strong as those of hawks, eagles, and falcons; their sturdy claws are strong but not so sharp as those of hawks and falcons. Their bills, not so powerful as in other hawklike birds, are rounded and hooked. Vocalizations are restricted to hisses and grunts. The sexes are alike. Vultures are usually solitary, but some gather in large roosts. They do not build nests; the eggs are laid in caves and hollow trees or on the ground. The 1–3 eggs are whitish or cream-colored, some blotched with browns. Both males and females incubate the eggs and care for the young. The hatchlings are downy, and their growth is rather slow.

TURKEY VULTURE (*Cathartes aura*)

Appearance: Medium-sized (26–32 in.) American vulture with a wingspan of 68–72 in.; plumage of the adults is dark grayish brown and grays, the bare head is reddish, the feet and legs dark pinkish. Immature birds are similar, but they have blackish heads and lighter-colored legs and feet. The long tail extends beyond the outstretched feet in flight, and there is no white showing on wings of birds soaring overhead. Wings are held in a steeper V and flapped less often than are those of the Black Vulture. Sometimes seen circling overhead in large numbers.

Voice: Hisses; sometimes grunts.

Range and status: Resident, except in more northerly parts, from s. Canada to s. S. America, including the Bahamas and Greater Antilles. In winter retreats south of a line extending coast to coast from n. Calif. to Md., rarely farther north. Common throughout most of range.

Habitat: Soars over all types of terrain; perches on dead trees, etc.

Seasonal movements: Spring movement in small numbers and generally unnoticed; some flocks may be seen moving southward in Oct.–Nov.

Biology: Nest: None. Eggs laid on ground under cover, in a hollow or a cave, or on exposed rock ledges. Eggs: 1–3, most often 2; dull or creamy white blotched

The Turkey Vulture, a valuable scavenger, feeds primarily on the remains of dead animals.

with light and bright browns. Incubation: 38–41(?) days by both sexes. Young are fed regurgitated food by both parents. Age at 1st flight: 8–10 weeks. Food: Carrion; sometimes small living animals.

Suggested reading: T. H. Work and A. J. Wool, "The Nest Life of the Turkey Vulture," *Condor*, vol. 44, pp. 145–159, 1942.

BLACK VULTURE (*Coragyps atratus*)

Appearance: Smaller (23–27 in.) than the Turkey Vulture, and blacker. Wingspan 54–60 in. Both adults and young have bare black heads. The legs and feet are whitish. The tail is short, and the extended feet are often longer than the tail in flight; also the tail is usually more fanned out and appears broader than that of the Turkey Vulture. In flight the wings are closer to horizontal than those of the Turkey Vulture, and the Black Vulture flaps its wings more and soars less. From below it has whitish patches near the tips of the wings.

Voice: Hisses and grunts only.

Range and status: Resident from the s., se., c., and e.-c. U.S. south to c. Argentina and Chile; not found regularly in Calif., N.Mex., Baja Calif., the Bahamas, or the W. Indies; has straggled to the Dakotas and se. Canada and is apparently extending its range northward. It is nowhere so common as the Turkey Vulture.

Habitat: Conducts its aerial searches over almost any terrain except those at higher altitudes.

Seasonal movements: There is some evidence that it is migratory within its range.

Biology: Nest: None. Eggs laid in situations similar to those chosen by the Turkey Vulture. Eggs: 1–3, normally 2; brown-blotched whitish or pale bluish, with the spots sometimes forming a wreath around the larger end. Incubation: 39–41 days. Age at 1st flight uncertain, but more than 60 days. Food: More restricted to carrion than the Turkey Vulture.

CALIFORNIA CONDOR (*Gymnogyps californianus*)

Appearance: The largest (43–55 in.) American vulture, with a wingspan of 100–132 in. (8½–11 ft.). Plumage is black, with a large area of white under the wings, and head is yellowish or orange. In flight the wings are held closer to a straight line than those of other vultures. Immature birds have blackish heads, but their much larger size and method of flight help separate them from the other similarly colored vultures.

Voice: Hisses.

Range and status: Now confined as breeding bird to coastal ranges from Monterey to Los Angeles Counties and mountains south of the San Joaquin Valley in Calif., where perhaps 40–60 individuals survive as residents. Sometimes reported in the foothills of the Sierra Nevadas in Calif. Formerly ranged through Ore. and Nev. and

The California Condor is one of North America's largest and rarest birds.

into Utah, Ariz., and Baja Calif. Man, practically the California Condor's only enemy, is responsible for almost eliminating this harmless bird.

Habitat: Mountains and adjacent open areas.

Seasonal movements: None.

Biology: At least 5 years old before 1st breeding. Nest: None. Eggs laid on rocks in caves or sheltered spots in cliffs. Birds desert nest at slightest disturbance. Eggs: 1, white. Incubation: Uncertain; 29–31(?) days (certainly not correct, as the S. American Condor incubates 55 days). Age at 1st flight: 3½–5 months; from this it is probable that the adults breed but once in 2 years. Food: Carrion, but the bird seems to prefer fresher meat than do other vultures; occasionally captures living prey.

Suggested reading: Carl Koford, *The California Condor*, Nat. Aud. Soc. Research Report, no. 5, 1953.

KING VULTURE (*Sarcoramphus papa*)

A robust vulture about the size of the Turkey Vulture, with plumage mainly a very light gray; flight feathers and tail are blackish, and a ruff of medium gray feathers circles the base of the bare head and neck. The head bears large caruncles, and the skin is patterned in black, yellowish, and reddish orange and is streaked with white. The bill is yellowish; legs and feet are pale gray; eyes are light yellow. It is found from c. Mexico south to n. Argentina; formerly in Fla. and Trinidad, accidentally in Ariz.

HAWKS, OLD WORLD VULTURES, AND HARRIERS (ACCIPITRIDAE)

These small to large (11–45 in.) diurnal, raptorial birds are absent only from the polar regions. The approximately 205 species are grouped into 8 subfamilies. There are 26 species in N. America; 2 of the subfamilies are not found here. These birds have a short bill that is strongly hooked; the legs are medium to long, and the claws are stout and sharply curved. Colors consist mainly of browns, black, and white; the birds are usually lighter beneath, with barred patterns predominating. Their wings are relatively large and powerful. Flight varies with their method of capturing food, from soaring to almost continual flapping, and aerial diving with folded wings. Their prey is largely animal, taken or killed by the feet from the air; some species live on fish, some on mollusks, and some on carrion. Generally the sexes are alike, but the female is usually larger. They nest in trees, on the ground, on cliffs, and in tree hollows. The nests are made of sticks, grasses, and weed stalks. The 1–6 whitish eggs, often spotted or blotched with brown, are incubated by the female alone or by both sexes; in all the American species apparently both parents participate. The downy hatchlings are reared by both parents.

The white-tailed kites subfamily (Elaninae) includes small to medium-sized (14–20 in.) hawks with very long, pointed wings and a medium-long tail that is commonly white. The plumage is soft. The nostrils are large and oval-shaped. The claws are smooth and rounded underneath. There are 6 species, ranging from the subtropics south through all the continents except Antarctica. Only 1 species, the White-tailed Kite, is found in N. America.

The honey buzzards and swallow-tailed kites (Perninae) are small to medium-sized (13–25½ in.) hawks with long, pointed or sharply rounded wings and a long, sometimes forked tail that is seldom pure white. Their claws are grooved beneath. The nostrils are oblique slits. There are 13 known species ranging over most of the world from c. se. U.S. and c. Europe and s. Siberia southward, exclusive of Antarctica. N. America has only the Swallow-tailed Kite.

True kites (Milvinae) are small to medium-sized (13–25 in.) hawks with long, somewhat pointed wings and a relatively long tail. There are 13 species found over much the same area as the Perninae; only 2 of these, the Mississippi Kite and the Everglades Kite, are found in N.

America. They have a featherless shield of flesh above each eye. Their flight is swift and graceful. Food consists mainly of large insects, snails, reptiles, amphibians, and small mammals; some extralimital species eat carrion.

There are about 50 species in the cosmopolitan Accipitrinae subfamily, small to medium-sized (10–27 in.) hawks usually called the bird hawks, but only 3 are found in N. America: the Goshawk, the Sharp-shinned Hawk, and Cooper's Hawk. Their tails are relatively long and their wings relatively short and rounded, an adaption to flight through thick forests and brush. They seldom soar, but fly with rapid wingbeats and occasional abbreviated glides. Females are considerably larger than the males; none of the N. American species shows any other difference in the sexes. Their food consists primarily of birds and small mammals. Of all avian predators, these birds are in man's highest disfavor; but without such predators helping to control bird populations, we could well have too many of the smaller birds. Dietary statistics of the bird hawks show that the most common birds (crows, Starlings, and blackbirds, for example) are eaten most often.

The subfamily of true hawks and eagles (Buteoninae) includes small to large (12–45 in.) heavy-bodied hawks, with broad, round-tipped wings and comparatively short, wide tails. Except for Antarctica, these birds range throughout the world. There are about 90 species; 18 occur in N. America. Many species have a light and a dark color phase, and in a few species there are also intermediate plumages. Flight is normally slow, with heavy flapping and much soaring. Most species are conspicuous because of their habit of circling high in the sky. They also like to perch on a high point, such as a tree, telephone pole, or cliffside, which gives them a wide view of the surrounding area. Not so swift of wing as the bird hawks, they are seldom able to capture the faster-flying birds and thus feed far more on mammals, reptiles, and fish. They usually take their prey, after sighting it from their vantage points or while soaring overhead, by diving toward it and overtaking the animal before it reaches cover. Some of the hawks that habitually soar over farmlands are called "chicken hawks," as they are erroneously believed to be hunting the farmers' poultry. Study of the stomach contents of a large number of these hawks shows that the most common item on their menu is rodents. Only 2% of the hawks manage to capture poultry, and these may have chanced upon a sick hen or one that wandered too far. These hawks are more properly referred to as buzzards, but in popular usage in America that word is used only for the vultures. Eagles, the largest members of this subfamily, usually soar high overhead on outstretched pinions held in a straight line. The true eagles are those belonging to the genus *Aquila*, but similar large hawks are also called eagles. The larger the hawk, the larger its prey is apt to be. Many eagles have become pirates, robbing the Osprey and other avian fishers of their catch, even though they are able to capture fish themselves. They also drive smaller hawks away from fresh kills or carrion.

The harriers and marsh hawks (Circinae) are a subfamily of long-legged, long-tailed, quite slim hawks with rather long, narrow wings. Because of their somewhat flattened faces, they have an owllike appearance. There are 17 species found all over the world except for Oceania, New Zealand, and the polar regions. There is only 1 species in America, the Marsh Hawk. Flight is rather slow, with much gliding, and adaption for hunting over swamps and open fields or prairies. There is considerable plumage difference between the sexes; the female is also larger. Nests are usually built on the ground; the 3–6 eggs are incubated by the female, but the male brings food to the female and helps raise the young. Small mammals make up a large bulk of their food, with birds, other vertebrates, and insects also being taken.

White-tailed Kite

Swallow-tailed Kite

Habitat: Marshes, river valleys, and well-watered foothills.

Seasonal movements: None.

Biology: Nest: In trees near marshes or near open country; a platform of twigs. Eggs: 2–6, usually 3–5: white or creamy, spotted or blotched with dark browns. Incubation: Not less than 30 days, by female alone; more data needed. Age at 1st flight: About 30(?) days. Food: Rodents, lizards, and large insects.

Suggested reading: J. B. Dixon, R. E. Dixon, and J. E. Dixon, "Natural History of the White-tailed Kite in San Diego Co., Cal.," *Condor,* vol. 59, pp. 155–165, 1957.

SWALLOW-TAILED KITE (*Elanoïdes forficatus*)

Appearance: The largest (19–25½ in.) member of the subfamily. The back, rump, wings, and deeply forked tail are blackish; the rest of the plumage is white, including the smaller feathers on the underside of the wing. Legs and feet are bluish or greenish gray, the bill is dark, and the eyes vary from dark brown to red. Head, neck, and upper breast of immature birds are streaked with brownish red. Flight is rapid and swallowlike. Wingspan is 45–50 in.

Voice: Squeals and loud, shrill, but sometimes soft, whistles.

Range and status: Now breeds locally and rarely from the Gulf Coast and S.C. south through e. Mexico and C. America to Ecuador, Bolivia, Brazil, and n. Argentina; possibly resident in much of this area. Winter range poorly defined. Formerly bred farther north in the Mississippi and Ohio Valleys to Minn. and Ohio and may still straggle there. Stragglers were recorded as far as N.Mex., Colo., s.-c. Canada, New England, Cuba, and Jamaica. May be considered rare and in danger of extirpation only in the U.S.

Habitat: At home in air over forests or open prairies, meadows, or brush, preferably in the vicinity of marshes, river bottoms, ponds, or lakes.

Seasonal movements: There is some movement of flocks within the range outlined above; in some places it is known only as a bird of passage.

Biology: Gregarious, but not colonial. Nest: In upper branches of trees (60–100 ft. or more); made of twigs interlaced with mosses, commonly "Spanish moss." Eggs: 2–4, most frequently 2; whitish with brown blotches. Incubation: Estimated as 21–24 days. Age at 1st flight unknown. Food: Lizards, frogs, snakes, and large insects snatched off the ground or captured in flight; much of it eaten while bird is still airborne!

Suggested reading: A. C. Bent, *Life Histories of North American Birds of Prey,* part 1, Dover, N.Y. (reprint of U.S. Nat. Mus. Bull. 167, 1937), 1961, pp. 44–53.

WHITE-TAILED KITE (*Elanus leucurus*)

Appearance: A small (15–17 in.) hawk. Adults are mostly white and light gray and show dark gray shoulders when perching. The eyes are scarlet, the legs and feet bright yellow. The bill is black with a yellow base. Immature birds have brown eyes; there is a broad band of brownish red across the chest, and the back has a scaled appearance from the buff-edged brown feathers that extend up to the crown.

Voice: A whistled, staccato *keep-keep-keep-keep* and a louder, higher-pitched *kreeeek.*

Range and status: Resident from Calif. west of the deserts, lowland Mexico, Tex., and peninsular Fla. south to Chile and Argentina, exclusive of the Bahamas and W. Indies. Very rare in Tex. and Fla. and not common in Calif.

MISSISSIPPI KITE (*Ictinia misisippiensis*)

Appearance: Small (13–17 in.), graceful, falconlike hawks. Adults gray, paler at the head; wings and tail darker gray. The eyes are bright red, the legs and feet yellow. The young are similar, but they are streaked with brown and have 3 gray bars on the tail. The pointed wings, dark at the tips and getting lighter toward the body, are distinctive. Wingspread is 34–37 in.

Voice: A high, weak double whistle.

Range and status: Breeds from e. Kans., Iowa, Tenn., and S.C. south to the Gulf Coast and n. Fla.; very rare in the n. parts of this area. Formerly north to Ill. and Ind. Winters from s. Tex. and Fla. to Guatemala and Paraguay. Has straggled farther west and north in U.S. The most common of our kites, but still a rare bird.

Habitat: Over open scrub forests, prairies, forested creek bottoms, and wooded areas where it can feed over nearby farmlands.

Seasonal movements: Withdrawal from n. regions is gradual, and there is no set timetable.

Biology: Gregarious, sometimes flying about in large flocks, but not colonial. Nest: In the tops of taller trees from 10 ft. in a scrub tree to over 100 ft.; a flimsy platform of small sticks and twigs lined with fresh green leaves. Eggs: 1–3, usually 2, plain bluish white. Incubation: 31–32 days. Age at 1st flight unknown. Food: Large insects, such as dragonflies and grasshoppers.

Suggested reading: G. M. Sutton, "The Mississippi Kite in Spring," *Condor*, vol. 41, pp. 41–53, 1939. T. S. Robinson, "Notes on the Development of a Brood of Mississippi Kites," *Trans. Kans. Acad. Sci.*, vol. 60, pp. 174–180, 1957.

EVERGLADE KITE (*Rostrhamus sociabilis*)

Appearance: A medium-small (16–18 in.) kite with rather broad wings. Wingspan about 45 in. Plumage of the male is blackish except for a narrow edge of white at the tip and upper half of the square-tipped tail; the feathers above and below the tail are also white. Female is browner, lighter-colored at the head, barred and streaked with darker browns and black; she is white where the male is white. Immatures resemble the females, but they have dark brown eyes. The legs, feet, eyes, and skin around the eyes and at the base of the bill are all bright red (female's duller or orangish); sharply decurved bill and claws are black. The downy young are pale brownish gray.

Voice: Rapidly repeated, high-pitched squeaks running into a chatter.

Range and status: Resident from Fla., e.-c. Mexico, and Cuba south to n. S. America and through e. S. America to Argentina. Draining of swamps in Fla., resulting in reduced snail populations, has lowered the popula-

A true kite, the Mississippi Kite has long, rather pointed wings and a relatively long tail.

The Everglade Kite uses its decurved bill to pry flesh from snails, its major source of food.

This immature Goshawk will retain its dark, streaked plumage through its second winter.

tion of this once common species alarmingly. The *New York Times* for Aug. 25, 1964, reported that fewer than 20 birds existed.

Habitat: Everglades and swamps of Fla. and bodies of water where its food may be found.

Seasonal movements: Contraction of its range in winter may have resulted from lowering of water levels and reduced food supply.

Biology: Gregarious, even nesting in small colonies. Nest: In low trees just above water, sometimes on reeds; a compact mass of twigs lined with grasses. Eggs: 2–5, usually 3–4; white, heavily spotted with brown. Incubation and age at 1st flight unknown. Food: Solely large freshwater snails of the genus *Ampullaria,* found throughout much of the American tropics; the bird pries the flesh from the shell with its pointed, strongly decurved bill (see illustration).

Suggested reading: A. Sprunt, Jr., "The Phantom of the Marshes," *Aud. Mag.*, vol. 47, pp. 15–22, 1945.

GOSHAWK (*Accipiter gentilis*)

Appearance: A large (19–27 in.) bird hawk, with a wingspan of 40–47 in. Adults are grayish; the back, most of the wings, and the tail are medium bluish gray, and the larger feathers of the wings are blackish; the tail, broadly barred with darker gray, is narrowly tipped with white. The underparts and thighs are finely barred gray and white. The face is white, and the rest of the head is dark gray, with a whitish line above the scarlet eyes. The

legs and feet are bright yellow, the bill and claws blackish. The immature plumage, worn through the second winter, is dark brown above, and white streaked with black and dark brown below; the tail, from below, is light gray, barred with darker gray. The eyes of the young are yellowish, the feet yellow; the whitish stripe above the eyes is more conspicuous in this species than in the otherwise very similar young of the Cooper's and Sharp-shinned Hawks. The adults in Europe and Asia are brown like the immatures, except that the underparts are finely *barred* with browns; the downy young are white and pale gray.

Voice: Alarm notes near nest are a deep, rapidly repeated *ka-ka-ka-ka-ka;* during courtship, a high, querulous *ey-ah, ey-ah.*

Range and status: Breeds from nw. and c. Alaska, nw. and s.-c. Mack., the n. Prairie Provinces, n. Ont., c. Que., and c. Lab. south to Calif., Nev., se. Ariz., Colo., n. Minn., the Great Lakes region, Pa., and Md. Also throughout Europe except the British Isles, and in Asia from the tree limits south to Asia Minor, s. Siberia, Mongolia, and Japan; also in Tibet and w. China. Winters from Alaska, B.C., and c. and se. Canada to s. Calif., c. Mexico, Tex., Mo., Tenn., and Va.; in Eurasia south to the Mediterranean, Iran, n. India, Burma, and s. China. Actively persecuted by man, it still survives to serve nature as a valuable population control. It is sparsely distributed, as are most large predators.

Habitat: Forested areas.

Seasonal movements: No regular migrations; invades more southerly areas irregularly, possibly because of food shortages within its normal range.

Biology: Nest: 20–60 ft. high in tree; large and bulky, and made of sticks lined with bark and fresh evergreen sprigs. Eggs: 2–5, most often 3–4, whitish. Incubation: About 28(?) days, mainly by female. Age at 1st flight: About 42 days. Food: About 60% birds and 40% mammals. Most of the birds taken are species like crows and blackbirds; a large percentage of the mammals eaten consists of red squirrels.

Suggested reading: Heinz Meng, "Food Habits of Nesting Cooper's Hawks and Goshawks in New York and Pennsylvania," *Wils. Bull.*, vol. 71, pp. 169–174, 1959.

SHARP-SHINNED HAWK (*Accipiter striatus*)

Appearance: Smallest (10–14 in.) of the bird hawks, with a wingspan of 20–27 in. Adults have a medium gray-blue nape, back, tail, and wings; the cap, larger feathers of the wings, and 4 bands on the tail are darker blue-gray; the tail also has a narrow white tip. The face and throat are white; the undersides and thighs are finely barred brownish red and white. The eyes are scarlet, the feet and legs bright yellow, the bill and claws blackish. Except for size, the immatures closely resemble immatures of the Goshawk and Cooper's Hawk; the tail of this species is notched or square, and the light stripe over the eye is distinct.

Voice: A shrill *keek-keek-keek*.

Range and status: N. America only. Breeds almost as far north as the Goshawk and farther south to s. Calif., c. Mexico, Tex. La., Ala., and S.C. Winters from s. Canada south to Costa Rica, the Gulf Coast, and s. Fla. Has straggled to Panama, Cuba, the Bahamas, and Bermuda. Fairly common.

Habitat: Forests and brushy areas.

Seasonal movements: Large migrating flocks may be seen in favored places Apr.–early May and Aug.–Oct.

Biology: Nest: 10–60 ft. above the ground; made of sticks and twigs, forming a platform in the branches of trees, usually conifers. Eggs: 3–8, commonly 4–5, brown-blotched white. Incubation: About 3 weeks, mostly by female. Age at 1st flight unknown. Food: 70% birds; also large insects and small mammals.

Suggested reading: A. C. Bent, *Life Histories of North American Birds of Prey*, part 1, Dover, N.Y. (reprint of U.S. Nat. Mus. Bull. 167, 1937), 1961, pp. 95–111.

COOPER'S HAWK (*Accipiter cooperii*)

Appearance: Middle-sized (14–21 in.) member of our bird hawk trio; larger than the Sharp-shinned, but almost a feather-for-feather match with that species in both adult and immature plumages. This species has a square or slightly rounded tip to its tail. The rather short, rounded wings and the relatively long shanks of the legs are typical of accipiters. In the immature birds, the streak over the eyes is obscure.

Voice: Similar to, but lower than, that of the Sharp-shin.

Range and status: Breeds from s. Canada to Baja Calif., nw. Mexico, Tex., Miss., Ala., and c. Fla. Winters from n. U.S. through Mexico to Costa Rica. It is a common forest hawk.

Habitat: Woodlands, usually with open areas.

Seasonal movements: Migrates in flocks, often accompanying Sharp-shins; late Mar.–early May and Sept.–early Nov.

Biology: Nest: 10–60 ft. up in trees; sometimes built in old Crow's nest; made of sticks and twigs lined with bark. Eggs: 3–6, usually 4–5; whitish, sometimes spotted

The Cooper's Hawk, a forest-dwelling species, preys mainly on smaller birds.

with brown. Incubation: About 24 days, mainly by female. Age at 1st flight unknown. Food: About 75% birds; the rest of the diet consists of small mammals.

Suggested reading: Heinz Meng, "Food Habits of Nesting Cooper's Hawks and Goshawks in New York and Pennsylvania," *Wils. Bull.*, vol. 71, pp. 169–174, 1959.

Harlan's Hawk

RED-TAILED HAWK (*Buteo jamaicensis*)

Appearance: A medium-sized (19–25½ in.) buzzard, with a wingspan of 46–58 in. Adult's head, nape, back, and top of wings are dark brown; throat and undersides, including thighs, are a buffy white with brown streaks and spots on the sides. The tail is a light brownish red with a thin dark terminal band, then a narrow buffy tip; the legs, feet, and base of bill are yellow; the claws and most of the bill are blackish. There are also dark phases, with all colors heavier or darker, and other variations, such as Krider's Red-tailed Hawk of the Great Plains; that bird is much lighter-colored, even whitish, and lacks most of the brownish red of the tail, which is replaced by very light tan. Immature birds have a brown tail, lighter below, barred with darker brown; their underparts are whiter, particularly the conspicuous breast, which is underlined by a band of brown streaks.

Voice: Down-slurred scream, usually long and drawn-out.

Range and status: Throughout N. America from c. Alaska and c. and e. Canada to Panama and the W. Indies. Winters from se. Alaska, sw. Canada and n.-c. and nw. U.S. southward. Common.

Habitat: Mountains, deserts, forests, meadows; generally more common near open areas than the Red-shouldered Hawk.

Seasonal movements: Migratory only in the n. parts of its range. Spring travels occur in Mar.–Apr., and fall in Sept.–early Nov., sometimes in large flocks.

Biology: Gregarious in migrations and during winter. Nest: Bulky platform of sticks lined with shredded bark; high in a tree, or in low trees or cactuses or on cliffs in treeless country. Eggs: 1–5, commonly 2–3, whitish with a few brown spots. Incubation: About 28(?) days, mostly by female, but male brings food to the hen. Age at 1st flight: 4–5 weeks. Food: About 80% mammals, mainly rodents; some birds, other vertebrates, and insects. They also eat some carrion; some of the larger items found in their stomachs, such as chickens, may have been found dead. It is one of the so-called chicken hawks.

Suggested reading: G. R. Austing, *The World of the Red-tailed Hawk*, Lippincott, Phil. and N.Y., 1964, 128 pp. H. S. Fitch, F. Svenson, and D. F. Tillotson, "Behavior and Food Habits of the Red-tailed Hawk," *Condor*, vol. 48, pp. 205–237, 1946.

HARLAN'S HAWK (*Buteo harlani*)

Appearance: About the same size (21–23 in.) as the Red-tailed Hawk, but its undersides and thighs are heavily streaked and barred with dark brown; the tail is whitish, becoming dark brown near the tip, which is white. The light phase (except for the back and wings, which are dark brown) is whitish, lightly streaked with brown and gray on the head, neck, and thighs. There is an intermediate phase. Immature birds resemble closely those of the Red-tailed Hawk.

Voice: Like the Red-tailed Hawk's.

Range and status: Breeds from e.-c. Alaska southeasterly to n. B.C. and c. Alta. Winters from Kans. and s. Mo. to c. Tex. and La., very rarely farther west and east. Rare; long believed only a variation of the Red-tailed Hawk.

Habitat: Like that of the Red-tailed.

Seasonal movements: Spring migration Apr.–early May; fall migration in Sept.

Biology: Very little known; considered a stronger, faster flier than the Red-tailed Hawk. Nest: Bulky mass of sticks in trees. Other data probably very similar to those of the Red-tailed Hawk.

Suggested reading: N. A. Wood, "Harlan's Hawk," *Wils. Bull.*, vol. 44, pp. 78–87, 1932.

RED-SHOULDERED HAWK (*Buteo lineatus*)

Appearance: About the same size (17–24 in.) as the Red-tailed Hawk, but it is less husky and has a smaller (32½–50 in.) wingspan. Adults are barred with white and brownish red below from the throat to the undertail feathers, on the thighs, and extending well out on the underside of the wings; head, nape, and back are dark brown streaked with lighter brown. The wings, except for the brownish red "shoulders," are dark brown, spotted with whitish; the tail is brownish black, with narrow white bars starting at the tip. Immature birds are similar but have white undersides streaked with dark brown. Does not soar so much as the Red-tailed.

Voice: A penetrating *keeee-ooo* scream.

Range and status: Mainly resident from n. Calif. to nw. Baja Calif. and from c. Minn., c. Wis., s. Ont., and s. Que. to c. and e.-c. Mexico, the Gulf Coast, and s. Fla. In the East it retreats in winter to the c. U.S. and s. New England. Locally common; rare in the West.

Habitat: Most common in broken, wet woodlands.

Seasonal movements: Scattered individuals may remain in n. parts of range; most have withdrawn by late Nov. and return by early Mar.

Biology: Nest: 20–60 ft. high in trees; made of sticks, with leaves, mosses, and bark; usually fresh leaves or mosses added daily. Eggs: 3–6, usually 3–4; whitish, blotched with browns. Incubation: 28 days, by both sexes. Age at 1st flight: 5–6 weeks. Food: Frogs, snakes, crayfish, large insects, mice, and shrews. The bird is also a scavenger, and most poultry found in stomachs probably obtained this way.

Suggested reading: R. E. Stewart, "Ecology of a Nesting Red-shouldered Hawk Population," *Wils. Bull.*, vol. 61, pp. 26–35, 1949.

Broad-winged Hawks migrate in loose flocks that sometimes number in the thousands.

BROAD-WINGED HAWK (*Buteo platypterus*)

Appearance: Smallest (13½–19 in.) of our buteos, with a wingspan of 32–39 in. Barred brownish red and white beneath but not extending to undersides of wings, which are mainly whitish; head, nape, back, wings, and tail are dark brown; the tail has 3 broad white bars and a narrow white tip; the throat is also white. Immatures are difficult to separate from young Red-shouldered Hawks, which have reddish shoulders and are larger.

Voice: Shrill, hissing whistled *wheeeeee*, diminishing in force after an explosive start.

Range and status: Breeds east of the Rockies from s. Canada south to Tex., the Gulf Coast, and s. Fla. Winters in Fla. and from Guatemala to nw. S. America. A common hawk.

Habitat: Deciduous woodlands.

Seasonal movements: Migrations often spectacular; may travel in loose flocks of thousands, both spring and fall. Movements Mar.–mid-May and Sept.–Oct.

Biology: Nest: 15–50 ft. high in trees next to the bole; loosely built of sticks and twigs, lined with bark and mosses. Eggs: 1–4, commonly 2; whitish with brown and purplish marks. Incubation: 21–25 days, by both sexes. Age at 1st flight: 40–50 days. Food: Large insects, frogs, toads, reptiles, some mice, and, very rarely, small birds.

Suggested reading: A. C. Bent, *Life Histories of North American Birds of Prey*, part 1, Dover, N.Y. (reprint of U.S. Nat. Mus. Bull. 167, 1937), 1961, pp. 236–253. R. Hatch, "Broad-winged Hawk: Symbol of the Northern Wilds," *Aud. Mag.*, vol. 58, pp. 70–71, 1956.

The Swainson's Hawk is fairly common through much of western North America.

SWAINSON'S HAWK (*Buteo swainsoni*)

Appearance: Like a small (19–22 in.) Red-tailed Hawk with lighter underparts, but the breast is crossed by a broad band of medium brown, and the tail is brown, barred with darker brown. The dark phase has undersides completely brown except for a whitish throat. Wingspan is 47–57 in. Immature birds are larger than young Broad-winged Hawks, but otherwise resemble them closely.

Voice: Like that of the Broad-winged, but higher-pitched and less of a hiss.

Range and status: Breeds from c. Alaska, nw. Mack., and the Prairie Provinces of Canada south to Baja Calif., n.-c. Mexico, and s.-c. Tex.; rarely in Ill. and Mo. Winters in Argentina, migrating through Mexico, C. America, and nw. S. America. Straggles casually through much of e. N. America. Common; sometimes seen in large migrating flocks.

Habitat: Forests, usually mixed conifers and deciduous trees; in prairie regions most abundant where some trees are found.

Seasonal movements: A long-distance migrant; according to Bent, the large flocks move southward through Mexico in Oct. and make the return trip in Apr.

Biology: Nest: From near ground level to 100 ft. or more above the ground in trees; bulky, made of sticks and branches lined with smaller sticks. Eggs: 2–4, most commonly 2; whitish, unmarked or spotted sparsely with brown. Incubation: Reported as about 28 days, probably by both sexes. Age at 1st flight: Reported as 28–35 days, a somewhat short period. Food: 66% of stomach contents consists of large insects, such as grasshoppers; some mammals and other vertebrates.

Suggested reading: J. G. Tyler, "Two Seasons with the Swainson Hawks," *Oologist*, vol. 25, pp. 9–12, 1908.

ZONE-TAILED HAWK (*Buteo albonotatus*)

About the size (18½–21½ in.) of Swainson's Hawk, with plumage mainly a medium gray, but tail has a narrow white tip and 3 broader white bands. Immature birds have white-spotted undersides and some white spots on the nape. It ranges from Baja Calif., c. Ariz., s. N.Mex., and w. Tex. south to n. S. America. In winter it becomes rarer in the n. parts of its range. In flight it resembles a vulture. It feeds on fish, amphibians, and reptiles; also some birds and mammals. The rest of its biology is probably similar to that of other buteos, but is little known.

WHITE-TAILED HAWK (Sennett's Hawk) (*Buteo albicaudatus*)

A moderate-sized (23–24 in.) hawk with gray upperparts and wings, light undersides, reddish shoulders, and a white tail tipped with a broad black band and a narrow terminal white band. It is resident from nw. Mexico, s. Ariz., and s. Tex. south to s. S. America. Little is known of its biology; probably much like that of buteos of similar size.

SHORT-TAILED HAWK (*Buteo brachyurus*)

A small (ca. 17 in.) buteo with a relatively short tail. The dark phase is uniformly medium gray all over, except for bars of darker gray on the tail. The light-phase

White-tailed Hawk

adults have clear white undersides. Immatures have dark-spotted buffy underparts. It is a rare resident in Fla. and is also found from c. Mexico to n. Argentina.

HAWAIIAN HAWK (Io) (*Buteo solitarius*)

A small buteo (15½–18 in.) found only on the island of Hawaii, where it was common in the late 19th century, but is now much reduced in numbers. One phase is almost entirely dark brown; another phase is almost all light buffy brown. An intermediate phase is dark brown above and buffy below. Although it occasionally kills birds, its principal foods are insects and small mammals.

ROUGH-LEGGED HAWK (*Buteo lagopus*)

Appearance: About the size (19–24 in.) of the Red-tailed Hawk. In 1 phase, plumage is all dark brown. In the light phase, however, the head, neck, underparts, and thighs are whitish to buffy, streaked and spotted with dark brown; the back, wings, and a broad band on the belly are dark brown; the lower third of the tail is dark brown, and the rest whitish. Immature birds of light phase are less whitish and more tawny; dark-phase immature birds have a mottled appearance. A large hawk (wingspan: 48–56 in.) with a habit of fluttering over 1 spot momentarily in its aerial searches.

Voice: High-pitched whistles reminiscent of the mewing of a cat, and outright squeals.

Range and status: Breeds in Scandinavia, n. Russia, and n. Siberia (southward in the east to Kamchatka), and in N. America from the n. edge of the continent and some of the s. islands of the Arctic Archipelago south to c. B.C., s. Prairie Provinces, c. Ont., c. Que., and c. Lab. Winters from the s. edge of the breeding range south to c. Calif., Ariz., N.Mex., Okla., Mo., Tenn., and Va., and in Eurasia to c. Europe, the Caspian area, n. China, and Japan; casually farther south. Abundance depends on populations of lemmings and other small rodents; very common some winters in U.S. when a shortage of food farther north causes the birds to move south in larger numbers than usual.

Habitat: Tundra and arctic coasts; in winter prefers marshes and other open areas.

Seasonal movements: Migratory, but erratic as to distance and direction.

Biology: Nest: On cliff ledges, rock outcrops, or the tops of the tallest of the stunted trees in its favored habitat; made of sticks and twigs lined with grasses and mosses. Eggs: 2–6, most often 3–4; whitish, blotched with varying shades of brown. Incubation: 28 days, by both sexes. Age at 1st flight: About 2 months. Food: In the breeding area, mainly lemmings, but includes other similar rodents as well as the ubiquitous field mouse in the U.S.; only rarely does it feed on other vertebrates and large insects. A most efficient "mousetrap"; this one chases the mice! Yet the greatest enemy of the Rough-leg is man, with his poisons and traps.

Suggested reading: D. A. Bannerman, *Birds of the British Isles,* Oliver and Boyd, Edinburgh, 1956, vol. 5, pp. 129–143.

In winter, the Rough-legged Hawk often strays far south of its arctic breeding range.

FERRUGINOUS HAWK (Ferruginous Rough-legged Hawk) (*Buteo regalis*)

Appearance: Somewhat larger (22½–25 in.) than the Rough-legged Hawk. Resembles the light-phase Rough-leg, except that it lacks the band across the belly, and has a whitish tail becoming light brownish red at the tip, reddish brown "pants," and more reddish upperparts, particularly the shoulders and back. Immatures are almost immaculate white below, and their tails are grayer. There is a dark-phase adult that is darker brown above and a dark brownish red below; it differs from the dark-phase Swainson's Hawk in having a completely whitish tail. Wingspan is about 56 in.

Voice: A loud, harsh cough and a higher-pitched *kree-ah*.

Range and status: Breeds from e. Wash. and the s. edges of the Canadian Prairie Provinces south to Nev., N.Mex., nw. Tex., and w. Okla. In winter mainly from the sw. U.S. to Baja Calif. and c. Mexico, but small numbers may be found throughout most of the breeding range. Fairly common.

Habitat: Open prairies, arid areas.

Seasonal movements: Returns to breeding grounds in Mar. and generally has left by mid-Oct.

Biology: Nest: On the surface of rocky outcrops, on cliff ledges, or in trees; made of sticks and twigs lined with grasses and rootlets. Eggs: 2–6, usually 3–4; white or whitish, well marked with varying shades of brown. Incubation: About 28 days, by both parents. Age at 1st flight: About 2 months. Food: About 95% small mammals, mainly mice and ground squirrels; sometimes other vertebrates and large insects. Should be fully protected whenever found.

Suggested reading: A. C. Bent, *Life Histories of North American Birds of Prey,* part 1, Dover, N.Y. (reprint of U.S. Nat Mus. Bull. 167, 1937), 1961, pp. 284–293.

GRAY HAWK (Mexican Goshawk) (*Buteo nitidus*)

Similar in size (16–18 in.) and appearance to the Broad-winged Hawk, but wings and upperparts are a medium gray and the undersides are barred white and gray. Immatures are usually whiter below than young Broad-wings. Ranges from s. Ariz., N.Mex., and Tex. to e. Bolivia, n. Argentina, and s. Brazil. Very little known about habits and biology.

HARRIS' HAWK (*Parabuteo unicinctus*)

Another tropical hawk about the size (17½–24 in.) of the Red-tail. Plumage is dark gray and brownish gray, with brownish red shoulders and thighs, and a narrow white tip to the tail; the base of the tail and the feathers beneath the tail are white. The feet and the rather long legs are yellow. It is resident from the s. border of the U.S. (Calif. to Tex.; formerly farther east) south to c. Chile and Argentina.

BLACK HAWK (*Buteogallus anthracinus*)

A medium-sized (20–23 in.) hawk, completely dark gray and black, except for a broad white band and a narrow white tip to the tail. Immature birds resemble young Broad-wings, except that their tails are barred black and white, not brown and whitish. Ranges from Ariz., N.Mex., and Tex. south to nw. S. America, the W. Indies, and Trinidad.

GOLDEN EAGLE (*Aquila chrysaëtos*)

Appearance: Large (30–41 in.), with a wingspan of 75–92 in. The full adult plumage attained after 4–6 years is largely brown, darker on the wings, with head and nape often a rich, golden brown; the tail is grayish brown with darker barring. From below, the large flight feathers of the wing appear brownish gray; head, body, and smaller feathers on the forepart of the spread wings are blackish. Immature birds are similar, but have light patches near the tips of the wings, and the tail is white with a broad dark tip. The legs are feathered all the way to the toes. In flight, the wings are usually held straight out from the body, not angled as in other hawks and vultures.

Voice: A seldom-heard barking yell; nestlings make faint squeals.

Range and status: Found from n. Eurasia and n. N. America south to n. Africa, Iran, Baluchistan, the Himalaya Mountains, China, Japan, c. Mexico, Tex., Tenn., and N.C.; in winter it moves casually farther south in the U.S. Despite its local "abundance," magnified by those who claim insufferable depredations on their livestock, it is rare and becoming rarer throughout most of its range; it is now exceedingly rare in the e. U.S. and Canada.

Habitat: Wild, usually open country from mountains to the plains and canyons.

Seasonal movements: Largely sedentary, except for n. population.

Biology: Nest: A mass of sticks and twigs, lined afresh each year; bits of green vegetation are added daily during incubation and rearing of young; usually on a

Coming in for a landing, a Harris' Hawk displays its typical tail pattern.

Burnished feathers on its neck help distinguish the Golden Eagle from the immature Bald Eagle.

high cliff ledge, sometimes in trees. Eggs: 1–4, commonly 2; whitish, clear or finely spotted with browns. Incubation: In Europe 41–42 days; in America, recorded as 43 days; in some works said to be performed by female alone, but observations in Scotland show male does his share. Age at 1st flight: 12 weeks; perhaps less in some parts of its range. Food: Predominantly medium-sized mammals, such as ground squirrels, rabbits, and hares; it will take lambs and other young animals when opportunity presents. It could even "kill" sheep and deer found helpless in blizzards. It has been demonstrated that a large Golden Eagle (up to 13 lb.) would not be able to lift prey half its weight off the ground; even carrying a 2-lb. animal presents difficulties, as birds so laden fly laboriously and must take advantage of every favorable wind. The great majority of animals taken are those that compete with man's domestic stock for forage. Some smaller mammals are also taken, as well as a few of the larger birds. Remarkably agile in the air, as demonstrated by its successful pursuit and capture of swift, dodging hares and rabbits.

Suggested reading: L. W. Arnold, *The Golden Eagle and Its Economic Status*, U.S. Fish and Wildlife Service Circular 27, 35 pp., 1954.

GRAY SEA EAGLE (*Haliaeetus albicilla*)

A large (31–40 in.; wingspan 84–96 in.) brownish eagle-like hawk with a white tail. Known as the Erne only to crossword puzzle fans. Resident in Greenland and Iceland, and from e. Europe and Asia Minor east to e. Siberia and Manchuria. It has straggled to Unalaska in Alaska and to Mass. off Nantucket Lightship.

BALD EAGLE (*Haliaeetus leucocephalus*)

Appearance: Large (34–43 in.), with a wingspan of 82–98 in. Adult plumage is well known, since this species is the national emblem shown on the Great Seal of the United States. Immature birds are rather uniform grayish brown and do not start to show any of the white feathering until their 3rd year; the head and tail may not be completely white until the 6th year. While soaring overhead, young birds are grayer and more uniformly colored than the much darker Golden Eagle. The bill is heavier, also.

Voice: Loud, staccato, squeaky laugh; sometimes a lower-pitched *kac-ka-ka-ka-kac*.

Range and status: Found from ne. Siberia and n. N. America generally south of the tree limit, south to Baja Calif. and s. U.S. Division into breeding and wintering ranges is difficult, as data are confused. Birds that breed early in the South (Fla.) move northward after nesting, then return with the more northerly breeders, which retreat in winter to regions of ice-free fresh water and to seacoasts. Recent investigations have shown that DDT and similar pesticides accumulate in the bodies of fish, which form the bulk of the Bald Eagle's diet. If the bird is not killed by the poison, it seemingly becomes unable to produce viable eggs. With the advent of large-scale use of such pesticides, Bald Eagle populations have dropped alarmingly. Today the bird may be called common only in Alaska, although there are fairly large concentrations in winter in the middle Mississippi Valley and in a few places along our Atlantic Coast. The large population in Fla. has dwindled, and the Bald Eagle has greatly diminished as a breeding bird over most of the U.S., except in Fla. and Alaska.

Habitat: From open areas to forests, but almost always near water, such as large streams, rivers, lakes, and seashores.

Seasonal movements: Nonbreeders wander considerable distances. There is also an extensive postbreeding dispersal, making it almost impossible to detect any regular migration routes or times.

Biology: Pairs apparently mate for life. Nest: From near ground level (10 ft. high in mangroves along Fla. coast) to about 150 ft. high in trees and higher on cliff ledges; made of sticks, twigs, and debris, added to each year of use; some nests, used more than 15 years, have weighed several tons. Eggs: 1–4, commonly 2, white. Incubation: 34–35 days, by both sexes. Age at 1st flight: 72–75 days. Food: Fish make up 50% or more of its diet, depending on location; most individuals probably eat more than 80% fish. Where it can, it prefers to rob the Osprey, rather than catch its own fish. In Alaska, and elsewhere when similar conditions prevail, it flies along the edges of streams and rivers during the salmon spawning season, catching its own fresh fish or gorging on dead and dying fish trapped in shallows or dragged to the shores by lesser predators. Other vertebrates, such as ducks, coots, rabbits, and rodents, are eaten, mostly as carrion.

Suggested reading: R. H. Imler and E. R. Kalmback, *The Bald Eagle and Its Economic Status*, U.S. Fish and Wildlife Service Circular 30, 51 pp., 1955.

STELLER'S SEA EAGLE (*Haliaeetus pelagicus*)

The largest (42–45 in.) hawk to reach our shores. Plumage generally dark browns and black; shoulders, tail, thighs, and feathers just under the tail are white; there is also a small white patch on the forehead. It breeds in e. Siberia and winters south to Korea and Japan; it has occurred in the Aleutians, the Pribilofs, and Kodiak I., Alaska.

MARSH HAWK (Harrier) (*Circus cyaneus*)

Appearance: An average-sized (17½–24 in.) hawk with a wingspan of 40–54 in. Adult males have gray head, nape, back, tail, and topside of wings; the tail is

Now rare over most of the United States, the Bald Eagle is common only in Alaska.

A female Mash Hawk stands guard over her nest in a cattail marsh.

barred with darker gray, and there is a conspicuous patch of white on the rump just above the tail. The underparts, including the thighs, are white, with short, sparse brownish red bars. The female is larger and predominantly brown, dark above and light buffy below; tail is tan with dark brown bars and narrow band of white at the tip. Her undersides are streaked with reddish brown, and she has a white rump patch like the male's. Both sexes have yellow legs, feet, and eyes; the dark bills have yellowish bases. Young birds resemble the female.

Voice: A soft, reedy whistled *pee-pee-pee* and a lower-pitched, sibilant *chew-chew-chew.*

Range and status: From south of the tundra areas in Europe, Asia, and N. America south to n. Baja Calif., Ariz., N.Mex., n. Tex., Mo., the Ohio River Valley, W.Va., and Va., and to s. Europe, the Caucasus, s. Siberia, Mongolia, and n. Manchuria. In winter it withdraws to the s. half of its breeding range and south to nw. S. America, the Greater Antilles, and the Bahamas and to n. Africa, Palestine, Iran, India, and s. China. Accidental in Hawaii. Not a rare hawk, but persecution by hunters and drainage of marshes are reducing its numbers and restricting its breeding places.

Habitat: Open areas; preferably marshes, wet fields, and prairies.

Seasonal movements: Resident over much of its range; where migrant, it is early in spring (Mar.–mid-May) and fall (Sept.–Nov.).

Biology: Nest: Of sticks and grasses on the ground or atop low vegetation, usually in a swamp or wet meadow. Eggs: 3–9, commonly 5; white or whitish, rarely spotted with light browns. Incubation: 31(?) days, by female alone; the male brings food to the brooding female and to the young. Age at 1st flight: 5–6 weeks. Food: More than 50 small mammals; also reptiles, amphibians, and some birds, as well as a few insects.

Suggested reading: W. R. Hecht, "Nesting of the Marsh Hawk at Delta, Manitoba," *Wils. Bull.*, vol. 63, pp. 167–176, 1951.

The Osprey dives from the air to catch fish in its sharp talons.

THE OSPREY (PANDIONIDAE)

There is only 1 species, the Osprey, or Fish Hawk, in this family. No other hawk has a reversible outer toe; it can rotate this toe so that it extends to the rear of the foot. Such a feature is an important adaptation to any bird that lives by catching slippery, squirming live fish, as it permits the bird to use 2 strongly hooked claws on each side of its prey. Otherwise it is obviously a hawk, and some ornithologists feel that it should rank only as a specialized subfamily of the Accipitridae.

OSPREY (*Pandion haliaetus*)

Appearance: A medium-sized (21–24½ in.) hawk with long, pointed wings spanning 54–72 in. The head, throat, and entire undersides are white; the nape, back, uppersides of the wings, a stripe running through the eye from the bill to the back of the head, and the tail are dark brown; the crown of the head is streaked with dark brown, and the tail is barred with lighter brown. From below, the wings are dark-edged whitish with large dark spots at the bend, and the tail is light-colored, with fine dark bars and a broad terminal band of dark edged with white. The female is larger, with some streaking on the forehead and crown; the crown of the young may be more heavily streaked. If a hawk dives into the water feet first, it is an Osprey. The bill is blackish, as are the long, strong, equal-sized, curved claws; the toes and thick legs are bluish gray. The soles of the feet are "spine-studded," an advantage in grasping slippery fish.

Voice: A succession of high, loud, and sharp whistled *cheep*'s or *whew*'s and a loud *sheer-reeek* alarm note near nest.

Range and status: Cosmopolitan, but not found in polar regions. Breeds from c. Alaska, nw., c., and se. Canada, Scandinavia, n. Russia, and c. Siberia south to Baja Calif., the s. U.S., the Bahamas, s. Russia, s. Siberia, s. China, and the Kuriles. It also breeds coastally in nw. Mexico, Yucatan, Cuba, s. Spain, islands of the Mediterranean, n., s., and e. Africa, Arabia, Japan, Formosa, Philippines, Celebes, New Guinea, Australia, smaller islands of Indonesia, the Solomon Is., New Caledonia, and also about the large lakes of e.-c. Africa; sporadically elsewhere in the tropics. It is sedentary in the tropical parts of its range, but n. breeders winter south to n. Chile, n. Argentina, s. Africa, and India; also appears occasionally in Hawaii, the Galápagos, Bermuda, and other oceanic islands, and has straggled to Greenland. Formerly common, but now becoming rare; in the U.S. it appears to be suffering the same fate as the Bald Eagle, since the Osprey also feeds almost exclusively on fish and its eggs fail to hatch. The Osprey is, and has been for years, vigorously persecuted by man.

Habitat: Seldom far from large bodies of water, rivers, lakes, streams, and marine shores.

Seasonal movements: Begins northward migrations in Feb. and reaches Alaska and Canada in May; starts leaving these areas in Sept. and reaches s. U.S. as late as early Dec.

Biology: Nest: Sometimes in loose colonies; on ground and ledges, in trees, on telephone poles and other man-made structures, a bulky mass of sticks and trash, added to each year of use. Eggs: 2–4, usually 3; whitish or brownish, thickly spotted with browns. Incubation: 28 days; reported as about 35 days in European literature, by both parents. Age at 1st flight: 8–10 weeks. Food: Almost exclusively fish; perhaps some other vertebrates and offal.

Suggested reading: D. A. Bannerman, "Osprey," *The Birds of the British Isles,* Oliver and Boyd, Edinburgh, 1956, vol. 5, pp. 335–348. P. L. Ames and G. S. Mersereau, "Some Factors in the Decline of the Osprey in Connecticut," *Auk,* vol. 81, pp. 173–185, 1964.

CARACARAS AND FALCONS (FALCONIDAE)

These are small- to medium-sized (6–25 in.) hawklike birds of prey with long, pointed wings and moderately long to long tails. There are 58 species throughout the world, 9 of which occur in N. America. The smallest is the sparrow-sized (6–7 in.) Red-thighed Falconet of se. Asia. The caracaras have naked faces and are relatively long-legged. They eat chiefly carrion and frequently associate with vultures, whose habits they seem to imitate. Falcons are the "streamlined" birds of prey par excellence, with wings and body contours designed for rapid, agile flight; they feed mainly on birds, rodents, and insects captured in or from the air. They dive at their victims with wings partially extended, in silhouette looking much like a modern jet fighter airplane, and strike with the talons. These high-speed dives are called "stoops" in the age-old language of falconry. It is the female that is properly referred to as the falcon; the male is called a tiercel (sometimes tercel). The legs are strong, the toes long, and the claws sharp, strong, and hooked. In both caracaras and falcons the sexes are usually alike, but the female is larger. The flight speed of falcons has been greatly exaggerated in the past, and few reliable statistics are available; the fastest falcon *may* exceed 100 miles per hour at times. The upper bill is deeply notched at each side near the tip, making it look as though the bird had sharp "canine" teeth there. The immature plumage is worn only through little more than 1 year.

CARACARA (Audubon's Caracara) (*Caracara cheriway*)

Appearance: Largest (20–25 in.) member of the family, with a wingspan of up to 48 in. It is the national emblem of the Republic of Mexico. Its naked face is pink, with a black cap over white cheeks and throat. Breast and upperpart of the back are buffy barred with black; thighs, belly, and wings are dark gray, and the feathers under the tail are white. Tail is barred black and white, with a broad band of blackish at the tip; legs, feet, and bill are yellowish. In flight white patches near the tips of the wings and the barred breast are distinctive. Immature birds are brownish instead of gray and black. Its habit of associating with vultures and perching on fence posts and other low vantage points also help to identify it.

Voice: Throws back its head and cackles, harshly and stridently.

Range and status: Resident from slightly north of the Mexican border south to Peru, Colombia, Venezuela, Surinam, and Trinidad; also in s. Fla., Cuba, and the Dutch W. Indies.

Habitat: Open lands.

Seasonal movements: None.

Biology: Nest: In the upper branches of trees or atop cactus 8–50 ft. above the ground; bulky, of sticks and twigs. Eggs: 2–4, commonly 2; whitish, heavily blotched with browns, very rarely immaculate. Incubation: 28(?) days, by both sexes. Age at 1st flight unknown; possibly 2–3 months. Food: A variety of animal life, but largely carrion; it can capture and kill rabbits, birds, and small rodents.

Suggested reading: A. C. Bent, *Life Histories of North American Birds of Prey*, part 2, Dover, N.Y. (reprint of U.S. Nat. Mus. Bull. 170, 1938), 1961, pp. 127–136.

GUADALUPE CARACARA (*Caracara lutosa*)

Similar in size and general pattern to the Caracara, but darker in color. Now extinct. It was found only on the island of Guadalupe off nw. Baja Calif.; formerly very common there, but slaughtered by natives because the birds reportedly attacked their very young goats.

GYRFALCON (*Falco rusticolus*)

Appearance: Largest of the true falcons. It has the typical falcon silhouette in flight, with long, sharp-pointed wings and long tail. There are 3 color phases: light, in which the birds are whitish with some dark markings; grayish, with darker markings; and dark brownish gray, almost blackish. The dark form is very rare in America. Wingspan is 44–52 in.

Voice: Silent, except for a rattling, complaining *kek-kek-kek* when nest or young seem in danger.

Range and status: Breeds along the n. edges of the N. American, European, and Asian continents; also

Gyrfalcon

Baffin and Ellesmere Is., Greenland, and Iceland, in e. Asia to s. Kamchatka and in barren, isolated areas of c. Asia. Resident in much of its breeding range, but irregularly south in irruptions as far as the n. U.S., c. Europe, and Japan. Rare, except during invasions, in more inhabited parts of range, as described.

Habitat: Tundra, open seacoasts, and barren mountain terrain.

Seasonal movements: No regular migrations; movements depend apparently on abundance or availability of food in regular range.

Biology: Nest: On cliff ledges; a hollow scraped in debris, sometimes with a few sticks and mosses or grasses added. Eggs: 4–5; creamy white, spotted with brownish reds and tans. Incubation: 28–29 days, largely by female. Age at 1st flight: 45 or more days. Food: Mammals and birds.

Suggested reading: T. J. Cade, "Behavior of a Young Gyrfalcon," *Wils. Bull.*, vol. 65, pp. 26–31, 1953.

PRAIRIE FALCON (*Falco mexicanus*)

Appearance: A large (17–20 in.) falcon. Generally tan above, with darker wings and mottling; whitish below, with dark brown or blackish markings, especially on the flanks. A dark brown or blackish streak extends toward the whitish throat from below the eye. In flight its undersides are whiter than those of other falcons, the belly is streaked, not barred, and there are dark spots on the wings next to the body. Immature birds are darker above and heavily streaked below.

Voice: Like the Gyrfalcon's, but higher-pitched, similar to the barking of a puppy.

Range and status: Resident from c. B.C., s. Alta., s. Sask., and N.Dak. south to Baja Calif. and the sw. U.S.; in winter some birds move south to c. Mexico. It has straggled to Man., Minn., Ill., Iowa, and Ind. Fairly common.

Habitat: Prairies, deserts, unforested mountains, canyons.

Seasonal movements: Migrates in flocks Aug.–Oct. and Feb.–Apr.

Biology: Nest: Usually none; occasionally uses old raven nests; eggs are laid on bare rocks of cliff ledges and crevices. Eggs: 3–6, usually 4–5; white or whitish, sprinkled with dots and spots of varying browns. Incubation: 31–33 days, almost entirely by female. Age at 1st flight: 5–6 weeks. Food: Over 50% birds; many mammals, some insects.

Suggested reading: H. Webster, Jr., "The Prairie Falcon in Colorado," *Auk*, vol. 61, pp. 609–616, 1944.

PEREGRINE FALCON (Duck Hawk) (*Falco peregrinus*)

Appearance: About the same size (15–20 in.) as the Prairie Falcon; same general pattern of light and dark

The Prairie Falcon is a rather common resident of dry open lands in the West.

colors, but upperparts and wings are dark bluish gray, mark under eye is blackish, and ground color of underparts is whitish to very pale rufous on the lower breast, becoming almost clear white on the throat. Except for the throat, the undersides are more or less barred with black. Airborne, the adults seem to be a more even gray color all over, except for the black-bordered head and throat area. Immature birds resemble the Prairie Falcon, but are much darker brown.

Voice: Heard only near aerie; notes similar to those of the Gyrfalcon, but more rapid: an iterated *weh-choo* and a drawn-out wail.

Range and status: Breeds over a wider geographical area than any other bird, from the n. edges of N. America, Asia, Europe, Greenland, and some of the more southerly islands of the Arctic to s. S. America, the Falklands, s. Africa, Madagascar, Australia, Tasmania, the Solomon Is., and other islands of w. Oceania. It occurs only during migration or in winter in wide areas such as the se. U.S., Mexico, C. America, the W. Indies, most of S. America (except s. Chile and s. Argentina), the Sahara Desert region, the Congo Basin area of Africa, and a broad belt from se. Russia to n. China, Korea, and Japan; its status in Burma, Siam, and Indo-China is uncertain. In N. America it winters from sw. Canada, Ariz., and N.Mex., Colo., Mo., the s. Great Lakes area, and New England south to n. Chile and c. Argentina. It is becoming rare in parts of its extensive range. In parts of N. America, evidence shows that many nestings are unsuccessful.

In cities, the cliff-nesting Peregrine Falcon sometimes nests on building ledges.

Habitat: Prefers open country from coasts to mountains. Has nested on roofs and ledges of tall city buildings and used such places through the year as hunting vantage points.

Seasonal movements: There are no regular or mass movements; unmated birds, unsuccessful nesters, and immature birds may wander long distances at any time.

Biology: Because of its grace, beauty, and spectacular method of capturing its prey in midair, this species has been the favorite of falconers. During the reign of King James II of England over £1,000 was paid for a single pair! Mating is apparently for life. Nest: Cliffs or in old raven or hawk nests in similarly high sites; a hollow scraped in shallow soil or debris. Eggs: 2–7, commonly 3–4; whitish or pinkish, heavily spotted and dotted with reds and browns. Incubation: 30 days in America, 33–35 days in Europe; almost entirely by female, but tiercel feeds falcon during this period and helps raise young. Age at 1st flight: 5–7 weeks. Food: So well equipped to capture birds in the air that it is not surprising that other items, such as mammals and large insects, make up less than 16% of the diet.

Suggested reading: H. Groskin, "Observations of Duck Hawks Nesting on Man-made Structures," *Auk*, vol. 69, pp. 246–252, 1952. R. A. Herbert and K. G. S. Herbert, "Behavior of Peregrine Falcons in the New York City Region," *Auk*, vol. 82, pp. 62–94, 1965.

APLOMADO FALCON (*Falco femoralis*)

A medium-sized (15–18 in.) falcon found from the U.S.–Mexican border south to Guatemala and from Panama through most of S. America. From above it looks like the Peregrine, but it has a white stripe over the eye; underneath it has a bright white throat and breast, dark gray-and-white-barred flanks, and reddish brown belly and thighs. Immatures have a black-streaked buffy breast, buffy belly and undertail feathers, and blackish flanks and thighs.

PIGEON HAWK (Merlin) (*Falco columbarius*)

Appearance: A small- to medium-sized (10–13½ in.) falcon. Adult male has blue-gray cap, back, rump, and top of wings (blackish at tips), a blackish tail barred with white, and a white throat. The rest of the underparts are whitish, streaked with dark brown or blackish. Females (and immatures) are dark brown where the males are blue-gray; they are buffy below, well streaked with dark brown, except for the plain throat. There is no dark mark below the eyes. In the air the streaked breast and belly and the barred tail help separate it from other falcons. In flight it does less gliding than the Sparrow Hawk.

Voice: Near nest, a high, chattering *ki-ki-ki-ki-ki*.

Range and status: Breeds in Iceland and the British Isles and in n. Europe, n. Asia, and n. N. America (rarely north of the tree limits) south to c. Russia, s. Siberia, the nw. and n.-c. U.S., and se. Canada; rarely to n. N.Y. and Maine. Winters from s. parts of breeding areas to nw. S. America, the W. Indies, Trinidad, n. Africa, Asia Minor, n. India, s. China, and Japan. Seldom seen in large numbers, although not rare in some areas.

Habitat: More open forests; also open areas, marshes, and hilly country, mainly in migration.

Seasonal movements: Migration periods Mar.–mid.-Apr. and Sept.–early Nov.; occasionally in small flocks in open areas and along coasts.

Biology: Nest: A scrape in the ground or on cliff ledge, in old tree nests of other birds, or in tree hollows; seldom more than a few grasses or sticks added. Eggs: 3–6, usually 4–5; whitish, sometimes unmarked, but more often spotted and flecked with browns and reds, obscuring the ground color. Incubation: 28–32 days (England), mainly by female. Age at 1st flight: 35–40 days. Food: 60% small birds; the rest mostly large insects, some small mammals.

Suggested reading: L. de K. Lawrence, "Notes on Nesting Pigeon Hawks at Pimisi Bay, Ontario," *Wils. Bull.*, vol. 61, pp. 15–25, 1949.

KESTREL (*Falco tinnunculus*)

A small- to medium-sized (12½–15½ in.) falcon found throughout most of Europe, Africa, and Asia (except n. and c. Siberia), Borneo, Japan, and the Philippines. Its tail is blue-gray with a terminal dark band, not brownish red like that of our Sparrow Hawk, which it resembles closely. (The English or European Sparrow Hawk is an accipiter, not a falcon!)

SPARROW HAWK (American Kestrel) (*Falco sparverius*)

Appearance: Our smallest (9–12 in.) falcon. Adult male has a rufous spot in the center of a blue-gray crown and a rufous back and upper tail. Tail has a broad dark terminal band and a narrow white tip; the back and upperside of tail are more or less barred with blackish; wings dark blue-gray at the tips; face and throat are whitish, with a black streak running from under the eye toward the throat. A similar streak runs behind the eye; near the rear of the head is a roundish black spot. The tiercel's undersides vary from whitish to tawny, with black spots along the flanks. The falcon (hen) and the young of both sexes lack the blue-gray on the wing and

Aplomado Falcon

The Sparrow Hawk, the smallest North American falcon, nests in holes in trees.

the rufous spot on the head, and the rufous upperparts are duller and more heavily barred with black. Undersides of the falcon are duller, and the brownish spots are more elongate. While the bird flies overhead, the virtually unbarred or unstreaked breast and belly and the broad terminal tail bar (no complete bars except this) are distinctive.

Voice: *Killy-killy-killy-killy,* shrill and rapidly repeated.

Range and status: Breeds from e.-c. Alaska, c. Mack., n. Man., n. Ont., s. Que., and N.S. south through all of Latin America to Tierra del Fuego. Winters from sw. Canada, c. U.S., s. Ont., and New England south. A common falcon.

Habitat: More open, wooded areas, prairies, deserts, fields, and cities.

Seasonal movements: Migration periods Mar.–Apr. and Sept.–mid-Nov.; sometimes seen in flocks during migration.

Biology: Nest: In hollows in tree or cactus, usually those dug by suitably sized woodpeckers; very rarely in old nests of other birds, such as crows or magpies. Eggs: 3–7, most commonly 4–5; whitish, finely speckled in varying degrees or heavily blotched with browns. Incubation: 29–30 days, by female with little assistance from male. Age at 1st flight: About 30–31 days. Food: More than 50% insects; small mammals, small birds, and snakes make up rest of diet.

Suggested reading: A. I. Roest, "Notes on the American Sparrow Hawk," *Auk,* vol. 74, pp. 1–19, 1957. E. J. Willoughby and T. J. Kape, "Breeding Behavior of the American Kestrel (Sparrow Hawk)," *The Living Bird,* vol. 3, pp. 75–96, 1964.

In the United States, the Chachalaca lives only in the Rio Grande Valley in Texas.

CHACHALACAS, CURASSOWS, AND GUANS (CRACIDAE)

These gallinaceous birds of medium to large size (20–40 in.) are restricted to the continental tropics and subtropics of N. and S. America from e. Mexico south to Peru, Paraguay, n. Argentina, and Uruguay. There are 38 species, but only 1 occurs north of the Mexican border: the Chachalaca. Attempts to introduce the Chachalaca, Curassow, and Guan into Hawaii were unsuccessful. Plumage is usually in black or browns with little pattern; the tail is long, the wings are rather small and rounded, and the legs and feet are strong. Many species are crested, some have casques on the bill, and some have bare areas on the throat or face. In some species the sexes are alike. These birds are mainly terrestrial, but they roost and occasionally feed in trees. They usually feed on fruit and vegetation. The young are precocial, which means they leave the nest shortly after hatching.

CHACHALACA (*Ortalis vetula*)

A small (20–24 in.) member of the family found from southernmost Tex. south through e. Mexico (including Yucatan) to Honduras and n. Nicaragua. It is dark grayish brown and looks like a long-tailed half-grown Turkey; sexes are similar. Well adapted to the thick brush of bottomlands, it is difficult to see but easy to hear, as it makes very noisy chickenlike cackles. Its "spring song" is a loud, grating repetition of its name from treetops, generally in chorus. The Chachalaca dawn chorus heard in good brush areas of the lower Rio Grande Valley is a true tropical jungle sound.

115

GROUSE AND PTARMIGAN (TETRAONIDAE)

This family includes the small- to medium-sized (12–35 in.) chickenlike birds of N. America north of Mexico, Europe, and c. and n. Asia. There are 18 species, 10 of which are found in our area. The legs are short, the feet large, and the bill short and rather stout. Plumages are generally barred, mottled, or scaled; browns, black, and white predominate. In some species the sexes are alike. The tail is prominent but seldom so long as in the pheasants. Ptarmigan differ from grouse in that their feet are fully feathered, even on the toes; also, they acquire an almost wholly white plumage in winter. Grouse and ptarmigan are not colonial, but some are seasonally gregarious. Most species are terrestrial. Flight is rapid and strong over short distances. Their nests are usually on the ground. For most species in this family the nest is a mere depression in leaves, grasses, or mosses, sometimes lined with nearby materials and, in some species, feathers. The young are all able to fly short distances at 1–2 weeks. The females alone incubate the eggs and care for the downy young, which leave the nest very shortly after hatching. The birds are nonmigratory. They eat seeds, buds, leaves, berries, other vegetable matter, and some insects.

BLUE GROUSE (Dusky Grouse, Sooty Grouse) (*Dendragapus obscurus*)

Appearance: A small- to medium-sized (15½–21 in.) grouse of dusky or bluish gray plumage with a square-tipped black tail; in some parts of its range it has

A male Blue Grouse in display exposes the inflatable sacs at the sides of its throat.

a broad terminal band of light color on the tail, and in other parts this band may be very narrow or even lacking. The male also has whitish feathers under the tail, white feathers on the throat, and a small bare patch of yellow or orange skin over the eyes. The female is mottled and barred brownish and blackish with a dark, light-tipped tail. The young resemble the females until winter, when they assume plumages much like the adults; full adult plumage is not acquired until after the 1st year. The males have small inflatable air sacs at the sides of the throat as an aid to vocalization.

Voice: Just prior to the nesting season, the males give a series of up to 7 low-pitched booms or hoots, which are often ventriloquial.

Range and status: Resident from se. Alaska, c. Yuk., and sw. Mack. south through mountains and highlands to w.-c. and s.-c. Calif., c. Nev., n.-c. and e.-c. Ariz., nw. N.Mex., c. Colo., and sw. Wyo. The common grouse of w. mountains.

Habitat: Aspen groves, coniferous forests, and edges of such; mainly mountains in U.S.

Seasonal movements: Moves into denser evergreen stands in winter, which may mean going *higher* up in many mountains.

Biology: Nest: A hollow lined with moss, leaves, and feathers; not always concealed, but near logs or under overhanging branches. Eggs: 7–16, most often 7–10; pale pinkish, spotted with browns. Incubation: Reported from various sources as 18–24 days; more accurate data needed. Age at 1st flight: The young can

The Sharp-shinned Hawk's short, rounded wings seem to be an adaptation for flying through dense forests, where it captures small birds and other prey.

When the Red-tailed Hawk flies overhead, the reddish upper surface of its tail usually is visible
only as the bird banks on turns.

Spruce Grouse

flutter short distances when only 1 week old; flight improves daily. Food: Seeds, berries, and leaves predominate; less than 7% is animal matter, mainly insects and spiders.

Suggested reading: J. L. Blackford, "Further Observations on the Breeding of the Blue Grouse Population in Montana," *Condor,* vol. 65, pp. 485–513, 1963.

SPRUCE GROUSE (Franklin's Grouse) (*Canachites canadensis*)

Appearance: A small (15–17 in.) grouse with black throat and undersides. Male's tail is black; the upperparts are brown, barred with darker brown, and marked with white at the flanks and sides of the throat. He has a small, bright red patch of bare skin just above the eyes. The female lacks the red spot, and the black of the male is replaced with browns.

Voice: None. Courtship "song" is replaced by weak drumming noises made by wing fluttering in the manner of the Ruffed Grouse, but not so loudly.

Range and status: Spruce, pine, cedar, larch, and fir areas of Alaska and Canada, also Wash., Idaho, w. Mont., nw. Wyo., n. Minn., n. Wis., n. Mich., ne. N.Y., Maine, Vt., and N.H.; not recorded from Nfld. Common except where civilization has forced it back; now especially rare in e. part of range.

Habitat: Coniferous forest regions, particularly upland bogs in such areas.

Seasonal movements: None, except for retreat to thicker forests in winter.

Biology: Nest: On ground, a hollow in mosses, etc., haphazardly lined with nearby litter. Eggs: 8–16, usually 10–12; buffy, variously spotted and blotched with browns. Incubation: 24 days, more or less. Age at 1st flight: Able to flutter within 1 week after hatching. Food: Buds and needles of spruce and other evergreens; some berries and other vegetable matter are consumed, also a few insects.

Suggested reading: H. G. Lumsden, "Displays of the Spruce Grouse," *Canadian Field Naturalist,* vol. 75, pp. 152–159, 1961.

RUFFED GROUSE (*Bonasa umbellus*)

Appearance: A small (16–19 in.) grouse that varies considerably throughout its extensive range. All forms have a large, square tail of reddish brown or grayish color with narrow dark barring; a narrow light-colored band is followed by a broader black band and a light-colored terminal band. At each side of the neck there is a ruff of blackish feathers (shorter in the females) that is spread wide during display. The upperparts range from brownish to grayish, mottled with darker colors, while the undersides are lighter, sometimes buffy, barred with dark browns and black. The head is crested, and there is a small red patch of bare skin above each eye. Birds of the West Coast are reddish-looking; those of the Rocky Mountain region are grayish; in the East most of the population is brownish, some being quite dark. Females and young are similar, but often duller-colored, with less pronounced ruffs. Hunters often call this bird a "partridge," but true partridges belong to the pheasant and quail family (Phasianidae).

Crest erect and tail spread, this Ruffed Grouse has just completed its drumming display.

Voice: None. Male grips his low perch tightly and snaps his wing back and forth, making a noise similar to that of heavy paper or cardboard shaken violently. The "drumbeats" start out slowly, gradually gather speed, and end in a rapid roll or flutter.

Range and status: Resident in the Yukon and Porcupine River Valleys of Alaska and Yuk. and from sw. and s. Mack., n. Sask., n. Man., n. Ont., s. Que., and s. Lab. south to nw. Calif., e. Ore., s. Idaho, c. Utah, w. Wyo., s. Alta., s. Sask., ne. N.Dak., c. Minn., s. Wis., and n. Ind., through the Appalachians to e. Tenn., n. Ga., nw. S.C., w. N.C., w. Va., w. Md., and s. N.J.; large outlying populations in S.Dak., Mo., w. Ill., and s. Ind. It is the common grouse in mixed or deciduous woodlands.

Habitat: Forested areas; deciduous or mixed deciduous and coniferous.

Seasonal movements: Normally sedentary.

Biology: Nest: Slight hollow on forest floor, sheltered by a nearby tree, log, or brush. Eggs: 8–14, generally 9–12; whitish or buffy, immaculate or spotted with dull browns. Incubation: 23–24 days. Age at 1st flight: Fluttering hops when 1 week old. Food: Nuts, seeds, buds, fruits, and leaves; about 10% of diet is insects.

Suggested reading: G. Bump, R. W. Darrow, F. C. Edminster, and W. F. Crissey, *The Ruffed Grouse*, N.Y.S. Conservation Dept., Albany, N.Y., 1947, 915 pp.

WILLOW PTARMIGAN (*Lagopus lagopus*)

Appearance: A small (15–17 in.) grouse. In summer this species has white wings, belly, legs, and feet; the tail, which is rather small, is black, and the rest of the male's plumage is reddish brown, including the throat. The small patch of bare skin above each eye (sometimes called the "comb") is bright scarlet, and the bill is black. The hen is mottled whitish, buff, and browns above. She has a white belly, legs, and feet, and the remainder of the undersides is wavy-barred with whitish, buff, and browns. In winter both sexes are all white except for the black tail and bill. The white plumage is gained and lost in "patches," so in early spring and fall pinto patterns prevail.

Voice: Low but strident warnings *go-out, go-out* or *go-back, go-back* and a stammering *c-c-c-caw* by the cock.

Range and status: Common in the open areas of Alaska and Canada from the arctic shores and c. islands of Franklin south to c. B.C., Alta., Sask., Man., c. Ont., c. Que., Lab., and Nfld., in Greenland, and in n. Europe and Asia south to c. Russia, c. Siberia, Sakhalin I., and Kamchatka. In winter it has wandered sporadically south, east of the Rockies, to the n. U.S.

Habitat: Tundra, alpine meadows, muskeg, and regions of scrub trees.

Seasonal movements: Flocks assemble, sometimes in

very large numbers, when snows start and move inland or south to more protected places, although they may be found within most of the range as outlined above.

Biology: Nest: A hollow on the tundra or open fields, lined with feathers and grass or moss. Eggs: 5–17, usually 7–10; whitish, yellowish, or pinkish, peppered and blotched with dark and light browns. Incubation: Recorded as 22 days. Age at 1st flight: Starts at end of 1st week with short fluttering "hops." Food: Leaves, buds, fruit, and some insects; in winter many twigs of trees and shrubs.

Suggested reading: A. C. Bent, *Life Histories of North American Gallinaceous Birds,* Dover, N.Y. (reprint of U.S. Nat. Mus. Bull. 162, 1932), 1963, pp. 178–201.

ROCK PTARMIGAN (*Lagopus mutus*)

One of the smallest (ca. 13 in.) of the family and the northernmost breeder. In summer it is darker brown than the Willow Ptarmigan and has white on the throat; in winter it has a black streak running through the eye to the bill. It is circumpolar, found on much of the Arctic Archipelago, except possibly islands off Europe and Asia, south through the tundra regions in America to n. B.C., n. Mack., n. Keewatin, n. Que., n. Lab., and in Nfld.; in n. Europe, the Pyrenees, the Alps, most of Siberia, the Amur coast, and c. Honshu I. of Japan. Biology similar to that of the Willow Ptarmigan.

Suggested reading: G. M. Sutton and D. F. Parmelee, "The Rock Ptarmigan in Southern Baffin Island," *Wils. Bull.,* vol. 68, pp. 52–62, 1956.

WHITE-TAILED PTARMIGAN (*Lagopus leucurus*)

Appearance: The smallest (12–13 in.) grouse; in summer much like the Willow Ptarmigan, but its tail is white and the browns are duller, usually barred buffy and spotted with darker browns. In winter the white of the plumage is relieved only by the dark eyes and blackish bill.

Voice: Henlike clucking and cackling; also pleasant low hoots.

Range and status: Resident from s. and sw. Alaska, c. Yuk., and sw. Mack. south through the mountains to w. Wash., w. Mont., w. Wyo., c. Colo., and n.-c. N.Mex. Common in out-of-the-way places.

Habitat: Treeless mountaintops; truly an alpine bird.

Seasonal movements: At times of deep snow covering its food supply, it descends to the edges of the tree zone.

Biology: Nest: A mere hollow on the open ground; lined with dried grasses and feathers. Eggs: 5–15, usually 6–8; whitish or buffy, spotted with browns. Incubation: Uncertain; possibly about 23 days. Like all members of the family, able to fly at a remarkably early age.

The full winter plumage of the White-tailed Ptarmigan is completely white.

Food: Buds, flowers, fruit, and some insects; in winter, subsists almost exclusively on twigs of dwarf willow.

Suggested reading: A. C. Bent, *Life Histories of North American Gallinaceous Birds,* Dover, N.Y. (reprint of U.S. Nat. Mus. Bull. 162, 1932), 1963, pp. 232–241. J. G. Edwards, "The Ptarmigan of Glacier National Park," *Aud. Mag.,* vol. 59, pp. 252–254, 1957.

GREATER PRAIRIE CHICKEN (Pinnated Grouse, Heath Hen) (*Tympanuchus cupido*)

Appearance: About the size (16½–18 in.) of the Ruffed Grouse; generally brown, barred dark brown and buff above and lighter brown and whitish below. There is a cluster of slender blackish pinnate feathers on each side of the throat (hence the name Pinnated Grouse). At just about the same position, the male has rather large inflatable air sacs of a bright golden yellow, which expand to the size of a tangerine during courtship "dances." At this time he also erects the blackish neck feathers into "horns." The extinct Heath Hen, the e. subspecies of the Greater Prairie Chicken, had 10 or fewer of these neck "epaulets"; the w. forms have more than 10. The tail is very dark, short, and rounded.

Voice: The males, with the aid of their inflated neck sacs, make a booming not unlike the noises from the jugs in a hillbilly band. Cackling is frequent on dancing grounds.

Range and status: Now resident in several discrete areas, formerly contiguous at least in the Midwest from s. Alta. and s. Man. to N.Dak., c. Minn., Wis., and n. Ill., from c. S.Dak. to ne. Colo., from coastal Tex. to sw. La., from s. Iowa to ne. Okla., from c. Ont. to n. Mich., from n. Ill. to n. Ind., and in s. Ill.; also small areas in w. Ont. Only locally common now. The extinct Heath Hen

Lesser Prairie Chicken

formerly occurred along the Atlantic Coast from N.H. to n. Va., Md., and Del. and inland to e. N.Y. and e. Pa.

Habitat: Prairies where grass grows tall; in the East, open areas in forests and along coasts.

Seasonal movements: None.

Biology: Nest: A grass-lined depression hidden in tall grass. Eggs: 7–17, commonly 10–12; olive, spotted with sepia. Incubation: 23–24 days. Age at 1st flight: 1–2 weeks. Food: 85% vegetable, all forms; 15% insects, mainly grasshoppers.

Suggested reading: C. W. Schwartz, "The Ecology of the Prairie Chicken in Missouri," Univ. of Missouri Studies, no. 20, 99 pp., 1945.

LESSER PRAIRIE CHICKEN (*Tympanuchus pallidicinctus*)

Appearance: Smaller (16 in.) and paler than the Greater Prairie Chicken; the air sacs on the throat are red, not orange.

Voice: Booming notes, but not so loud as Greater's; also henlike cackles and clucks, and a gobbling noise.

Range and status: Se. Colo. and sw. Kans. to e. N.Mex., n. Tex., and w. Okla. Not common. Possibly established in Hawaii (Nihoa I.).

Habitat: Sagebrush country, sand hills.

Seasonal movements: None.

Biology: Nest: Grass-lined depression under brush. Eggs: 11–13; whitish to buffy, unspotted or finely spotted with lavender. Incubation period unknown. Age at 1st flight: 1–2 weeks. Food: Seeds, grasses, and grasshoppers.

SHARP-TAILED GROUSE (*Pedioecetes phasianellus*)

Appearance: About the size (15–20 in.) of Ruffed Grouse, but slimmer-looking, with long, pointed tail. Barred light brown with dark brown and black above; whitish below, scaled with brown on the breast and barred with brown and black on the flanks. The wings are grayish above, spotted with white. The elongated central tail feathers are the same colors as the back; the rest of the tail is white. It has a small crest and an air sac only at the throat and lacks long feathers on the side of the neck. During the spring "dances," the cock inflates his air sac at the throat, erects and spreads his tail, and, with a rustle of quivering wings and tail feathers, challenges all nearby male Sharp-tailed Grouse and displays for the hens.

Voice: In spring, cooing notes and a faint rattling made by shaking the wing quills; also a harsh cackle.

Range and status: Resident in the Yukon River Valley of Alaska and Yuk. and from w. Mack., Sask., Man., n. Ont., and nw. Que. south through c. B.C. to ne. Ore., ne. Nev., n. Utah, c. Colo., c. S.Dak., c. Minn., c. Wis., and n. Mich.; formerly farther south. Common, but being extirpated from much of its territory by land clearing.

Habitat: Grasslands, brushy areas, forest clearings and edges, prairies.

Seasonal movements: Retreats somewhat from more exposed areas in winter, but movements are local and irregular.

Biology: Nest: A slight hollow sparsely lined with grasses, partially concealed under brush or tall grass.

Eggs: 7–14, usually 10–12; grayish greens or grayish browns, immaculate or spotted with darker browns. Incubation: About 21(?) days. Age at 1st flight: 1–2 weeks. Food: Seeds, fruit, grass, leaves, and twigs make up 90% of diet, and insects the rest.

Suggested reading: F. N. Hamerstrom, Jr., "A Study of Wisconsin Prairie Chicken and Sharp-tailed Grouse," *Wils. Bull.*, vol. 51, pp. 105–120, 1939.

SAGE GROUSE (*Centrocercus urophasianus*)

Appearance: Our largest (22–30 in.) grouse, with long, pointed tail feathers. The male is noticeably larger than the female and has a black belly, black throat set off with a small white "necklace," and prominent long-feathered white breast; the rest of his plumage is mottled or barred with black, white, dark brown, and light brown; the small bare-skinned patch above the eye is yellow. In his dancing displays to the female, he inflates the pair of air sacs at the upper breast into bright yellow balloons and spreads his "spiked" tail feathers in an erect position. The hen is mottled and barred in browns, black, and white overall but does sport a black belly flanked with white.

Voice: A series of clucks when flushed. During courtship the male sounds as though he were popping his "balloons."

Range and status: Resident from e. Wash., s. Idaho, se. Alta., sw. Sask., and sw. N.Dak. south to the Sierra Nevadas of e. Calif., c. Nev., s. Utah, w. Colo., sw. Wyo., and nw. Nebr. Range was formerly more extensive; population dropped because of hunting pressure and mainly through overgrazing by sheep in its native areas, but now on the increase and may be called abundant through much of its range.

Habitat: Sagebrush; feeding and nesting requirements are closely tied to sage, so that it is much rarer in areas even closely marginal to the sagebrush.

Seasonal movements: None.

Biology: Gregarious; sometimes found in flocks of several hundred. Nest: Often a mere hollow in the ground, sheltered by sagebrush or other vegetation; sometimes a meager lining of grasses. Eggs: 7–15, mostly 9–12; pale green or grayish green, evenly spotted with dark browns. Incubation: About 22(?) days. Age at 1st flight: 1–2 weeks. Food: Tender, succulent vegetation and some insects; adults eat mostly leaves of sage; stomach and gizzard not built to accept harsh foods.

Suggested reading: J. R. Simon, "Mating Performance of the Sage Grouse," *Auk*, vol. 57, pp. 467–471, 1940. J. W. Scott, "Mating Behavior of the Sage Grouse," *Auk*, vol. 59, pp. 477–498, 1942.

The Sharp-tailed Grouse has relatively small, purplish throat pouches.

As it displays, the Sage Grouse makes loud popping sounds.

Despite its small size, the Bobwhite is a popular game bird.

QUAILS, PARTRIDGES, AND PHEASANTS (PHASIANIDAE)

This family includes small- to large-sized (5–90½ in.) chickenlike birds with rather long, strong legs. The bills are stout and similar to those of the grouse. Some species have spurs on the legs. Most pheasants have very long tails, but quails and partridges have short tails. There are about 165 species found throughout the world, except for the polar regions, n. and c. Canada, Alaska, n. Europe, n. Asia, and Oceania (except as introduced by man); 9 species occur in N. America, and 3 of these were introduced. In addition, 7 species not on the N. American list have been introduced successfully in Hawaii, and 1 other has hybridized with the Ring-necked Pheasant on 1 of the Hawaiian Is. The birds are grouped in 3 subfamilies: Pheasants (Phasianinae), Old World quails and partridges (Perdicinae), and New World quails (Odontophorinae). All true partridges in N. America were introduced by man. Many species in the family are gregarious. In only a few species are the sexes alike. Most species are terrestrial, obtaining their food by scratching or digging in the soil. They usually roost in trees; flight is strong but of short duration. The nest is on the ground. Only rarely does the cock assist in incubation, though in many species he does help rear the young. The hatchlings are downy, but they grow quickly; the flight feathers develop rapidly, and the young learn to fly quite early. The birds feed mainly on seeds, buds, flowers, berries, and other fruit, together with some animal matter, such as insects and worms.

BOBWHITE (*Colinus virginianus*)

Appearance: A small (8½–10½ in.) member of the family Phasianidae, but a little less than average size for a quail. There is considerable variation of color from 1 part of its large range to another. In general it is brownish, lighter below and barred with white (in Sonora the underparts resemble those of a robin); above, the brown is marked with darker browns, occasionally by dark browns spotted with whitish. The head is dark brown, slightly crested, with a white eye stripe and white throat. Some populations lack the white throat. The female is similar, but the white is replaced with duller yellowish or buffy colors. The tail is short and dark. A covey, when flushed, "explodes" in all directions at once, like a Roman candle on the 4th of July.

Voice: A loud, clear whistled recital of its name; often rendered in 3 notes, as *bob-bob-white*, and a rather liquid 3-part answering whistle of the hen. The covey is called together by *kwoy-hee* notes of the parents.

Range and status: Introduced and well established in e. Ore., e. Wash., and w. Idaho. A discrete population is resident in s. Ariz. and the Mexican state of Sonora. Elsewhere resident from S.Dak., c. Minn., c. Wis., c. Mich., s. Ont., c. Pa., N.J., se. N.Y., s. Conn., R.I., and se. Mass. south to c. and s. Mexico and w. Guatemala, also in Cuba, and the Isle of Pines. Removal of hedgerows and other cover by many farmers seriously reduced the population and restricted its range; reestablishment of cover and restocking from game farms has helped somewhat. Locally common in many areas.

Habitat: Farmlands, open areas with scrub growth.

Seasonal movements: Gathers in large flocks during nonbreeding periods, sometimes more than 30 birds. No migration.

Biology: Nest: Well hidden in tall grass and tangled brush, usually in a fencerow; lined with grass and arched over with surrounding vegetation. The hen is very difficult to flush from the eggs. Eggs: 12–20, commonly 14–16, white. Incubation: 23–24 days, by both parents. Age at 1st flight: Less than 2 weeks. Food: About 85% plant matter of all types and 15% animal matter, mainly insects. It is reported that 1 captive ate 568 mosquitoes in 2 hours!

Suggested reading: H. L. Stoddard, *The Bobwhite Quail*, Scribner, N.Y., 1931, 559 pp. Thane S. Robinson, *The Ecology of Bobwhites in Southcentral Kansas*, Univ. Kans. Mus. Nat. Hist. and Soc. Bio. Surv. Kans. Misc. Publ., no. 15, 84 pp., 1957.

SCALED QUAIL (*Callipepla squamata*)

Appearance: Larger (10–12 in.) than the Bobwhite; the neck, shoulders, breast, and belly look as though they were covered with dark-edged whitish or gray scales. The head is gray with a whitish topknot; the back, wings, and tail are medium grayish brown; the legs and feet are blue-gray. The sexes are alike.

Voice: A whining whistled *pay-cos.*

Range and status: Native in arid Southwest and Mexican plateau, from se. Ariz., s. and c. Colo., and sw. Kans. south to c. and ne. Mexico. Successfully introduced into e. Wash. Common, but often widely scattered.

Habitat: Arid and semiarid, brushy grasslands.

Seasonal movements: None; large coveys of up to 200 birds gather from late summer to early spring.

Biology: Nest: A hollow scraped in ground in shelter of clump of grass or bush; lined with grass and a few feathers. Eggs: 9–16, usually 12–14; whitish, thickly peppered with dull, light browns. Incubation: About 21 (?) days. Age at 1st flight: Uncertain; probably about 2 weeks. Food: Almost 30% insects; seeds, buds, leaves, and other plant material make up the rest.

Suggested reading: S. D. Schemnitz, *Ecology of the Scaled Quail in the Oklahoma Panhandle*, Wildlife Mono., no. 8, 47 pp., 1961.

CALIFORNIA QUAIL (*Lophortyx californicus*)

Appearance: Small, only a little larger (9½–11 in.) than the Bobwhite. The adult male has a long, large-ended, saucy black plume curving forward from the front of his dark reddish brown cap. The forehead, and a line extending from it to the rear of the head above the eye, is white, as is a necklace that starts behind the eye and borders the black face and throat. Breast and back of the neck are bluish gray, the nape being spotted with white; the feathers of the belly are whitish edged with black, except in the center of the abdomen, where they are brownish red. The back, tail, and flanks are medium brown with white slashes on the flanks. The hen lacks the brownish red patches and the black-and-white-patterned head. Her plume is browner and more demure; her face is whitish, marked and spotted with dull browns; otherwise she resembles the male but is duller.

Voice: A querulous, 3-note *key-car-go* call; low, henlike clucks; and the male's loud whistled springtime "battlecry," *t'work.*

Range and status: Resident along the coasts and Coast Ranges from sw. B.C. to s. Baja Calif. and inland from s. Ore. through w. Nev. to s.-c. Calif. Successfully introduced in e. Wash., e. Ore., s. Idaho, c. Nev., and n. and c. Utah; also Hawaii, Chile, and New Zealand. Not so common as formerly, but making excellent comeback.

Habitat: Open areas in and edges of forests, scrub growth of coastal regions, parklands, farmlands, and suburbs.

Like many of its relatives, the California Quail has a conspicuous head plume.

Seasonal movements: None; found in large flocks during nonbreeding periods.

Biology: Nest: A slight depression in the ground lined with grass and leaves, sometimes well hidden in rock crevices or under vegetation. Eggs: 10–17, most often 12–16 (larger numbers probably the result of another hen getting into the nest); yellowish or whitish, speckled or blotched to varying degrees with browns and/or grays. Incubation: 18–21(?) days, almost entirely by hen. Age at 1st flight: About 10 days. Food: Seeds, grass, leaves, grain, fruit; less than 5% of diet consists of insects and other animal matter.

Suggested reading: E. L. Sumner, "A Life History Study of the California Quail, with Recommendations for Its Conservation and Management," *Calif. Fish and Game,* vol. 21, pp. 167–256 and 275–342, 1935.

GAMBEL'S QUAIL (*Lophortyx gambelii*)

Appearance: About the size (10–11½ in.) of the California Quail and similarly plumed. The males differ in that this species has a black forehead, lacks the white spots on the rear of the neck, has a buffy belly with a large central blackish spot, and has brownish red flank feathers slashed and streaked with white. The hens may also be separated from the California Quail, as the female Gambel's has a buffy belly and white-streaked reddish brown flanks.

Voice: Like that of the California Quail, but often adds a preliminary note: *yuk-key-car-go;* the male's courtship challenges are more nasal in quality.

Range and status: Resident in the arid Southwest from se. Calif., s. Nev., c. Utah, w.-c. Colo., and n.-c.

Gambel's Quail, a native of southwestern deserts, feeds on seeds and other plant material.

White bars on its sides and a long, erect head plume readily identify the Mountain Quail.

N.Mex. south to ne. Baja Calif., c. Sinaloa, c. Chihuahua, and sw. Tex.; introduced successfully in e. N.Mex. Fairly common.

Habitat: Desert scrub, not far from water.

Seasonal movements: None; gathers in flocks during nonbreeding seasons.

Biology: Nest: A hollow in shelter of mesquite, sagebrush, or other shrub, lined with sticks, grasses, and feathers. Eggs: 9–14, usually 10–12; whitish, irregularly spotted and blotched with grays and browns. Incubation: 21–24(?) days, by female alone. Age at 1st flight: Uncertain; probably about 10 days, but both young and adults prefer to escape by running. Food: Seeds, leaves, and plant shoots; some grain and fruits; very few insects are consumed (usually only about 2%).

Suggested reading: D. M. Gorsuch, *Life History of the Gambel Quail in Arizona,* Univ. Ariz. Biol. Sci. Bull., no. 2, 89 pp., 1934.

MOUNTAIN QUAIL (*Oreortyx pictus*)

Appearance: Small (10½–11½ in.), like Gambel's Quail, but with grayish blue crest; the plume rising from its noticeable crest is longer, more pointed, and stiffer than those of California and Gambel's Quail. Head, shoulders, and lower breast are grayish blue; throat and upper breast are brownish red, separated from the gray-blue of the neck by a white line; the face is white, and there is white about the eye. The flanks are brownish red, with an upper edging of white and a series of broad, roundish white bars covering the lower part. The back, tail, and wings are neutral brown. The female is like the male but generally duller.

Voice: A tremolo whistle of alarm; the cock in spring makes a 1- or 2-part hooting bark, *too-wook* or *wook*.

Range and status: Resident of the Coast Ranges from s. Vancouver I., B.C., to n. Baja Calif. and in the Sierra Nevada and other ranges of Calif. and e. Nev.; successfully introduced in se. Wash., e. Ore., w. Idaho, and c. Nev. Common in some areas.

Habitat: Mixed forests and scrub growth, mainly in mountainous areas; most abundant in the more humid areas.

Seasonal movements: None; some birds retreat from higher altitudes in autumn and return in spring.

Biology: Nest: Under cover of log or vegetation, a hollow lined with grasses, leaves, pine needles, and a few feathers. Eggs: 8–22, most commonly 10–12; unmarked yellowish or pinkish. Incubation: About 21 days, probably by both sexes. Possibly 2 broods raised each year; male cares for young after hatching. Age at 1st flight: About 2 weeks; generally escape by running. Food: Leaves, flowers, buds, seeds, plant shoots, fruit; very few insects.

Suggested reading: A. C. Bent, *Life Histories of North American Gallinaceous Birds,* Dover, N.Y. (reprint of U.S. Nat. Mus. Bull. 162, 1932), 1963, pp. 40–51.

HARLEQUIN QUAIL (Mearn's Quail) (*Cyrtonyx montezumae*)

Appearance: Bobwhite-sized (8–9½ in.), with brownish red breast and undersides; sides of neck and flanks are grayish, with prominent round white spots. The crest, composed of rather long buffy feathers at the rear of the head, accents the large-headed appearance of the stocky bird; the white head is separated from the breast by a blackish neck ring and is marked with a neat black throat patch, earmarks, and mustaches. The back, tail, and wings are variegated patterns of browns, white, and black. The hen is dull brownish, lighter below and on the head and throat; there are dark markings behind the eye and at the lower edge of the throat.

Voice: A trembling, stuttering whistle.

Range and status: Resident in se. Ariz., c. and sw. N.Mex., and w. and c. Tex. south through the more mountainous and less arid regions to s. Mexico. Locally common in remote areas; prominent, as it shows very little fear of man.

Habitat: Grassy edges of oak forests on mountain slopes and in canyons and other grassy areas amid pine-oak forests.

Seasonal movements: Moves higher up mountain slopes in early fall and retreats in winter.

Biology: Nest: Well hidden under arched-over grasses near sheltering tree or shrub; lined with grasses and sometimes reached by bird through a tunnel of grasses. Eggs: 8–14, usually 10–12, white. Incubation:

Unknown; by both male and female. Young cared for by both parents. Age at 1st flight unknown; dependence of bird on protective coloration is so complete that it seldom attempts flight until it is too late. Food: Acorns, piñon nuts, other seeds, grasses, leaves, etc.; some insects.

Suggested reading: O. C. Wallmo, "Nesting of Mearn's Quail in Southeastern Arizona," *Condor,* vol. 56, pp. 125–128, 1954.

CHUKAR (*Alectoris graeca*)

Appearance: Small (ca. 13 in.), short-tailed, grayish brown above, with tail and wings of the same color. A black line starting at the forehead runs through the eyes and then downward, forming a V with the line from the other side on the upper breast and thus completely enclosing the yellowish cheeks and throat. The breast below this is gray, and the rest of the undersides, including the dark-barred flanks, is yellowish. The bill, legs, and feet are pink or red. Sexes are alike, but immature birds are duller in color.

Voice: *Chuck-chuck-chuck-chuck,* sometimes in longer series; a piercing whistled *wheee-too.*

Harlequin Quail

Range and status: Native to s.-c. and se. Europe through Asia Minor and Mesopotamia to n. India, s. Siberia, and n. China; introduced in semiarid mountain regions of w. U.S. in e. Wash., w. and s. Idaho, locally in Calif., w. and c. Nev., nw. Wyo., and sw. Colo. Resident; has become common enough in some areas to permit hunting.

Habitat: Rocky slopes with sparse vegetation and sagebrush areas of dry mountain regions.

Seasonal movements: None.

Biology: Nest: Grass-lined depression in ground or rock crevice. Eggs: 8–16, average 9; buffy, spotted with browns. Incubation: About 23(?) days. Age at 1st flight unknown. Food: Seeds, leaves, and fruit about 60%; remainder, insects, spiders, etc.

Suggested reading: J. R. Alcorn and Frank Richardson, "The Chukar Partridge in Nevada," *Jour. Wildlife Management*, vol. 15, pp. 265–275, 1951.

GRAY PARTRIDGE (Hungarian Partridge) (*Perdix perdix*)

Appearance: About the size (12–14 in.) of the Chukar, with gray nape and breast, brownish red face and throat, and brownish cap, back, wings, and tail. The back is barred with a redder brown, and the wings are spotted with white. The undersides are buffy, and the flanks buffy gray, barred with reddish brown. There is a large dark brown spot in the center of the breast. The legs, feet, and bill are grayish. Sexes are alike.

Voice: *Kee-urck;* the 1st part nasal in quality, but higher in pitch than the raspy 2nd part.

Range and status: Native to Europe (except s. Spain and n. Scandinavia), Turkey, and sw. Siberia. Introduced in N. America and established over wide areas and locally from s. B.C., c. Alta., c. Sask., s. Man., w. and e.-c. Ont., and s. Que. south to ne. Calif., c. Nev., n. Utah, c. Wyo., n. Nebr., n. Iowa, n. Ill., c. Ind., c. Ohio, and c. N.Y.; also in s. N.B. and P.E.I. Most successful in prairie regions, where common enough for open hunting seasons; also common in e. Wash. and Ore.

Habitat: Prairies, irrigated croplands, open farmlands.

Seasonal movements: Sedentary.

Biology: Nest: A slight depression among tall grass or near bushes, lined with leaves and grass. Eggs: 6–20, usually 8–12; when more than 20, probably from more than 1 hen; plain olive, sometimes lighter colors. Incubation: 23½–24 days, mainly by hen; cock helps with family after hatching. Age at 1st flight: About 2 weeks. Food: Shoots and leaves of grasses, clover, etc., seeds, berries, grain; in season, many insects, spiders, etc.

Suggested reading: R. E. Yeatter, *The Hungarian Partridge in the Great Lakes Region*, Univ. Mich. School Forestry and Conservation Bull., no. 5, 92 pp., 1934.

Reeve's Pheasant, a spectacular native of Asia, was introduced in Hawaii in 1957.

ERCHEL'S FRANCOLIN (*Francolinus erckelii*)

Larger (15–17 in.) than the Chukar. Native of Ethiopia, introduced on the main island of Hawaii; success uncertain.

CHINESE QUAIL (Japanese Quail) (*Coturnix coturnix*)

A small (7 in.) quaillike bird of Europe, c. Asia, n. and s. Africa, Madagascar, and Japan that has been established in many islands of Hawaii (Kauai, Molokai, Lanai, Maui, Hawaii). Light reddish brown with very short tail, prominent streaks through plumage, and striped face.

PECTORAL QUAIL (*Coturnix pectoralis*)

Very similar to the Chinese Quail. Established on Niihau I., Hawaii; native to Australia and Tasmania.

KING QUAIL (Pygmy Quail) (*Excalfactoria chinensis*)

A very small (ca. 5–6 in.) quail native from India and s. China south to Indonesia, Australia, and the Philippines. Established on Kauai I., Hawaii. Brownish above. Male has blue-gray underparts and a brownish red center spot on the breast. Female is buffy below, streaked with blackish. Heads of both sexes patterned in black and white.

RED JUNGLE FOWL (*Gallus gallus*)

Medium-sized (17–30 in.) ancestor of the domestic chicken, brought to the Hawaiian Is. by the Polynesians and now found wild on Niihau and Kauai Is.; formerly throughout the archipelago. Native to India, se. Asia, Hainan, and n. Indonesia; introduced throughout most of Polynesia and Indonesia.

REEVE'S PHEASANT (*Syrmaticus reevesii*)

According to the measurements, a seemingly very large (28–83 in.) bronzy, silver, and black pheasant. The cock has a very long tail, averaging 55 in.; only the Peafowl has a longer tail. This species was released on Molokai I., Hawaii, in 1957 and *may* have become established there; it is native from se. Mongolia to c. China.

COPPER PHEASANT (*Syrmaticus soemmerringi*)

Another long-tailed pheasant, native to all Japanese islands except Hokkaido; liberated on Kauai, Oahu, and Maui Is., Hawaii, and believed to have hybridized with the Ring-necked Pheasant there. This species is generally copper-colored, with some reds, white, and dark browns. The hen is about 30 in. and the cock about 55 in. long.

RING-NECKED PHEASANT (*Phasianus colchicus*)

Appearance: A medium-sized (21–36 in.) pheasant; the cock is, on the average, about 10 in. longer than the hen and is much more colorful. His head and neck are dark metallic green, separated from the rest of the body by a white ring. There is a patch of bright red bare skin on the cheek and about the eye. The feathers just above the eyes on each side are elongated into a double crest. The plumage of the underparts, upper back, and shoulders is a rich, bronzy, brownish red, with markings of dark brown, black, and white; the rump feathers, extending up the lower back, are greenish gray. The flank feathers are light golden brown marked with dark brown streaks. The slender, pointed tail feathers, making up a bit more than half the total length of the bird, are a dull bronze barred with dark brown. The bill is yellowish, and the legs and feet grayish. From 1 part of its extensive range to another, there is considerable variation in details of coloration and in size and completeness of the white neck ring. The hen is brownish; much paler below, and

The Ring-necked Pheasant, another Asian species, is one of our most valuable game birds.

Only the male Peafowl has the spectacular taillike train.

marked with darker browns and blackish above. The long yellow-brown tail feathers are barred with darker brown and whitish. The young resemble the female at first, but young males quickly acquire a patchwork of brighter feathers.

Voice: The crow of the cock is like a loud, strident double *caw* of the Common Crow, but higher in pitch. Also harsh croaks when flushed, and chickenlike double clucks by both sexes.

Range and status: Introduced as a game bird and established in many areas throughout the world; in N. America, resident in river valleys, open lands, and prairies from s. B.C., c. Alta., s. Sask., s. Man., c. Minn., Wis., s. Mich., s. Ont., and N.Y. south to n. Baja Calif., n. Ariz., s. N.Mex., n. Tex., n. Mo., c. Ill., Ind., Ohio, and w. Pa., and along the Atlantic coastal plains from P.E.I. to N.J. and in se. Pa.; also established in Hawaii. Natural range from area between the Black and Caspian Seas east to Manchuria, se. Siberia, Korea, s. China, and Formosa. Common; in some places where cover is not ideal for the species, populations are maintained by pen breeding and stocking.

Habitat: Ideally, open grasslands, steppes, open river bottoms; does well in irrigated farmlands.

Seasonal movements: None.

Biology: Nest: A slight depression lined with grasses on the ground in grassy or brushy fields. Eggs: 6–15, more commonly 10–12, dark greenish buff. Incubation: 23–25 days; only very rarely does the male assist. Age at

1st flight: Able to fly 4–5 ft. when only 7 days old. Food: Up to 25% of stomach contents may be insects; also many seeds, plant shoots, nuts, and other fruit.

Suggested reading: W. H. Hudson, "The Sacred Bird," *Adventures among Birds,* Hutchinson & Co., London, 1913, pp. 85–94.

GREEN PHEASANT (*Phasianus versicolor*)

A Japanese pheasant very similar to the Ring-necked Pheasant, but lacking the white neck ring and having green on the rump, back, and mantle. It has become established in Hawaii on the islands of Molokai, Kauai, Maui, Lanai, and Hawaii; hybridizes with the Ring-necked Pheasant.

PEAFOWL (*Pavo cristatus*)

The beautiful Indian Peafowl is so well known to us that it hardly needs description. The large (80–90½ in.) male is bright blue, with a long green train spotted with bronze and blue "eyes." The train is not its true tail, but is made up of elongated feathers from just above the tail. The train may be over 60 in. long. The hen is smaller (36–39 in.) and browner, and she lacks a train. Introduced in Hawaii and established on the islands of Maui, Hawaii, Molokai, Kauai, Oahu, and Niihau; native to India and Ceylon.

The Helmet Guineafowl has escaped from captivity on several Hawaiian islands.

THE GUINEAFOWL (NUMIDIDAE)

Guineafowl are gallinaceous birds of small to medium size (17–30 in.) with large strong feet; short, stout bills; short, rounded wings; and medium-sized tails, usually overdraped by elongated feathers just above. Their heads are sparsely feathered or have large bare areas, wattles, combs, and crests. The sexes are alike or nearly so. Plumage is mainly dark, with uniform spotting or streaking; exposed skin is red, blue, yellow, or grayish. Guineafowl are terrestrial, and their flights are generally short, but they roost in trees. There are 7 species, 1 of which has been introduced in Hawaii, the W. Indies, and C. America. They are restricted naturally to Africa and Madagascar. Guineafowl nest on the ground. Incubation is by the hen alone, but the cock helps raise the young, which are downy on hatching and are able to leave the nest immediately. Food consists mainly of plant products, insects, and snails.

HELMET GUINEAFOWL (*Numida meleagris*)

This is the most commonly domesticated species; it has escaped from captivity and established itself as a wild bird in Cuba, Hispaniola, and Hawaii (various islands). It is native through most of Africa and Madagascar. Exposed skin is bluish, except for the dark brown "helmet." Plumage is dark, liberally spotted and peppered with white.

THE TURKEYS (MELEAGRIDIDAE)

Turkeys are large (33–48 in.) birds related to the chickens. Their heads and necks are sparsely feathered, and the large tails are not overly long. Plumage is of dark metallic colors marked with black, white, and grays. They have relatively short, rounded wings and large, strong legs and feet. Their bills are large, sturdy, rather long, and moderately hooked. The sexes are generally similar, the male being larger and brighter-colored. There are but 2 species in the family, which ranges from Ariz. and the e. U.S. south to British Honduras and Guatemala, but only 1 species occurs in the U.S. Turkeys roost in trees but feed on the ground, eating much vegetable matter and some insects and other animals. Incubation and care of the young are by the hen; the downy hatchlings are able to leave the nest shortly after emerging from the eggshell.

TURKEY (*Meleagris gallopavo*)

Appearance: Large (36–48 in.); the hen averages about 10 in. shorter than the cock. Slimmer and longer-legged than the familiar domestic variety. The head, neck, and wattles are reddish, grading to bluish; the plumage is iridescent bronze, barred blackish; the tail, fanned out in display by the male, is tipped with buff. A

Unable to fly long distances, the Turkey does most of its traveling on foot.

long hank of hairlike feathers protrudes from the breast, but the hen often lacks this "beard."

Voice: The wild birds gobble just like their domesticated "descendants." They also have a *pit-pit* alarm call and a loud *kyow-kyow* flock-rallying signal.

Range and status: Present natural range is from n. Ariz., s. Colo., Okla., c. Mo., c. Ky., e. W.Va., s. N.Y., and e. Va. south through the mountains of e. and w. Mexico to s.-c. Mexico, the Gulf Coast, and s. Fla.; formerly resident to n. Colo., se. S.Dak., s. Great Lakes area, and s. New England. Recently it has been established locally in Hawaii, Calif., Wyo., and sw. S.Dak. and reestablished in e. N.Y. and w. Mass. As domestic poultry it is found throughout the civilized world. The wild bird is still rare in the U.S. but is gaining in population under better management and restocking.

Habitat: Deciduous forests in the East, mesquite and oak in the West, and cottonwood-bordered streams in the prairielike regions.

Seasonal movements: Not migratory, but may wander extensively in fall and winter in search of food.

Biology: Gregarious, but not colonial. Nest: A slight, well-hidden hollow on ground in woods or brush, lined with leaves. Eggs: 8–20, usually 8–15 by 1 hen; 2 hens may lay in 1 nest and alternate in incubation duties and care of young. The eggs are light sandy-colored, peppered with brownish red. Incubation: 28 days. Age at 1st flight: Probably about 1 week; they are able to fly to roosts in trees at 2 weeks. Food: About 85% twigs, nuts, fruit, and seeds; animal food mainly insects, some spiders, snails, and other invertebrates.

Suggested reading: A. W. Schorger, *The Wild Turkey*, Univ. of Okla. Press, Norman, 1966, 626 pp.

BUTTON-QUAILS AND HEMIPODE-QUAILS
(TURNICIDAE)

These small (4½–7½ in.) quaillike birds are more closely related to cranes, rails, bustards, and the Limpkin than they are to any of the gallinaceous birds. They have sturdy legs but lack a hind toe on their feet. Their feathers are rather short and soft; grays, browns, and black predominate. The sexes are similar, but the cocks are a bit smaller and duller, probably because they incubate the eggs and care for the young. Each hen accommodates several males. There are 15 species found in s. Europe, s. Asia, Africa, Indonesia, the Philippines, Australia, and the Solomon Is.; 1 species, the Painted Quail, is perhaps established in Hawaii. In food, feeding habits, and general habitat, they resemble the true quails.

PAINTED BUTTON-QUAIL (*Turnix varia*)

This typical button-quail, native of Australia and Tasmania, was introduced in Hawaii and possibly established on Maui I.

Painted Button-quail

Four rare Whooping Cranes swoop in for a landing near a pond in Saskatchewan.

THE CRANES (GRUIDAE)

Cranes are large (31–60 in.), long-legged, long-necked birds of N. America (s. to c. Mexico), Cuba, Europe, Asia, Africa, Australia, and Tasmania. There are 14 species, represented in America regularly only by the Whooping and Sandhill Cranes; the Common Crane of Europe and Asia has straggled to America. The wings are long, and the tail is short; in flight the neck is always extended. A single bird overhead is a picture of symmetry; a flock is spectacular. The impression they give in flight is more of power than grace; aground they may seem awkward, but the courtship dances displayed by most species are airy and graceful, banishing forever the idea that these birds are clumsy. They are omnivorous. Their voices are loud; the convolutions of the windpipes within parts of the skeleton add materially to the resonant qualities. Except in the breeding season, they are gregarious. The sexes are alike or nearly so. Their nests are flimsy or large masses of vegetation on the ground or in shallow water. They lay 2–3 eggs. The downy hatchlings are able to leave the nest shortly after hatching. Incubation and care of the young are shared by both parents.

GRAY CRANE (Common Crane) (*Grus grus*)

A medium-sized (ca. 44 in.) gray crane with black head and throat, and a prominent white cheek patch. This species has been recorded twice in Alta. and once in Alaska. It breeds in n. and se. Europe and c. and s. Siberia; winters in s. Europe, nw. and e. Africa, n. India, and c. and s. China.

WHOOPING CRANE (*Grus americana*)

Appearance: Our largest (49–56 in.) crane, and our tallest bird. Its plumage is white, except for the black tips of the wings (which span 7–7½ ft.) and dark red face, throat, and cap; the young are light brown about the head and neck. The red of the face and cap is the color of the skin showing through very sparse blackish feathering. Except for the long, trailing legs, it might possibly be mistaken for a Snow Goose or White Pelican (the only roughly similar birds occurring in the same regions).

Voice: Loud, shrill bugling *ker-loo, ker-lee-oo.*

Range and status: Only about 30 birds now exist in the wild (33 in 1963); it is possible to make an accurate census each year because the only known wintering area today is on the Aransas National Wildlife Refuge, Tex. Each year this remnant of a once widespread, but never abundant, bird (total population in 1869 estimated as 1,300 birds) flies northward to its nesting places (only 1 definite locality known) in n. Sask. or c. Mack., and returns. Some years it is hopefully reported that reproduction has added 4 or 5 to the population; only too often the birds just grimly hold to the same numbers. Formerly bred in the area between Great Slave Lake, Mack., and Iowa and n. Ill.; also in s. La. Formerly wintered from the Gulf Coast to c. Mexico and s. Fla.

Habitat: Muskeg, prairie marshes, coastal lagoons, brackish marshes, grasslands.

Seasonal movements: Departs for breeding grounds Mar.–early May, most commonly in mid-Apr.; usually reaches wintering grounds before mid-Nov. Family groups are usually the last to arrive in Texas. Migration was formerly in flocks of up to 50 birds.

Biology: Breeding preceded by courtship dance in which both sexes participate. Nest: A heap of grasses, sedges, and other vegetation near water in marsh, with slight depression in top. Eggs: 1–2, most often 1; buffy, blotched with browns. Incubation: Probably about 33 days. Age at 1st flight: Probably about 3 months. Food: 28 animal species and 17 plants are listed; crabs, shrimp, crayfish, worms, razor clams, and acorns are major items in Texas wintering area.

Suggested reading: Robert P. Allen, *The Whooping Crane*, Nat. Aud. Soc. Research Report, no. 3, 246 pp., 1952.

SANDHILL CRANE (*Grus canadensis*)

Appearance: A medium-sized (34–48 in.) all-gray crane. Forehead and most of cap are bare-skinned and dull red in color; sparse, hairlike brownish feathers to rear of this area. Legs, feet, and bill are blackish. Immature birds are dull brownish and have fully feathered head.

Voice: In flight a high, resounding, rolling *gar-ooo-ooo-ooo* repeated often; a guttural series of *took*'s and a gooselike *awnk*.

Range and status: Breeds from ne. Siberia and n. N. America (including s. half of Canadian Arctic Archipelago) south to Ore., ne. Calif., nw. Utah, Wyo., Mont., Colo., S.Dak., Wis., Mich., and n. Ohio. Resident from s. Miss., s. Ala., and s. Ga. to s. Fla. and Cuba; formerly more widespread. Winters from Calif. and s. Tex. south to n. Baja Calif. and s.-c. Mexico. After suffering a great decline in the latter half of the 19th century, the population is increasing slightly and the species is beginning to reoccupy some of its former range.

Habitat: Tundra, alpine fields (breeding only), grasslands, wetlands, grainfields.

Seasonal movements: Some of the cranes nesting in the Great Lakes region migrate to Fla. for the winter, moving southward west of the Appalachian Mountains. It is not known whether they fly both day and night or rest overnight. Northward movement starts as early as Feb., and some individuals linger in Midwest until early Nov.

Biology: Nest: A mound of grasses and weeds in a marsh. Eggs: 1–3, usually 2; light olive, spotted and marked with grays and browns. Incubation: 29–30 days. Age at 1st flight uncertain; possibly 3 months. Food: Roots, tubers, seeds, grain, and other plant matter; also worms, insects, fish, amphibians, reptiles, and small mammals on occasion.

Suggested reading: L. H. Walkinshaw, *The Sandhill Cranes*, Cranbrook Inst. Sci. Bull. 29, 202 pp., 1949.

The Sandhill Crane seldom lays more than two eggs in its simple, moundlike nest.

Like the Everglade Kite, the Limpkin feeds primarily on large freshwater snails.

THE LIMPKIN (ARAMIDAE)

Only 1 species makes up this family. The Limpkin is a medium-sized cranelike bird. It has a longer, much more functional hind toe and is somewhat more specialized, owing to its more restricted food habits, than are the true cranes.

LIMPKIN (*Aramus guarauna*)

Appearance: A medium-sized (23–28 in.), long-necked, long-legged, long-billed bird. The plumage is medium brown with a greenish metallic sheen, streaked with white on the back, neck, breast, flanks, and shoulders. Bill blackish at tip, yellowish at base above, and reddish at base below; legs and toes are dark, greenish gray.

Voice: Loud humanlike wailing, somewhat variable, described as *kurr-r-ee-ow* or *kr-ow*, repeated several times or joined in by several birds at once.

Range and status: From s. Ga., Fla., and c. Mexico through the W. Indies and C. America to Colombia, Brazil, e. Argentina, and Uruguay. Resident throughout. Often common in preferred habitat.

Habitat: Tropical freshwater marshes and riverbanks.

Seasonal movements: Sedentary.

Biology: Behavior somewhat like that of rails: resorts to flight infrequently and then only for short distances; skulks about in reeds and grasses. Nest: Among clumps of tall grasses in shallow water; made of weeds and grasses, a dense mass interwoven with the growing plants. Eggs: 4–8, commonly 5–6; buffy to brownish green, spotted and blotched with grays and browns. Incubation period unknown; by both sexes. Age at 1st flight unknown. Food: Snails of the genus *Ampullaria* (the same species that form the main diet of the Everglade Kite) constitute the main part of the food consumed, but other mollusks, as well as worms, crustaceans, reptiles, amphibians, and aquatic insects, are eaten.

Suggested reading: H. M. Hall, "Wakulla Limpkins," *Aud. Mag.,* vol. 52, pp. 308–314, 1950.

RAILS, GALLINULES, AND COOTS (RALLIDAE)

Small- to medium-sized (5½–20 in.) marsh and water birds are included in this family. The chickenlike appearance of some species has led to their being called "marsh hens" and "mud hens." All rails can swim, but coots regularly swim about on the water like ducks with the aid of lobe-webbed feet much like those of the grebes. The gallinules are also expert swimmers, and their very long toes also enable them to walk easily on floating vegetation, as do the jaçanas. When swimming, coots and gallinules pump their heads back and forth. They are all excellent divers. Their plumage is soft, tails are short, bills are of varying length, and their wings are short and rounded. The bodies of most rails are compressed laterally, an adaptation that enables them to stalk among the dense vegetation more easily. The expression "as thin as a rail" means that a person is as thin as one of these birds, not as thin as a fence rail. There are 132 species, found all over the world except for the colder regions; 16 of these species occur in America or Hawaii. The sexes are alike and share duties of incubation and care of the young. Most species are noisy, and they are much more often heard than seen. The downy hatchlings leave the nest shortly after emerging from the shell. Their food is mainly aquatic animals and plants. Draining of marshes is seriously reducing the ranges and populations of the rails. Among the rails, evasion of enemies by running through plant growth is much preferred to flight by air. Rails that colonize islands where the climate enables them to survive throughout the year, where land enemies are lacking, "forget" their wings and become "flightless." While airborne, rails characteristically "dangle" their legs.

KING RAIL (*Rallus elegans*)

Appearance: A large (15–17 in.) rail with a long, strong bill (longer than head). As with almost all our rails, the rear half of the underside is barred; in this rail there are thin white bars alternating with broader black-edged bluish gray bars. Except for a white throat, a whitish lower eyelid, and a whitish streak running from the bill to just above the eye, the rest of the plumage is yellowish brown streaked and spotted with blackish on the back, tail, and wings; the cap is a somewhat darker brown. The bill is dark at the tip, becoming yellowish at the base; the legs and feet are light brownish gray. The downy young are black, with a bill of very pale buff. There is a light-phase bird in which the browns are more buffy.

Voice: A series of tubalike *oomp-oomp-oomp* notes and clicking and clucking notes; in some areas used to be called the "stage-driver," as its notes resembled those of a man starting up a team of horses.

Range and status: Breeds from e. Nebr., Iowa, s. Minn., s. Wis., s. Mich., s. Ont., N.Y., Conn., and Mass. south to Vera Cruz, Tex., the Gulf Coast, and s. Fla.; also in s.-c. Mexico, Cuba, and the Isle of Pines, where it is resident. Winters from Gulf Coast and s. Ga. to e.-c. Mexico; casually farther north even to n. limits of breeding range. Has straggled to N.Dak., Maine, and Nfld. Not common; exact status difficult to determine, as it is heard more often than seen, and notes of marsh dwellers are not always certainly identifiable.

Habitat: Freshwater marshes; sometimes into adjacent high grass and wet meadows. Where its range overlaps that of the Clapper Rail, it is more apt to be restricted to wooded swamps. Only rarely found in brackish or saltwater marshes during migration.

Seasonal movements: A retreat before freezing waters in fall and a readvance with melting ice in spring; arrival in n. limits usually Apr.–May and departure Sept.–Nov.

Biology: Nest: A pile of dry dead stems of water plants, concealed in the aquatic vegetation in shallow water; the rim of the nest is usually about 6–8 in. above the water. Also woven into supporting rushes or bushes about 1 ft. above water; where possible, the nest is arched over by surrounding plants. Eggs: 6–15, usually 8–11; pale buffy, lightly and sparsely marked with dark browns. Incubation: Uncertain; about 22 days. Age at 1st flight unknown. Food: Invertebrates, such as crayfish, insects, leeches, worms, and slugs, and a variety of aquatic plant seeds, roots, and tubers. Consumption of plant food highest in winter season.

Suggested reading: Brooke Meanley, "Nesting of the

King Rail in the Arkansas Rice Fields," *Auk,* vol. 70, pp. 261–269, 1953. Brooke Meanley, "Notes on the Courtship Behavior of the King Rail," *Auk,* vol. 74, pp. 433–440, 1957.

CLAPPER RAIL (*Rallus longirostris*)

Appearance: Like a faded and graying King Rail, and about the same size (14–16½ in.) and pattern. The barring below is whitish alternating with medium gray. It is impossible to separate the downy young from those of the King Rail. The 2 species occasionally interbreed where their ranges are contiguous.

Voice: A long series of harsh, rasping *kak-kak-kak* notes gradually lowering in volume and pitch at the finish, sometimes irregularly spaced; also some grunting sounds.

Range and status: Along coasts from w.-c. Calif. to nw. Peru; from Conn. through Mexico, C. America, and n. S. America to se. Brazil, and in the W. Indies; also along the lower Colorado River and in the Valley of Mexico. Mainly resident, but retreats in winter from Conn. to N.J. Formerly abundant. Status much affected by conversion of so many of the small coastal marshes

An incubating Clapper Rail uses its long bill to rearrange the eggs in its nest.

into marinas and by the spraying of these places for mosquito control; becoming rare from Conn. to Md.

Habitat: Saltwater and brackish marshes; in some areas freshwater marshes.

Seasonal movements: Hardly noticed; a gradual withdrawal.

Biology: Nest: Very much like that of the King Rail. Eggs: 6–14, commonly 9–12; yellowish or greenish buff, boldly marked or finely spotted with browns and grays. Incubation: 21–23 days. Age at 1st flight unknown. Food: Crabs, insects, mollusks, worms, and other marine animals; in fresh waters, crayfish and amphibians.

Suggested reading: E. L. Kozicy and F. V. Schmidt, "Nesting Habits of the Clapper Rail in New Jersey," *Auk,* vol. 66, pp. 355–364, 1949.

VIRGINIA RAIL (*Rallus limicola*)

Appearance: A medium-sized (8½–10½ in.), long-billed rail resembling the King Rail. Its cheeks are grayer; broad blackish lines on underparts alternate with narrow, wavy white lines; bill, legs, and feet are pinkish. Young birds, at least until end of 1st winter, appear almost black; the browns, except on the wings, are preceded by medium and dark grays, and the white is more subdued. Downy young are black, glossed greenish or bluish on the head and neck; bill yellowish white with blackish ring near middle.

Voice: In spring a resonant, metallic note, like the sound of a hammer on an anvil, repeated many times, or the double *click-ick* of an old-fashioned telegraph key. Also a large variety of reiterated grunts and *wak*'s usually descending in tone and volume.

Range and status: Breeds from s. Canada to Guatemala and through the mountains to Ecuador and Peru; also from c. Chile and Argentina to the Strait of Magellan. In our winter retreats from more northerly regions. It is probably one of the most common rails, but it is suffering because of drainage of marshes and mosquito-control poisoning.

Habitat: Marshes; fresh, and in winter, mainly, salt.

Seasonal movements: Those observed during winters in secluded open-water spots in the North are silent. Old dates of arrival, based on voice identification, are thus misleading. During migration seasons, enough birds are killed by colliding with telephone wires, etc., strung near swamps, to indicate that there is some movement.

Biology: Nest: Near fresh water (very rarely salt), sometimes in the water; made of coarse grasses and reeds, often 7–8 in. high and well concealed. Eggs: 5–12; buffy, spotted with browns. Incubation: About 20 days. Age at 1st flight unknown. Food: Worms, aquatic insects, slugs, mollusks, amphibians, small fish, and occasionally seeds.

Suggested reading: L. H. Walkinshaw, "The Virginia Rail in Michigan," *Auk,* vol. 54, pp. 464–475, 1937.

Although common in many marshes, Virginia Rails are heard more often than seen.

WATER RAIL (*Rallus aquaticus*)

A small (10–12 in.) European and Asian rail resembling the Virginia Rail, but with a shorter bill and grayer breast. The form resident in Iceland has straggled to Greenland.

SPOTTED CRAKE (*Porzana porzana*)

A small (ca. 9 in.) rail; short-billed (shorter than head). Brownish above, marked with blackish, and spotted with white; light below. Found in Europe and w.-c. Asia, wintering through Africa and to c. India. Has straggled to Greenland.

SORA (*Porzana carolina*)

Appearance: Small (8–10 in.), short-billed rail with brownish cap, nape, back, wings, and tail; the back and wings are marked and spotted with blackish and buff. The barring below is irregular, thin white on medium gray; the breast and rest of the head are warm gray except for the black face and bib. The bill is yellowish with a blackish tip; the legs and feet are yellowish green. The eye of the adult is vermilion; in the duller, browner immature birds, it is yellow. The downy young are glossy black with stiff, curled, bright orange chin feathers; their bills, reddish and enlarged at the base, are yellow.

Voice: A rapid series of clear, bell-like notes, warm and pulsating, like the whinny of a horse, descending in pitch and volume. Also a *keek* of alarm and in spring a high-pitched *er-eee*.

Range and status: Breeds from B.C., w. Mack., Sask., Man., Ont., c. Que., P.E.I., and N.B. south to n. Baja Calif., Nev., Ariz., N.Mex., Okla., Mo., Ill., Ind., c. Ohio, W.Va., and Pa. Winters from sw. U.S., the Gulf Coast, and S.C. south through Mexico, C. America, and the W. Indies to Peru, Venezuela, Trinidad, and Guyana; occasionally remains as far north as n. U.S. Has straggled to Greenland, Bermuda, Ireland, England, and Wales. Our most abundant rail.

Habitat: Brackish and marine marshes in winter; prefers freshwater swamps and wet meadows rest of year and as long as water remains open.

Seasonal movements: Very pronounced migration; sometimes in flocks of about 100 birds traveling long distances with slow, labored beating of tiny wings. Arrives on breeding grounds Mar.–May and departs Sept.–mid-Nov.

Biology: Nest: Hidden among reeds, cattails, or grasses in shallow water; made of dry grasses, reeds, and other vegetation supported by growing plants, the edge 3–6 in. above the water. Eggs: 6–18, commonly 10–12; buffy yellow or greenish buff, irregularly spotted with reddish and grayish browns. Incubation: 18–20 days. Age at 1st flight unknown. Food: More vegetarian than most other rails; seeds of aquatic plants predominate; small mollusks, worms, and insects are eaten in great numbers, especially in spring.

Suggested reading: L. H. Walkinshaw, "Summer Life of the Sora Rail," *Auk*, vol. 57, pp. 153–168, 1940.

Soras, our most abundant rails, feed on reeds, aquatic plants, and small animals.

The flightless Laysan Rail, once common in Hawaii, is thought to be extinct.

LAYSAN RAIL (*Porzanula palmeri*)

A very small (ca. 5 in.) flightless rail, pale grayish brown above and grayish below; belly and flanks are spotted with white. It is probably extinct. Was introduced on Midway I.; 1 seen there in June, 1944, was probably the last Laysan Rail seen alive. Formerly common on Laysan I. in Hawaii. Introduced rabbits, rats, and man eliminated most of the covering vegetation, and man's mosquito-control projects changed its habitat. Attempts to protect it and restock it have failed.

HAWAII RAIL (Sandwich Rail) (*Pennula sandwichensis*)

A small (ca. 5½ in.) flightless brown rail last seen alive in 1884 (possibly 1893) on the island of Hawaii. It could run very swiftly, but unfortunately it often took refuge in rodent holes. This was certainly a dangerous habit when the burrow was made by a Norway rat. Alteration of natural habitat and introduction of new enemies by man had much to do with the extermination of this bird.

Suggested reading: J. C. Greenway, Jr., "Hawaiian Rail," *Extinct and Vanishing Birds of the World,* Amer. Comm. Internat. Wildlife Protection Spec. Publ. 13, pp. 235–237, 1958.

YELLOW RAIL (*Coturnicops noveboracensis*)

Appearance: Small (6–7½ in.), short-billed, yellowish brown rail, little bigger than a House Sparrow; almost impossible to flush without a dog. In flight, a white patch is visible on the wings. The cap, nape, back, tail, and wings are streaked and spotted with dark browns and blackish; the barring underneath, mainly on the flanks, is dark brown with thin, wavy white lines. The bill is yellow, the legs and feet pale grayish yellow. The downy young are black with a slight greenish gloss on the cap and neck and a brownish tinge on the back.

Voice: A rhythmic 2, 3, 2, 3, 2, 3, 2, 3 clicking or clucking.

Range and status: Breeding records few and scattered; generally breeds east of Rockies from s.-c. Mack., n. Man., Ont., w.-c. and se. Que., N.B., and Maine south to Alta., Sask., N.Dak., Minn., Wis., Ohio, Mass., and Conn. Bred once in e.-c. Calif.; scattered summer records indicate its breeding range may extend farther south. Winters from Ore. to s. Calif. and along the Gulf Coast from Tex. to s. Fla. Another subspecies, perhaps extinct, may be resident in s.-c. Mexico. Because of its secretive habits and difficulty of observation, its true status is impossible to ascertain; reports are rare.

Habitat: Freshwater grass marshes and wet meadows; rarely upper reaches of grassy saltwater marshes in winter.

Seasonal movements: Early spring and late fall migrant.

Biology: Nest: Woven of fine grasses placed on a tussock of coarse grass, canopied and well hidden, in grassy, shallow-water marsh. Eggs: 7–10; yellowish buff, peppered or wreathed with spots of brown. Incubation period unknown. Age at 1st flight unknown. Food: The only food reported is small snails.

Suggested reading: L. H. Walkinshaw, "The Yellow Rail in Michigan," *Auk,* vol. 56, pp. 227–237, 1939.

BLACK RAIL (*Laterallus jamaicensis*)

Appearance: A little smaller (5–6 in.) than the House Sparrow; short-billed and very dark-looking. The entire rear half of the body is blackish barred with thin, wavy white lines below and interrupted thin white lines above; the forward half of the body is dark gray tinged with reddish on the top of the head and the nape. Bill is black; legs and feet bright yellowish green. The downy young are black with a greenish sheen above.

Voice: Ticking notes, higher in pitch than those of other American rails; other calls not definitely assigned to this species.

Range and status: Breeds from c. Calif. to nw. Baja Calif.; from Kans., Ind., Ohio, s. N.Y., Conn., and se. Mass. south to Okla., Mo., Ohio River Valley, w. Va., w. and c. Fla., Cuba, Jamaica, Puerto Rico; and from Peru to c. Chile. In winter it withdraws to coastal areas in Calif. and south to s. La. and s. Ga. in e. U.S. Exact status impossible to determine because of difficulty of observation and secretive habits.

Habitat: Mainly tidal marshes and inland grassy edges of swamps.

Seasonal movements: Leaves inland and more

northerly limits before early Nov. and returns before the end of May.

Biology: Nest: Of grasses and sedges near edges of marshes, under clumps of grasses or glasswort (*Salicornia*), well hidden but not arched over by bird. Eggs: 4–13, usually 6–8; whitish, evenly spotted with bright browns and drabs. Incubation period unknown. Age at 1st flight unknown. Food: Insects and some seeds of aquatic plants; in marine habitat, isopods—small marine crustaceans.

Suggested reading: A. C. Bent, *Life Histories of North American Marsh Birds*, Dover, N.Y. (reprint of U.S. Nat. Mus. Bull. 135, 1927), 1963, pp. 326–331.

CORN CRAKE (Land Rail) (*Crex crex*)

A medium-sized (9–11 in.), short-billed brownish rail of Europe and w.-c. and c. Asia wintering in Africa, Madagascar, and Arabia. It has straggled many times to e.

Removal of foreground grass clearly reveals the nest of a shy Black Rail.

Canada, e. U.S., Bermuda, Australia, and New Zealand. It is whitish below, with white-barred brownish red flanks. It inhabits drier meadows and grainfields.

PURPLE GALLINULE (*Porphyrula martinica*)

Appearance: Medium-sized (ca. 13 in.) rail with unusually long toes and very bright colors; it is much more of an extrovert than its relatives. Head, neck, and undersides are a deep, rich purple; the back, wings, and upper tail feathers are dark green with a bronzy sheen; the feathers under the tail are white. The legs and feet are bright greenish yellow. The bill is bright yellow at the tip and bright red at the base; a hard fleshy casque starts at the base of the upper bill and flares out to the center of the head; it is red at the bill and pale bluish white over the eye. Immature birds are dark gray above and light gray and white below; their bills and casques are dull grayish. The chicks are glossy black with whitish bristles on the forehead, chin, cheeks, and cap; they have black-tipped yellow bills.

Voice: Very noisy; henlike cackles in flight; shrill, harsh "laughing" and "giggling" notes and slower *hic-cup* calls.

Range and status: Breeds along coastal lowlands and up large river basins from Tenn. to La.; from sw. La. to S.C.; through the W. Indies, Tobago, and Trinidad; from Nayarit, Mexico, to Peru; and from s. Tex. to Uruguay and n. Argentina, including the Amazon and Orinoco river basins. In winter from the Gulf Coast southward. Has straggled through most of U.S. into se. Canada, Bermuda, and Tristan da Cunha and S. Georgia I.

Habitat: Marshes, edges of lakes and ponds overgrown with aquatic vegetation, lagoons.

Seasonal movements: Mainly resident; withdrawal not pronounced.

Biology: Nest: A shallow bowl of stalks, stems, and grasses supported by vegetation above the water of marshes on "floating" islands; sometimes several dummy nests are made nearby. Eggs: 5–10, usually 6–8; pinkish buff, evenly peppered with brown. Incubation period unknown. Age at 1st flight unknown. Food: Rice, grain, other seeds, insects, small mollusks, and amphibians.

Suggested reading: D. A. Bannerman, *Birds of the British Isles*, Oliver and Boyd, Edinburgh, 1963, vol. 12, pp. 226–229.

BLUE-HEADED GALLINULE (*Porphyrio poliocephalus*)

Hen-sized (ca. 20 in.) purplish blue gallinule with vermilion legs, feet, bill, and casque. Found from c. and s. Asia through Indonesia and w. Oceania to Australia, Tasmania, and New Zealand. Introduced from Australia to Oahu, Hawaii, and established, but nowhere common.

The Blue-headed Gallinule, found only on Oahu in Hawaii, was introduced from Australia.

Like all coots and gallinules, the Common Gallinule is an excellent swimmer and diver.

COMMON GALLINULE (Florida Gallinule, Moorhen)
(*Gallinula chloropus*)

Appearance: Similar in size (12–14½ in.) and general appearance to the Purple Gallinule, but is rather dark gray where that species is purple; its casque and yellow-tipped bill are bright red, and its legs and feet are yellowish green. The upper edge of the flank is white and shows as a white streak down the side of a swimming bird. The central undertail feathers are dark gray. The downy young are glossy black; the skin at the base of the black-tipped reddish bill is bright red; the stiffish, curled feathers of the chin and forehead are white.

Voice: Froglike *cr-r-oak,* henlike notes, *kek-kek-kek-kek* calls, and loud, noisy complaints.

Range and status: Breeds from the British Isles, s. Scandinavia, n. Russia, s. Siberia, and Japan south to s. Africa, Madagascar, s. India, Ceylon, c. Indonesia, Philippines, Bonin and Marianas Is., and Hawaii. In the Americas from c. Calif., c. Ariz., Okla., Kans., Nebr., Iowa, c. Minn., s. Wis., Mich., s. Ont., s. Que., Vt., and Mass. south to Peru, n. Argentina, se. Brazil (including the W. Indies), also Bermuda and the Galápagos Is. Large gaps in this range, particularly in desert regions. In winter retires to warm temperate and subtropical areas; in America from c. Calif., s. Ariz., c. Mexico, the Gulf Coast, and e. N.C. southward. Common.

Habitat: Freshwater ponds and marshes, edges of large rivers and lakes; prefers reedy and brushy cover.

Seasonal movements: Mainly sedentary; it has been said, without proof, that some hibernate! Disappears from n. regions about mid-Nov. and seen again in these areas about mid-Apr.

Biology: Nest: Sometimes in small colonies; sometimes 1 pair builds several nests. A shallow cup of stems of aquatic plants, usually reeds and rushes over water, woven into supporting vegetation and often partially floating. An entrance ramp is usually built on 1 side. Eggs: 6–17, commonly 10–12; reddish buff, irregularly marked and spotted with dark browns. Incubation: 18–21 days. Age at 1st flight: 6–7 weeks. Food: Largely underwater plants, grasses, herbs, seeds, and berries and some insects, snails, worms, etc.

Suggested reading: A. C. Bent, *Life Histories of North American Marsh Birds,* Dover, N.Y. (reprint of U.S. Nat. Mus. Bull. 135, 1927), 1963, pp. 346–355.

EUROPEAN COOT (*Fulica atra*)

About the same size (14–16 in.) as the American Coot; differs from it only in having the feathers under the tail slate gray like the rest of the plumage. Ranges from Iceland, Europe, and nw. Africa across Asia to Sakhalin I., Japan, s. India, Burma, and s. China; also in Java, New Guinea, Australia, and Tasmania. Has straggled to Greenland, Lab., and Nfld.

The American Coot nests on the marshy fringes of lakes and ponds.

AMERICAN COOT (*Fulica americana*)

Appearance: About the size (13–16 in.) of a small chicken; on water looks like a small-headed duck. Plumage dark gray, slightly lighter below, with a patch of white under the short tail. The eye is reddish, the legs and feet greenish, and the rather stout, conical bill is china-white. Immature birds are paler and have brownish eyes and a grayish bill. The downy young are black with an orange bill, and the feathers about the head, neck, and shoulders are orange or orange tipped.

Voice: Very vociferous; harsh, loud cackles, grunts, and croaks. A rhythmic *ca-ha, ca-ha, ca-ha;* monotonous *kaakaakaakaakaa.*

Range and status: Breeds from B.C., s. Mack., Alta., c. Sask., Man., w. Ont., Wis., Mich., s. Ont., s. Que., and N.B. south to s. Baja Calif., Nicaragua, Panama, the Gulf Coast, s. Fla., Cuba, Isle of Pines, Jamaica, and Grand Cayman I.; also in the Andes from Colombia to Ecuador, Hawaii, and through the W. Indies. Winters from s. B.C., Ariz., N.Mex., Tex., the Ohio River Valley, and Md. south to Panama, Greater Antilles, and the Bahamas; casually farther north and to Bermuda. Has straggled to Alaska, n. Ont., Lab., Nfld., and Greenland. A common water bird.

Habitat: Freshwater lakes, ponds, and marshes; fields, meadows, saltwater estuaries and bays, mainly in winter.

Seasonal movements: Rather sedentary; begins returning to more northerly breeding grounds in early Mar. and may not leave until late Nov.

Biology: Nest: A floating platform of aquatic vegetation anchored firmly to new growths or a cup fashioned of reeds among the rushes. Eggs: 6–22, most often 8–12; reddish to dark buff, evenly and heavily spotted with dark browns. Incubation: 23–24 days. Age at 1st flight: Probably about 7–8 weeks. Food: Omnivorous; all types of vegetable matter; also fish, tadpoles, snails, worms, and crustaceans.

Suggested reading: G. W. Gullion, "Displays and Calls of the American Coot," *Wils. Bull.,* vol. 64, pp. 83–97, 1952. G. W. Gullion, "The Reproductive Cycle of American Coots in California," *Auk,* vol. 71, pp. 366–412, 1954.

THE JAÇANAS (JACANIDAE)

These are small- to medium-sized (6½–21 in.) birds that resemble rails, more particularly the gallinules, but they have several characteristics that lead ornithologists to place them closer to the plovers. There are 7 species ranging around the world in the tropical regions; the Jaçana is the only species to reach our area. According to Webster's, the correct pronunciation (but seldom used) is *zha′ sa na′*. The bills are thin and moderately long, about the same length as the head. The legs are long, the toes very long, and the toenails extremely long. The wings are broad and have a spur or knob at the forward bend. Flight is slow. They commonly walk about on floating aquatic vegetation, although they are excellent swimmers and divers. Insects, snails, and seeds of water plants form the bulk of their diet. The sexes are similar, except that the females are larger. In the winter some species are gregarious. Nests are built of plant material on floating vegetation. The 3–6 eggs are brown, marked with darker brown and black. Incubation and care of the young are mainly by the male. The downy young are able to leave the nest shortly after hatching.

Long, slender toes and toenails enable the Jaçana to walk on floating vegetation.

JAÇANA (*Jacana spinosa*)

This is a small (8–9 in.) brownish red jaçana (darker toward the head), with greenish yellow flight feathers, yellow bill, yellow forehead wattles, and yellowish green legs and feet. It is resident from w.-c., c., and ne. Mexico south to Panama, Ecuador, and c. Argentina. It occurs in the Greater Antilles, has straggled occasionally into Tex., and has been taken once in Fla.

The American Oystercatcher's simple nest is little more than a hollow in the sand.

THE OYSTERCATCHERS (HAEMATOPODIDAE)

Oystercatchers are medium-sized (15–21 in.) shorebirds with moderately long, stout pinkish or reddish legs and feet. The strong red bill is compressed laterally and is longer than the head. They have long, pointed wings and 3 toes only (all directed forward). Tails and necks are short. There are 6 species, ranging along almost all the seacoasts of the world except those of the polar regions and some of the cool temperate areas. They are found inland in c. and w.-c. Asia and e. Europe. Only 3 species have been recorded in America: European Oystercatcher, American Oystercatcher, and Black Oystercatcher. They fly well and are noisy and gregarious. The nest is a hollow in the ground, sometimes lined with grasses or pebbles. Both sexes, which are alike, incubate the eggs and care for the young. The downy young leave the nest shortly after hatching. The design of the bill makes it fairly easy for them to pry open bivalve mollusks, such as clams, mussels, and oysters, which form the bulk of their diet; they also eat worms and other invertebrates.

EUROPEAN OYSTERCATCHER (*Haematopus ostralegus*)

A medium-sized (ca. 17 in.) bird with black head, neck, upper breast, back, and wings; the rest of the plumage is white, including a broad streak on the wing; most of the tail is white, with the terminal third black. It breeds on the seacoasts of Iceland, the British Isles, Europe, s. Africa, e.-c. Asia, Australia, Tasmania, and New Zealand, and in the interior of c. and w.-c. Asia and se. Europe. In winter it ranges over the remainder of the seacoasts of Africa, Asia, and Indonesia from its more northerly nesting grounds. It has straggled to s. Greenland.

AMERICAN OYSTERCATCHER (*Haematopus palliatus*)

Appearance: Largest (17–21 in.) of the oystercatchers. Head, neck, and upper breast are black; the back, wings (except for a broad white streak), and terminal third of the tail are medium brownish gray; the rest of the plumage is white. The legs and feet are

145

pinkish; bill and eyelids are red. Immature birds are duller black and more brownish and show some white at the base of the bill. The downy hatchlings are grayish or brownish gray, mottled with darker shades.

Voice: A loud, clear, dominating *wheep,* repeated many times in flight; also a shorter *pi* note and a few double, more mellow notes.

Range and status: Mainly resident along coasts from Baja Calif. to n. Chile, from se. N.Y. (Long I.) and N.J. to e.-c. Argentina, and through the W. Indies. In winter it is very rarely found north of N.C. Formerly common in parts of its range, it is now rare through most of the U.S. areas. The bird still straggles casually north to Calif. and N.B.

Habitat: Almost all types of marine coasts, tidal zones, and beaches.

Seasonal movements: Scatters during breeding seasons, but gathers in flocks at other times of year; on the Atlantic Coast these flocks gradually withdraw to N.C.

Biology: Nest: A mere hollow in the sand of flat, dry beaches, well above high tide. Eggs: 2–4; most often 3; greenish brown, sparsely and irregularly marked, spotted or scrawled with dark browns. Incubation period unknown; probably like that of the European Oystercatcher, 24–27 days. Age at 1st flight: About 34–37 days. Food: About 70% bivalve mollusks; some crustaceans and worms.

Suggested reading: H. M. Hall, *A Gathering of Shore Birds,* Devin-Adair, N.Y., 1960, pp. 28–32. H. M. Hall, "The Oystercatcher," *Aud. Mag.,* vol. 62, pp. 214–217, 1960.

BLACK OYSTERCATCHER (*Haematopus bachmani*)

Appearance: Smaller (17–17½ in.) than the American Oystercatcher; adult plumage entirely black, bill and eyelids red, and bill and feet pinkish. Young birds are browner, with a paler bill. The downy hatchlings are brownish gray, with a light spot on the abdomen, a blackish tail, and 2 black streaks down the back; they are mottled overall with blackish.

Voice: Very similar to that of the American Oystercatcher.

Range and status: Resident on coasts of islands and mainland from the w. Aleutian Is. to sw. Calif. and offshore islands of Baja Calif. Straggles to the Pribilof Is. in winter. Sometimes common locally.

Habitat: All types of marine coasts, tidal areas, and beaches.

Seasonal movements: Sedentary.

Biology: Almost identical with that of the American Oystercatcher; some ornithologists feel that this is only a subspecies of the latter.

Suggested reading: J. D. Webster, "The Breeding of the Black Oystercatcher," *Wils. Bull.,* vol. 53, pp. 141–156, 1941.

PLOVERS, TURNSTONES, AND SURFBIRDS (CHARADRIIDAE)

These are small (6–15½ in.) shorebirds with straight, medium-long bills; long, usually pointed wings; short to medium tails; and rather short necks. Some extraterritorial species have long crests, some have spurs on their wings, and some have wattles about the face. The Lapwing, a straggler to our territory, is crested. Their hind toes are lacking or vestigial, and there is usually some webbing between the toes. There are 63 species ranging throughout the world; 16 of these occur in America. Except during the breeding season, they are gregarious. They spend much time on the ground and can run swiftly. Their flight is rapid and strong. Sexes are alike or nearly so. The eggs, usually 4, are generally laid in a depression in the ground. Normally, incubation and care of the young are by both male and female. In most species the adults protect the eggs and young by a "broken wing" display until the intruder is lured safely away. The downy young are able to leave the nest shortly after hatching. Some plant matter is eaten, but the greater part of the food of most species consists of small animals, such as insects, crustaceans, and various kinds of worms.

LAPWING (*Vanellus vanellus*)

A fairly large (ca. 12 in.) black-crested plover with buffy plumes originating behind each eye. It has a black throat and chest, a subterminal black band on the white tail, and blackish flight feathers on the wings; the rest of the head and underparts are white, and the back and small feathers of the wings are metallic greens and browns. Breeds from the British Isles and c. Europe across Asia to ne. China and se. Siberia. Winters from Iceland (where it bred in 1922) and n. Eurasia south to n. Africa and s. Asia. It occasionally reaches Greenland and has straggled to the e. seaboard of America from Baffin I. and Lab. to S.C. and the Bahamas.

RINGED PLOVER (*Charadrius hiaticula*)

A small (ca. 7½ in.) plover; resembles our Semipalmated Plover, but, according to some, it has much less webbing between the toes, and the tip of the tail is not so black. It is perhaps the same species as our Semipalmated Plover. Breeds from Ellesmere I. and Baffin I. through Greenland, Iceland, the British Isles, Spitsbergen, Novaya Zemlya, New Siberian Is., n. Europe, and n. Asia to East Cape and the base of Kamchatka Peninsula. Winters from the British Isles, the Mediterranean region, Asia Minor, and China south to s. Africa and c. India. The birds breeding in ne. Canada migrate eastward through Greenland. A straggler once reached Barbados, B.W.I.

SEMIPALMATED PLOVER (*Charadrius semipalmatus*)

Appearance: Small (6½–8 in.) plover, dark grayish brown above and white below, with a white forehead and a light gray patch just behind the eye. The throat and a conjoining ring around the neck are white, and just below this is another ring of black (sometimes not complete in front). The feet are yellowish or flesh-colored, as is the black-tipped bill. The flight feathers of the wing are blackish, and the tail is blackish near the narrow white tip. In winter the black markings are replaced with grayish brown.

The Ringed Plover, a European species, is very closely related to the Semipalmated Plover.

147

Voice: A querulous, buzzy *chiwe.*

Range and status: Breeds around the coasts of n. N. America from Queen Charlotte Is., B.C., to the n. shore of the Gulf of St. Lawrence, on the coasts of Victoria I., s. Somerset I., s. Baffin I., Nfld., Magdalen I., and Sable I.; inland to s. Mack. and s.-c. Lab. and in nw. B.C.; formerly to s. N.B. Nonbreeders remain much farther south. Winters along coasts of N. America, the W. Indies, and S. America from c. Calif. and S.C. to Chile and Argentina; casually farther north. Has straggled to Greenland, ne. Siberia, Bermuda, and England. Migrates through the interior of N. America, but more commonly along coasts. Sometimes abundant in migration.

Habitat: Marine and freshwater coasts, intertidal flats; freshly plowed fields or almost any large, flat, muddy area.

Seasonal movements: Large flocks begin arriving from wintering areas Apr.–mid-May and begin to return in July, with largest fall flights in Aug.

Biology: Nest: A slight hollow in the sand above high tide, sometimes lined with bits of shells or grasses. Eggs: 3–4, most often 4; pale, medium greenish brown, spotted and blotched with black and dark browns. Incubation: 23(?) days; closely related Ringed Plover of Eurasia 23–26 days. Age at 1st flight unknown. Food: Small crustaceans, small mollusks, insects, and worms.

Suggested reading: G. M. Sutton and D. F. Parmelee, "The Breeding of the Semipalmated Plover on Baffin Island," *Bird-banding,* vol. 26, pp. 137–196, 1955.

PIPING PLOVER (*Charadrius melodus*)

Appearance: Small (6–7½ in.); resembles the Semipalmated Plover but is much paler; the upperparts are a light brownish gray, with much white on the head. The only black on the head is a narrow band running from eye to eye above the forehead; it does have the black ring around the neck, not always complete across the chest. The legs, feet, and blackish-tipped bill are flesh-colored or yellowish. In winter the black feathers are replaced with brownish gray.

Voice: A clear, piping whistle, *peep-peep-peeplo;* it is often difficult to determine its point of origin.

Range and status: Breeds east of the Rockies from s. Canada south to nw. N.Dak., se. S.Dak., the s. shores of the Great Lakes, and along the Atlantic seaboard from sw. Nfld. to Va. Winters along the coasts of U.S. from S.C. to Tex.; rarely to the Bahamas and the Greater Antilles. Has straggled to Wyo. and Colo. A rather common plover.

Habitat: Sandy marine beaches and lake shores.

Seasonal movements: Starts northward migrations in Mar. and begins to return in mid-July.

Biology: Not colonial, but gregarious. Nest: A hollow in the sand, often well back from the high-water line, with a meager lining of shell fragments or pebbles. Eggs: 3–5, commonly 4; light brownish or pale buffy, sparsely but evenly spotted with dark browns and black. Incubation: 27–31 days. Age at 1st flight: 30–35 days; usually

The Semipalmated Plover generally lays a clutch of four large mottled eggs.

Piping Plover

remains within 500 ft. of nest until 1st flight. Food: Insects, small crustaceans, small mollusks, annelid worms, etc.

Suggested reading: Le Roy Wilcox, "A Twenty Year Banding Study of the Piping Plover," *Auk,* vol. 76, pp. 129–152, 1959.

SNOWY PLOVER (*Charadrius alexandrinus*)

Appearance: About the same size (6–7 in.) as the Piping Plover, but much lighter in color and with a thinner black bill, greenish black legs and feet, a black spot behind the eye, and, in place of a black ring around the neck, a black slash at the sides of the lower throat. It does have black at the top of the forehead. The female is sometimes a duller black where the male is black, and in winter the black marks on both sexes are replaced by brownish gray.

Voice: Not vociferous; sometimes in flight a low, staccato trill. The most common call is a pleasant whistled *pee-wee-ah.*

Range and status: Breeds along the coasts from w. Wash. to Baja Calif.; from Tex. to w. Fla.; from Peru to c. Chile; the Greater Antilles; and from s. England and s. Scandinavia south around Europe, the Mediterranean, Africa, Madagascar, Arabia, w. India, Australia, and Tasmania; e. Asia from Manchuria to Thailand, Ceylon, Java, and Honshu I. of Japan. It breeds inland in N. America from e. Ore., w. Nev., and Utah south to s. Baja Calif. and locally in e. Colo., s. N.Mex., sw. Kans., nw. Okla., and n. Tex.; perhaps casually or locally southeastward of these areas to s. La., and in c. Asia (and around the shores of the Black and Caspian Seas), Persia, se. Europe, parts of n., w., and e. Africa, and parts of s. Australia. In winter it deserts the inland breeding grounds for the nearby coastal areas but is seldom found north of w. Ore. Once straggled to e. Fla. Formerly common; increased use of beaches by humans has reduced populations by depriving them of nesting and feeding sites.

Habitat: Beaches; flat, sandy, vegetation-free lands near water; also salt plains.

Seasonal movements: Moves into more northerly and inland areas late Mar.–mid-Apr. and leaves Sept.–early Dec.

Biology: Nest: A depression in sand, sometimes

Like most of its relatives, the Snowy Plover builds a simple, unlined nest.

lined with shell fragments and bits of rock, or a hollow in flat rocky terrain; near water, but above high-tide line. Eggs: 2–5, normally 3; pale to medium buff, spotted and scrawled with black, browns, and gray. Incubation: 24 days; it is possible that 2 broods are raised each year, at least in warmer regions. Age at 1st flight unknown. Food: Insects and larvae, small mollusks, small crustaceans, worms, and spiders.

Suggested reading: H. M. Hall, *A Gathering of Shore Birds,* Devin-Adair, N.Y., 1960, pp. 46–49.

MONGOLIAN PLOVER (*Charadrius mongolus*)

Small (ca. 7½ in.), white below, sandy above, with a light, reddish brown chest (replaced by a gray ring in winter) and a white throat. It breeds in se. Siberia, nw. India, Tibet, Mongolia, e. Siberia, Komandorskie Is., and w. Alaska (St. Lawrence I., Goodnews Bay). Winters from s. Asia and the Philippines to Mozambique, Ceylon, Indonesia, and Australia. It has also been recorded at Cape Prince of Wales and on Nunivak I., Alaska.

WILSON'S PLOVER (*Charadrius wilsonia*)

Appearance: Larger (7–8 in.) than the Semipalmated Plover, which it resembles somewhat, except that it is a lighter brown above. The white forehead is extended into a stripe above the eye, the black neck "ring"

is broader and does not extend around the back of the neck, the black bill is almost as long as the head, and the legs and feet are a pale, pinkish gray. In the female the blacks are duller or are replaced with dark gray; in winter both species have a brownish gray in place of black.

Voice: A loud, strong *wheet.*

Range and status: Breeds along coasts and on coastal islands from c. Baja Calif. and Sonora to Peru, from s. N.J. to s. Fla., and around the Gulf Coast and Caribbean area to Venezuela and Guyana; also through the W. Indies. In winter it retreats south of S.C. on the Atlantic Coast and may reach e.-c. Brazil. Not rare; may be locally common.

Habitat: Bars, mudflats, sandy strands, beaches, and islets.

Seasonal movements: Remains in more northerly regions until Oct. and returns. Mar.–Apr.

Biology: Sometimes nests in loose colonies. Nest: A depression in the sand well back of high tide, sometimes partially sheltered by driftwood or plant growth and frequently lined with broken shells or stones. Eggs: 2–4, usually 3; yellowish buff, thickly covered with splotches, spots, and scrawls of black and browns. Incubation: 24–25 days. Age at 1st flight unknown. Food: Insects, marine crustaceans, tiny mollusks, and worms.

Suggested reading: I. R. Tompkins, "Wilson's Plover in Its Summer Home," *Auk,* vol. 61, pp. 259–269, 1944.

In the United States, the Caracara is found in Florida and along the Mexican border. This relative of the falcons feeds mostly on carrion but also captures live prey.

The secretive King Rail inhabits freshwater marshes over much of the eastern United States but is nowhere common. Like most rails, it is heard more often than seen.

KILLDEER (*Charadrius vociferus*)

Appearance: Slightly larger (9–11 in.) than a Robin; in general pattern and color it resembles a Semipalmated Plover, but it has some white extending from the forehead to under the eye and a second black breast band below the complete upper ring. It also has a slim black bill, flesh-colored legs and feet, and a bright rufous rump patch extending partway down the dark-tipped, white-edged tail. In flight a white streak runs from the inner, trailing edge almost to the tip of the wing. Immature birds are browner above.

Voice: A loud, querulous continued repetition of its name, *kill-deer, kill-deer,* and variations of this 2-note call; also a deep trill.

Range and status: Breeds from nw. B.C., s. Mack., ne. Man., n. Ont., s. Que., and N.B. south to s.-c. Mexico, the Gulf Coast, the Greater Antilles, and the Bahamas; also from n. Peru to n. Chile. Winters from s. B.C., Ore., n. Utah, Colo., Okla., the Ohio Valley, and se. N.Y. south to Chile, Peru, Colombia, and Venezuela. Since protected by law, it has managed to regain its former numbers and is now common; often locally abundant.

Habitat: Open fields, lawns, riverbanks, seacoasts, irrigated lands. This is the plover most apt to nest on your gravel driveway or walks.

Seasonal movements: Resident over much of its range; where it does migrate, it leaves late in the fall and returns early in spring.

Biology: Nest: A depression in the ground, lined with stones, wood chips, or stalks; often lays eggs in slight hollow of gravel flats, rooftops, etc. Eggs: 3–5, usually 4; yellowish buff, irregularly spotted, blotched, and scrawled with blackish and dark browns. Incubation: 24–29 days; most records are 27–28 days. Age at 1st flight unknown. Food: Very largely insects, such as beetles and grasshoppers; also crustaceans, worms, mollusks, and spiders. Some seeds (less than 3%) are eaten.

Suggested reading: W. P. Nickell, "Observations on the Nesting of the Killdeer," *Wils. Bull.,* vol. 55, pp. 23–28, 1943.

MOUNTAIN PLOVER (*Eupoda montana*)

Appearance: Resembles a small (8–9½ in.), drab Killdeer, but it has no black neck ring or chest band. The white forehead is continued into a stripe above the eye, and the forepart of the cap is blackish. Upperparts are light grayish brown, and some of this color continues on

Because of its heavy bill, the Wilson's Plover is also called the Thick-billed Plover.

Mountain Plover

known. Age at 1st flight unknown. Food: Insects, mainly locusts; no seeds have been found in its stomach.

Suggested reading: H. M. Hall, *A Gathering of Shore Birds,* Devin-Adair, N.Y., 1960, pp. 56–59. L. W. Walker, "The Mountain Plover," *Aud. Mag.,* vol. 57, pp. 210–212, 1955.

DOTTEREL (*Eudromias morinellus*)

Medium-sized (ca. 8½ in.); brownish gray above and on chest, with a white eye stripe, a white throat, a white band under the chest, and white undertail feathers; the rest of its underparts are rich reddish brown. The legs and feet are yellowish, and the bill is black. In winter this species becomes whitish below and grayish brown above, with just a trace of the white eye stripe and the white chest bar remaining. It breeds locally in the mountains of Scotland, England, c., n., and e. Europe, and n. and c. Asia (and at least once in n. Alaska). Winters in s. Europe, n. Africa, and sw. Asia. It has straggled to w. Wash.

EURASIAN GOLDEN PLOVER (*Pluvialis apricaria*)

Very similar in size (ca. 11 in.), pattern, and color to the American Golden Plover; the most obvious difference is that the smaller feathers of the underside of the wing are white in this species. It breeds in Iceland, Great Britain, n. Europe, and nw. Asia. Winters from n.-c. Europe to n. and e.-c. Africa, Baluchistan, and nw. India. It occurs regularly during migration in s. Greenland and has straggled to Jan Mayen, Bear, Azores, Canary, Madeira, and Cape Verde Is.

AMERICAN GOLDEN PLOVER (*Pluvialis dominica*)

Appearance: Medium-sized (9½–11 in.) plover with black face, throat, and undersides; above, it is golden brown mottled and spotted with blackish. There is a white line running from the forehead, above the eye, down the side of the neck and broadening out at the shoulders, where it ends. The bill is black, and the feet and legs are blackish. In the nonbreeding seasons the white and black plumage is replaced by grayish white, marbled with dull light brown on the flanks and chest and about the face.

Voice: In flight, a penetrating *quee-ee-ee-a,* tremulous in the middle and dropping at the end; also a series of notes often described as *coodle-coodle-coodle.*

Range and status: Breeds from the coasts of Siberia and Alaska and Banks, Parry, and N. Devon Is. of the Canadian Arctic south to c. Siberia, sw. Alaska, c. Mack., ne. Man., and s. Baffin I. Winters from e. India, s. China, and Hawaii south to Australia, Tasmania, New Zealand, and s. Oceania; also from Bolivia and s. Brazil to e.-c. Argentina. Only now recovering from hunting pressure of

to the side of the breast, fading out completely in the center of the chest. The tail is grayish brown with a narrow white tip and a subterminal dark band or spot. The bill is black, and the legs and feet are dull, pale brownish yellow. In winter the blackish cap is replaced with a duller grayish brown one, and the white eye streak is less distinct.

Voice: A pleasant deep, drawling whistle; often a higher, harsher note.

Range and status: The higher plains and plateaus from n. Mont. and ne. N.Dak. south to se. N.Mex., w. Tex., and w. Okla.; winters from c. Calif., s. Ariz., and c. Tex. to s. Baja Calif. and c. Mexico. Rather rare, but may be locally common.

Habitat: Drier grasslands, prairies, and plateaus.

Seasonal movements: Arrives at breeding grounds mid-Mar.–mid-May and reaches wintering areas Sept.–mid-Oct.

Biology: Nest: A slight hollow in the ground; linings of fine rootlets and grasses are probably adventitious. Eggs: 2–4, commonly 3; dark greenish buff, spotted and scrawled with black; these marks are sometimes wreathed around the larger end. Incubation period not

former years, when hunters were permitted to kill them for the markets; thanks to protection rendered in time, one may now occasionally see large migrating flocks in America.

Habitat: Tundra in summer; grasslands, extensive mudflats, and seacoasts.

Seasonal movements: Rare as a migrant west of the Rockies; common through the Great Plains and sometimes common along the Atlantic Coast, particularly in the Northeast. Its main flight to Argentina passes near Bermuda and the Lesser Antilles. The spring flight evidently passes over c. S. America, through Panama, and over the e. shores and waters of both the Caribbean and Gulf of Mexico, then up the Mississippi Valley. Fall movements occur July–Nov.; spring movements Feb.–May.

Biology: Nest: Hollow in tundra, lined with leaves. Eggs: 3–5, usually 4; reddish to yellowish buff, or creamy, boldly and thickly but irregularly marked with black or dark brown spots, blotches, and dots. Incubation period unknown, but Eurasian Golden Plover incubates 27½–34 days. Age at 1st flight unknown. Food: Largely insects, some crustaceans, mollusks, and worms; also some seeds and berries.

Suggested reading: G. H. Mackay, "The Habits of the Golden Plover in Massachusetts," *Auk*, vol. 8, pp. 17–24, 1891.

BLACK-BELLIED PLOVER (*Squatarola squatarola*)

Appearance: Our largest (10½–13½ in.) plover; resembles the Golden Plover, but upperparts are light gray marked and spotted with black, except on the head and nape, where the gray fades into white. The bill is heavier, and the undertail feathers are white. In nonbreeding plumage it lacks any yellowish or golden tints on the back, and the grayish plumage below is more distinctly spotted with dull grayish brown on the throat, breast, and flanks.

Voice: Rich, querulous, run-together whistled *pee-u-wee* and a loud, bell-like *wherrell*.

Range and status: Breeds in tundra from n. Russia across n. Siberia, n. Alaska, and n. Canada to Banks, Baffin, and Southampton Is. Winters from British Isles, s. Europe, n. India, s. China, and s. Japan south to s. Africa, Madagascar, Mauritius, Ceylon, Australia, New Zealand, and the Solomon Is., and coastally from sw. B.C. to Chile and the Galápagos Is., from N.J. south along the Gulf and Caribbean shores, and through the W. Indies to s. Brazil. Has straggled to Hawaii and Argentina. Not so common as the Golden Plover; travels in small flocks, never large concentrations.

Habitat: Tundra in summer; prairie mudflats and sloughs, seacoasts, marshes.

Seasonal movements: Migrates across country and along seacoasts, moving south July–Nov. and north Mar.–mid-June.

Biology: Nest: A hollow in tundra, lined with mosses. Eggs: 3–4, usually 4; pinkish, greenish, or brownish, spotted and scrawled with dark browns and blacks in a wreath about the larger end. Incubation: 23(?) days. Age at 1st flight not known. Food: Crustaceans, insects, small mollusks, worms, etc.

Suggested reading: D. A. Bannerman, *Birds of the British Isles*, Oliver and Boyd, Edinburgh, 1961, vol. 10, pp. 224–229.

SURFBIRD (*Aphriza virgata*)

Appearance: About the size (10 in.) of the American Golden Plover. It is brownish gray above, spotted

Black-bellied Plover

The Surfbird winters on rocky western coasts but breeds in the mountains of Alaska.

with black and dark brown, and white below, heavily marked with dark gray, particularly on the chest and flanks. Its white tail has a broad subterminal black band. It has a whitish eye stripe, yellowish legs and feet, and a blackish bill with yellow at the base of the lower mandible. In flight a white streak extends most of the way along the dark wings. During the nonbreeding seasons it is dark gray with a white abdomen and undertail feathers, a whitish throat, and a faint whitish eye stripe; wings and tail are like the breeding plumage.

Voice: A keen, piercing *kee-a-wee* or *kee-wee;* about the nest a low *tee-tee-teet.*

Range and status: Breeds in the higher parts of the c. Alaska Range, in and near Mount McKinley National Park; nonbreeders wander farther north in Alaska; some may breed in the Kotzebue Sound region. Winters along the Pacific Coast from se. Alaska to Chile. It has straggled to Yukon; nonbreeders may remain as far south in summer as Panama. Not a common bird.

Habitat: Rocky, surfridden coasts; nests on rocky mountainsides.

Seasonal movements: Probably reaches breeding grounds in mid-May and departs in July.

Biology: Nest: A natural depression in the rock, sparsely lined with lichens and plant leaves. Eggs: 4; reddish buff, marked with dark reddish brown. Incubation period unknown; almost entirely by male. Age at 1st flight unknown. Food: Insects, crustaceans, small mollusks.

Suggested reading: J. Dixon, "The Surf-bird's Secret," *Condor,* vol. 29, pp. 3–16, 1927.

RUDDY TURNSTONE (*Arenaria interpres*)

Appearance: Somewhat smaller (8–10 in.) than the Killdeer but plumper-looking. In spring and summer plumage it is mainly brownish red on back and wings, with white below, and its white head has a grayish cap and nape. In addition, a black upper chest band loops down to the sides of the lower chest and back up, continuing as streaks down the back. Fingers of black run from the side of the throat to the base of the bill, the eye, and the rear of the head. There is a small black oval behind the eye and a thin black line from the eye to the forehead. The white tail has a broad subterminal band of black; the bill is blackish, and the legs and feet are orange-red. In flight the wings have a large triangle of white near the shoulders and a white streak across the blackish flight feathers. The large white rump patch is separated from the white of the tail by a black V. In fall and winter the bird is white below and brownish above, including the head; the black of the breeding plumage is suggested by a darker brown, and the throat is whitish.

Voice: Metallic, staccato twitter *kitititit* and less frequently a clear-whistled *kee-oo;* on the breeding grounds a distinctive *quitta-quitta-quitta, quit-it-it.*

Range and status: Breeds along arctic shore (including islands) from Bristol Bay, Alaska, to Southampton I., N.W.T., and from the Baltic states around Scandinavia and n. Eurasia almost to the base of Kamchatka Peninsula, on the shores of Novaya Zemlya, the New Siberian Is., and Wrangel I., and on parts of the shores of Banks, Somerset, Devon, Baffin, and Ellesmere Is. of the

Black Oystercatcher

Black Turnstone

The gregarious Ruddy Turnstones almost always move about in small flocks.

Canadian Archipelago, parts of nw., n., and e. Greenland, and parts of Spitsbergen. Winters coastally from c. Calif., the Gulf Coast, and S.C. south to c. Chile and s. Brazil, and from Britain, the Mediterranean, coasts of w. Asia, and Hawaii south to s. Africa, s. India, Indonesia, Australia, New Zealand, Oceania, and the Galápagos. Common.

Habitat: All types of marine shores from mudflats to surf-pounded rocks.

Seasonal movements: Migrating flocks fly high; when landing en route, flocks scatter. Leaves breeding grounds before mid-July and is in wintering areas in s. U.S. by mid-Oct. In spring most migrations occur in May; nonbreeders may linger or remain anywhere along the way. Moves commonly along coasts and through Great Lakes region; very rare in Mississippi Valley and elsewhere in interior.

Biology: Gregarious, but not colonial. Nest: An unlined depression in tundra near coasts. Eggs: 3–5, usually 4: grayish yellow to dark greenish buff, spotted and/or marbled, mainly on large end, with browns, grays, and black. Incubation: 21–22 days, by both sexes. Age at 1st flight not known. Food: earns its name by turning over stones with its stout bill in search of small animals hiding underneath; shells, clods of soil, and other objects are also rolled over in this search; the stone may be levered up by the bill and pushed over by the breast. Major items of food are small mollusks, crustaceans, and insects.

Suggested reading: D. A. Bannerman, *Birds of the British Isles,* Oliver and Boyd, Edinburgh, 1961, vol. 9, pp. 207–222.

BLACK TURNSTONE (*Arenaria melanocephala*)

Appearance: About the same size (9 in.) as the Ruddy Turnstone. In spring and summer the lower chest, belly, and feathers under the tail are white; the white tail has a broad dark gray subterminal band; the rest of the plumage is very dark gray with subjoined white spots forming streaks on the sides of the breast and on the nape and a line over the eye. There is a squarish patch of white between the eye and the bill, and there are white streaks and marks on the wings. The bill, legs, and feet are dark grayish. During the nonbreeding seasons the gray becomes lighter, and the white spots and patterns disappear. In flight the light and dark pattern is similar to that of the Ruddy Turnstone.

Voice: Apparently similar to the Ruddy Turnstone's but higher in pitch.

Range and status: Breeds on the coasts of w. and s. Alaska. Winters from se. Alaska south to s. Baja Calif. and Sonora. Casual inland; nonbreeders may linger in parts of winter range. Commoner on the Pacific Coast than the Ruddy Turnstone.

Habitat: Seacoasts, particularly surf-pounded stretches.

Seasonal movements: Generally an early migrant both spring and fall, but nonbreeding lingerers make accurate construction of schedule impossible.

Biology: Very much like that of Ruddy Turnstone. Nest sometimes lined with a few blades of grass.

Suggested reading: H. M. Hall, *A Gathering of Shore Birds,* Devin-Adair, N.Y., 1960, pp. 79–81.

WOODCOCK, SNIPE, AND SANDPIPERS (SCOLOPACIDAE)

These small- to medium-sized (5–26 in.) wading birds have long legs, short to long necks, and long, rather slender bills (at least as long as head, some several times as long). Some ornithologists consider that the Surfbird and turnstones belong to this family. Without these, there are about 77 species distributed throughout the world; 44 have been recorded in America. The wings are long and rounded or pointed; the tail is short to medium. Flight is strong and usually rapid, and all species are able to swim. Many species indulge in spectacular courtship flights and displays, accompanied by "songs" produced by voice or special sound-making feathers. Most species are gregarious, except in the mating season. With few exceptions, the sexes are alike. Nests are generally on the ground, though a few species build in old or deserted nests of tree-nesting birds. The commonly 2–4 eggs are light brownish or greenish and heavily spotted. Incubation is usually performed by both parents, but sometimes by male or female alone. Young leave the nest shortly after hatching, while still in the downy stage; they are cared for, in most species, by both parents. Food is largely animal matter, very seldom vegetable.

AMERICAN WOODCOCK (*Philohela minor*)

Appearance: Somewhat smaller (10–12 in.) than a Robin, but much chunkier, with a very short neck and a straight bill almost twice as long as its head. Rufous below and a variegated pattern of browns, black, and grays above; the forehead is grayish, and the crown has 3 broad blackish bands separated from each other and the forehead by narrow rufous bands. The bill, legs, and feet are dark flesh-colored. The tail is very short. Depending on excellent protective coloration, the bird remains quietly among the dead leaves (the bill resembling a dead weed or stem) until almost trod upon; it then vaults into the air on wings that whistle at every beat. The outer wing feathers are modified and stiffened so that they produce a whistling sound, especially when the bird is startled into vigorous flight.

Voice: Rather silent except during the remarkable courtship flights that occur in the early evening dusk, again in early morning, and sometimes throughout moonlit nights. The male spirals upward and then down on twittering wings; at the peak of the flight and during the descent, it makes a bubbling, vocal whistle. While on the ground between these aerial performances, it emits a nasal *peent* much like the call of the Nighthawk.

Range and status: Breeds from s. Man., w. and c. Ont., s. Que., P.E.I., c. N.S., and s. Nfld. south to La., Miss., Ala., and c. Fla. Winters from e. Okla., s. Mo., sw. Tenn., n. Miss., n. Ala., w. S.C., w.-c. N.C., and w. and se. Va. south to e. Tex., the Gulf Coast, and s. Fla. Has straggled to Colo., Mont., and Bermuda. Still common; clearing of lands actually increased available habitat.

Habitat: Wet woodlands, alder thickets, particularly with nearby clearings; very rare in old, mature forest lands.

When the American Woodcock flies, its outer wing feathers produce a distinct whistling sound.

Seasonal movements: Moves southward as forced by freezing ground and returns as earth thaws in spring. Migration occurs at night, apparently never in large flocks.

Biology: Nest: Slight hollow in ground, thinly lined with leaves; most often at edge of covering second-growth woodland or in thickets, sometimes in open at edge of field. Eggs: 3–5, most often 4; buff, with a scattering of reddish brown specks. Incubation: 20–21 days, by female; male assists in raising young. Age at 1st flight: 2 weeks; it has been reported that the adults will carry the young in flight, supported between their legs, but this is only accidental. Food: Largely earthworms, but also insect larvae; occasionally seeds and berries. The bird obtains animal food by probing soft soil with its long, sensitive mobile-tipped bill.

Suggested reading: O. S. Pettingill, Jr., *The American Woodcock, Philohela minor*, Mem. Bost. Soc. Nat. Hist., no. 9, pp. 169–391, 1936. W. G. Sheldon, *The Book of the American Woodcock*, Univ. of Mass. Press, Amherst, 1967.

EUROPEAN WOODCOCK (*Scolopax rusticola*)

Larger (ca. 13½ in.) than the American Woodcock, but similar in appearance; the underparts are buffier and barred with blackish, and the wing is somewhat more pointed. The outer flight feathers are not specialized and thus do not make the whistle produced by the American Woodcock in its display flight. When this species is startled into flight, the noise it makes with its wings sounds like stiff paper being torn. Breeds in the mountains and n. parts of Eurasia and in the Azores, Madeira, and Canary Is. Winters to n. Africa, s. Asia, and the Philippines. Straggles to Greenland, Iceland, the Faeroes, and Spitsbergen; it has reached Nfld., Que., N.J., Pa., Ohio, Va., and Ala.

COMMON SNIPE (*Capella gallinago*)

Appearance: About the size (10½–11½ in.) of the American Woodcock, but less stocky, with a somewhat longer bill (more than twice as long as head), and with a medium-long tail. The lower chest, belly, and undertail feathers are white; the upper chest and neck are buffy streaked with dark brown. The pale buff head has a streak of dark brown running from the bill to the nape, a thinner streak of brown through the eye, and lighter streaking on the cheek. The back and wings are blackish and dark brown with buffy and whitish streaking; the tail is buffy with dark brown barring and a narrow terminal band of white. The legs, feet, and blackish-tipped bill are greenish gray.

Voice: When the bird is startled into flight, a rather nasal *'scape;* around nest, a loud whistled *wit-wit-wit,* repeated often. While flying back and forth overhead

The Common Snipe probes in mud and shallow water for insects, worms, and other food.

during the breeding season, the bird (possibly both sexes) produces a peculiar, hollow-sounding, undulating whistled *who-who-who-who* for minutes on end; this is done mechanically with the outer tail feathers.

Range and status: Breeds from just south of the tundra in N. America and Eurasia, including Iceland and Great Britain, to Calif., Ariz., Colo., Nebr., Ill., Ohio, Pa., N.J., s. Europe, the Himalayas, se. Siberia, and the Kurile Is. Winters from s. parts of breeding range to Colombia, Venezuela, s. Brazil, nw. and s.-c. Africa, s. India, Ceylon, c. Indonesia, the Philippines, and Japan. No longer abundant, but still common locally.

Habitat: Freshwater marshes, bogs, wet meadows, streamsides, etc.

Seasonal movements: Moves northward as soon as frost leaves the ground; is forced south in late fall by advancing frost line. Migration is at night, apparently in small flocks that scatter during the day to feed.

Biology: Nest: A hollow in a dry clump of grass in or at the edge of a bog or marsh, lined with dead grass and leaves. Eggs: 3–6, usually 4; yellowish or greenish brown; sometimes rather dark and boldly spotted and blotched about larger end with dark browns and black. Incubation: 19½–20 days, by both parents. Age at 1st flight not known, but probably quite early. Food: Insects, largely aquatic forms and their larvae; crustaceans, worms, snails, and a very few seeds of marsh plants.

Suggested reading: D. A. Bannerman, *Birds of the British Isles*, Oliver and Boyd, Edinburgh, 1961, vol. 9, pp. 127–146.

EUROPEAN JACKSNIPE (*Lymnocryptes minimus*)

A smaller (ca. 7½ in.) version of the Common Snipe, but with a wedge-shaped tail that lacks any white. It breeds in n. Europe and c. Siberia (south of the tundra) and winters from c. Europe, the Near East, and India south to c. Africa, Ceylon, and Formosa. It has straggled to Alaska, Calif., and Lab.

LONG-BILLED CURLEW (*Numenius americanus*)

Appearance: Largest (20–26 in.) member of the family, with a very long, decurved bill (more than 3 times as long as the head); buff-colored, unmarked below, and only slightly darker and streaked and mottled with dark brown above. It has a thin dark streak through the eye and a broader streak running above the eye from the bill to the back. The legs and feet are grayish; the bill is brownish, with dull flesh color at the base of the lower mandible. In winter the adults are somewhat more pinkish below.

Voice: Rather noisy, making a great variety of loud, clear whistles, trills, and guttural calls. A loud, rattling *que-he-he-he-he-he*, a guttural *coy-coy-coy*, and a clear, loud, drawn-out *curl-e-e-e-u-u-u* rising and then falling in pitch and volume. This last is probably responsible for the name "curlew."

Range and status: Breeds from sw. and s.-c. Canada south to Utah, N.Mex., and Tex.; formerly east to Wis. and Ill. Winters from Calif., w. Nev., Ariz., Tex., and La. south to Baja Calif. and Guatemala, and from S.C. to Fla. Casual on the Atlantic Coast and in the W. Indies, much rarer farther north. Once abundant on the prairies, now rare.

Habitat: High, dry prairies in summer; at other seasons, farmlands, saltwater marshes, beaches, and tidal flats.

Seasonal movements: Moves south mid-July–Sept. and returns Mar.–Apr., flying in long V-shaped flocks.

Biology: Nest: A grass- and weed-lined depression in the open prairie or a damp, green hollow in the range; sometimes in loose colonies. Eggs: 3–5, most often 4 (higher numbers the product of more than 1 hen); dark greenish buff, more or less evenly spotted with browns and greenish grays. Incubation period not known; possibly about 30 days. Age at 1st flight unknown. Food: Mainly insects on the prairies; also worms, toads, crustaceans, small mollusks, and an occasional berry.

Suggested reading: J. W. Sugden, "Range Restriction of the Long-billed Curlew," *Condor*, vol. 35, pp. 3–9, 1932.

EURASIAN CURLEW (*Numenius arquata*)

Very similar in size (19–25 in.) and appearance to the Long-billed Curlew, but belly and undertail feathers are whitish, and entire undersides are streaked and spotted with brown. Breeds from Great Britain and c. and n. Europe east to c. China. Winters south to s. Africa, Madagascar, the Seychelles Is., India, Ceylon, Indonesia, and the Philippines. Has straggled to Greenland, Iceland, and N.Y.

WHIMBREL (Hudsonian Curlew) (*Numenius phaeopus*)

Appearance: Smaller (15–19 in.) than the Long-billed Curlew, but with a somewhat proportionally shorter bill, and whitish instead of buffy below. The back, nape, and wings, and to some extent the sides of the chest and flank, are streaked and mottled with grayish brown. There is also a dark brown streak above the eye from the bill to the rear of the head as well as a thinner streak through the eye. In winter the Eurasian races of this species sport a white rump patch.

Voice: In migration and flight a 4-note call, *kwip-pip-pip-pip*, sometimes prolonged by additional *pip*'s given more rapidly and developing into a bubbling trill.

The Long-billed Curlew's nest is a shallow grass-lined depression on the prairie.

During migrations, the Whimbrel is a fairly common sight along both coasts.

On breeding grounds it is noisy and gives, among other calls, a *curlew* cry.

Range and status: Breeds in Iceland, the Faeroes, n. Scandinavia, n. Russia, nw. Siberia, inland in ne. Siberia, sw. Alaska; coastally from Seward Peninsula, Alaska, to nw. Mack., and along the w. coast of Hudson Bay; possibly elsewhere in Mack., Franklin Territory, and Spitsbergen, and locally in Scotland. Winters from British Isles, Mediterranean region, s. Asia, the Philippines, and the coasts of s. U.S. south to s. Africa, Madagascar, Mascarene Is., Ceylon, Australia, Tasmania, New Zealand, Fiji, the Caroline Is., the Galápagos Is., s. Chile, and Brazil. Relatively common and increasing.

Habitat: Grasslands, tidal flats, grassy marshes, shorelands, and tundra.

Seasonal movements: Spring migration Mar.–May; fall migration July–mid-Oct.; very rare in the interior of the U.S. Birds breeding in Alaska move through the Bering Sea and down the Pacific Coast, while birds breeding in the Hudson Bay region move eastward, then down the Atlantic Coast.

Biology: Nest: A slight hollow in a clump of moss or grass, often with water around the clump. Eggs: 3–5, commonly 4; bluish green, brownish green, or grayish green, dotted and splotched, most thickly about the larger end, with browns and lavender. Incubation: 27–28 days, by both sexes. Age at 1st flight unknown. Food: Insects, crustaceans, mollusks, worms, spiders, and a few berries.

Suggested reading: P. A. Taverner, "The Distribution and Migration of the Hudsonian Curlew," *Wils. Bull.*, vol. 54, pp. 3–11, 1912.

BRISTLE-THIGHED CURLEW (*Numenius tahitiensis*)

Appearance: About the same size (17 in.) as the Whimbrel, but more pinkish about the neck and breast; its tail is rufous with brown barring, and it has a light rufous rump patch.

Voice: A slow 3-part *whee-u-wheet* call somewhat like that of the Black-bellied Plover, and a *weet-feeo* "wolf whistle."

Range and status: Breeds in w. Alaska, certainly near the mouth of the Yukon River and probably elsewhere; winters in Oceania from the Marshall Is. and Hawaii south to Fiji, Samoa, and the Marquesas and Tuamotu Is. Has straggled to the Marianas, the Caroline Is., and Japan. A rare bird.

Habitat: Open areas and tundra of the Arctic and shores of oceanic islands; breeds in uplands.

Seasonal movements: Flies directly over the ocean between the small islands and its breeding grounds, arriving in Alaska as early as mid-May and departing before the end of Aug.

Biology: Nest: Found for 1st time in 1948; a slight

Eskimo Curlew

Biology: Nest: A mere scrape in mosses of the tundra. Eggs: 3–4, most often 4; light brownish green, marked with irregular blotches of bright, dark browns. Incubation period not known. Age at 1st flight unknown. Food: Berries and insects.

Suggested reading: V. L. Emanuel, "Texans Rediscover the Nearly Extinct Eskimo Curlew," *Aud. Mag.*, vol. 64, pp. 163–165, 1962. D. A. Bannerman, *Birds of the British Isles*, Oliver and Boyd, Edinburgh, 1961, vol. 9, pp. 81–88.

UPLAND PLOVER (*Bartramia longicauda*)

Appearance: Medium-sized (11–12½ in.) sandpiperlike bird called a plover; similar to the Eskimo Curlew, but its bill is not decurved and is only about as long as the head. Tail is light brown, barred with blackish; bill, legs, and feet are yellowish brown.

The Upland Plover, once abundant on prairies and grasslands, is becoming rather rare.

depression in the tundra, lined with mosses. Eggs: 4; dark buff, blotched with grayish browns. Incubation period not known. Age at 1st flight unknown. Food: Definitely known to eat berries; probably also eats insects, mollusks, crustaceans, etc.

Suggested reading: A. A. Allen, "The Curlew's Secret," *Nat. Geog. Mag.*, vol. 94, pp. 751–770, 1948.

ESKIMO CURLEW (*Numenius borealis*)

Appearance: Smaller (12–14 in.) than, but very similar to, the Whimbrel; bill proportionately shorter and less decurved, underparts lighter, and legs a dark greenish gray.

Voice: Pleasant, soft, almost trilling whistles in flight; also a light, squeaky note and faint whistles.

Range and status: Formerly bred on the tundra of n. Mack.; probably east along the coast of Alaska to Norton Sound. Wintered from s. Brazil to Chile, s. Argentina, and Uruguay. Occasional sightings reported (1 reported at Galveston, Tex., in 1959 and another in 1960), but at the brink of extinction; once abundant. Subjected to extremely heavy hunting pressure as it moved through c. N. America, its numbers dropped rapidly. More were killed than could be eaten.

Habitat: Tundra, prairies, and coastal plains.

Seasonal movements: Moved north through the Great Plains during spring in large numbers; in fall moved eastward, then down the coast of New England, then apparently directly to S. America, accounting for stragglers recorded in Iceland and Great Britain in autumn.

In summer, the Spotted Sandpiper is common near almost any body of fresh water.

Voice: A melancholy, pleasantly haunting, whistled *ip-ip-ip-ip*, frequently stirring the night air; also an eerie, hollow, long, drawn-out whistle that starts on a rattling call, then rises and falls: *t-t-t-tre-ee-eeeee, treelooooooo.*

Range and status: Breeds from s. Alaska, sw. Yuk., sw. Mack., c. Sask., s. Man., Mich., s. Ont., s. Que., and c. Maine south to ne. Ore., Idaho, s. Mont., se. Wyo., c. Colo., n.-c. Tex., c. Mo., c. Tenn., n. and e. W.Va., c. Va., and Md.; formerly farther south. Winters from s. Brazil to s.-c. Argentina; casually to Chile. Formerly abundant; now rather rare.

Habitat: Meadows, fields, prairies.

Seasonal movements: Starts its long southward journey before mid-July, generally flying in evening and into night, and arrives on the pampas in Sept. as the last ones are leaving the breeding areas. Leaves pampas in Feb. and arrives in s. U.S. in Mar.

Biology: Nest: Slight hollow in grassland, often in tufts of grass, sparsely lined with dead grasses. Eggs: 3–5, usually 4; light pinkish brown, buffy, or greenish white, evenly spotted with dark browns, reddish browns, and grays. Incubation: 21–24 days; 1 report of 26 days. Age at 1st flight: About 30–31 days. Food: 97% animal

matter, chiefly insects injurious to man's interests; some seeds.

Suggested reading: A. C. Bent, *Life Histories of North American Shore Birds,* part 2, Dover, N.Y. (reprint of U.S. Nat. Mus. Bull. 146, 1929), 1962, pp. 55–68. W. C. Grimm, "Spirit Bird of the Grasslands," *Aud. Mag.,* vol. 55, pp. 152–155, 1953.

SPOTTED SANDPIPER (*Actitis macularia*)

Appearance: Small (7–8 in.); dark grayish brown above and white below. Throat, breast, and belly marked with roundish dark brown and blackish spots during the breeding season; the white outer feathers of the tail are barred with light or medium brown. The bill, about the length of the head, is blackish above and yellowish below; the legs and feet are pale grayish flesh color or very pale grayish green. In the nonbreeding plumage a triangular patch of grayish brown at the side of the breast joins the similar color of the back; the bird is then immaculate white below. At every pause, as it paces the shores, it teeters nervously on its legs.

Voice: Usually a simple, clear-whistled *peet* or *pee-weet;* when near nest or greatly alarmed, it adds a long series of *weet* notes that may diminish in pitch and volume at the end.

Range and status: Breeds from n. continental N. America south to mountains of s. Calif., s. Nev., c. Ariz., n. N.Mex., c. Tex., c. Miss., n. Ala., w. N.C., Va., and e. Md. Winters from sw. B.C., sw. Ariz., s. N.Mex., the Gulf Coast, and coastal N.C. south through C. America and the W. Indies to n. Chile, c. Bolivia, and s. Brazil; rarely south to Argentina. Nonbreeders may remain in wintering areas during our summer. Has straggled to Greenland and Europe. Probably the most common and best-known sandpiper in the U.S. and Canada, especially in the interior.

Habitat: Shores of almost any body of fresh water, sometimes salt water; in breeding season particularly, pebbly beaches preferred. Frequents marine coasts in migration and winter more often than in summer.

Seasonal movements: Rather inconspicuous during migration, as it does not travel in flocks and often flies at night. Moves north late Mar.–mid-May and returns July–Oct.; some may not reach S. America until Nov.

Biology: Swims and dives well; has even been reported walking on the beds of streams underwater like the dippers. Nest: Near, but not always next to, a body of water, usually at least partially concealed by grasses, shrubs, rocks, logs, or debris; a mere hollow lined with grasses or weed stalks. Eggs: 3–5, commonly 4; brownish, pinkish, or greenish buff, evenly spotted with browns; only rarely are these small spots wreathed about the larger end of the egg. Incubation: 20–24 days (apparently varies through wide geographic range), almost entirely by male, as is subsequent care of young. Age at 1st flight: 15–16 days; downy young are able to swim and dive. Food: Apparently entirely animal matter, mainly aquatic insects, also small crustaceans and small fish.

Suggested reading: H. Mousley, "Nesting Habits of the Spotted Sandpiper," *Auk*, vol. 54, pp. 445–451, 1937.

SOLITARY SANDPIPER (*Tringa solitaria*)

Appearance: Somewhat larger (7½–9 in.) than the Spotted Sandpiper; upperparts much darker, almost blackish (lighter on neck and head), and spangled with whitish. It is white below, with brown mottlings along the flank, upper breast, and cheeks; it has white around the eye. The central feathers of the tail are blackish; the outer feathers are white, distinctly barred with blackish. The bill is black, and the legs and feet are dark grayish green. In winter the plumage is grayer with less distinct light spots on the back, and the mottlings on the sides and breast are grayish streaks or patches. It does not teeter so much as the Spotted. In flight its wings are dark, lacking the white streak of the Spotted's wing.

Voice: Like that of the Spotted, but shriller.

Range and status: Breeding range difficult to define, as nests are not easily located, and transients and non-breeders may linger anywhere south of the true limits. Probably breeds from c. Alaska, n. Mack., n. Man., n. Ont., c. Que., and c. Lab. south to e.-c. B.C., s. Alta., c. Sask., s. Man., c. Ont., s.-c. Que., and s.-c. Lab.; possibly south to n. U.S. Winters from Baja Calif., s. and e. Mexico, the Gulf Coast, Fla., and se. Ga. through C. America and the W. Indies (rarely) to s.-c. Argentina. Has straggled to Greenland, Iceland, Bermuda, and Great Britain. Rather rare.

Habitat: Along almost any type of freshwater habitat in spruce-fir forest region; very rarely near marine waters, even in winter or during migration.

Seasonal movements: Moves south July–Oct. and returns late Mar.–mid-June; almost always singly or in small flocks.

Biology: Nest and eggs not reliably recorded until 1903. Nest: In old or deserted nests of tree nesters such as robins, blackbirds, etc., near a stream or body of fresh water; little, if any, lining added by sandpiper. Eggs: 4–5, most often 4; greenish or buffy, blotched with browns and grays. Incubation period unknown. Age at 1st flight unknown. Food: Mostly aquatic insects; probably also small crustaceans.

Suggested reading: J. F. Street, "On the Nesting

Unlike its ground-nesting relatives, the Solitary Sandpiper uses deserted nests in trees.

Grounds of the Solitary Sandpiper and the Lesser Yellowlegs," *Auk,* vol. 40, pp. 577–583, 1923.

WOOD SANDPIPER (*Tringa glareola*)

Small (ca. 8 in.) and very similar to the Solitary Sandpiper, but dark markings on breast are barred rather than mottled or streaked. Breeds south of the tundra in the n. half of Eurasia and winters from s. Europe and s. Asia to s. Africa, Ceylon, Indonesia, and Australia; has straggled to Hawaii and Alaska.

WANDERING TATTLER (*Heteroscelus incanum*)

Appearance: Medium-sized (10½–11¼ in.); dark gray above and whitish below, thickly barred and streaked with thin dark gray lines. The blackish bill is slightly longer than the head; the legs and feet are light grayish yellow. The nonbreeding plumage is similar, but the throat, lower breast, belly, and undertail feathers are white, and the rest of the underparts are medium gray. In both plumages there is a whitish streak above the eye.

Voice: A call similar to that of the Spotted Sandpiper's *pee-weet-weet* notes and a less staccato *wee-wee-wee-wee* whistle.

Wandering Tattler

Range and status: Breeds above timberline in mountains of Alaska, nw. B.C., and possibly Yuk. Winters along coasts and on islands from s. Calif. to the Galápagos Is., Colombia, and Ecuador and from the Philippines, the Marianas, and Hawaii through islands of Oceania to Fiji, Samoa, the Society Is., and the Tuamotu Is.; sometimes farther north in winter to w. Wash. Has straggled inland in B.C. and Ore. and to Japan, Formosa, New Guinea, Australia, and New Zealand. Rather rare.

Habitat: Breeds along mountain streams; at other times found along rocky coasts, tidal flats, and stony beaches.

Seasonal movements: Moves north Mar.–May and south July–Oct. Nonbreeders that remain behind in spring retain the winter plumage.

Biology: Nest: A hollow in dry part of gravel bar in mountain stream; sometimes twigs used in lining. Eggs: 4: greenish gray, spotted with browns (nest and eggs not found until 1912!). Incubation period unknown. Age at 1st flight unknown. Food: Small marine animals (crustaceans, mollusks, worms, etc.) and probably insects on breeding grounds.

Suggested reading: J. Dixon, "Nesting of the Wandering Tattler," *Condor,* vol. 35, pp. 173–179, 1933.

POLYNESIAN TATTLER (*Heteroscelus brevipes*)

Very similar in size (ca. 11 in.) and appearance to the Wandering Tattler; possibly only a subspecies of that bird. Feathers of upper tail are barred with white; in the breeding plumage the belly and undertail feathers are plain white. Probably breeds in mountains of e. Siberia and winters from Malaya and the Philippines to Indonesia and Australia; has straggled to the Pribilof Is. and St. Lawrence I., Alaska.

WILLET (*Catoptrophorus semipalmatus*)

Appearance: Fairly large (14–17 in.), with a sturdy, straight blackish bill about 1½ times as long as the head; the upperparts are medium brownish gray; whitish with mottlings of brownish gray on the flanks, neck, and upper chest; and a whitish stripe through the eye. The outer flight feathers of the wing are black, with a broad white streak across the centers; the tail is the same color as the back, but the feathers just above and below it are white. The legs and feet are bluish or greenish gray. In spring the brownish gray areas are spotted and streaked with blackish and dark browns.

Voice: Noisy on the breeding grounds; most commonly a *wek-wek-wek* or *kerwek-kerwek-kerwek* and a pleasant *pill-o-will-o-willet;* in flight a loud, ringing *kie-yuk,* apparently rather variable.

Range and status: Breeds from e. Ore., Idaho, c. Alta., c. Sask., and s. Man. south to ne. Calif., Nev., n. Utah, n. Colo., and e. S.Dak.; also in places along the

As it flies, a Willet displays its characteristic black-and-white wing pattern.

coasts in N.S. and from N.J. along the Atlantic and Gulf Coasts to Fla. and Tex., and in the Bahamas and Greater Antilles. Winters along coasts from n. Calif., the Gulf Coast, and the Bahamas south to nw. Peru (rare along coast of C. America), Bolivia (rare), and the coasts of n. S. America east to the mouths of the Amazon in Brazil. Numbers much reduced in the past by heavy hunting; now recovering, so that it is locally abundant although not yet reestablished in all of former range.

Habitat: Swales, wet prairies, freshwater marshes; in winter mainly, tidal flats, marine marshes, and beaches.

Seasonal movements: Those that breed inland east of the Rockies move eastward and down the Atlantic Coast of the U.S., down the Mississippi Valley, and southwest to coast of Calif. Birds of N.S. apparently fly over ocean to the W. Indies and n. S. America; on the return flights there is much less movement along the Atlantic Coast. Spring migration Mar.–May; fall migration late July–Oct.

Biology: Nest: A depression in grassy land, upper edges of beaches, or drier, grassy areas near marshes; lined with grasses, sedges, or small sticks. Eggs: Usually 4; greenish buff or yellowish gray, irregularly spotted and blotched with browns and grays. Incubation period unknown. Age at 1st flight unknown. Food: Insects and small marine animals, such as worms, mollusks, crustaceans, and fish, plus some vegetable matter, including roots, leaves, and seeds.

Suggested reading: W. Vogt, "Preliminary Notes on the Behavior and Ecology of the Eastern Willet," *Proc. Linn. Soc. N.Y.,* no. 49, pp. 8–42, 1938.

GREATER YELLOWLEGS (*Totanus melanoleucus*)

Appearance: Smaller (12½–15 in.) than the Willet, which it resembles somewhat, except that the legs and feet are bright yellow, the bill is slenderer, and the upperparts are browner; its tail is lightly barred, and it has no white on the wing. Its bill is proportionally longer and stockier than that of the very similar Lesser Yellowlegs.

Voice: Famed "tattlers," giving the alarm to all within hearing at any invasion of their neighborhood; mainly in a series of 2–5 clarion whistles, *whew-whew-whew,* often given in flight. Also a pleasing liquid "yodeling" *touwhee-touwhee-touwhee* call from grounded flocks.

Range and status: Breeds from c. Alaska, c. B.C., and c. Alta. east to Lab., se. Que., and Nfld.; non-breeders may remain in wintering and migrating areas

A Greater Yellowlegs perches in a treetop near its nest in a northern spruce bog.

during our summer. Winters along coasts from sw. B.C. and S.C. through the W. Indies and Latin America to Tierra del Fuego and inland from Nev., c. Ariz., c. N.Mex., c. Tex., and the Gulf Coast through the lowlands. Fairly common.

Habitat: Breeds in spruce bogs and forested muskeg regions; at other times, marshes, mudflats, streams, ponds, and beaches.

Seasonal movements: Migration periods, Mar.–May and July–Nov.

Biology: Nest: A hollow in the mosses of muskeg or spruce bogs. Eggs: 3–5, usually 4; buffy, irregularly spotted and blotched, mainly about larger end, with dark browns and grays. Incubation: 23 days. Age at 1st flight unknown. Food: Small fish, insects (mainly aquatic), worms, small mollusks, and crustaceans.

Suggested reading: H. M. Hall, *A Gathering of Shore Birds*, Devin-Adair, N.Y., 1960, pp. 126–130.

LESSER YELLOWLEGS (*Totanus flavipes*)

Appearance: Smaller (9½–11 in.), but otherwise almost identical to the Greater Yellowlegs; its bill is much more slender and straighter.

Voice: This species characteristically gives a 1- or 2-note *yew* or *yew-yew* call, which further differs from the Greater's call in being weaker. Also a low-pitched yodel *toodle-ooo-ooo*, and other notes.

Range and status: Breeds from n.-c. Alaska, n. Yuk., nw. Mack., s. Keewatin, n. Man., n. Ont., and nw. Que. south to c. B.C., c. Alta., c. Sask., s. Man., n.-c. Ont., and w.-c. Que. Winters along coastal lowlands from Mexico, the Gulf Coast, and S.C. south through C. America and the W. Indies to Chile and Argentina; rare on the Pacific Coast of Mexico and on the C. American coasts. Casually farther north in winter; nonbreeders may linger in wintering areas. Common.

Habitat: In summer, more open woods in areas south of tundra; tidal flats, beaches, edges of streams, ponds, lakes, and marshes.

Seasonal movements: Main spring flight (Mar.–mid-May) through the W. Indies and up the Mississippi Valley; much more common along Atlantic Coast in fall (July–Oct.).

Biology: Nest: A small depression in the ground, lined with a few dried leaves or grasses. Eggs: 3–5, usually 4; buffy or light brownish green, spotted, blotched, and splashed with dark browns, grays, and blackish, with marking sometimes heaviest at large end of egg. Incubation: 22–23 days. Age at 1st flight: Early, possibly 2–3 weeks. Food: Insects, small crustaceans, small fish, and worms.

Suggested reading: J. F. Street, "On the Nesting Grounds of the Solitary Sandpiper and the Lesser Yellowlegs," *Auk*, vol. 40, pp. 577–583, 1923.

REDSHANK (*Totanus totanus*)

About the same size (11 in.) and appearance as our Lesser Yellowlegs, but with red legs and feet and a blackish-tipped reddish bill. Found from Iceland, the British Isles, n. Europe, and c. Siberia south to s. Africa, s. India, Ceylon, n. Indonesia, the Philippines, and Japan. Has straggled to Greenland.

KNOT (*Calidris canutus*)

Appearance: About the same size (10–11 in.) as the Lesser Yellowlegs, but with shorter legs and a much stockier body. In the breeding season, the head, neck, back, and underparts (except for the undertail feathers) are robin's-breast red; the crown, nape, and back are streaked and spotted with blackish, and there are a few blackish marks on the flank. The larger flight feathers of the wing are blackish, and the rest of wing is gray, as is the tail; just above the tail is a whitish patch plainly marked with short dark bars. The black bill is about as long as the head; the feet and legs are green. In fall and winter the birds lose all the reddish color, becoming gray above and whitish below; the legs and feet are then a much duller grayish green.

Voice: In the breeding areas, on the wing, a loud, shrill *wah-quoi* and a similarly toned *iwee-a-whit*, as well as a long, drawn-out, flutelike *coo-a-hee*. In migration and winter it repeats the *wah-quoi* notes, but then they are low and much subdued, though still far-carrying; also a variety of clucklike notes, usually uttered singly, sometimes transliterated as *knut*.

Range and status: Breeds in scattered localities among the arctic islands from Ellesmere I. and n. Greenland south to n. Alaska, Victoria I., Melville Peninsula, Southampton I., e.-c. and w.-c. Greenland, and in Spitsbergen Is., Taimyr Peninsula of Siberia, the New Siberian Is., and Wrangel I. Winters along coasts from s. Calif., Mass., British Isles, s. Scandinavia, and s. Asia south to s. S. America, w.-c. and e.-c. Africa, Australia, and New Zealand. Concentration in large flocks along seashores in winter and during migration gives a false impression of abundance; total population not so large as those of seemingly scarcer birds such as the Purple Sandpiper.

Habitat: Intertidal zones, especially flatter type, and shorelines; for nesting: flat, high, dry tundra, rather stony, with sparse vegetation, not far from shores or low swampy spots.

Seasonal movements: Main migration spring and fall along Atlantic Coast in America and along Pacific Coast of Asia; largest concentration of wintering birds in North Sea area. Fall movement July–Oct. and in spring Apr.–June.

Biology: Nest: Among pebbles on rocky ground,

usually where some lichens grow. Eggs: 2–5, usually 4; pale or medium greenish brown, with largest concentration of brown and gray spots and scrawls at larger end. Incubation: 21–22 days. Age at 1st flight: About 18 days. Food: Insects, small mollusks and crustaceans, worms, and, in early summer, berries, buds, and other plant material.

Suggested reading: D. A. Bannerman, *Birds of the British Isles*, Oliver and Boyd, Edinburgh, 1961, vol. 9, pp. 223–231.

GREAT KNOT (*Calidris tenuirostris*)

Larger (11½ in.) than the Knot, but rather similar to it. Lacks the rufous coloring and has a black white-spotted breast band on the whitish undersides. Breeds in the mountains of ne. Siberia; winters from the coasts of s. Asia and the Philippines south to Indonesia and in Australia. Has straggled once to nw. Alaska.

PURPLE SANDPIPER (*Erolia maritima*)

Appearance: Rather small (8–9½ in.) sandpiper; dark above, somewhat lighter below. In spring the buffy breast is spotted with dark brown, as is the whitish head and neck; the whitish flanks are streaked with blackish, and the rest of the undersides is white. The feathers of the back are dark brown, edged with light buff; those at the shoulders are black, edged with whitish, resulting in a scaly appearance; the central feathers of the tail are blackish, the outer ones are brownish gray. The black bill, yellowish at the base, is about as long as the head;

the legs and feet are yellowish. In fall the breast is brownish gray with darker mottling; the head and back are a more even brownish gray. At this time also it has a white throat, a white eye-ring, and a small spot of white before the eye.

Voice: A rather low *twit* or *tweet-whit;* a flock makes a swallowlike twittering.

Range and status: Breeds on arctic coasts and islands from n. Ellesmere I., nw. and e.-c. Greenland, Spitsbergen, Franz Josef Land, Severnaya Zemlya, and New Siberian Is. south to Banks I., Victoria I., Southampton I., islands along e. coast of Hudson Bay, Baffin I., s. Greenland, Iceland, n. Scandinavia, Novaya Zemlya, and Taimyr Peninsula. Winters from P.E.I., N.S., Nfld., sw. Greenland, and Iceland south to Md., Great Britain, shores of the North and Baltic Seas, rarely to the Mediterranean. Has straggled to Man., Wis., Ill., Ind., Ohio, s. Ont., w. N.Y., coastally to Fla., and to the Azores. Rather rare.

Habitat: Tundra, rocky coasts, barren mountaintops, intertidal zones.

Seasonal movements: Early spring and late fall migrant; at both seasons a gradual movement Mar.–May and Sept.–Dec.

Biology: Gregarious but not colonial. Nest: A slight hollow above high tide or near mountaintop, lined with grasses or mosses and lichens. Eggs: 3–4, usually 4; pale greenish gray to pale yellowish brown, spotted, streaked, and blotched with purples and dark browns. Incubation: 21–22 days, reportedly by males alone, as is care of the young. Age at 1st flight: About 3 weeks. Food: Insects, various small marine animals, and some vegetable matter, such as seeds, berries, algae, etc.

Suggested reading: D. A. Bannerman, *Birds of the British Isles,* Oliver and Boyd, Edinburgh, 1961, vol. 9, pp. 326–339.

ROCK SANDPIPER (*Erolia ptilocnemis*)

Appearance: So similar in size (8–9 in.), appearance, and habits to the Purple Sandpiper that many ornithologists consider it only a variation of that species. In the nonbreeding plumage the two species can hardly be separated; in spring the adults have a large gray patch in the center of the breast and are more reddish above than the Purple Sandpiper.

Voice: A loud, clear note, much reiterated, like the call of a flicker.

Range and status: Breeds from ne. Siberia, islands in the Bering Sea, and w.-c. Alaska south to Sakhalin I., Kurile Is., the Aleutians, w. Alaska Peninsula, and the Shumagin Is.; winters from the Komandorskie Is., the Aleutians, and s. coastal Alaska south to the Kuriles and the coast of n. Calif. Rather rare, but tameness allows close approaches.

Habitat: Tundra and rocky coasts.

Seasonal movements: Retreats before heavy ice and readvances with thaw.

Biology: Nest: A depression in the mosses and lichens above the beaches or on alpine hills or mountaintops. Eggs: 4; light greenish gray to dark greenish brown, with dark brown or purplish roundish spots or streaks. Incubation: About 20 days, by both sexes. Age at 1st flight unknown. Food: Small mollusks, insects, crustaceans, worms; some algae, seeds, and berries are also consumed.

Suggested reading: H. M. Hall, *A Gathering of Shore Birds,* Devin-Adair, N.Y., 1960, pp. 140–143.

SHARP-TAILED SANDPIPER (*Erolia acuminata*)

Rather small (ca. 8½ in.). In migration, when seen most often in U.S., white below, with a pale buff band across the front of the neck and the breast; buff, streaked and spotted with blackish above; crown is streaked with reddish brown and dark brown. In breeding season buff is replaced by light reddish brown on back and chest. Breeds along arctic coast of ne. Siberia; winters from New Guinea, New Caledonia, and Tonga to Australia, Tasmania, and New Zealand; migrates along Pacific Coasts—in the e. part of its range from Alaska to Calif. Rare south of B.C. and casual in Hawaii; has straggled to n. India, Guatemala, and England. In U.S. prefers edges of grassy saltwater marshes.

PECTORAL SANDPIPER (*Erolia melanotos*)

Appearance: Similar in size (8–9½ in.) and general appearance to the Sharp-tailed Sandpiper. Light grayish buff, streaked and spotted with blackish above and on breast; undersides white; large flight feathers of wing blackish, rump and central tail feathers dark brown or black, outer tail feathers buffy. The neck is relatively long; the bill, which is about as long as the head, is blackish, and the legs and feet are dull greenish yellow. Grayer and less buffy in winter and fall. The male is larger than the female, not the reverse, as stated in some books.

Voice: The male has inflatable sacs at the throat and upper breast that are used in spring courtship to give a resonant quality to its whistles, like the noise made by blowing across the mouth of an empty bottle. When deflated, the sacs hang empty but noticeable in the pectoral region, hence the bird's name. A creaky, whiny *kerr* or *kerr-kerr.*

Range and status: Breeds on the arctic coasts and tundra of w. and n. Alaska, n. Yuk., nw. Mack., Victoria I., and Southampton I. south to e.-c. Mack., s. Keewatin, and w. and s. coast of Hudson Bay; possibly along Siberian coast from Taimyr eastward. Winters from Peru, s. Bolivia, n. Argentina, and Uruguay south to Chile and s. Argentina; casually in small numbers to Australia, New

The Pectoral Sandpiper summers on the tundra and winters in southern South America.

Voice: A weak, whispery whistled *jeet* or *tzeep*.

Range and status: Breeds from the Canadian Arctic Archipelago (Melville I. and n. Baffin I.) south to coast of n. Alaska, n. Yuk., n. Mack., n. and e. Keewatin, Southampton I., and sw. Baffin I.; possibly farther north. Winters from Paraguay and s. Brazil to Tierra del Fuego and the Falkland Is. Has straggled to Franz Josef Land, England, Switzerland, and the Azores. Rare in the U.S. compared with numbers on breeding and wintering grounds.

Habitat: Tundra, tidal flats, water edges, grasslands.

Seasonal movements: Spring migration starts in Mar., moving through the W. Indies and through the interior of N. America in May. In fall it is rare in the interior and south of New England; large flocks probably fly over the ocean to S. America; moves south July–Oct.

Biology: Nest: A slight hollow in grasses or mosses just above water, sparingly lined with grass. Eggs: 4; deep greenish brown, heavily blotched with dark browns about the larger end, sparsely spotted over rest of surface. Incubation period unknown; by female alone. Age at 1st flight unknown. Food: Insects; probably various small marine animals—not much known.

Suggested reading: D. A. Bannerman, *Birds of the British Isles,* Oliver and Boyd, Edinburgh, 1961, vol. 9, pp. 320–325.

Zealand, and Samoa, possibly elsewhere in Oceania; it may remain much farther north. Has straggled to Greenland, Iceland, Europe, and Hawaii. Fairly common.

Habitat: Tundra in summer; wet grasslands, saltwater marshes, edges of grassy ponds, pools, and shores.

Seasonal movements: Northward movement Feb.–May and return July–Oct., moving up N. America between the Rockies and Appalachians in spring and coast to coast in the fall, even out to sea, crossing Bermuda and the Lesser Antilles.

Biology: Nest: A depression in the tundra, lined sparsely with dry grasses. Eggs: 4; whitish to light yellowish buff, and deep greenish brown, spotted and blotched with browns and grays, usually more heavily at the larger end. Incubation: 21–23 days, by hen alone; she also does all the work of raising the young. Age at 1st flight: About 3 weeks. Food: Mostly insects; also some small crustaceans, worms, etc.; very rarely seeds.

Suggested reading: F. A. Pitelka, "Breeding Schedule and Territoriality in Pectoral Sandpipers of Northern Alaska," *Condor,* vol. 61, pp. 233–264, 1959.

WHITE-RUMPED SANDPIPER (*Erolia fuscicollis*)

Appearance: Much like a small (7–8 in.), short-necked Rock Sandpiper with a white rump. Those seen in most of the U.S. are in nonbreeding plumage, which is grayish above, including the crown and smaller feathers of the wing, with a light gray band across the breast; the larger feathers of the wing are blackish, as are the central feathers of the tail, the outer feathers of which are grayish. The bill, legs, and feet are blackish. In breeding plumage the back and crown are reddish brown, streaked and spotted with dark brown and black; the gray band of the chest is replaced with parallel rows of spots.

White-rumped Sandpiper

BAIRD'S SANDPIPER (*Erolia bairdii*)

Appearance: Small (7–7½ in.); similar to the White-rumped Sandpiper, but without the white rump. The band across the chest is buffy, very faintly streaked with darker brown; the upperparts are more brownish, with a scaled effect on the back. The bird is whiter below; the bill, legs, and feet are blackish. In winter it is more brownish above and less whitish below.

Voice: A *kreeep* call given in flight and a shrill, trilling whistle.

Range and status: Breeds coastally in ne. Siberia, Alaska (Cape Romanzov to Demarcation Point), Yuk., n. Mack., n. Keewatin, and the Arctic Is. from Victoria I., Melville I., Ellesmere I., and nw. Greenland south to King William I. and sw. Baffin I. Winters locally in the Andes Mountains from Ecuador to Chile and from sw. Bolivia to s. Argentina; very rarely north to El Salvador and Costa Rica. Migration mainly through the interior of the U.S. and Canada. Has straggled to the Galápagos Is., Falkland Is., England, and s. Africa. Fairly common.

Habitat: Tundra, grasslands, shores, and mountain-tops.

Seasonal movements: In fall, only a rare but regular migrant along the Atlantic and Pacific shores; through the interior in spring. Northward flights Mar.–May and return July–Oct.

Biology: Nest: A shallow hollow in the ground, well hidden in grasses, sparsely lined with leaves. Eggs: 3–4, usually 4; light pinkish brown to dark buff, streaked and spotted with browns and grays. Incubation period un-known. Age at 1st flight unknown. Food: Insects and small crustaceans.

Suggested reading: J. Dixon, "The Home Life of the Baird Sandpiper," *Condor*, vol. 19, pp. 77–84, 1917.

LEAST SANDPIPER (*Erolia minutilla*)

Appearance: Smallest (5–6½ in.) of our sandpipers; very much like Baird's Sandpiper, but the grayish chest band is more distinctly streaked, and feet and legs are yellowish or greenish. In the breeding season coloration is more brownish.

Voice: A reedy, almost double-noted *kree-eet*.

Range and status: Breeds along the coasts and on offshore islands of n. N. America south to se. Alaska, Anticosti and Magdalen Is. of Quebec, Sable I. off N.S., and Nfld. and in the interior to s. Yuk., e.-c. Mack., and s. Keewatin; possibly also on Victoria I. Nonbreeders found south to Calif., Utah, the Gulf Coast, and S.C. Winters from coastal Ore., s. Nev., c. Ariz., c. N.Mex., c. Tex., the Gulf Coast, and N.C. south through the rest of N. America and the W. Indies to the Galápagos Is., Peru, and c. Brazil. Has straggled to Europe. Common.

Habitat: Intertidal zones, beaches, wet grasslands, marshes, puddles, and tundra.

Seasonal movements: In spring mid-Apr.–early June, and in fall July–Nov., along both coasts and through intermontane interior.

Biology: Nest: A simple depression molded by bird's body in grasses of marshes or mosses of tundra or bogs. Eggs: 4; pale to medium brownish green or light pinkish

The Least Sandpiper is one of several small sandpipers known collectively as "peeps."

Migrating flocks of Dunlins often are made up of thousands of birds.

brown, boldly blotched and spotted with reddish and greenish browns. Incubation period unknown. Age at 1st flight unknown. Food: Insects and small crustaceans.

Suggested reading: D. A. Bannerman, *Birds of the British Isles*, Oliver and Boyd, Edinburgh, 1961, vol. 9, pp. 272–278. H. M. Hall, "The Least Sandpiper," *Aud. Mag.*, vol. 59, pp. 222–223, 1957.

LONG-TOED STINT (*Erolia subminuta*)

Small (ca. 5 in.) and very much like the Least Sandpiper, but its legs and toes are much longer. Breeds on islands of ne. Asia from Bering I. south to Sakhalin I. and the Kurile Is. Winters from e. India, se. Asia, e. China, and the Philippines south to Ceylon and in n. Indonesia. Straggles to Pribilof Is., Alaska.

RUFOUS-NECKED SANDPIPER (*Erolia ruficollis*)

Small (6½ in.); resembles the Least Sandpiper, but cheeks and upper chest are a tawny color; in winter it is like the Semipalmated Sandpiper, but bill is more slender. Breeds in ne. Siberia and w. end of Seward Peninsula, Alaska; winters from s. China to Indonesia, Australia, Tasmania, and New Zealand. Has straggled to the Pribilof Is. and Nome, Alaska.

CURLEW SANDPIPER (*Erolia ferruginea*)

A small (ca. 7½ in.) sandpiper with a bill somewhat longer than its head and slightly decurved. In fall and winter it resembles the Dunlin, but is browner and has a more slender bill and a white rump patch. In breeding

plumage it has a bright, reddish brown head, neck, breast, and belly. It breeds in n. Siberia and winters from the British Isles, the Mediterranean region, s. Asia, and the Philippines south to s. Africa, Madagascar, Ceylon, Australia, Tasmania, and New Zealand and has straggled to Alaska (it bred at Point Barrow in 1962), B.C., Ont., N.B., Maine, Mass., Conn., N.Y., N.J., Tex., La., Lesser Antilles, and s. Argentina.

Suggested reading: R. T. Holmes and F. A. Pitelka, "Breeding Behavior and Taxonomic Relationships of the Curlew Sandpiper," *Auk*, vol. 81, pp. 362–379, 1964.

DUNLIN (Red-backed Sandpiper) (*Erolia alpina*)

Appearance: Small (8–9 in.); in fall and winter it is grayish above and whitish below, with a buffy gray chest and neck; the central feathers of the tail are dark gray, and the outer feathers buffy gray. In spring and summer the back becomes reddish brown marked with blackish, giving a scaly appearance; there is a tinge of reddish on the crown, and the undersides are whitish, except for buffy gray spots on the neck and chest and a large black spot in the center of the belly. The bill, decurved and slightly longer than the head, is blackish; legs and feet are grayish or blackish.

Voice: In flight a loud, grating *purre,* and in spring a pleasant trill that becomes lower in pitch and more rapid at the end.

Range and status: Breeds on tundra and along arctic coasts from e. Greenland and Iceland east to Somerset I. and Southampton I. in the Canadian Arctic Archipelago, south to Great Britain, n. Germany, Denmark, the Baltic States, the base of Kamchatka Peninsula, sw. continental Alaska, ne. Man., and possibly to n. Ont.; not positively known to breed along the coasts of n.-c. Mack. Winters coastally from se. Alaska, Mass., Great Britain, the Mediterranean, the Red Sea, s. Asia, and Japan south to Baja Calif., the Gulf Coast, s. Fla., Cape Verde Is., n. Africa, Somaliland, s. India, and Formosa. Common, sometimes and in some places abundant.

Habitat: Tundra, alpine mountaintops, beaches, tidal areas, mudflats, and pools.

Seasonal movements: In spring Apr.–early June, and in fall Aug.–Nov. Mainly along coasts, sometimes in immense flocks; rarely in interior of continents.

Biology: Nest: A depression in fairly dry ground of tundra or alpine meadow, usually near a pool or other water; lined with grass and dry leaves and well concealed. Eggs: 2–6, most often 4; pale grayish green to medium greenish brown, spotted and blotched with dark browns and grays, usually more heavily on the larger end of the egg. Incubation: 21–22 days, by both sexes. Age at 1st flight: About 25 days. Food: Small mollusks, crustaceans, insects; some seeds and other plant food.

Suggested reading: R. T. Holmes, "Breeding Ecology and Annual Cycle Adaptations of the Red-backed Sandpiper in Northern Alaska," *Condor,* vol. 68, pp. 3–46, 1966.

SHORT-BILLED DOWITCHER (*Limnodromus griseus*)

Appearance: Small (10½–12 in.), with bill considerably longer than the head; neck and breast are

The Long-billed Dowitcher frequents mudflats near pools and marshes and in tidal areas.

reddish brown, fading to whitish from the belly to the undertail feathers; dark brown above, spotted and streaked with reddish brown. The face is grayer, with a dark streak passing through the eye, and there are varying amounts of dark brown spotting on the flank and side of the neck. The rump is white; the tail is white, with fine blackish barring. The bill is blackish at the tip, becoming grayish at the base; the legs and feet are greenish gray. In fall and winter the reddish hues are lost; the bird becomes dark grayish brown above and whitish below, with grayish upper breast and grayish streaking and barring along the flank.

Voice: Confusing, as this and the next species were once considered variations of the same species; voice differences were therefore not carefully noted. The call of this species is similar to that of the Greater Yellowlegs, but a lower-pitched *peu-peu-peu.*

Range and status: Breeds on the coast of s. Alaska and from s. Mack. and s. Keewatin to n. Alta., n. Sask., and n. Man.; probably also in n. Ont. and n. Que. Winters from s. U.S. (S.C. on the Atlantic Coast) through Mexico, C. America, and the W. Indies to nw. Peru and e.-c. Brazil. Casual in Bermuda, Greenland, and Europe. Formerly very common, but suffered from overhunting, from which it is only now beginning to recover.

Habitat: Tidal flats, particularly muddy areas, marshes, and ponds.

Seasonal movements: Largest migration occurs along coasts Apr.–June and July–mid-Nov.

Biology: Nest: A hollow in a clump of grass or moss in muskeg region; sparingly lined with twigs, leaves, or grasses. Eggs: 3–5, usually 4; light greenish gray, spotted and flecked with dark browns. Incubation period unknown. Age at 1st flight unknown; male apparently assumes full care of young upon hatching. Food: Insects and small marine animals; also some seeds and roots of aquatic plants.

Suggested reading: F. A. Pitelka, *Geographic Variation and the Species Problem in the Shorebird Genus Limnodromus,* Univ. Calif. Publ. in Zool., vol. 50, no. 1, 108 pp., 1950. D. A. Bannerman, *Birds of the British Isles,* Oliver and Boyd, Edinburgh, 1961, vol. 9, pp. 158–165.

LONG-BILLED DOWITCHER (*Limnodromus scolopaceus*)

Appearance: Slightly larger (11–12½ in.) than the Short-billed Dowitcher, with a somewhat longer bill; otherwise very similar, differing mainly in having more barring and less spotting along flank.

Voice: A single, squeaky, often quavering *keek;* other notes on breeding grounds.

Range and status: Breeds in ne. Siberia and along the coasts of w. and n. Alaska, n. Yuk., and n. Mack.;

somewhat inland in Mack. Winters from c. Calif., w. Nev., s. Ariz., s. N.Mex., w.-c. Tex., the Gulf Coast, and Fla. south to Guatemala; has straggled to the W. Indies and Argentina. Has been recorded in summer in Calif., Tex., and La. Becoming common again, but rarer than the Short-billed.

Habitat: Mudflats, tidal areas, pool and marsh edges; frequents fresh water more often than the Short-billed Dowitcher.

Seasonal movements: Migrates mainly through w. N. America; rare eastward, then mainly in fall along coast from Maine to Ga. Mar.–mid-May and July–Oct.

Biology: Nest: A depression in grass or moss in tundra, usually near water. Eggs: 4; brownish green or greenish, spotted and streaked with browns and grays. Incubation period unknown. Age at 1st flight unknown. Food: Aquatic insects and their larvae; probably small marine animals, etc.

Suggested reading: F. A. Pitelka, *Geographic Variation and the Species Problem in the Shorebird Genus Limnodromus*, Univ. Calif. Publ. in Zool., vol. 50, no. 1, 108 pp., 1950.

STILT SANDPIPER (*Micropalama himantopus*)

Appearance: Small (7½–9 in.), with bill much longer than head and with rather long legs (longer than those of dowitchers). During spring and summer grayish brown, with some streaking on neck, and with a brownish red patch just behind the eye; the flight feathers of the wing are blackish. The bill is blackish, and the legs and feet are a grayed, yellowish green. In fall and winter it loses the barring below; the sides of the breast are then mottled with grayish.

Voice: Low but harsh *whu*, sometimes ending in a drawn-out rasp, most commonly given in flight.

Range and status: Breeds in tundra and coastal regions from ne. Alaska east to se. Keewatin and ne. Man., on Victoria I., and probably in n. Ont., south to continuous forest region. Winter range poorly known; probably from Bolivia, w.-c. Brazil, and Paraguay south to e.-c. Argentina and Uruguay. Migration mainly between the Rockies and the Mississippi and through Mexico, C. America, and S. America east of the Andes. Rare.

Habitat: Tundra near shallow pools and ponds in summer; mudflats, marshes, and wet spots in prairies.

Seasonal movements: Mar.–May and July–Oct.; rare west of the Rockies and east of the Mississippi to the Atlantic Coast, where only casual north of Mass.

Biology: Nest: A slight hollow in tundra, lined with a few leaves and grasses. Eggs: 4; light grayish yellow, blotched with browns. Incubation period unknown. Age at 1st flight unknown. Food: Insects and small aquatic animals; sometimes as much as 30% vegetable matter, such as seeds, roots, and leaves of aquatic plants.

The Stilt Sandpiper often wades breast-deep in water as it probes the bottom for food.

Suggested reading: D. A. Bannerman, *Birds of the British Isles*, Oliver and Boyd, Edinburgh, 1961, vol. 9, pp. 340–346.

SEMIPALMATED SANDPIPER (*Ereunetes pusillus*)

Appearance: Small (5½–7 in.), with a blackish bill shorter than head and rather stout; white below and grayish above; tail grayish, legs and feet blackish. In spring and summer it has a gray upper breast and throat marked with dark chevrons and spots.

Voice: Flight note a *cherr*; sometimes a *ki-i-ip*; also in courtship flight a high, liquid trill and a "whinny" call.

Range and status: Breeds in the tundra regions of N. America from n. Alaska, n. Yuk., Victoria I., King William I., Boothia Peninsula, c. Baffin I., and n. Lab. south to sw. Alaska, e.-c. Mack., se. Keewatin, ne. Man., s. coast of Hudson Bay, and n. Que.; nonbreeders may remain as far south as Panama. Winters from Gulf Coast and S.C. through e. Mexico and the W. Indies to n. Chile, Paraguay, and s. Brazil. Has straggled to the Pribilofs, Argentina, Bermuda, and Europe. Common.

Habitat: Tundra in summer; beaches, shores, and tidal zones.

Seasonal movements: Apr.-May and mid-June–Sept.; usually east of the Rockies and often very common on coasts.

Biology: Nest: A depression in ground or sands, exposed or amid herbage; sparsely lined with grasses,

The Western Sandpiper migrates mostly along the Pacific Coast and is seldom seen in the East.

moss, and leaves. Eggs: 3–4, usually 4; whitish to light brownish green and yellowish, spotted with browns. Incubation: 17–19 days. Age at 1st flight: About 1 month. Food: Insects and small marine animals.

Suggested reading: H. M. Hall, *A Gathering of Shore Birds*, Devin-Adair, N.Y., 1960, pp. 176–179.

WESTERN SANDPIPER (*Ereunetes mauri*)

Appearance: Small (6–7 in.); much like the Semipalmated, but bill longer (at least as long as head). In spring and summer its upperparts and cheeks are reddish brown, spotted and marked with blackish. The underparts are white, with black spots and tiny chevrons across the chest. In fall and winter it is white below and gray above, with some reddish brown at the shoulders. The bill, legs, and feet are blackish.

Voice: A plaintive *cheep* or *cherp*, not so drawn-out as the call of the Least Sandpiper.

Range and status: Breeds on the coasts of Alaska from Nunivak I. and the Kashunuk River to Point Barrow; nonbreeders may remain as far south as Panama. Winters from se. Alaska (rarely), the Gulf Coast, and N.C. south to coasts of Colombia, Ecuador, Peru, Venezuela, and the W. Indies. Migration mainly along Pacific Coast; rarer in interior and very rarely along Atlantic Coast. Fairly common.

Habitat: Marine coasts, tundra, marshes, and mudflats.

Seasonal movements: Apr.–May and July–mid-Oct.; apparently spring migration is almost entirely coastal, as the bird is seldom found in interior.

Biology: Nest: In drier parts of tundra amid bunchgrass; a small depression with scant lining of grass and leaves. Eggs: 3–5, usually 4; yellowish white, profusely marked and spotted with reddish and dark brown. Incubation: About 21 days. Age at 1st flight unknown. Food: Insects, worms, small shellfish, and other small marine animals.

Suggested reading: H. M. Hall, *A Gathering of Shore Birds*, Devin-Adair, N.Y., 1960, pp. 179–182.

BUFF-BREASTED SANDPIPER (*Tryngites subruficollis*)

Appearance: Small (7½–9 in.), with slender blackish bill about as long as head. Entire underparts, neck, and face buff; above, the buff is marked and streaked with blackish and dark brown, giving a somewhat scaly effect. The legs and feet are yellow.

Voice: A low *chrup* as it takes flight and a low trilled *pr-r-r-reet*.

Range and status: Breeds in n. Alaska, n. Yuk., n. Mack., Melville I., Bathurst I., and King William I.; winters in c. Argentina. Migrates through the interior of N. America, C. America, and Colombia; very rare along the Pacific or Atlantic Coasts, e. Siberia, the W. Indies, and Venezuela. Has straggled to Europe and Egypt. Rather rare.

Habitat: Tundra, prairies, grassy fields.

Seasonal movements: Mar.–May and mid-July–Oct.; in spring, the main movement is apparently across the Gulf of Mexico to Tex. and w. La., then up the e. slope of the Rockies to the breeding area; in fall, many return by the same route, but others apparently fly eastward, then offshore of e. Canada and over the ocean to S. America.

Biology: Nest: A depression in the tundra, scantily lined with leaves. Eggs: 4–5, most often 4; whitish, yellowish brown, or greenish gray, spotted and blotched with browns and grays. Incubation period unknown. Age at 1st flight unknown. Food: Insects and their larvae; very few seeds.

Suggested reading: D. A. Bannerman, *Birds of the British Isles*, Oliver and Boyd, Edinburgh, 1961, vol. 9, pp. 383–392.

MARBLED GODWIT (*Limosa fedoa*)

Appearance: Large (16–20 in.), with a slightly upcurved bill more than twice as long as head. Buffy, with dark brown and blackish streaks and spots on back and cap, along flank, and sometimes on chest; a whitish throat and stripe just above the eye. The tail is dark buff, barred with blackish; the wings are dark brown and reddish. The long legs and feet are bluish gray. The flesh-colored bill is blackish at the tip, and the neck is rather long. The female is slightly larger. In winter both male and female are more grayish, the chest is unmarked, and the flanks are only indistinctly marked.

Voice: A large variety of sounds; most common is a *terwhit, terwhit, terwhit,* or *godwit, godwit, godwit,* which increases in vigor, length, and stress as the bird becomes more excited. Also a rather musical whistled *ker-koit* and a loud, disturbing *eradica-radica-radica-radica* or *you're-crazy-crazy-crazy.*

Range and status: Breeds from c. Alta., s. Sask., and s. Man. to c. Mont., c. N.Dak., ne. S.Dak., and w.-c. Minn.; formerly farther south and possibly farther north. Nonbreeders found as far south as Mexico and S.C. Winters from c. Calif. and w. Nev. south, mainly along coasts, to Guatemala and British Honduras, rarely to Ecuador, Peru, and Chile, and from S.C. to Fla. In fall migration, reaches the W. Indies and the Atlantic Coast north to Mass. Has straggled to Alaska, B.C., and N.S.

A drop of water at the tip of a Marbled Godwit's bill accentuates its slight curve.

Formerly abundant throughout most of U.S. and only now recovering from injudicious hunting pressure, but e. populations and migrants are still low.

Habitat: Prairies, pools, lakes, and shores; in winter, marine coasts and intertidal areas.

Seasonal movements: Spring migration along w. coast and through w. interior, scattering to e. coast in fall; Apr.–mid-June and July–Nov.

Biology: Nest: A slight hollow in the short prairie grass, not usually concealed; lined with grass. Eggs: 3–5, commonly 4; light greenish gray or greenish brown, irregularly and sparsely spotted and blotched with browns. Incubation period unknown. Age at 1st flight not known. Food: Mainly aquatic; mollusks, insects, worms, and other small invertebrates.

Suggested reading: H. M. Hall, *A Gathering of Shore Birds,* Devin-Adair, N.Y., 1960, pp. 187–189.

BAR-TAILED GODWIT (*Limosa lapponica*)

Rather large (15–18 in.) and similar to the Marbled Godwit, but underparts, neck, face, and throat are grayish rufous. Rump is white, and the white tail is barred with gray or blackish. Female and male in fall and winter are grayish brown above and whitish below (including neck, throat, and face), with irregular barring on chest and flanks. It breeds in arctic Eurasia and w. and n. Alaska; winters coastally from North, Baltic, and Black Seas and s. Asia to Gambia, Somaliland, Australia, Tasmania, New Zealand, and the Philippines, migrating through the Aleutians. Also winters through Oceania from Hawaii to the Gilbert, Samoa, and Tonga Is. Has straggled to Mass., N.Y., N.J., and B.C.

HUDSONIAN GODWIT (*Limosa haemastica*)

Appearance: Medium-sized (14–17 in.); similar to the Marbled Godwit, brownish gray above, with underparts, including lower throat, a rich brownish red. The black tail has a narrow white tip and a broad white band at the base; the larger feathers of the wing are blackish, with a streak of white running from the body nearly to the tip. The black-tipped bill is bright pinkish flesh color, and the legs and feet are grayish blue. In fall and winter it is a more even brownish gray above and a pale buff below, with brownish gray at the sides of the chest.

Voice: A *godwit* higher in pitch than that of the Marbled.

Range and status: Breeds locally on arctic coasts and tundra from nw. Mack. to ne. Man., on Akimiski I. in James Bay, and possibly in highlands of Southampton I. Winters from n. Chile, Paraguay, and s. Brazil to Tierra del Fuego and Falkland Is. Migration mainly through interior of Canada and U.S. Has straggled to New Zealand. Rare; nowhere near former abundance, when flocks of thousands were recorded in Argentina.

Habitat: Tundra, prairie pools, marine and fresh-water shores.

Seasonal movements: Mar.–May and July–early Nov.; in spring through interior; in fall se. to Maritime Provinces and then over ocean to S. America; very rare in Great Lakes region or along Atlantic Coast of U.S. and only casually on Pacific Coast of N. America.

Biology: Very little known. Nest: A hollow in tundra mosses, sparingly lined with dry leaves. Eggs: 3–4, usually 4; greenish brown, irregularly spotted with dark browns. Incubation period unknown. Age at 1st flight unknown. Food: Insects, worms, small crustaceans, small mollusks, and other small marine organisms.

Suggested reading: J. A. Hagar, "Nesting of the Hudsonian Godwit at Churchill, Manitoba," *Living Bird*, 5th Ann., pp. 5–44, 1966.

BLACK-TAILED GODWIT (*Limosa limosa*)

Medium-sized (15–17 in.); very similar to Bar-tailed Godwit, but rear half of underparts whitish, tail wholly black, and rump white; except for black tail and blackish shoulder patch, hardly distinguishable from Bar-tailed in fall and winter. Breeds in Iceland and in c. Europe and c. Asia. Winters from Great Britain, the Mediterranean, s. Asia, and the Philippines to e.-c. Africa, Borneo, Australia, and Tasmania. Has straggled to Greenland and Nfld.

RUFF (*Philomachus pugnax*)

Small (8½–12 in.); cocks are remarkably variable, especially about the head, crest, throat, and breast, where erectile feathers may be all blackish, barred yellow and black, whitish, yellowish, or variegated in color. The male's underparts are whitish, and his back is brownish and blackish. The yellowish black-tipped bill is about as long as the head; the legs and feet are yellowish. The hen, known as the Reeve or Ree (and the cock in fall and winter), is brownish gray mottled with darker grays above and whitish below, with brownish gray mottling on the chest. In all plumages of both sexes there is a conspicuous white oval patch on each side of the dark tail. Ranges through Afro-Eurasia and Indonesia; has

A group of Sanderlings in winter plumage hunt for food on a surf-washed beach.

straggled to Iceland, Greenland, the Maritime Provinces, Maine, N.C., Ont., Ohio, Ind., and Iowa and, fairly often, to the coasts of New England and the Middle Atlantic states.

SANDERLING (*Crocethia alba*)

Appearance: Small (7–9 in.); legs, feet, and bill (which is about as long as the head) are blackish. It is rather chunky and short-necked. In spring and summer it is reddish brown, streaked and spotted with blackish above and on head, neck, and breast; it is whitish below and has blackish wings. Rump is white, with a central streak of medium gray extending through central tail feathers; outer tail feathers are light gray. In fall and winter it is white below and pale gray above, with a small black patch at shoulder; wing and tail about as in spring.

Voice: A strident *twick*, *twick* on taking flight, and melodious twittering and cheeping while feeding.

Range and status: Breeds in high arctic islands and coasts from Ellesmere I., n. Greenland, Spitsbergen, North Land (Severnaya Zemlya), and the New Siberian Is. south to n. Mack., e. Keewatin, Southampton I., e.-c. Greenland, Taimyr Peninsula, and the delta of the Yenisei River; nonbreeders may remain as far south as Calif., n. Venezuela, Tunisia, and Somaliland. Winters coastally from B.C., the Gulf Coast, Mass., the British Isles, the Mediterranean, the Caspian Sea, n. India,

Burma, China, the Marianas, and Hawaii to s. S. America, Madagascar, Maldive Is., s. India, Ceylon, Indonesia, Australia, and the Phoenix and Union Is. Common to locally abundant.

Habitat: Northernmost arctic beaches, tundra, lakeshores and seashores, intertidal areas.

Seasonal movements: Most common as a migrant on seacoasts and shores of larger inland bodies of water; Apr.–early June and July–Nov.

Biology: Nest: Grasses, leaves, and mosses in shallow depression in stony tundra or arctic coasts. Eggs: 3–4, normally 4; yellowish white or pale greenish white, evenly speckled with dull browns. Incubation: 23–24 days. Age at 1st flight: 2 weeks. Food: Small crustaceans, insects, worms, and other small invertebrates.

Suggested reading: D. A. Bannerman, *Birds of the British Isles*, Oliver and Boyd, Edinburgh, 1961, vol. 9, pp. 347–360.

SPOON-BILL SANDPIPER (*Eurynorhynchus pygmeum*)

A small (6½ in.) sandpiper, grayish above and whitish below, with black legs, feet, and bill. The bill is stout and flares out laterally near the tip into a "spoon shape." In spring and summer the head, neck, and upper breast are reddish brown, and there are dark streaks on the upper chest and flank. It breeds in ne. Siberia and winters in se. Asia. It has straggled to nw. Alaska.

AVOCETS AND STILTS (RECURVIROSTRIDAE)

Avocets and stilts are small- to medium-sized (11½–20 in.) wading birds with rather long necks; long, slender legs; and long, thin bills. The bill, usually 2–3 times as long as the head, is straight, decurved, or recurved (curved upward at the tip). The tail is short and square, and the wings are long and pointed; the feet may be well webbed or only slightly webbed, and the hind toe is entirely lacking or very rudimentary. The sexes are alike, or very similar. They are found from c. Europe, c. Asia, and the U.S. south to s. Africa, Madagascar, Ceylon, Australia, New Zealand, the Philippines, Hawaii, the Galápagos, and s. S. America; there are 7 species, of which only 2, the American Avocet and the Black-necked Stilt, occur in America. Though they are excellent fliers and good swimmers and are able to dive beneath the water, mainly they are waders. They are gregarious and colonial. Their nests are bare hollows in sand or mud, sometimes lined with grass or pebbles; rarely do they build a bulky platform of sticks and twigs. The 2–7 eggs (commonly 4) are grayish brown or grayish green, spotted, blotched, and streaked with black and reddish browns. Both sexes share incubation and duties of raising young. The downy young leave the nest shortly after hatching. Food consists mainly of insects, shellfish, and other small invertebrates; very little vegetable matter is consumed.

AMERICAN AVOCET (*Recurvirostra americana*)

Appearance: Medium-sized (15½–20 in.), but largest member of family. Tail, entire body, and feathers at base of bill are white; rest of head and long, graceful neck are tawny (gray in fall and winter). The outer, larger flight feathers of the wing and a broad band extending from these to the body are black, and the feathers from the shoulder to the inner rear edge of the wing shade from black to dark gray. From below, the flight feathers are dark, and the rest of the wing is white. The black bill is nearly 3 times as long as the head and is curved gently upward at the tip; the legs and webbed feet are light grayish blue. Swims frequently and flies with neck extended. Flocks at times indulge in rather complex aerial maneuvers.

Voice: A loud, piercing *weet-weet-weet*, repeated many times; sometimes recorded as *plee-eek*. Also a lower, softer *whick-whick-whick*.

Range and status: Breeds from e. Wash., s. Idaho, c. Alta., s. Sask., and s. Man. south to s. Calif., s. Nev., n. Utah, s.-c. Colo., s. N.Mex., w. Tex., and n.-c. Okla.; winters from c. Calif. and s. Tex. to Guatemala. It may once have nested as far east as the Atlantic Coast, as there is an old record of nesting in N.J. Locally common.

Habitat: Swamps; flat, muddy edges of lakes and ponds (particularly more alkaline bodies of water in semiarid regions); tidal flats and more muddy bay coasts in winter.

Seasonal movements: Mar.–May and Sept.–Oct.

Biology: Nest: A slight hollow in ground of dry, sunbaked flats, gravelly beaches, or isles where vegetation is sparse; lined with grasses, weed stems, and sticks. Eggs: 3–5, normally 4; light grayish yellow to medium greenish brown, evenly spotted and blotched with dark browns and black. Incubation period unknown, but European Avocet takes 22–24 days. Age at 1st flight unknown; estimated as 6 weeks in European species. Food: Feeds by wading in water and swinging bill from side to side in bottom mud, obtaining aquatic insects, small crustaceans, and other small animals thus stirred up; about 35% of the food consists of seeds of aquatic plants obtained in same way as animal food.

Suggested reading: A. C. Bent, *Life Histories of North American Shore Birds*, part 1, Dover, N.Y. (reprint of U.S. Nat. Mus. Bull. 142, 1927), 1962, pp. 37–46.

BLACK-NECKED STILT (*Himantopus mexicanus*)

Appearance: Smaller (13–17 in.) than the Avocet; top of head to below the eye, back of neck, back, and wings are black, and there is a small white patch above the eye. All the rest of the plumage, including the rump, is white; the tail, however, is pale gray. The bill, which is almost twice as long as the head, is black; eyes, legs, and feet are red. The feet are not so well webbed as those of the Avocet, and the Stilt is therefore not so good a swimmer or diver. The adult female is grayish on the back, and the black is duller. Immature birds have a light mottling of buff on the black of the back and neck.

Voice: A loud, throaty *whuk-whuk-whuk* or a high-

The American Avocet lines its shallow nest with grass and other plant material.

pitched yelp: *clee-eek, clee-eek, clee-eek* or *kyip-kyip-kyip*.

Range and status: Breeds from s. Ore., Idaho, n. Utah, s. Colo., e. N.Mex., and the Gulf Coast of Tex. and La. south to n. Baja Calif., the Galápagos Is., the coast of Ecuador, and probably the coast of Peru; and from S.C. and c. and e. Fla. through the W. Indies to the coasts of n. S. America. Apparently only a local breeder in Mexico and C. America; perhaps not breeding at all from Costa Rica to n. Colombia. In winter retreats south of c. Calif., the coasts of Mexico, the Rio Grande Valley of Texas, and the Gulf Coast from the Mississippi Delta west. Has been recorded, mainly as a migrant, from Sask., N.Dak., Wis., N.B., Nfld., and Bermuda south. Once bred north along the Atlantic Coast to N.J. Relaxation of hunting pressure has permitted the bird to regain some of its former numbers, so that it is now at least locally common.

Habitat: Shallow-water lakes, marshes, and ponds, either alkaline or fresh; also mudflats, especially intertidal.

Seasonal movements: Mainly resident, but retires from n. part of range Oct.–early Nov. and returns late Mar.–Apr.

Biology: Nest: In small colonies in swamps, wet meadows, or in such places as mangrove swamps near open areas; a slight hollow in dry ground or on hummocks, sparingly lined with twigs, weed stalks, and grasses. Eggs: 3–7, usually 4; light brownish yellow or buff, irregularly spotted or blotched with dark browns and black. Incubation period unknown. Age at 1st flight unknown. Food: Insects (mostly aquatic stages), other small invertebrates, a few small fish, and generally less than 2% vegetable matter that may be ingested accidentally.

Suggested reading: H. M. Hall, *A Gathering of Shore Birds*, Devin-Adair, N.Y., 1960, pp. 205–210.

In breeding plumage, the female Red Phalarope (left) *is more colorful than her mate.*

THE PHALAROPES (PHALAROPODIDAE)

Phalaropes are small (6½–10 in.) aquatic sandpiperlike birds with long (slightly longer than the head), thin bills (somewhat stouter in the Red Phalarope) and lobe-webbed toes. The wings are rather long and pointed, and the tails are moderately long and squarish. The females are larger and more brightly colored than the males. The birds are thoroughly at home on both land and sea; they float high and corklike on the water, constantly bobbing and spinning, seemingly so light and airy as to be at the mercy of every wind and wave. Phalaropes breed in the arctic and subarctic regions and winter mainly in the colder oceans of the S. Hemisphere (1 species in the interior of s. S. America). In migration they fly over most of the world's oceans and occasionally inland. There are 3 species, all of which occur in N. America. These are gregarious birds, often nesting in small colonies; their nests may be sparsely lined depressions in the ground or may be well built of grasses on the ground near water. The eggs, usually 4, are greenish brown, spotted with dark browns and black. Incubation is by the male alone, but the female may return to assist in caring for the young. The downy chicks leave the nest shortly after hatching. They feed mainly on small crustaceans and insects, rarely on plant matter.

RED PHALAROPE (Gray Phalarope) (*Phalaropus fulicarius*)

Appearance: Medium-sized (7½–9 in.—smaller than a Robin), with a rather stout blackish bill that is yellowish at the base. In spring and summer the female has a black cap and a white cheek patch, and the rest of the upperparts are light brown, marked and spotted with dark brown and blackish. The underparts are brownish red, the wing is grayish brown with blackish flight feathers, and the tail is brown with darker central feathers. Feet and legs are yellowish. The male is much duller, with a brownish cap, a less distinct cheek patch, and more rufous underparts. In fall and winter both sexes are gray above and white below; the head is then mostly white, with a blackish spot behind the eye; the back of the neck is grayish, merging with a dark gray at the back of the head. Immature birds are like the male, but grayer. The downy young are dull buffy gray, streaked and mottled with darker browns and black.

Voice: Not noisy; a low, musical, metallic *clink-clink* and a sharp *kit-kit*.

Range and status: Breeds on arctic coasts and tundra from Ellesmere I., e.-c. and w.-c. Greenland, Spitsbergen, s. Novaya Zemlya, New Siberian Is., and Wrangel I. south to coasts of n. Siberia, w. and n. Alaska, n. Yuk., n. Mack., e. Keewatin, ne. Man., Southampton I., Coats I., n. Que., and n. Lab.; possibly Iceland. Winters at sea off both coasts of S. America and w. Africa south to New Zealand, s. Chile, the Falkland Is., and S. Africa. In migration very rare through the interior of N. America and only casually in the interior of Eurasia. Has straggled to India. Fairly common.

Habitat: Arctic coasts and tundra in summer; open seas, estuaries, bays, and marine coasts in winter.

Seasonal movements: Arrives in N. America May–early June. Fall migrations extended, as some birds leave the Arctic in early July and others linger to late Oct.; some may be seen off New England and Wash. in late Nov.

Biology: Nest: Built by male alone; a shallow scrape in the ground, grass tussocks, or mosses, sparingly lined with fine grasses. Eggs: 3–6, commonly 4; pale to dark greenish buff, boldly marked with irregular spots and pepperings of dark brown and black. Incubation: 23–24 days, by male alone. Age at 1st flight unknown, but early. Food: Small crustaceans (almost entirely these while the bird winters at sea), insects, tiny fish, and very little plant food (mainly algae).

Suggested reading: D. A. Bannerman, *Birds of the British Isles*, Oliver and Boyd, Edinburgh, 1961, vol. 9, pp. 166–181.

WILSON'S PHALAROPE (*Steganopus tricolor*)

Appearance: Largest (8½–10 in.) of the phalaropes. In spring and summer the hen is largely gray above and whitish below, with white on the back of the neck and a small white spot just above the eye. A rather broad black streak runs through the eye and down the side of the neck, where it becomes a brownish red that extends down the back, forming a V with the line from the other side. There is a suffusion of the brownish red across the front of the neck and the upper breast, and a brownish red streak runs across the upper wing. The male is brownish above and whitish below, with a white spot at the back of the head and a whitish streak above the eye. The neck is dull brownish red at the back and buff at the front. Both sexes have white rump patches, grayish legs, and thin blackish bills. In fall and winter both cock and hen are gray above and white below, with a white streak above the eye. The gray of the back extends onto the sides of the breast. The legs and feet are yellowish gray. Immature birds resemble the male but are buffier. Downy young are light tawny above and whitish below, with a broad blackish streak down the back and thinner streaks and spots of blackish above. The feet are less prominently lobed and webbed than in the other species, and the bill is proportionately longer.

Voice: A soft, nasal grunt or quack and a croaking *oit-oit-oit.*

Range and status: Breeds from c. B.C., c. Prairie Provinces, c. Minn., s. Wis., and s. Ont. south to s.-c. Calif., c. Nev., n. Utah, ne. Colo., c. Kans., w. Nebr., and e. S.Dak., formerly farther southeast; nonbreeders range farther north. Winters mainly in Chile, Argentina,

and the Falkland Is.; casually from s. Tex. southward. Some migration along Atlantic Coast, but most move through the interior west of the Mississippi River and then along the coasts of Mexico and C. America. This is the phalarope most familiar to the majority of Americans, if not the most common phalarope.

Habitat: Shallow fresh and salt water, shores, tidal flats, marshes; bound to the land more than the other phalaropes.

Seasonal movements: Apr.–May and Aug.–Sept.

Biology: Nest: Well concealed in wet, grassy meadows or marshes; a slight hollow in the ground, well or sparsely lined with grasses. Eggs: 3–4, most often 4; light brownish yellow, thickly spotted and blotched with browns and black. Incubation: 20–21 days. Age at 1st flight unknown. Food: Mainly insects and small crustaceans; some seeds of aquatic plants. On mudflats and in very shallow water, it feeds with probing sweeps of the bill, as do the sandpipers; in deeper water it probes the bottom with only the tail and part of the back marking the site of its activity; while swimming, it continually spins completely around, stabbing at floating food in every direction.

Suggested reading: E. O. Höhn, "Observations on the Breeding Biology of Wilson's Phalarope (*Steganopus tricolor*) in Central Alberta," *Auk*, vol. 84, pp. 220–244, 1967.

Wilson's Phalarope

NORTHERN PHALAROPE (Red-necked Phalarope)
(*Lobipes lobatus*)

Appearance: Small (6½–8 in.); generally medium gray above, including the head, with some gray on the sides of the breast and in spots on the flank. A patch of white covers the throat and sweeps back to the sides of the upper neck. A band of brownish red crosses the chest, extending to the sides and up along the throat; the rest of the underparts are whitish. There are 3 slashes of rufous from the bend of the wing to the back; the central tail feathers are dark gray, and the outer ones are lighter gray. The male is browner above; the brownish red of the neck and breast is replaced with dull, dark buff, and there is a whitish streak above the eye. In fall and winter both sexes are dark gray above and white below, including most of the head; a dark gray cap covers the rear half of the head, and a patch of dark gray begins just before the eye and reaches well behind the eye. The bill is blackish and the legs and feet are grayish in all seasons. Immature birds are like the male, but somewhat duller and browner. The downy young are tawny above, with black cap and a black spot behind the eye. The back is marbled with blackish; the underparts are whitish.

Voice: A faint, plaintive *wit-wit* or *pe-et-pe-et-pe-et.*

Range and status: Tundra and n. tree zone of subarctic n. Eurasia and n. N. America, from Southampton I., s. Baffin I., w.-c. and e.-c. Greenland, Iceland, Spitsbergen, s. Novaya Zemlya, and northernmost coasts of both continents south to the Komandorskie and Aleutian Is., s. Alaska, n. Ont., n. Que., c. Lab., s. Greenland, n. British Isles, the Baltic States, and n. Kamchatka; possibly farther south in interior of Eurasia and N. America. Winters at sea south of the Azores, n. Africa, s. Asia, s. Japan, the Galápagos, and s. Argentina south almost to antarctic waters. Common; an abundant coastal migrant, rare in the interior, particularly in e. N. America.

Habitat: In summer near shallow fresh waters with abundant tundra grass, shrubby tundra edges, and such waters in n. edges of tree limit; in winter open seas, bays, marine coasts.

Seasonal movements: Mar.–June and late Aug.–Oct.

Biology: Nest: Small, deep hollows in ground or on tussocks, scantily lined with grasses and sedges. Eggs: 3–5, most often 4 (more than 5 usually the product of more than 1 female); pale to dark greenish brown, with various patterns in dark browns and black spots or blotches. Incubation: About 20 days, by male alone. Age at 1st flight unknown; young are able to swim when half grown. Food: Insects, crustaceans, and tiny fish; at sea known to eat small jellyfish, and often follows gams of whales.

Suggested reading: D. A. Bannerman, *Birds of the British Isles,* Oliver and Boyd, Edinburgh, 1961, vol. 9, pp. 182–197.

As with other shorebirds, the Killdeer's downy, protectively colored chicks are able to leave their nest almost immediately after hatching.

The Black-necked Stilt's nest usually is simply a hollow on dry ground, but the bird sometimes builds a more elaborate structure on hummocks in shallow water.

JAEGERS AND SKUAS (STERCORARIIDAE)

These are moderate-sized (16–24 in.), somewhat heavy-bodied seabirds related to the gulls, but more adapted to predatory ways. The wings are falconlike: long, narrow, rather pointed, and angled backward from the bend of the wing in flight. The strong bill, more than half as long as the head, is rounded and hooked, with a horny sheath, or cere, covering the nostrils. The tail is medium long and wedge-shaped; in some species the central feathers are much elongated. The legs are rather short and stout; the feet are well webbed, the toenails are strong and hooked, and the hind toe is almost rudimentary. The sexes are alike, the female perhaps being slightly larger. There are various plumage phases from light to dark, with black, white, grays, brownish, and yellowish hues predominating. All species display a white flash near the tip of the wing while in flight. There are 4 species, all found in N. America. They breed in arctic, subarctic, and antarctic regions and range over the world's oceans except the w. and c. Pacific and c. and e. Indian Oceans; they are rare in continental interiors. Except during the breeding seasons, they are mainly pelagic; they are often gregarious and sometimes nest in loose colonies. Their nests are slight depressions in ground, with or without lining. Usually there are 2, but sometimes as many as 4, eggs. Incubation is by both sexes; care of downy young, which remain near the nest for some time, is also shared. The fledgling period, the time from hatching to 1st flight, is usually short. Food, mainly animal matter, consists of eggs and young stolen from the nests of other birds; small adult birds are attacked and killed, as are mice and lemmings. They obtain marine animals by forcing other seabirds to drop or disgorge their catch. They also eat fish captured from the water, carrion, offal, mollusks, and other small invertebrates found along shores and inland. Very little plant matter is eaten; possibly it is picked up inadvertently with other food.

POMARINE JAEGER (Pomatorhine Skua) (*Stercorarius pomarinus*)

Appearance: Large (20–23 in.); the dark-phase adults are dusky brown all over, somewhat lighter below, and the cap is almost black. The rather stubby projection of the elongated central tail feathers beyond the rest of the tail varies from 1–2½ in. The bill is yellow with a blackish tip, and the legs and feet are blackish. The light phase differs only in being white below, with the white of the throat joined to a yellowish cheek patch; a band of dusky brown crosses the upper breast. Immature birds of the light phase lack the yellow cheek patch, and the white areas are brownish white, with barring of darker brown; those of the dark phase are somewhat paler than the adults. The downy young are unmarked, pale grayish brown, with brown bills, buffy legs, and buffy feet.

Voice: A strident *which-yew;* also squeaky whistles and a thin, shrill *week-week.*

Range and status: Breeds on tundra and coasts of Eurasia from n. Russia to ne. Siberia and the coasts of N. America from w. Alaska to n.-c. Mack. and ne. Keewatin; on Novaya Zemlya, New Siberian Is., Wrangel I., and from Melville, Bathurst, Cornwallis, and Devon Is. south to Victoria, Southampton, and s. Baffin Is., and on w.-c. Greenland. Winters at sea, mainly in the N. Atlantic but appears south of the equator and straggles into w. Mediterranean; rarer in N. Pacific, chiefly on e. shores, but has been taken and reported in good numbers off se. Australia. Has been recorded in Greater Antilles and, in migration, in the interior of N. America and Eurasia. Rather common.

Habitat: Tundra in summer; open seas and a variety of marine coasts in nonbreeding seasons.

Seasonal movements: Apr.–May and mid-Aug.–mid-Nov.; not so much a migration as a retreat before ice and a readvance with opening waters, in company with the seabirds from which they pirate their food; a movement irregular as to time, numbers participating, and final "destination."

Biology: Nest: A slight depression formed at the crest of some slight elevation on the tundra; lining seems to be debris accidentally blown in by wind, etc. Eggs: Invariably 2; varying shades of brownish green, sparingly spotted with browns and grays. Incubation: About 27–28 days. Age at 1st flight: 5–6 weeks. Food: Favored items seem to be fish and other marine organisms taken by gulls and terns, which it forces them to disgorge in flight. These items are usually caught in midair before they have fallen very far. Nests of other birds, such as gulls

The predatory Parasitic Jaeger nests on arctic tundra.

and terns, are robbed of their eggs and young, small mammals are captured, and much offal and refuse are consumed.

Suggested reading: D. A. Bannerman, *Birds of the British Isles,* Oliver and Boyd, Edinburgh, 1963, vol. 12, pp. 33–46.

PARASITIC JAEGER (Arctic Skua) (*Stercorarius parasiticus*)

Appearance: Smaller (16–21 in.) than the Pomarine, with sharp-pointed, elongated central tail feathers. The dark-phase adults are a medium dusky brown above, with a darker cap, and are light grayish brown below and on the cheeks. The light-phase birds have a white abdomen and throat, a grayish chest band, and a yellowish cheek patch, sometimes extended around back of the neck in an indistinct collar. Immature birds are brown above, with some lighter mottlings; they are dull whitish below, and the head is heavily streaked and barred with brown. The bill is grayish yellow with a blackish tip, and the legs and feet are blackish. The downy young are blackish brown above, somewhat lighter below.

Voice: A whining *wheee-ah, wheee-ah* squeal, harsh *cack-cack-cack*'s, and a loud *eea-ow* alarm note.

Range and status: Breeds on marine coasts and arctic islands and tundra from Melville I., Somerset I., c. Ellesmere I., w.-c. and e.-c. Greenland, Spitsbergen, Franz Josef Land, and n. Siberia south to the Aleutians, s. Alaska, the coasts of Hudson Bay, n. Que., n. Lab., s. Greenland, Iceland, n. British Isles, s. Scandinavia, s. Kamchatka, and the Komandorskie Is.; seldom south of

tundra. Winters at sea, mainly in N. Atlantic; greatest concentration is apparently off w. Europe, with some numbers off se. Australia. Its range is very similar to that of the Pomarine Jaeger in nonbreeding seasons. Probably the most numerous of the family.

Habitat: Tundra, rocky coasts with nearby flat islands, and shores; in winter open seas and offshore marine waters.

Seasonal movements: Like those of Pomarine: Apr.– June and mid-Aug.–Nov.

Biology: Nest: A simple depression in ground; scant lining of leaves and grasses may be purely adventitious. Eggs: 1–4, commonly 2; various shades of grayish green, spotted, blotched, and scrawled with browns. Incubation: 24–28 days, with 25–26 being more common. Age at 1st flight: 28–35 days, apparently with much variation. Food: Same food items as Pomarine Jaeger, obtained same way; eats more insects.

Suggested reading: A. C. Bent, *Life Histories of North American Gulls and Terns,* Dover, N.Y. (reprint of U.S. Nat. Mus. Bull. 113, 1921), 1963, pp. 14–20.

LONG-TAILED JAEGER (Long-tailed Skua) (*Stercorarius longicaudus*)

Appearance: Same size (20–23 in.) as the Pomarine Jaeger, but resembles the Parasitic Jaeger closely in general coloration. Its lengthened central tail feathers are much longer than those of the Parasitic (almost twice as long as the tail when fully grown), but growth stages make this an uncertain character. It is a lighter gray-brown above, with a more distinct blackish cap; the underparts are whiter, with no breast band; and the white of the throat and yellowish of the cheeks extend around the back of the neck, forming a more complete collar than in the Parasitic Jaeger. Apparently there is no dark phase. Immature birds have mere stubs of central tail feathers, are dull whitish, streaked and barred (heavily above) with dark brown and blackish. The bill is brownish with a blackish tip; the legs and feet, but for the blackish-tipped toes, are bluish gray. The downy young are rather light grayish brown.

Voice: Rather silent; a shrill, tremulous *kr-r-r-r, kri-kri-kri*, a loud *kree*, and a shrill *few-few-few-few* from the air.

Range and status: Breeds on tundra and marine coasts from Prince Patrick I., Melville I., n. Ellesmere I., n. Greenland, Spitsbergen, c. Novaya Zemlya, and Wrangel I. south to coasts of w. and n. Alaska, n. N.W.T., ne. Man., Southampton I., s. Baffin I., w.-c. and e.-c. Greenland, n. Eurasia (to s. Kamchatka in east).

Winters at sea in Atlantic, mainly south of the latitude of s. Europe, rarely in e. Pacific; recorded through interior of N. America and Europe in migration. Not so common as Pomarine and Parasitic Jaegers.

Habitat: Tundra and open seas.

Seasonal movements: Like that of other jaegers; Apr.–May and mid.-Aug.–Nov.

Biology: Nest: A scrape or natural depression on a small elevation, usually near a pond; apparently sometimes intentionally lined with grasses and small twigs. Eggs: 1–3, most often 2; a variety of greenish browns, irregularly spotted and blotched with browns. Incubation: 23 days. Age at 1st flight: 3 weeks. Food: As other jaegers, but noted more often catching its own fish or other marine organisms by ternlike dives, and also noted hunting lemmings and large insects more frequently.

Suggested reading: W. H. Drury, Jr., "Breeding Activities of Long-tailed Jaeger, Herring Gull, and Arctic Tern on Bylot Island, Northwest Territories, Canada," *Bird-banding*, vol. 31, pp. 63–78, 1960.

Strikingly elongated central tail feathers distinguish the adult Long-tailed Jaeger.

Skua

SKUA (Great Skua) (*Catharacta skua*)

Appearance: Large (20–24 in.); more gull-like than other jaegers, with the tail only slightly wedge-shaped and lacking any elongated central feathers. The adults are dark brown, mottled and streaked with lighter browns, with blackish flight feathers in the wing and tail. The larger flight feathers of the wing are white at the bases, showing as a whitish patch during flight. Immature birds are dull brownish gray where the adults are brown. The bill, legs, and feet are blackish. The Skua of the Antarctic is similar but larger.

Voice: A sharp, gull-like *skua-skua* or *skui*.

Range and status: Breeds in Iceland, the Faeroes, Shetland Is. and Orkney Is.; also the coasts of Antarctica, s. S. America, the Falklands, s. New Zealand, and islands in the antarctic seas south of the Atlantic and Indian Oceans. In the nonbreeding season this bird ranges through the N. Atlantic, rarely to the N. Pacific, and through the s. parts of the S. Hemisphere oceans. Very abundant in S. Hemisphere, locally common in c. and e. N. Atlantic; less common off Maritimes and New England; has straggled to B.C., Wash., and Calif.

Habitat: Rocky and barren marine coasts favored for nesting; disperses over open seas.

Seasonal movements: A wide dispersal after breeding; difficult to schedule, as nonbreeders remain at sea.

Biology: The Skua resents any intrusion by man (or any other enemy) at its nesting colonies and will continually harass any invader with vigorous diving attacks until it withdraws. Nest: In colonies; a shallow depression in higher ground, usually at base of cliff, inadvertently lined with grasses or debris. Eggs: 1–3, usually 2; grayish yellow to greenish browns, spotted and blotched with browns and purples. Incubation: 28 days. Age at 1st flight: 6–7 weeks. Food: As for other members of family. Fierce and rapacious, even eating its own young, should these wander too far from nest; able to pirate food from the larger species of seabirds, such as gannets and shearwaters. It sometimes gorges itself so much on offal and other food that it must eject some before it is able to fly.

Suggested reading: C. R. Eklund, "The Antarctic Skua," *Scientific American*, vol. 210, pp. 94–100, 1964.

GULLS AND TERNS (LARIDAE)

Gulls and terns are small to medium-sized (8–32 in.) aquatic birds with long, rather narrow pointed wings, short to medium legs, and feet webbed between the front toes only. They have a small, sometimes vestigial, hind toe. The bill is moderate in size, usually about as long as the head, rather straight and sharp-pointed in some and rounded and hooked in others. The tail also is moderate in size, seldom long; it is usually square, sometimes graduated or deeply forked. Plumage colors are most often grays, browns, black, and white; the bill, legs, and feet are often bright yellows or reds. The females are slightly smaller than the males; otherwise the sexes are alike. Of the 82 species found throughout the world, 46 occur in America. They fly and swim well, occupying both marine and a variety of freshwater habitats. Many species are migratory. They are gregarious and colonial. Nests vary from simple scrapes in the ground or debris of cliff ledges to burrows, including heaps of plant material on the ground, in trees, or even floating. Usually 1–4 eggs are laid. Incubation and care of young are performed by both sexes. The downy young usually remain in the vicinity of the nest until almost fledged. Food consists of a large variety of marine animals, insects, carrion, offal, berries, and some other vegetable matter. The family is divided into two subfamilies: gulls (Larinae) and terns (Sterninae).

Gulls are somewhat larger (10–32 in.) and heavier-bodied than the terns; their bills are stouter, more rounded, and slightly hooked. Their legs are proportionately longer than those of the terns; tails are moderate-sized, square or slightly rounded, very seldom forked. There are 43 species throughout the world; 24 of these occur or have been recorded in America. Generally feathers of the upper surface of the wing (often the flight feathers too) and the back are of the same color; this contiguous area is referred to as the mantle. In most species there are summer, winter, and immature plumages; often the full adult feathering is not attained until after the 3rd or 4th year. Gulls very rarely dive into the water for food as do terns. When swimming, they float higher on the water than do most ducks. They nest in colonies near both fresh water and salt water. The downy young swim readily. Gulls eat a larger variety of food than do the terns, partaking more often of garbage and offal. They also frequently prey on nests and young of other birds, primarily nearby colonial water birds; some species are active predators. Man's commercial fishery activities, with attendant disposal of food remains from barges offshore, have probably contributed considerably to increased numbers of many gull species; the concomitant range extensions cannot all be explained by climate amelioration over the last century.

Terns are slim-bodied, graceful seabirds, smaller (8–24 in.) than gulls. There are about 40 species found all over the world; 22 of these have been recorded in America. Their bills are usually sharp-pointed, fairly long, and commonly more slender than those of the gulls. Their legs are rather short, and their tails are long and commonly forked. A word of warning about using fork of tail for identification: when spread wide, forked tails may look straight and square tails may appear rounded. Like the gulls, the terns usually have a uniformly colored mantle and most species have a cap that contrasts with the color of the head and neck. Most species have 3 distinct plumages: breeding, nonbreeding, and immature, although the change from breeding to nonbreeding is not so extensive as that of most gulls. Most terns hover over the water, then plunge headfirst after their food, which consists mainly of small fish and plankton; those species nesting inland eat large numbers of insects. They swim well, but very infrequently. Nesting colonies are near water, either marine or fresh. Many species are strongly migratory.

GLAUCOUS GULL (*Larus hyperboreus*)

Appearance: One of the largest (26–32 in.) gulls; adults completely white-plumaged, including the tip and trailing edge of the wing, except for a very light gray mantle. In winter the head and neck are lightly streaked with pale grayish brown. The bill is yellow, with a red spot near the end of the lower mandible; the legs and feet are pinkish (paler in winter). Plumage of immature birds is streaked, barred, and mottled with light brownish gray; full adult plumage not attained until 4th year.

Voice: Usually silent, but makes some wailing notes

Except for its light gray mantle, the Glaucous Gull is completely white.

similar to those of Herring Gull; also croaks. It may be noisier on breeding grounds.

Range and status: Breeds on almost all arctic islands (including coasts of Greenland) south to the continental coasts of Eurasia from n. Russia to ne. Siberia and in N. America from sw. Alaska to n. Keewatin, Southampton I., n. Que., and c. Lab.; also locally in Iceland. Winters from s. edge of breeding area south to s. Calif., Great Lakes region, N.Y., n. and c. Europe, n. China, and Japan; casually to Ga., the Mediterranean, Black, and Caspian Seas. Rare in comparison with most gulls, but fairly common for a large predator.

Habitat: Mainly marine coasts; very rare in interior and then usually in large bodies of water or tundra.

Seasonal movements: Forced south by rigors of winter (mid-Oct.–mid-Dec.); it moves north as soon as possible, reaching the Far North May–June.

Biology: Nest: In colonies on cliff ledges, preferably facing sea; of grasses and mosses. Eggs: 2–4, usually 3; varying shades of yellowish or greenish brown, irregularly peppered, spotted, or blotched with darker browns and purplish grays. Incubation: 27–28 days. Age at 1st flight unknown. Food: Practically omnivorous; consumes any kind of animal food, captured living or found dead, or the remains of animal activity. Pursues, captures, and eats many smaller birds and mammals.

Suggested reading: I. J. Fergusen-Lees, "Studies of Less Familiar Birds: 123—Glaucous Gull," *British Birds,* vol. 56, pp. 263–267, 1963.

ICELAND GULL (*Larus glaucoides*)

Appearance: Smaller (23–26 in.) than the Glaucous Gull, but otherwise nearly identical in every plumage. However, it has a proportionately smaller bill.

Voice: Similar to Herring Gull's.

Range and status: Breeds from Ellesmere I., w. Greenland, and Iceland south to s. Baffin I. Winters from s. Lab. to N.Y. and N.J. (rarely in Great Lakes area) and from Iceland and n. British Isles to n. Europe. Rare.

Habitat: Marine coasts.

Seasonal movements: Pushed out of high arctic areas by winter, reaches more southerly parts of winter range Oct.–Nov. and returns to more northerly parts of breeding range May–June.

Biology: Nest: In colonies, on cliff ledges and along sandy beaches; a bulky affair of mosses and grasses. Eggs: 2–3; clay-colored, with brown markings. Incubation period unknown. Age at 1st flight unknown. Food: Almost any marine animal small enough to be swallowed or helpless enough to be killed and torn apart; offal, garbage, and some plant matter.

Suggested reading: D. A. Bannerman, *Birds of the British Isles,* Oliver and Boyd, Edinburgh, 1962, vol. 11, pp. 333–343.

GLAUCOUS-WINGED GULL (*Larus glaucescens*)

Appearance: Smaller (24–27 in.) than the Glaucous Gull, which it resembles closely, except that the larger flight feathers at the tip of the wing are gray with small white spots. In winter the adults' head and neck are clouded with pale brownish gray marks. Immatures are almost a uniform dark gray, more mottled above.

Voice: 3–5 *ka-ka-ka* notes in varying cadences; a high-pitched, buglelike *keer-keer-keer;* low, somber *klook-klook-klook* calls; low, somewhat braylike *ooo-anh, ooo-anh* notes; and others.

Range and status: Breeds in Komandorskie Is., islands in Bering Sea, Aleutian Is., and coast from se. Alaska to nw. Wash. Winters from breeding area to n. Japan and s. Baja Calif. and into Gulf of Calif. Has straggled to China, Hawaii, and Okla. Often, in winter, the most numerous large gull around West Coast garbage dumps.

Habitat: Great variety of marine coastal habitats, around fishing piers, fish canneries, garbage dumps, etc.

Seasonal movements: Mar.–May; Oct.–Nov.

Biology: Nest: In colonies; on rocks, cliff ledges, on ground under bushes; large, well made of seaweed, grasses, weeds, and debris. Eggs: 2–4, normally 3; buff and greenish brown, uniformly spotted and blotched with darker browns. Incubation: 26–28 days. Age at 1st flight: 35–54 days. Food: Omnivorous scavenger; consumes many marine animals, including sea urchins.

Suggested reading: Kees Vermeer, *The Breeding*

The downy young of the Great Black-backed Gull stay near the nest until almost fledged.

Ecology of the Glaucous-winged Gull on Mandarte Island, B.C., Occ. Papers B.C. Prov. Mus., no. 13, 104 pp., 1963.

GREAT BLACK-BACKED GULL (*Larus marinus*)

Appearance: Large (28–31 in.) black-mantled white gull with pink legs and feet, and a yellow bill having a red spot near the tip of the lower mandible. From above, only the very tip and trailing edge of the wing is white. In the 1st year the immature has a dark brown-mottled buffy mantle, and the head and neck are faintly streaked with pale brown. The tail has a narrow white tip, then becomes blackish brown, gradually fading into a pale brown mottling on a whitish rump. The bill is large and blackish. Full adult plumage assumed during the 4th year.

Voice: A harsh barking *arrg-arrg-arrg;* sometimes a guttural *oorg-oorg.*

Range and status: Almost strictly a coastal breeder on sw. Greenland, Iceland, British Isles, n. France, n. Russia, all of Scandinavia, and in N. America from n. Que., around Lab., Gulf of St. Lawrence, Nfld., the Maritimes, and New England to Long I., N.Y. Disperses in winter along seacoasts from Nfld., Greenland, and n. Europe to Fla., the Azores, Canaries, and Madeira Is., the Mediterranean, Black, and Caspian Seas; regularly into the Great Lakes region. Accidental inland. Becoming more common and expanding its range.

Habitat: Mainly seacoasts, sometimes open seas, and coasts of large bodies of fresh water.

Seasonal movements: Some populations sedentary; no migration, simply dispersal before adverse weather in winter and return in spring.

Biology: Nest: Sometimes in large colonies; a rather well made structure of seaweeds, grasses, sticks, other plant matter, and debris on ground, cliff ledges, etc. Eggs: 2–5, usually 3; varying from pale greenish brown to medium browns and murky yellows, more or less heavily spotted and blotched with darker browns, grays, and purplish grays. Incubation: 26–28 days. Age at 1st flight: 7–8 weeks. Food: Varied menu of fish, garbage, offal, and eggs and young of other colonial seabirds, as well as a great variety of shellfish and other marine animals.

Suggested reading: D. A. Bannerman, *Birds of the British Isles,* Oliver and Boyd, Edinburgh, 1962, vol. 11, pp. 310–322.

SLATY-BACKED GULL (*Larus schistisagus*)

Very similar to the Great Black-backed Gull, but smaller (27 in.) and with a mantle not quite so dark. Breeds on the coasts of e. Siberia, the Kurile Is., and n. Japan, ranging south to e. China, casually to Formosa and Amoy in winter. Casual in the Aleutians, the Pribilofs, and the coasts of Alaska.

WESTERN GULL (*Larus occidentalis*)

Appearance: Fairly large (24–27 in.) white gull with dark gray mantle; very similar to Great Black-backed, but mantle is lighter and has less white at tip of wing. Immature birds also resemble Great Black-backed but are generally a darker brown in 1st year. Legs and feet are pale pink; bill is yellow with a reddish spot.

Voice: Low, throaty *kuk-kuk-kuk* and a high, quavering, rather nasal *whee-ee-ee;* also other *kee-ah* notes.

Range and status: Resident along Pacific Coast from n. Wash. to w.-c. Baja Calif. and in the Gulf of Calif.; dispersal after breeding, north to B.C. and south to w.-c. Mexico. Recorded once from Chicago, Ill. Common.

Habitat: Marine coasts and estuaries; frequents beaches, piers, and dumps.

Seasonal movements: Only dispersal after breeding and by nonbreeders.

Biology: Nest: On rock ledges, grassy hillsides, near, sometimes on, beaches; made of weeds or grasses, often used several years and then becoming quite bulky. Eggs: 2–4, usually 3; various shades of yellowish or greenish brown, spotted and blotched with darker browns and purplish grays. Incubation: 24 days. Age at 1st flight: 7–8 weeks. Food: Now obtains much of its food from garbage dumps, refuse from fishing operations, etc., but formerly to a great extent, and frequently still, captures own fish and other marine animals; it is also a scavenger of dead animals along beaches. In common with other gulls, is able to eat mollusks and other shellfish by dropping them from a height onto rocks (which unhappily includes highways) to crack the shells.

Suggested reading: A. C. Bent, *Life Histories of North American Gulls and Terns*, Dover, N.Y. (reprint of U.S. Nat. Mus. Bull. 113, 1921), 1963, pp. 89–98.

LESSER BLACK-BACKED GULL (*Larus fuscus*)

Smaller (20–22 in.) than the Great Black-backed Gull, which it otherwise resembles very closely, except that its legs and feet are bright yellow in the breeding season and brownish yellow in nonbreeders and immatures. Ranges from Iceland and n. Europe to c. Africa and the Persian Gulf; has straggled to Greenland, N.Y., and Md.

HERRING GULL (*Larus argentatus*)

Appearance: Medium- to large-sized (22½–26 in.), with a medium gray mantle and black-tipped wings. There are white spots in the black at the tip, the entire trailing edge of the wing is narrowly bordered with white, and the rest of the plumage is white. Legs and feet are pinkish (varying from 1 geographical area to another, somewhat duller in winter), and the rather sturdy bill is yellow, with a red spot near the tip of the lower mandible. In winter the adults are streaked with brownish gray above on the head and neck. During the 1st year, birds are streaked and mottled with dark brownish gray, and the flight feathers of the wing and tail are blackish brown; in the 2nd year, the browns become considerably lighter, almost whitish below, and the gray of the mantle begins to appear at the shoulders. The rump also becomes whitish, and white mottlings show on the base of the tail.

Lesser Black-backed Gull

Voice: A variety of calls: *keee-kee ek, kee-ek kee-kee;* a *yuk-yuk-yuk-yuckle;* squeals, nasal caws, and mewing.

Range and status: Breeds on arctic coasts and tundra from Iceland, n. Eurasia and n. N. America (Banks I., s. Ellesmere I., and nw. Greenland) south through a variety of inland freshwater and saltwater habitats and seacoasts to n. France, s. Scandinavia, s. Russia, islands in the Mediterranean, Black, and Caspian Seas, Lake Baikal, ne. Siberia, s. Alaska, s. B.C., n. Alta., e. Mont., s. Man., the Great Lakes region, the Gulf of St. Lawrence, Nfld., and along the Atlantic Coast to Md.; also recorded in Azores, Madeira, and Canary Is. Winters from s. half of this range to Panama, Barbados, n. and c. Africa, Arabia, n. India, se. Asia, and n. Philippines. Most common of the larger gulls; possibly most widespread of the Laridae; rare, however, in interior of c. and w. U.S. Probably the best-known and most widely studied gull in N. America and Europe.

Habitat: Almost ubiquitous; appears fairly well out to sea, along all sorts of shores, on farmlands, and at garbage dumps.

Seasonal movements: Returns to n. areas as soon as thawing permits; disperses over wide area, and nonbreeders may remain outside normal breeding range in summer.

Biology: Nest: Colonial; on ground above highwater marks along coasts and near shores of inland bodies of water; a rather crude structure of sticks, weeds, seaweeds, and/or grasses; material seldom brought any distance. Eggs: 2–6, normally 3; color ranges from pale blues to dark brownish greens, varyingly spotted and blotched with dark browns, black, and grays. Incubation: 25–27 days. Age at 1st flight: About 6 weeks. Food: As with other gulls, a great variety of marine animals found along beaches or on ground, stolen from other seabirds, or taken by the gull itself, as well as eggs and young of other birds, small mammals and other vertebrates, offal, large insects, and both plant and animal remains culled from garbage heaps.

Suggested reading: N. Tinbergen, *The Herring Gull's World*, Collins, London, 1953, 255 pp.

CALIFORNIA GULL (*Larus californicus*)

Appearance: Smaller (20–23 in.) than, but very similar in all plumages to, the Herring Gull; its bill is a little slimmer, there are larger white spots (mirrors) in the black wing tips, and the legs and feet are greenish yellow. In immature birds, the dark spot near the tip of the bill may be almost a ring.

Voice: A great variety, similar to noises made by other gulls; 1 is a high, thin *kee-ah, kee-ah.*

Range and status: Breeds from n.-c. Mack. and c. Man. south to se. Ore., ne. Calif., nw. Nev., n. Utah, nw. Wyo., c. Mont., and e.-c. N.Dak. Winters from s. Wash.

Hovering in midair, two Herring Gulls scan the land or water below for edible refuse.

and e. Idaho south, mainly along the Pacific Coast, to s. Baja Calif., the Gulf of Calif., w. Mexico, and s. Guatemala. Has straggled to Alaska, Kans., Tex., Vera Cruz, and Hawaii. Common.

Habitat: Marshes, freshwater lakes and rivers in summer; in addition, in winter and during nonbreeding seasons, farmlands and seacoast.

Seasonal movements: Northeastward Apr.–May and to south and southwestward mid-Aug.–early Nov.

Biology: Nest: On ground of islets or near lake or marsh shores; made of grasses, sticks, and/or weeds; sometimes bulky. Those found in water were probably built before level of lake or pond rose. Eggs: 2–5, most often 3; light to dark greenish browns, evenly marked with spots and blotches of browns and grays. Incubation: 23–27 days. Age at 1st flight unknown. Food: Inland, consumes large numbers of the larger insects; the gulls that did so much to control the plague of locusts descending on the early Mormon settlers in Utah were mostly this species. Also eats various invertebrates, small fish, small mammals, young birds, and some birds' eggs;

The Ring-billed Gull commonly breeds on islands and along the shores of inland lakes.

along marine coasts it scavenges actively and is also active at dumps.

Suggested reading: W. H. Behle and W. A. Goates, "Breeding Biology of the California Gull," *Condor*, vol. 59, pp. 235–246, 1957.

RING-BILLED GULL (*Larus delawarensis*)

Appearance: Medium-sized (18–21 in.) gray-mantled white gull with black wing tips. Further differs from the larger Herring Gull and California Gull in having yellowish legs and feet, black at the very tip of the 2 outermost flight feathers of the wing, and a black ring around the bill near the tip. During the 1st year immatures are streaked brownish above, with a brownish gray mantle and dark gray flight feathers. The rump is whitish, and the tail has a rather narrow black band almost at the tip. They are also whitish below; their legs and feet are pinkish, and the yellow bill is black-tipped.

Voice: A loud, shrill *kree-kreee* of alarm, softer *kow-kow-kow* notes from circling flocks, and occasionally a low, somber *kowk*.

Range and status: Breeds from c. Wash., Alta., Sask., and c. Man. south to ne. Calif., Idaho, Colo., se. Wyo., and ne. S.Dak. and from c. Que. and ne. Nfld. to n. Mich., s. Ont., and n. N.Y. Winters along the Pacific Coast from s. B.C. to El Salvador, in the interior of Mexico, and in e. U.S. from the s. Great Lakes region to the Gulf Coast, and along the Atlantic Coast from the

Maritimes to s. Fla. and Cuba. Accidental in Hawaii, Bermuda, Jamaica, Martinique, and the Azores. Common.

Habitat: Lakes, rivers, seacoasts, estuaries; breeds mainly on shores and islets of freshwater lakes. Ranges over fields, garbage dumps, and sand flats.

Seasonal movements: Mar.–May and Sept.–Nov.; large movement through Mississippi Valley.

Biology: Nest: On ground of upper beaches, usually among boulders; made of small sticks, weeds, and grasses. Eggs: 2–4, commonly 3; various shades of yellowish, pinkish, or greenish browns, irregularly speckled, spotted, and blotched with browns and grays. Incubation: About 21 days. Age at 1st flight unknown. Food: Large insects, worms, small mammals and other small vertebrates in interior; also fish and, on seacoasts, other marine animals and refuse on beaches. Eats eggs and young of other birds and culls various items from garbage dumps.

Suggested reading: A. C. Bent, *Life Histories of North American Gulls and Terns*, Dover, N.Y. (reprint of U.S. Nat. Mus. Bull. 113, 1921), 1963, pp. 132–140.

BLACK-TAILED GULL (*Larus crassirostris*)

Medium-sized (ca. 19 in.), with yellow legs, feet, and bill, and a dark gray mantle. The bill has both a red spot and a black ring, and the tail has a rather broad black band almost at the tip. The immature bird resembles that of the Ring-billed, but its tail is almost entirely black. Breeds in e. Asia from se. Siberia to China, and winters from n. Japan southward; has straggled to Calif.

MEW GULL (Short-billed Gull) (*Larus canus*)

Appearance: Small (16–18 in.) gray-mantled white gull with black wing tips. Very similar to the Ring-billed, but its bill is noticeably shorter and entirely yellow, the mantle is somewhat darker, and white spots in the black wing tips are larger. Head, neck, and underparts of 1st-year birds are light brownish gray; upperparts are medium grayish brown, and the rump is grayish, mottled with brownish. The tail has a narrow white tip, then a rather broad dark brown band; the rest is grayish, marked with brownish.

Voice: A mewing, from which it acquires its name, and a *hiya-hiya-hiya* in a high-pitched querulous voice.

Range and status: Breeds in n. British Isles, n. Europe, c. and s. Siberia, Sakhalin I., the Caucasus, s. Caspian Sea, and c. Alaska, c. Yuk., and nw. Mack. south to se. Alaska, n. B.C., n. Alta., and n. Sask. Winters from s. edge of breeding area to Mediterranean Sea, s. China, Formosa, Japan, and s. Calif. Straggles to Greenland, Iceland, Spitsbergen, Canary Is., Wyo., and Mass. Common in Alaska; rather rare along Pacific Coast of U.S.

Habitat: In breeding season, mainly lakes, rarely seacoasts; in winter, favors coastal waters and estuaries.

Seasonal movements: Along w. U.S. coasts, Apr.–May and late Aug.–mid-Dec.

Biology: Nest: In small colonies, on ground or in trees near water (tops of spruces near Alaskan lakes); made of twigs and grasses. Eggs: 2–5, usually 3; light yellowish brown to greenish brown, spotted, blotched, and sometimes scrawled with darker browns and grays. Incubation: 23–26 days. Age at 1st flight: 4–5 weeks. Food: At breeding lakes, insects (many water beetles) and small fish; elsewhere, mollusks (habitually drops these from a height of about 30 ft. on rocks until cracked open), small fish, and other marine animals; also found near garbage dumps.

Suggested reading: D. A. Bannerman, *Birds of the British Isles*, Oliver and Boyd, Edinburgh, 1962, vol. 11, pp. 270–279.

BLACK-HEADED GULL (*Larus ridibundus*)

Small (14–15 in.) white gull with dark brown head, bright red bill, legs, and feet, and light gray mantle; only the very tips of the larger flight feathers of the wing are black. In winter the head becomes white, with a dark brownish spot behind and below the eye. Immature birds resemble those of Laughing Gull, but they are much lighter brown and have yellow legs and feet. Breeds in Iceland and n. and c. Eurasia. Winters south to n. Africa, s. Asia, and the Philippines. Has straggled to Greenland, Lab., Nfld., Mass., N.Y., Mexico, Barbados, the Grenadines, and the Aleutians. Has summered in N.S. and may some day breed there.

LAUGHING GULL (*Larus atricilla*)

Appearance: Small (15½–17 in.) white gull, with a slate-gray head and dark gray mantle; there is no white in the wing tip. In the breeding season the white underparts become pink. In fall and winter the head and neck are white, with brownish gray mottling on top of the head and about the eyes. The young in their 1st winter have a grayish brown head, neck, and mantle; the rump is grayish, becoming white at the tail. The tail is white, with a broad black band almost at the tip; the throat and underparts are white. The legs, feet, and bill of the adult, summer and winter, are dark brownish red; those of the young are dusky.

Voice: A hoarse, gooselike *ka-ha, ka-ha,* most commonly during flight; elsewhere a loud, piercing *ha-ha-ha-ha-ha-ha-haa-haa-haa,* earning it its common name.

Range and status: Breeds locally along the coasts of e. N. America from N.S. to Yucatan; the shores of the W. Indies and n. Venezuela, the coasts of Sonora and Sinaloa, and the shores of the Salton Sea in s. Calif. Nonbreeding birds range, in addition, to the e. Great

The Mew Gull, named for its distinctive cry, is sometimes called the Short-billed Gull.

The handsome Black-headed Gull is a rare straggler in North America.

The graceful Franklin's Gull often hawks for insects as it flies.

Lakes, British Honduras, Panama, and Trinidad. Winters from s. Mexico to n. Peru and from the Gulf Coast and N.C. to n. S. America. Moves inland along larger rivers. Has straggled to Greenland, N.Mex., Colo., Nebr., S.Dak., Wis., and Tenn. Formerly more common; besides collecting it for millinery purposes, man has usurped many of the beaches on which it bred.

Habitat: Marine coasts, bays, and saltwater marshes.

Seasonal movements: Returns to breeding areas Apr.–early May and departs mid-Sept.–mid-Oct.

Biology: Nest: In compact colonies, on ground or on clumps of grass of salt marshes or marshy beaches; large and well made of grasses and sedges, with a lining of finer grasses. Eggs: 2–5, usually 3; yellowish or greenish browns, irregularly spotted, splotched, and scrawled with dark browns and grays. Incubation: About 20 days. Age at 1st flight unknown. Food: Mainly small fish, mostly fry, caught at the water surface or stolen from pelicans (the gull often perches on the pelican's head as it completes its catch of fish and steals them from the pouch). It also eats the eggs and nestlings of other seabirds, small invertebrates gleaned from the beaches, and some garbage.

Suggested reading: A. C. Bent, *Life Histories of North American Gulls and Terns*, Dover, N.Y. (reprint of U.S. Nat. Mus. Bull. 113, 1921), 1963, pp. 154–162.

FRANKLIN'S GULL (*Larus pipixcan*)

Appearance: A small (15½–17 in.) black-headed white gull with a gray mantle. The tip of the wing is white, with a large central black patch; the bill, legs, and feet are deep red. In the breeding season the breast becomes rosy. In fall and winter the head is entirely white, except for a small brownish gray patch at the back. The bill, legs, and feet are darker red; otherwise the plumage is the same as in summer. Resembles Laughing Gull, but legs are shorter and trailing edge of wing has more white; both are good marks when bird is on the ground. Immature birds resemble the adults in winter, but the mantle and patch at the back of the head, which are conjoined, are much browner, and there is a rather broad subterminal band of black on the tail.

Voice: While feeding, a shrill *kuk-kuk-kuk-kuk;* also a soft *krrruk* and low clucks, plus a loud, pleasant, nasal *pway.*

Range and status: Breeds from se. Alta., s. Sask., and sw. Man. south to c. Ore., c. Mont., n. Utah, ne. S.Dak., sw. Minn., and nw. Iowa; nonbreeders straggle beyond this range. Winters along the Pacific Coast from Guatemala to the Galápagos Is. and Chile, and along the Gulf Coast from Tex. to La. Migrates through the U.S. between the Rockies and the Mississippi River, rarely farther east, and through c. Mexico. Has straggled to Hawaii, N.B., Mass., Va., and the W. Indies. Common.

Habitat: The prairies (often follows the plow and has thus earned the name of prairie pigeon); marshes and lakes; marine coasts in winter.

Seasonal movements: Arrives at breeding marshes late Mar.–mid-June and departs Aug.–early Nov. Fall migration more erratic in timing and direction. Large flights in daytime.

Biology: Nest: Large colonies (1 recorded as 15,000–20,000 nests) among reeds and rushes in 1–6 ft. of water; a floating mass of old reeds with well-formed cups anchored to fresh vegetation. Eggs: 2–4, usually 3; dull browns and greenish browns, spotted, splotched, and scrawled with darker browns. Incubation: 18–20(?) days. Age at 1st flight unknown. Food: During the nesting season, almost exclusively insects; also worms and other small invertebrates. During the winter, small marine invertebrates and small fish. Very rarely eats eggs of other birds.

Suggested reading: A. C. Bent, *Life Histories of North American Gulls and Terns*, Dover, N.Y. (reprint of U.S. Nat. Mus. Bull. 113, 1921), 1963, pp. 163–174.

BONAPARTE'S GULL (*Larus philadelphia*)

Appearance: Slightly smaller (12–14 in.) than Franklin's Gull, with dark gray head and light gray mantle. The wing tip is white with narrow, black edging. The bill is blackish, and the legs and feet are bright red.

High in a spruce, a Bonaparte's Gull incubates its eggs on a nest built of twigs and moss.

In fall and winter the head becomes white, except for a blackish spot behind the eye. Immature birds resemble winter adults, but they have more black on the wing tips, a brownish streak angling across the gray mantle of the wing, and a narrow subterminal black band on the tail.

Voice: A strident *cheer* and, while feeding, low, muttering whistled notes.

Range and status: Breeds from the Yukon River Valley of Alaska, s. Yuk., nw. Mack., n. Sask., ne. Man., and w.-c. Ont. south to c. B.C., s. Alta., and w.-c. Sask.; nonbreeders range farther south and east. Winters along coasts from sw. B.C. to s. Baja Calif. and w.-c. Mexico, from Long I., N.Y., to e.-c. Fla., and along the Gulf Coast from Tex. to w.-c. Fla.; casually farther north and to Bermuda, Cuba, and Haiti. Has straggled to Hawaii, the Bahamas, Greenland, Iceland, and n. Europe. Uncommon but widespread.

Habitat: Marshes, lakes, bays, marine waters and shores; breeds in muskeg and coniferous swamps.

Seasonal movements: Moves northward and inland late Mar.–early June and returns Aug.–Nov.

Biology: Nest: Usually solitary pairs or small groups, about 10–20 ft. above water surface in conifers of muskegs; made of twigs and moss. Eggs: 2–4, usually 3; light reddish brown to darker browns, evenly spotted or irregularly blotched with dark browns and greenish browns. Incubation and age at 1st flight unknown. Food:

Insects, worms, and other small invertebrates inland; from ocean waters, small fish, crustaceans, snails, etc.

Suggested reading: A. C. Twomey, "Breeding Habits of Bonaparte's Gull," *Auk,* vol. 51, pp. 291–296, 1934.

LITTLE GULL (*Larus minutus*)

A small (10–11½ in.) white gray-mantled, black-headed gull of Eurasia that has straggled to Sask., Ont., Ohio, w. Pa., N.Y. (5 scattered records), Maine, Mass., N.J., the Maritime Provinces, Bermuda, and Greenland. The wings are gray above and below, becoming darker at the tip, and each of the flight feathers is tipped with white. The bill, legs, and feet are red. In winter the head becomes white, except for the black spot behind the eye and the grayish rear half of the cap. The immature bird resembles the winter adult, but the rear half of the cap is dark brown, as is the back. The blackish of the wing tips extends in a diagonal line across the wing to the body; it also has a low, broad blackish triangle near the tip of the white tail.

HEERMANN'S GULL (*Larus heermanni*)

Appearance: Medium-sized (18–21 in.) grayish gull with a whitish head, dark gray mantle, and white-tipped black tail. Legs and feet are dark gray, and the red bill is ringed with grayish near the tip. In winter the head and neck are grayish brown. The immature bird is brownish

Heermann's Gull

gray all over, somewhat darker on the head and mantle, with a narrow white tip to the tail.

Voice: Low, muted cackles in winter; also a rather high *whee-ee* and a *cow-auk, cow-auk, cow-auk*.

Range and status: Breeds on islands off w. Mexico from nw. Baja Calif. and the Gulf of Calif. to w. Nyarit and Sinaloa; nonbreeders range north to sw. B.C. Winters from Ore. to Guatemala. Fairly common.

Habitat: Marine shores and open water.

Seasonal movements: Returns to breeding islands in Mar. and departs May–June.

Biology: Nest: Large colonies; an unlined, small depression in ground of island. Eggs: 2–3; light yellowish gray to bluish gray, faintly spotted with grayish browns, lavenders, and grayish blues. Incubation and age at 1st flight unknown. Food: Largely fish, often stolen from pelicans, cormorants, etc., and animal matter found on beaches.

Suggested reading: A. C. Bent, *Life Histories of North American Gulls and Terns*, Dover, N.Y. (reprint of U.S. Nat. Mus. Bull. 113, 1921), 1963, pp. 148–154.

IVORY GULL (*Pagophila eburnea*)

A small (15–17 in.) all-white, rather pigeonlike gull, with black feet and a small yellow-tipped greenish bill. The immature has a light brownish gray head, and its mantle is mottled with brownish gray. It breeds on the northernmost arctic islands and coasts south to n. Melville I., n. Baffin I., n.-c. coasts of Greenland, n. Spitsbergen, n. Novaya Zemlya, and n. Severnaya Zemlya. Winters over the drift ice south to coasts of n. N. America and n. Eurasia; casually to Maine, rarely to Mass., N.Y., N.J., and Great Britain. Has straggled inland to B.C., Colo., Man., Wis., Ont., and Europe. Very rare in s. parts of range.

Suggested reading: S. D. MacDonald and A. H. MacPherson, *Breeding Places of the Ivory Gull in Canada*, Nat. Mus. Can. Bull. 183, pp. 111–117, 1960.

BLACK-LEGGED KITTIWAKE (*Rissa tridactyla*)

Appearance: A smallish (16–18 in.) white gull with a light gray mantle and solid, straight-edged black wing tips (no white spots). It has black legs and feet, and a yellow bill. From below, the wing is almost immaculate white, except for the black tip. In winter a patch of light gray extends from the crown to the rear of the neck (sometimes to the side of the chest). There is also a spot of dark gray before the eye and another behind it. The immature has a blackish collar on the nape, a blackish spot behind the eye, black-tipped tail feathers, more extensive black wing tips (with some whitish spots), and a dark gray line angling toward the body from the bend of the wing.

Black-legged Kittiwakes nest in colonies on rocky cliffs near the sea.

Voice: A loud, harsh, strident rendition of its name *kittiwake*, or a rough approximation, as *kakaweek*, and catlike moans *a-a-a.*

Range and status: Breeds coastally from Somerset I., n. Baffin I., w.-c. and ne. Greenland, Spitsbergen, Franz Josef Land, Severnaya Zemlya, New Siberian Is., Wrangel I., and nw. Alaska south to se. Que., Nfld., British Isles, nw. France, n. Scandinavia, s. Novaya Zemlya, scattered localities on n.-c. Siberian coast, ne. Siberia, Kurile Is., the Aleutians, sw. Alaska, and Kodiak I. There are large gaps in this range, particularly in ne. N. America. Winters from s. edge of polar ice cap to Japan, nw. Baja Calif., N.J., Bermuda, nw. Africa, and in the Mediterranean Sea; rarer at s. edge. Has been recorded from Wyo., Colo., Mo., Iowa, Wis., Ill., Ohio, nw. Pa., and the interior of Eurasia. Common.

Habitat: Marine coasts during breeding season; pelagic other seasons. Seldom comes so close to land outside nesting times as do other gulls.

Seasonal movements: Returns to nesting sites Mar.–mid-June and departs mid-July–mid-Oct.

Biology: Nest: On cliff ledges near sea; made of mud and algae stuck to bare rock and lined with grasses and mosses. Eggs: 1–3, most commonly 2; bluish gray or browns, with pinkish, yellowish, or greenish casts, spotted, splotched, and scrawled with darker browns and grays. Incubation: 21–24 days. Age at 1st flight: At least 5 weeks; some longer than 6 weeks. Food: Fish and crustaceans picked from surface of sea; beginning to feed more commonly than in years past on offal from fishing vessels, etc.

Suggested reading: J. C. Coulson and E. White, "A Study of Colonies of the Kittiwake," *Ibis,* vol. 98, pp. 63–79, 1956.

RED-LEGGED KITTIWAKE (*Rissa brevirostris*)

Smaller (14–16 in.) than the very similar Black-legged Kittiwake, but the legs and feet are bright red, and the wings are gray below, especially near the black tip. Immature birds lack the dark gray streak on the wing and the black on the tail, but otherwise they resemble young Black-legged. The voice is very similar, although said to be higher in pitch than that of the other kittiwake. Breeds on the Komandorskie and Pribilof Is. in the Bering Sea and winters on open waters of same region; a straggler was recorded from nw. Ore. Habitat and biology are much like those of the Black-legged Kittiwake.

ROSS' GULL (*Rhodostethia rosea*)

Appearance: Small (13–14 in.) white gull, with a light gray mantle, a wedge-shaped white tail, and a narrow black necklace. The blackish bill is relatively small; the legs and feet are bright red. In spring and summer the head and body are bright pinkish. The wing is gray to the tip, with white on the trailing edge. In fall and winter the necklace is lost, a patch of gray appears on the rear part of the crown, and the pink fades to almost white. Immature birds have the gray of the mantle extending up the back to the forehead. A black line extends from the wing tip to the bend of the wing, then angles backward to the body. The longer, central tail feathers are tipped with black, and the rest of the plumage is white.

Voice: A rather high, melodic *a-wo, a-wo, a-wo* and a quarreling *mi-aw, mi-aw.*

Range and status: Breeds in lower reaches of rivers in ne. Siberia that empty into the Arctic Ocean; disperses throughout neighboring seas, seldom leaving them even in winter; recorded regularly along n. and w. Alaskan coasts. Rather rare.

Habitat: Arctic shores and seas.

Seasonal movements: Reaches nesting grounds late May–June and departs Aug.

Biology: Nest: In small colonies; hollows in dead grasses and mosses, lined with similar material. Eggs: 2–3, usually 3; deep olive-green, spotted with chocolate-brown. Incubation: More than 3 weeks. Age at 1st flight unknown. Food: Insects on breeding grounds; crustaceans, fish, mollusks, marine worms, offal from fishing boats, etc.

Suggested reading: S. A. Buturlin, "The Breeding Grounds of the Rosy Gull," *Ibis,* vol. 6, series 8, pp. 131–139, 333–337, 1906.

Ross' Gull

SABINE'S GULL (*Xema sabini*)

Appearance: Small (13–14 in.) gray-headed white gull with a black edging separating the gray from the white of the neck. The mantle is medium gray, and there is a triangle of white on the wing extending from the bend of the wing and the black tip to the inner rear edge. The tail is well forked; the legs and feet are dark gray, and the blackish bill has a yellow tip. In winter the adults have white heads, with some grayish mottling at the nape. Immature birds have a black-tipped tail and a brownish gray mantle that extends over the back to the white forehead.

Voice: A harsh, grating ternlike note and a high-pitched chatter.

Range and status: Breeds along arctic coasts from nw. Alaska to Melville Peninsula, Southampton I., Victoria I., Ellesmere I., Baffin I., Greenland (except s. part), n. Spitsbergen, Franz Josef Land, and Siberia from Taimyr Peninsula to Anadyr. Winters in Pacific south to n. Peru and also in the Atlantic (winter range poorly known). Somewhat common.

Habitat: Arctic coasts and tundra in summer; pelagic in winter.

Seasonal movements: A very few migrate through the Great Plains, Great Basin, and lower Colorado River regions. Moves north May–early July and south late Aug.–Oct.

In winter, the gray head of the Sabine's Gull becomes almost pure white.

Biology: Nests: In loose colonies on low, wet, or marshy ground near the sea or lakes; a depression in the moss or among low tundra plants. Eggs: 2–3, usually 3; yellowish and greenish browns, irregularly spotted and blotched with darker browns. Incubation: 23–26 days. Age at 1st flight unknown. Food: Insects, small crustaceans, small fish, offal, and eggs of neighboring nesting species.

Suggested reading: D. A. Bannerman, *Birds of the British Isles*, Oliver and Boyd, Edinburgh, 1962, vol. 11, pp. 201–219.

GULL-BILLED TERN (*Gelochelidon nilotica*)

Appearance: Medium-sized (13–14½ in.) white tern with a fairly stout, rather sharp-pointed black bill, a black cap, a light gray mantle, and a shallowly forked tail. The legs and feet are black. In winter the head and neck become white, the nape is tinged with gray, and there is a crescent before the eye and a streak behind the eye, both brownish gray. The immature bird resembles the adults in winter, but the patch on the hind neck is brownish, and it lacks the crescentic mark before the eye.

Voice: A low, rather buzzy *za-za-za;* a loud, monotoned, 2-syllabled *gaawaak*, and a soft *gor-rok* at the nest.

Range and status: Breeds discontinuously along marine coasts and in isolated inland areas; in s. Calif., around Baja Calif., and down w. Mexico to Guerrero, around the Gulf Coast from ne. Mexico to s. Fla., in c. Fla., from Md. to s. Fla., from se. Panama to nw. Peru, in the Bahamas, and coastally in the Greater Antilles. Also around Europe and in se. Europe, in Asia Minor, in se. Siberia, in Mesopotamia, along the coasts of Iran and into nw. India, along the coasts of s. China and into lower river valleys, on the coasts of e. and w. Australia, and in se. Australia. Retreats from more northerly regions in winter and ranges more extensively to the south, especially into e. Africa and s. Asia. Common in some areas.

Habitat: Seacoasts, lakes, marshes, grasslands.

Seasonal movements: Arrives on n. breeding grounds Apr.–May and returns south Sept.–Oct.

Biology: Nest: In colonies (mostly outside U.S.); solitary, or in small, scattered groups at edges of larger colonies of other tern species; on the ground; a mere scrape in the sand of beaches or mud edges of lakes and rivers, sparsely lined with stones, bits of shells, and grasses, or a more substantial structure of grasses and weeds on ground near water. Eggs: 2–5, usually 3; light yellowish or pinkish brown, irregularly spotted and blotched with dark browns. Incubation: 22–23 days. Age at 1st flight: 4–5 weeks. Food: Almost entirely insects caught in midair; some crustaceans, small fish, and other small vertebrates.

Suggested reading: D. A. Bannerman, *Birds of the*

The Gull-billed Tern is so named because of its rather stout black bill.

British Isles, Oliver and Boyd, Edinburgh, 1962, vol. 11, pp. 119–127.

TRUDEAU'S TERN (*Sterna trudeaui*)

A medium-sized (14 in.) pale gray tern with a white head and upper neck. It has a small spot of black before the eye and a black streak behind the eye. It breeds in Argentina and Uruguay, ranging into Chile. Audubon described the 1st specimen known to science from 1 taken at Egg Harbor, N.J., the only known N. American record.

FORSTER'S TERN (*Sterna forsteri*)

Appearance: Medium-sized (14–16½ in.) black-capped white tern with a light gray mantle and deeply forked tail. Very similar to the Common Tern, but with lighter wings when viewed from above, especially near the tips. The tail is pale gray, and the black-tipped bill is more orange, less red. The legs and feet are bright orange-red. In fall and winter the head is white, except for a streak of black extending backward from the eye; the bill becomes blackish, and the legs and feet are duller and more yellowish. The immature is like the adult in winter, but sides of head, back of neck, and mantle are brownish.

Voice: A low, harsh, grating or buzzing *tza-a-ap*, a nasal *kee-ar*, shorter than the similar call of the Common Tern, and a soft *weet-weet*.

Range and status: Breeds from the s. Prairie Provinces of Canada south to s.-c. Calif., n. Utah, e. Colo., w. Nebr., n. Iowa, s. Minn., and se. Wis., and along the coasts from Tamaulipas and s. Tex. to se. Md. Winters, mainly but not entirely, along marine coasts, from c. Calif. to sw. Guatemala, from Vera Cruz around the Gulf Coast to w. Fla., and from Va. to ne. Fla.; in migration throughout c. U.S. and from the Great Lakes region and New England south. Rather common.

Habitat: Freshwater and saltwater marshes, lakes, marine shores, oceans.

Seasonal movements: Apr.–May and Aug.–Oct.; dispersal of nonnesters confuses timetable.

Biology: Nest: In loose or small colonies, even solitary near water (sometimes on floating masses of vegetation); a depression in matted reeds or grasses, lined with reeds and fine grasses, or a depression in mud or sand, lined with bits of shell and grasses. Sometimes grebes' nests are appropriated and refurbished. Eggs: 2–6, usually 3; various shades of greenish or reddish brown, spotted, splotched, and scrawled with darker browns. Markings may be wreathed around larger end of egg or spread evenly over entire surface. Incubation: 23 days. Age at 1st flight unknown. Food: Insects caught on wing or plucked from surface of water, fish, mollusks, other invertebrates snatched from waters or scavenged from beaches; also dives into water after prey.

Suggested reading: A. C. Bent, *Life Histories of*

Forster's Tern breeds near inland lakes but winters along marine coasts.

North American Gulls and Terns, Dover, N.Y. (reprint of U.S. Nat. Mus. Bull. 113, 1921), 1963, pp. 229–235.

COMMON TERN (*Sterna hirundo*)

Appearance: Medium-sized (13–16 in.) black-capped white tern with light gray mantle (darker than that of Forster's Tern) and deeply forked tail. The black-tipped bill is redder than Forster's, the tail is whiter, and the wing appears much darker near the tip. In fall and winter the head becomes white, except for a black streak starting behind the eye confluent with the black nape and rear of head. During these seasons the bill is blackish, and the legs and feet are a duller red than in spring and summer. The immature may be separated from the very similar young Forster's Tern by the darkish patch on the forward part of the inner wing.

Voice: A more drawn-out, less harsh *tee-ar-r-r-r* than Forster's; also a rapid, pulsating *tut-tut-tut-tut* and a loud, piercing *tee-ar.*

Range and status: Breeds from s. Mack., s. Keewatin, c. Que., Nfld., n. Europe, and n.-c. Siberia (to Anadyr) south to n. U.S. (east of the Rockies), s. Europe, Iraq, n. Iran, n. India, c. China, Sakhalin I., and the Kuriles; the Azores, Madeira, and Canary Is.; coastally from Tex. to s. Fla., N.S. to Mass.; locally on the coasts of Spain, w. and n. Africa, Asia Minor, and Palestine. Winters from s. edges of breeding range south to Ecuador, Argentina, Falkland Is., s. Africa, Madagascar, s. Asia, New Guinea, and the Solomon Is. In migration occurs throughout U.S. Properly named; a common tern.

Habitat: Lakes (mainly in summer), seacoasts, and at sea.

Seasonal movements: Mar.–mid-May and Aug.–Dec.; there is a wide dispersal after the breeding season in almost every direction.

Biology: Nest: In colonies; a hollow in sand or pebbly beach, or matted vegetation with some nesting materials such as grasses, pebbles, and seashells added. Eggs: 2–4, usually 3; light buff, greenish buff, and medium browns, spotted to varying degrees with dark browns, sometimes blotched and splashed with grays and dark colors. Incubation: 21–30 days (a considerable variation). Age at 1st flight: About 4 weeks. Food: Mainly small fish; also insects and various small marine invertebrates.

Suggested reading: R. S. Palmer, "A Behavior Study of the Common Tern," *Proc. Bost. Soc. Nat. Hist.,* no. 42, pp. 1–119, 1941.

ARCTIC TERN (*Sterna paradisaea*)

Appearance: Medium-sized (14–17 in.) black-capped white tern with gray mantle and deeply forked tail. It resembles the Common Tern in all plumages; in spring and summer its bill is entirely red, with no black tip, but some Common Terns may lack the black tip in late summer.

Voice: Very similar to that of the Common Tern; a high-pitched, whistled *kee, kee* during preliminary courtship performances and a mouselike squeak are said to be diagnostic between the species.

Range and status: Breeds on almost all arctic islands and coasts south to the Aleutian Is., se. Alaska, s. Yuk., c. Mack., s. Keewatin, n. Ont., n. Que., Lab., Mass., s. Greenland, Iceland, n. Europe, tundra of Siberia, base of Kamchatka Peninsula, and the Komandorskie Is. Winters in subantarctic and antarctic waters of Atlantic, Indian, and Pacific Oceans north to s. S. America and S. Africa. Has straggled to Hawaii, New Zealand, the Black Sea, and to interior of Alta., Colo., N.Y., and Ont. Common.

Habitat: Tundra lakes in summer, marine coasts, and open seas.

Seasonal movements: A champion long-distance migrant. Migrates through open seas of e. Pacific and in Atlantic off w. Europe and nw. Africa, then off e. S. America; rare along U.S. shores. Mar.–mid-June and Aug.–Nov.

Biology: Nest: In colonies; a scrape in sand or depression in mosses or rock, sometimes lined with a few grasses or mosses. Eggs: 1–4, usually 2; cannot be distinguished from those of Common Tern. Incubation: 21–22 days. Age at 1st flight unknown. Food: Fish, insects, small marine invertebrates.

Suggested reading: O. Hawksley, "Ecology of a Breeding Population of Arctic Terns," *Bird-banding,* vol. 28, pp. 57–92, 1957.

ROSEATE TERN (*Sterna dougallii*)

Appearance: About the same size (14–17 in.) and general appearance as the Common Tern, but with much longer tail (when perching, tail extends beyond wing tips). In summer, the bill is blackish, very seldom with any red. The pinkish bloom on the breast is not always visible.

Voice: A ripping, rasping *aaark* and a distinctive *chee-wee* whistle are best field "marks."

Range and status: Breeds locally on coasts and islands from N.S. to Va., s. Fla., Yucatan, Bahamas, W. Indies, Azores, Madeira, Great Britain, France, Denmark, Tunisia, w. Red Sea, e. and s. Africa, Madagascar, Seychelles Is., Ceylon, Malaya, China, Formosa, New Guinea, Australia, and New Caledonia. Retires to tropical and s. seas in winter and such areas near breeding grounds. Nearly exterminated by plume hunters and only now making a comeback.

Habitat: Almost never seen inland; ranges offshore and in open seas.

Seasonal movements: Apr.–May and Sept.–Oct.; many populations almost sedentary.

Biology: Nest: In colonies; a hollow in the sand, with some lining of grasses. Eggs: 1–3, commonly 1–2; like the Common Tern's in coloration, but somewhat less heavily marked. Incubation: 21–25 days. Age at 1st flight unknown. Food: Small fish.

Suggested reading: D. A. Bannerman, *Birds of the British Isles*, Oliver and Boyd, Edinburgh, 1962, vol. 11, pp. 147–155.

ALEUTIAN TERN (*Sterna aleutica*)

A medium-sized (15 in.) black-capped white tern with a gray mantle, a deeply forked tail, and a black bill. Its white forehead extends to just above the eye, narrowing there to a point; the body is grayish. It breeds on Sakhalin I., Siberia, and islands in Norton Sound, Goodnews Bay, and near Yakutat, Alaska; winters in the nw. Pacific.

SOOTY TERN (*Sterna fuscata*)

Appearance: Medium-sized (15–17 in.), with a deeply forked tail; entirely sooty black above, including wings and tail. It has a white forehead, however, and is white below. The immature is all brown, lighter below, with some white spotting on the back.

Voice: Called the Wide-awake because of its whining 3-part call; also other harsh barking notes.

Range and status: Breeds on oceanic islands and some nearshore islands of Pacific (Ryukyu, Marcus, Midway, Hawaiian, Revilla Gigedo, and Tres Marias Is., south), reefs off Yucatan, La., and w. Fla. coasts, the Bahamas, the W. Indies, and islands in the S. Atlantic and Indian Oceans. Ranges over adjacent seas in nonbreeding seasons. Carried by storms to Tenn., W.Va., N.Y., Vt., Ga., N.C., and c. Fla. Fairly common, sometimes abundant.

Habitat: Pelagic (although feathers are not waterproof); on or near land only during breeding season.

Seasonal movements: Too little known; some individuals, at least, breed every 9–10 months; large flocks almost never encountered at sea.

Biology: Nest: In dense colonies; a scrape in the sand, sometimes lined with leaves of nearby plants. Eggs: 1–3, usually 1; variable marking of dark brown and grays on whitish or buff. Incubation: 26 days. Age at 1st flight unknown. Food: Fish, squid, etc., plucked gracefully from surface of water, hardly wetting a feather.

Suggested reading: J. P. Chapin, "The Calendar of Wideawake Fair," *Auk*, vol. 71, pp. 1–15, 1954.

BRIDLED TERN (*Sterna anaethetus*)

Medium-sized (14–15 in.); white below and grayish brown above, with a black cap, white face, and a black line running through the eye from the cap to the black

In flight, the black-backed Sooty Tern is distinguished by its deeply forked tail.

Hawaii's Gray-backed Terns are found throughout much of the central Pacific Ocean.

bill. The outer feathers of the deeply forked tail are white. Immature birds are similar, but without the black cap and eye streak. They are light brown, mottled with grayish above. Breeds locally along coasts and on islands of tropic lands and seas around the world (including Hawaii), ranging into the s. warm temperate areas in the nonbreeding seasons. It has straggled to the coasts of Ala., Fla., and S.C.

BLACK-NAPED TERN (*Sterna sumatranas*)

Medium-sized (13½–14½ in.) white tern with gray mantle, rump, and central tail feathers. It has a crescent of black on the nape and a black spot before the eye. The tail is well forked. Breeds on small islands of tropical and subtropical regions of the Indian Ocean and the S. Pacific, straggling casually to Hawaii.

GRAY-BACKED TERN (*Sterna lunata*)

Medium-sized (13½–15 in.); very similar to Aleutian Tern, but its mantle is dark gray, and its undersides are pure white. Breeds throughout Oceania; Feb.–June on islands of nw. Hawaii and off Oahu.

LEAST TERN (*Sterna albifrons*)

Appearance: Small (8½–9½ in.) white tern with gray mantle, black cap, and a white forehead extending to just above the eye. The tail is moderately forked. The bill, legs, and feet are yellow. The 2 outer flight feathers of the wing are dark gray or blackish. In winter the crown is grayish, whiter toward the bill, with a crescent of blackish at the back of the head. A blackish line runs from the back of the head to the eye. Immature birds resemble the winter adults, but they have brown at the back of the head. Wing tips, mantle, and the upper side of the tail are dark gray. The forward half of the wing is mottled brownish and gray.

Voice: A rapid twittering *kirri-kiki, kirri-kiki,* a *kweet* squealed in alarm, and a *kik-kik-kik* about the nesting grounds; many variations.

Range and status: Breeds locally along coasts and in broad river valleys from s. Calif. to s. Baja Calif., from ne. Mexico and from Mass. to s. Fla., in the Colo., Red, Missouri, and Mississippi river systems (north to Nebr., Iowa, Ind., and Ohio), the e. coast of the Yucatan Peninsula, the shores of the Greater Antilles, the Bahamas, n. Venezuela, the coasts of Europe (north to Scotland, Denmark, and Estonia), the shores of the Gulf of Guinea and up the Niger and Benue Rivers, nw. Africa, e.-c. Africa, s. and e. Asia (north to Korea), c. Japan, the Philippines, and n. and e. Australia, in the river valleys of c. Russia and w.-c. Siberia, the Caspian and Aral Seas area, the valleys of the Indus, Ganges, and Brahmaputra Rivers, and in river valleys of se. Asia and China. Ranges farther south in W. Hemisphere to Peru and Brazil, especially in winter, when it also retreats from its more northerly nesting areas. Considerably reduced in numbers by demands of millinery trade in late 19th century, but, thanks to activity of the Audubon Society, it is now common, even locally abundant.

Habitat: Mud, sand, and gravel beaches of oceans, estuaries, lagoons, and larger rivers in breeding seasons; all types of shallow marine coasts in other seasons.

Seasonal movements: Sedentary through most of range; arrives at n. stations mid-Apr.–mid-May and departs mid-July–Oct.

Biology: Nest: Solitary or in small colonies; a hollow in sand, gravel, or rock, very rarely lined with plant matter. Eggs: 2–4, usually 2; ground color from yellowish to greenish brown and whitish, with scattered spots and blotches of dark brown. Incubation: 20–21 days. Age at 1st flight: About 4th week. Food: Crustaceans, worms, fish, and mollusks.

Suggested reading: I. R. Tomkins, "Life History Notes on the Least Tern," *Wils. Bull.*, vol. 71, pp. 313–322, 1959. J. W. Hardy, *The Least Tern in the Mississippi Valley*, Mich. State Univ. Biol. Series, vol. 1, pp. 1–60, 1957.

ROYAL TERN (*Thalasseus maximus*)

Appearance: Large (18–24 in.) white tern with a rather prominently crested black cap, light gray mantle, well-forked tail, bright orange bill, and blackish legs and feet. From midsummer to early spring the cap is white, except for the bushy crest to the rear of the head. Immature birds are like the winter adults, but they have less of a crest and are spotted with brownish gray above.

Voice: A loud, high-pitched *keer*, a penetrating, squawked *kowk*, notes resembling the bleating of sheep, and a musical, liquid *tourrrreee* whistle.

Range and status: Breeds along coasts from Baja Calif. to w.-c. Mexico, from S. Tex. to s. La., from Md. to Ga., locally in the W. Indies, and w. Africa. Winters coastally from c. Calif. to Peru, from S.C. and the Caribbean area to Argentina, and w. Africa. Straggles north to Mass. Common.

Habitat: Seacoasts.

Seasonal movements: Largely sedentary; arrives N.C. Apr.–May and departs Sept.–Nov.

Biology: Nest: In dense colonies; a scrape in sand of upper beaches. Eggs: 2–4, usually 2; whitish to buffy or yellowish, with small, evenly scattered spots and dots of dark browns, sometimes heavily blotched with browns. Incubation period unknown. Age at 1st flight unknown. Food: Small fish.

Suggested reading: A. C. Bent, *Life Histories of North American Gulls and Terns*, Dover, N.Y. (reprint of U.S. Nat. Mus. Bull. 113, 1921), 1963, pp. 211–218.

ELEGANT TERN (*Thalasseus elegans*)

Medium-sized (16–17 in.); very similar to the Royal Tern in all plumages, but with slimmer, more yellowish bill. Breeds on and off both coasts of Baja Calif. and winters from Peru to Chile. In fall it ranges north to c. Calif. It has been recorded once at Corpus Christi, Tex.

SANDWICH TERN (Cabot's Tern) (*Thalasseus sandvicensis*)

Appearance: Medium-sized (14–16 in.) black-capped, gray-mantled white tern with deeply forked tail, a rather long yellow-tipped black bill, and black legs and feet. It has a somewhat prominent crest. In winter only the crest is black, and even this is spotted with white. The immature has a white-spotted blackish crest, and its back and mantle are marked with blackish.

Like many terns, Royal Terns breed in dense, noisy colonies.

Voice: A loud, insistent *kirhitt, kirhitt* and short, shrill *creee* screams.

Range and status: Breeds along coasts from Va. to S.C., from Tex. to La., off Yucatan, in the Bahamas, from the British Isles, Denmark, and s. Sweden to nw. Africa, Sardinia, Sicily, and the Black and Caspian Seas. Winters from s. Mexico to Panama, from Fla. and the Caribbean to s. Brazil and in the Mediterranean, Red Sea, and Persian Gulf areas, and adjacent seas. Accidental in s. Ont. Spreading and becoming more common.

Habitat: Seacoasts.

Seasonal movements: Arrives Apr., departs Sept. in n. part; largely sedentary.

Biology: Nest: In large colonies; a hollow in sand dunes or gravelly beaches, sometimes sparsely lined with grasses. Eggs: 1–3, usually 1–2; pale pinkish or pinkish brown, some whitish; very dark brown markings vary considerably in shape and size. Incubation: 20–23 days. Age at 1st flight: About 5 weeks. Food: Small fish; some shrimp and squid.

Suggested reading: D. A. Bannerman, *Birds of the British Isles*, Oliver and Boyd, Edinburgh, 1962, vol. 11, pp. 136–146.

CASPIAN TERN (*Hydroprogne caspia*)

Appearance: Large (19–23 in.); very similar to the Royal Tern, but with heavier, redder bill, darker gray wing tips, and a moderately forked tail. The crest at the rear of the head is not so prominent as that of the Royal Tern, and in winter the cap is brownish black marked with whitish. It appears lighter near the bill.

Voice: Coarse, lower than that of the Royal Tern, *k-kaaar* and a *kuk-kuk-kuk-kuk*.

Range and status: Breeds in scattered localities, inland and along coasts, on every continent but S. America; in Europe only in the se. and in the Baltic Sea region. Breeding localities in N. America include s.-c. Mack., e.-c., c., and s. Man., s. Ont., se. Que., e. Ore., Calif., w.-c. Nev., n. Utah, nw. Wyo., ne. Wis., Mich., s. Tex. to s. La., e. Va. to se. S.C., w.-c. Baja Calif., and w. Sinaloa. Largest concentration in sw. Asia, particularly sw. Siberia in Caspian-Aral-Ozero region; also breeds in Madagascar, Ceylon, and New Zealand. Winters mainly along marine coasts from c. Calif. to s. Baja Calif., from the Gulf Coast and N.C. south to the Greater Antilles, and from the Mediterranean region to s. Africa, Aus-

Sandwich Tern

The Caspian Tern broods its downy chicks for several days after hatching.

tralia, and New Zealand. Accidental in w. and c. Europe. Locally common.

Habitat: Large lakes, marine coasts, estuaries.

Seasonal movements: Those breeding in interior apparently move east and west to coasts before going south, and return the same route; Apr.–mid-May and Sept.–Oct.

Biology: Nest: In large colonies on sandy or pebbly beaches and islets; a simple hollow or depression. Eggs: 1–4, most commonly 2–3; pale pinkish or yellowish brown, sparingly and evenly marked with small spots, sometimes blotches and scrawls of darker browns and reddish grays. Incubation: 20–22 days. Age at 1st flight: 4–5 weeks. Food: Small fish; sometimes robs nests of nearby seabirds of eggs or young.

Suggested reading: C. L. Hayward, "The Breeding Status and Migration of the Caspian Tern in Utah," *Condor,* vol. 37, pp. 140–144, 1935.

BLACK TERN (*Chlidonias niger*)

Appearance: Small (9–10¼ in.) black-headed, black-bodied, gray-winged, gray-tailed tern with white undertail feathers and very dark red bill, legs, and feet. The tail is moderately forked. In fall and winter its underparts, face, forehead, and nape are white; the rear of the crown and back of the head are dark gray, with a finger of dark gray extending to just behind the eye. The immature is like the adult in winter, but the dark gray of the head region becomes grayish brown, and the back

and inner half of the mantle is yellowish brown, marbled with dark gray. In fall the black pattern of the head and body of the adult becomes spotted with patches of white that gradually merge, so that for a while the bird presents a curiously mottled or pied appearance.

Voice: A rather monotonous, high *kik-kik-kik* in flight (mainly silent in migration), lengthening and becoming a shriller *keek-keek* when the bird is alarmed; also an occasional *kleeaa.*

Range and status: Breeds from e.-c. B.C., ne. Alta, c. Sask., n. Man., and n. Ont. south, east of the Coast Ranges to s.-c. Calif., n. Nev., n. Utah, Colo., Nebr., Mo., Ill., w. Ky., Ohio, Pa., w. N.Y., nw. Vt., Maine, and c. N.B.; also in c. and s. Europe and sw. Siberia. Winters from Panama to Chile, from Colombia to Surinam, and from n. to s.-c. Africa. Has straggled to Alaska and Bermuda. Locally common; congregates in large flocks in winter.

Habitat: Freshwater marshes and lakes in summer, mainly marine coasts in winter.

Seasonal movements: Apr.–early June, mainly through interior; Aug.–early Oct., east and west to coasts at irregular intervals, then south.

Biology: Nest: Usually a floating mass of reeds and waterweeds, rather neatly lined with finer plant materials; sometimes a mere scrape in firm ground near marshes, scantily lined with grasses. Eggs: 2–4, usually 3; light yellow or greenish browns, heavily splotched with dark browns; markings often heavier at larger end. Incubation: 21–22 days. Age at 1st flight: About 4 weeks.

In winter, much of the Black Tern's dark plumage is replaced by white.

Food: Largely aquatic insects, both adult and larval forms; also spiders, leeches, small fish, tadpoles, and frogs.

   Suggested reading: N. L. Cuthbert, "A Nesting Study of the Black Tern in Michigan," *Auk,* vol. 71, pp. 16–35, 1954.

WHITE-WINGED BLACK TERN (*Chlidonias leucopterus*)

Small (8½–9½ in.); similar in all plumages to the Black Tern, but legs and feet are red, and bill is more reddish. Also the tail is white (in summer), and "shoulder" of wing is white. Breeds from e. Europe and Turkey to se. Siberia; winters in Africa, s. Asia, Indonesia, Australia, and New Zealand. Recorded from Wis., Mass., Barbados, and Guam.

BLUE-GRAY NODDY (*Procelsterna caerulea*)

Small (9½–11 in.); all bluish gray (darker gray flight feathers at wing tip), with black bill, legs, and toes; webbing between toes is light-colored. Immature birds are dark brownish gray above and whitish below. It breeds on tropical and subtropical islands of the Pacific, including several of the Hawaiian Is. It lays 1 egg in a bare hollow in sand or on rock ledges or in cavities in a rock.

BROWN NODDY (Noddy Tern) (*Anoüs stolidus*)

A medium-sized (15–16 in.) dark brown tern with a light grayish cap that is almost white on the forehead, a rounded blackish tail, a black bill, and dark brown legs and feet. The immature bird has less grayish white on the head. Almost never swims or dives. Its voice is a harsh, staccato *karrk,* somewhat crowlike. Breeds on islands in tropical seas throughout the world, including Hawaii, Dry Tortugas in Fla., and the Bahamas; winters in adjoining seas. It is fairly common. Nonmigratory. The bulky nest is made on the ground or in low bushes, of twigs, branches, and seaweeds, sometimes lined with shells and coral. Eggs: 1–3, usually 1; pale pinkish or yellowish brown, sparingly speckled or spotted with browns and grayish lavender. Incubation has been reported as taking 35–36 days, which seems rather long. Young birds are at least 30 days old at time of 1st flight. Food: Small fish.

Suggested reading: A. C. Bent, *Life Histories of North American Gulls and Terns,* Dover, N.Y. (reprint of U.S. Nat. Mus. Bull. 113, 1921), 1963, pp. 301–310.

BLACK NODDY (White-capped Noddy) (*Anoüs tenuirostris*)

Small (12–14 in.); resembles the Brown Noddy, but is darker, with a whiter cap and a gray tail that is lighter-colored than the back. Breeds and is resident in Hawaii and tropical islands of Indian, Pacific, and S. Atlantic Oceans and islands off the coast of British Honduras. This species is now thought to include a formerly separated species, the Least Noddy, *Anoüs minutus.* A specimen of the form breeding on the islands of the S. Atlantic was recently taken on the Dry Tortugas, Fla. A common dark tern in Hawaii.

FAIRY TERN (*Gygis alba*)

A small (10½–13 in.) pure white tern with black bill and legs; its toes are black, and the webbing between is yellow. Breeds and is resident in w. Hawaii and islands of the tropical S. Atlantic, Indian, and Pacific Oceans (east to Hawaii and the Marquesas). It lays its single egg balanced on a limb or in the crotch of a tree. Sometimes seen off main Hawaiian Is.

The delicate, wide-ranging Fairy Tern is only slightly larger than a Robin.

The Black Skimmer fishes by skimming the water with its long lower mandible.

THE SKIMMERS (RYNCHOPIDAE)

Skimmers are medium-sized (14½–20 in.) seabirds closely related to the gulls and terns; major differences are related to the specialized bill and feeding habits of the skimmers. There are 3 species, only 1 occurring in America. The lower bill is longer than the upper, and both are flattened laterally to knife-blade thinness at the tips. In feeding, the birds fly over shallow waters with the tip of the lower mandible slicing through the upper layer of water, scooping small surface-feeding fish and crustaceans into the mouth; most of this feeding is done at dusk, at dawn, or during the night. The long, pointed wings are never swept through a full downward arc, during the feeding flights at least, so as to keep them free of the water. Because of the special way of flying, they may be said to fly well but not strongly. Their legs are rather short, and the tail is moderately long and forked. They make loud, strident calls and "barks" and softer, more pleasant notes during courtship. These birds range over S. America, tropical Africa, s. Asia, and the coasts of N. America from N.Y. south; they are restricted mainly to marine coasts, large rivers, and lakes. Skimmers are colonial. Their nests are unlined hollows in sand or soil; the 2–5 eggs are incubated by the female, possibly with the male's help. The downy young remain at the nest for some time, fed by both parents.

BLACK SKIMMER (*Rynchops nigra*)

Appearance: About the size of a crow (16–20 in.); the cap, back of neck, mantle, rump, and tail feathers are black, except for some gray bordering the black in the tail. The rest of the plumage is white, including the trailing edge of the wings. The black-tipped bill, legs and feet are bright red. Immature birds are streaked brownish where the adults are black, except for the flight feathers of the wings, which are blackish.

Voice: Low, throaty grunts or barks: *kak-kak-kak* or *kuk-kuk-kuk;* during courtship a lower, more plaintive, gull-like *keow, keow.*

Range and status: Breeds locally on coasts of e. and se. U.S. from Mass. to e.-c. Fla. and from s. Tex. to w.-c. Fla., from Yucatan around the shores of the Caribbean, and n. and e. S. America to c. Argentina (up the large rivers of ne. and e. S. America), and along the Pacific coast from nw. Mexico to the Strait of Magellan. In winter, retreats to Gulf Coast and w.-c. Mexico south to Chile and Argentina. Has straggled north to N.S. and N.B. and into interior of e. U.S. Rather common.

Habitat: In N. America, strictly a bird of the marine coasts, lagoons, bays, and lower estuaries.

Seasonal movements: Largely sedentary, but arrives in n. parts of range mid-Apr.–early May and leaves mid-Sept.–mid-Nov.

Biology: Nest: A bare hollow in sand of beaches or islands above high water. Eggs: 1–5, usually 4–5; whitish, pale buff, light bluish green, or pinkish buff, heavily marked with dark brown spots, blotches, and scrawls. Incubation period and age at 1st flight unknown. Food: Small surface-feeding fish and crustaceans.

Suggested reading: Witmer Stone, *Bird Studies at Old Cape May,* Delaware Ornith. Club at Acad. of Nat. Sci., Phil., vol. 2, pp. 598–608, 1937. O. S. Pettingill, Jr., "Behavior of Black Skimmers of Cardwell Island, Virginia," *Auk,* vol. 54, pp. 237–244, 1937.

AUKS, MURRES, AND PUFFINS (ALCIDAE)

These are small- to medium-sized (6–30 in.) seabirds related to the gulls and terns, but are more completely aquatic. There are 22 species and 1 recently extinct species; all but 1 of these occur in some part of N. America. They breed in arctic and subarctic regions, with a few species breeding farther south, 1 even to the warmer parts of the temperate zone. Most species are nonmigratory but disperse after breeding over adjacent seas; a few, however, migrate south almost to the tropic zone. Strictly marine, with occurrences in the interior accidental, they are at home along seemingly inhospitable rocky coasts. Their plumage is mainly black, white, grays, and browns, usually whitish below and dark above; many species have bright-colored bills, legs, and feet. Their bills, often ornamented with grooves and ridges, are quite variable: some are short and stout (auks and auklets), others are moderately long and slender (murres and murrelets), while still others are large and compressed laterally (puffins). Their large heads are set on rather short necks, and their bodies are comparatively compact and heavy-looking. Their wings are small and pointed, while their legs are short and attached toward the rear of the body; the feet are webbed, and the tails are rather short. The sexes are alike. There is a winter plumage, but it is little modified from the summer pattern. Immature birds usually resemble the winter-plumaged adults. The extinct species was flightless, but existing species fly "heavily" on rapidly beating wings; they are expert divers and swimmers and are much at home in the water. The wings are used in underwater swimming. Their voices consist mainly of moans, barks, grunts, and hisses. Courtship includes water parades and dances similar to those of the grebes, usually with much bowing and scraping. They are gregarious, nesting in colonies. The 1–2 eggs are laid on rock ledges or crevices or in burrows dug mainly by the male, seldom with benefit of lining. The eggs of some species are pear-shaped or rounded conical, of light colors, marked or plain. Incubation is by both sexes or by the female alone; the young are cared for by both parents. The downy young of many species remain at the nest site for about 1–2 weeks, taking to the sea before they are able to fly. The young of other species remain at the nest up to 7 weeks. Food consists mainly of fish and small marine invertebrates; several species feed mostly at night or during dusky hours of the day.

GREAT AUK (Gare-fowl) (*Pinguinus impennis*)

Appearance: Extinct. Large (ca. 30 in.); black above, including head and neck, and white below, with a large oval patch of white between the eye and the bill. The wings were very small, quite incapable of sustaining flight, but useful in underwater swimming. The black bill was large and compressed laterally, with several ridges near the forehead and grooves near the tip. The legs and feet were black. The adults in fall and winter and the immature birds differed from the above description somewhat, but no exact details have been recorded. On land it walked upright like a penguin; in fact, this was the original penguin, but now that name is reserved for birds of an entirely different family.

Voice: Uttered a croak and a gurgling noise.

Range and status: Bred on islands in the Gulf of St. Lawrence, isles off Nfld., Greenland, Iceland, the Outer Hebrides, the Faeroes, and Lundy I. Wintered south to Mass., s. Spain, n. France, Great Britain, and Scandinavia; casually to Fla. The last 2 specimens known to science were killed at Eldey, Iceland, June 3, 1844. They were so easy to kill and so numerous that early mariners counted them as a sure source of food in n. waters, collecting them by the thousands and preserving them in salt as provision. After they became too rare for such practices, they might have survived and even regained some of their former numbers had not egg collectors become so eager to possess a set. An egg sold in England for £330 in 1900.

Habitat: Entirely marine, nesting on small islets accessible to nonflying animals.

Seasonal movements: Very little known; eggs were available in June, and young were taken in July.

Biology: No nest was built. Eggs: 1, laid on bare rock; pyriform, whitish or yellowish, spotted, blotched, and scrawled with black, browns, and grays. Incubation period and age at 1st flight unknown. Food: Fish, crustaceans, and other marine invertebrates.

Suggested reading: D. A. Bannerman, *Birds of the British Isles*, Oliver and Boyd, Edinburgh, 1963, vol. 12, pp. 81–92.

RAZORBILL (*Alca torda*)

Appearance: Medium-sized (16–18 in.); black above, including entire head and neck, and white below,

with a white streak running from the eye to the top of the base of the upper bill. There is also a thin white bar on the wing. The large, deep black bill is somewhat laterally compressed and has a white groove near the tip; the legs and feet are black. In fall and winter there is no line between the eye and the bill; the white extends up over the underside of the head and in a lobe to behind the eye. The immature is like the winter adult, but it has a smaller, more slender, ungrooved bill.

Voice: Hoarse croaks and growls; chicks, a whistled *whee-oo.*

Range and status: Breeds along coasts from c. Lab. to e. Maine, including sw. and e. Nfld., w.-c. to s. Green-

Great Auk

land, Iceland, the British Isles, Bear I., Norway, Sweden, Finland, and n. Russia. Winters south to S.C., the Canary Is., Portugal, and w. Mediterranean Sea. Has straggled to Lake Ontario, Pa., and c. Europe. Formerly locally abundant, now somewhat common.

Habitat: Rocky seacoasts and offshore waters; in the Baltic Sea area it occurs in brackish water regularly, and in Lake Ladoga, Finland, it breeds in freshwater habitats —the only member of the family to do so.

Seasonal movements: Starts leaving s. wintering areas Mar.–Apr. and returns Nov.

Biology: No nest. Eggs: Usually only 1 laid on rock of clifftop near sea, seldom on ledges; slightly pear-shaped, bluish or greenish white or pale pinkish or yellowish buff; brown, black, and gray markings vary in size, shape, and density. Incubation: 34–39 days. Age at 1st flight: Young leave nest site when only 12–14 days old and before wings are feathered. They leap off cliffs, some higher than 600 ft., into the sea; usually this dive is performed at dusk or early evening. Most of them survive this initial harsh introduction to the sea and from that moment are adept swimmers and divers. The adults follow them down to the water and protect them from predacious gulls, at least until the young are able to fly, some 2 weeks later. Food: Fish and marine invertebrates, usually captured near or at surface, but some Razorbills have been trapped in fish nets 60 ft. below the surface.

Suggested reading: W. J. Plumb, "Observations on the Breeding Biology of the Razorbill," *British Birds*, vol. 58, pp. 449–456, 1965.

COMMON MURRE (*Uria aalge*)

Appearance: Medium-sized (16–17 in.); sooty black above, including head and neck; white below, with a sharp-pointed, rather slender black bill somewhat longer than the head. Some have a narrow white ring around the eye and a thin line extending toward the rear of the head. While the bird flies overhead, there is a conspicuous broad band of white from the body almost to the tip of the wing. The legs and feet are blackish. In fall and winter the white of the undersides conjoins the white throat, cheek patch, and front of the neck. There is a narrow blackish line running from the eye back into the cheek. Immature birds resemble the adults in winter, but they have smaller bills and a mottling of grayish brown on the white of the foreneck. In silhouette it resembles a small loon, but with a much shorter neck.

Voice: Loud, coarse, low *arrrr* moans and a squab-bling *gwoo-err, gwoo-err;* the chicks, a whistled *weeoo* and a shriller *quee-wee.*

Range and status: Breeds from Bering Strait to Sakhalin I., e. Korea, n. Japan, and c. Calif. and from w. Greenland, Iceland, Bear I., and Novaya Zemlya to N.S. and n. France. Winters in adjacent offshore open seas

south to N.J. and the Mediterranean Sea. Often locally abundant.

Habitat: Rocky islands, sea cliffs and ledges, and large bays and seas.

Seasonal movements: Arrives at nesting cliffs Jan.–Apr. and departs Aug.–mid-Sept.

Biology: No nest. Single pear-shaped egg laid on bare rock of clifftop or cliff ledges; the shape lowers incidence of egg's rolling over edge of cliff. Some murres said to place a few pebbles on downhill side of egg, but this is more likely accidental. Eggs: Only a single egg in a clutch. Highly variable in ground color and marking;

The handsome Razorbill breeds on rocky North Atlantic seacoasts.

Breeding colonies of Common Murres sometimes are made up of thousands of birds.

whitish, deep blue-green, reddish, bluish; spotted, splotched, and scrawled with browns or black, sometimes unmarked. Incubation: Varies, usually 28–30 days, but as many as 37 recorded. Age at 1st flight: Like the Razorbill, leaves nest site and dives off cliffs into sea when only half grown and minus flight feathers in wing, at 18–25 days. Starts flying some 20 days later. Both parents escort flightless young at sea for some time; but after young are fledged, usually only 1 parent remains with it. Food: Fish, marine invertebrates, and a very small percentage of seaweed.

Suggested reading: Leslie Tuck, *The Murres*, Canadian Wildlife Series, no. 1, 260 pp., 1961.

THICK-BILLED MURRE (*Uria lomvia*)

Appearance: Slightly larger (17–19 in.) than the Common Murre, which it resembles closely in all plumages. Its bill is slightly thicker and shorter than that of the Common Murre. Of more help in separating the 2 species, however, is the whitish "lip" on the bill, showing as a streak running almost half the length of the bill from center to rear, and the inverted V pointing up the throat, where the white of the breast joins the back of the neck of the Thick-billed. In winter the black of the head extends farther behind the eye as a patch, not as a finger of black, into the white cheek.

Voice: Like Common Murre's.

Range and status: Breeds along coasts from Ellesmere I., Greenland, Jan Mayen, Iceland, Spitsbergen, Franz Josef Land, Novaya Zemlya, ne. Siberia, and n. Alaska south to the Gulf of St. Lawrence, n. Russia, and the Komandorskie and Aleutian Is. Winters from open waters near breeding colonies south to S.C., n. France,

the Netherlands, the Baltic, Sakhalin I., Japan, and B.C. Has straggled in winter to Lakes Huron, Erie, and Ontario and inland to Ont., Que., Mich., Iowa, Ind., Ohio, Pa., N.Y., Mass., N.H., Conn., N.C., and S.C., also in Germany. Much more common along Atlantic Coast than Pacific Coast of the U.S.

Habitat: Rocky isles, sea cliffs, and oceans.

Seasonal movements: Arrives at breeding sites Mar.–mid-June and departs Aug.–Sept.

Biology: Almost identical in detail to that of the Common Murre, but apparently young remain on land a bit longer (21–28 days) and start flying later (41–48 days).

Suggested reading: D. A. Bannerman, *Birds of the British Isles*, Oliver and Boyd, Edinburgh, 1962, vol. 12, pp. 115–124.

DOVEKIE (Little Auk) (*Plautus alle*)

Appearance: Small (7½–9 in.) and stocky; blackish above, including head and neck, and white below, with a series of white slashes running across the back from shoulder to shoulder. There is also a small white spot above the eye and another below. The black bill is short and sturdy; the legs and feet are black. In winter the white extends up to the base of the lower bill and as a broad lobe to the region of the ear behind the eye. Immatures resemble winter adults, but the black is duller, and the bill is smaller and weaker-looking.

Voice: A shrill, high-pitched, laughing *kraak-ack-ack-ack-ack* chatter at breeding colonies.

Range and status: Breeds from e.-c. Ellesmere I., w.-c. and e.-c. Greenland, Jan Mayen, Spitsbergen, and Franz Josef Land south to s. Greenland, n. Iceland, Bear

Thick-billed Murre

I., and Novaya Zemlya; may also breed on New Siberian Is. Winters in ice-free waters of Arctic Ocean south to N.J., the Azores, n. France, and the Baltic Sea, casually to Fla., Bermuda, Madeira, and the w. Mediterranean Sea. Has straggled to n. Alaska, Keewatin, Man., Minn., Wis., Mich., Ont., and New England. Abundant despite numerous enemies, including man (Eskimos use the bird as a major source of food and clothing).

Habitat: Rocky shores for breeding, coasts and open seas.

Seasonal movements: Arrives at breeding colonies Mar.–mid-May and departs mid-July–Sept.

Biology: Nest: None. Eggs: 1, very rarely 2; laid on bare rock, in crevice, and sometimes in an existing burrow partly deepened by Dovekie (whether male or female is uncertain), commonly at foot of cliff; unmarked bluish white. Incubation: 24(?) days. Age at 1st flight: Said to be about 28 days, but young enter sea before fledging and begin flying clumsily for short distances soon afterward. Food: Mainly surface-feeding crustaceans, also other marine invertebrates; most individuals at breeding grounds seem to feed at sea between 10 P.M. and 6 A.M.

Suggested reading: P. P. G. Bateson, "Studies of Less Familiar Birds: 112—The Little Auk," *British Birds*, vol. 54, pp. 272–277, 1961.

BLACK GUILLEMOT (*Cepphus grylle*)

Appearance: Small (12–14 in.), with a completely sooty black plumage, except for a large smooth-edged patch of white on the wing. The rather slender, pointed bill, about as long as the head, is black; legs and feet are bright reddish orange. In fall and winter the adult retains the white patch on the black wing, but it becomes predominantly white, with a mottling of dark brown starting at the crown and extending over the neck and back to the rump. The tail is black. The immature is sooty black above, mottled with white on the back and especially on the wing, where the adult has the white patch; it is whitish below, including the throat and ear region of the head. The flanks are buffy, barred with brownish.

Voice: A hissing when disturbed; on breeding grounds a weak, buzzy *peeeeee.*

Range and status: Breeds along coasts from n. Ellesmere I., n. Greenland, Spitsbergen, Franz Josef Land, Severnaya Zemlya, New Siberian Is., and Wrangel I. south to Hudson Bay, James Bay, Maine, N.S., Nfld., Iceland, Ireland, Scotland, s. Norway, s. Sweden, s. Finland, Novaya Zemlya, n.-c. Siberia, ne. Siberia, and n. Alaska. Winters in shallow, open waters off breeding sites south to N.J., n. Europe, and s. Alaska. Rather common.

Habitat: Rocky coasts and open seas.

Seasonal movements: Arrives at breeding colonies Apr.–May and departs Sept.–Oct.

In breeding plumage, the Black Guillemot is all black except for its white wing patches.

Biology: Nest: An unlined burrow dug by the bird; a crevice or cleft in cliff facing sea. Eggs: 1–2, usually 2; dull white, sometimes tinged with blue, green, or yellow, evenly covered with small spots or with large spots, blotches, and scrawls of dark browns and grays ringed around larger end of egg. Incubation: 21–30 days; generally shorter periods in more southerly breeding colonies. Age at 1st flight: 34–36 days. Food: Fish and other small marine animals, generally obtained at bottom of shallow marine waters.

Suggested reading: H. E. Winn, "The Black Guillemots of Kent Island, Bay of Fundy," *Auk,* vol. 67, pp. 477–485, 1950.

PIGEON GUILLEMOT (*Cepphus columba*)

Appearance: Small (12–14 in.), and so similar to the Black Guillemot that some ornithologists think it only a geographic variation of that species. In this species the white wing patch is disrupted by 2 fingers of black entering from the lower edge in both summer and winter. It is impossible to tell the immature birds of the 2 species from each other.

Voice: Same as Black Guillemot's.

Range and status: Breeds on coasts and islands of the Bering Sea south to Kamchatka, the Kuriles, n. Japan, and s. Calif. Winters in adjacent ice-free seas. Common and widespread along Pacific Coast.

Habitat: Rocky coasts, preferably shallow, and oceans.

Seasonal movements: Sedentary; starts nesting

Mar.–Apr. and leaves breeding colonies as soon as young are able to swim.

Biology: Identical with that of Black Guillemot, but incubation period recorded at 30–32 days.

Suggested reading: R. H. Drent, "Breeding Biology of the Pigeon Guillemot, *Cepphus columba,*" *Ardea,* Leiden, Neth., vol. 53, pp. 99–160, 1965.

MARBLED MURRELET (*Brachyramphus marmoratum*)

Appearance: Small (9½–10 in.) and chunky, with a very short neck; sooty black above, feathers of rump edged with brown; white below, broadly edged with brown, giving a marbled effect to plumage. The rather short bill, legs, and feet are blackish. In fall and winter it becomes spotless white below, with the white of the neck almost meeting at the back. A white patch in the wing shows as a horizontal slash while the bird is swimming. Immatures resemble the winter adults, but they have a less distinct wing patch; the breast and sides are mottled with brownish.

Voice: A rather high *meer-meer-meer* and a lower-pitched *kee.*

Range and status: Probably breeds on coasts and islands from se. Siberia to Japan and from s. Alaska to nw. Calif. Winters north into the Bering Sea and south to s. Calif. May be fairly common locally.

Habitat: Coasts, bays, and sounds; seems to prefer more sheltered waters than other murrelets.

Seasonal movements: Moves north Feb.–Mar. and returns Sept.–Nov.

Biology: First, and only, nest found "in a rock slide far above timberline at 1900 ft. on Chichagof I., Alaska, on June 13, 1931" (Gabrielson and Lincoln, *Birds of Alaska*). Eggs: Light pinkish brown, blotched, splashed, and spotted with dark browns. Food: Small fish. Very little else is known of this species, and even the 1 nest recorded gave little information of use in establishing general biology or geographic range.

Suggested reading: A. C. Bent, *Life Histories of North American Diving Birds,* Dover, N.Y. (reprint of U.S. Nat. Mus. Bull. 107, 1919), 1963, pp. 141–145. C. J. Guiguet, "Enigma of the Pacific," *Aud. Mag.,* vol. 58, pp. 164–167, 1956.

KITTLITZ'S MURRELET (*Brachyramphus brevirostre*)

Small (9 in.) and similar in shape to the Marbled Murrelet; dark brown or dark grayish, heavily streaked with light buff above and light buffy below. Barred and mottled on the throat, breast, and flanks with dark brown. The small bill, legs, and feet are blackish. In fall and winter it has a slate-gray cap, back, rump, and wings. A narrow band of slate gray runs across the breast, and there is a small black crescent just before the

The Laughing Gull, a fairly common species, breeds in scattered colonies along our coasts from
Nova Scotia to Mexico and on the shores of the Salton Sea in California.

Like most terns, the graceful Arctic Tern hunts by hovering over the water and then plunging headfirst to snatch up small fish and other aquatic prey.

Swimming at or just beneath the surface of the water, the Common Puffin is adept at catching fish and other marine animals with its seemingly awkward bill.

eye. The rest of the plumage is white, including a patch on the wing similar to that of the Marbled Murrelet. It probably breeds above timberline of mountains and on some islands along the Alaskan coast from Point Barrow to Wrangel. It winters in adjacent open seas and from se. Siberia to n. Japan. It is rather rare and very little is known of its habits and biology.

XANTUS' MURRELET (*Endomychura hypoleuca*)

About size and shape of Marbled Murrelet (9½–10½ in.); dark slate gray above and white below (including lower half of head) with *no* white slash on wing, which is whitish beneath; in fall and winter the white is more extensive on the head. Breeds from Santa Barbara Is., Calif., south to coastal islands of c. Baja Calif. In non-breeding season wanders farther north along Pacific Coast, casually to Wash. Rather rare. Nesting season apparently lasts from Mar. to July.

CRAVERI'S MURRELET (*Endomychura craveri*)

Slightly smaller (8½ in.) than Xantus' Murrelet; otherwise differs from that species in having gray rather than whitish on the underside of the wing. It breeds on islands in the Gulf of Calif. In winter it has ranged as far north as Monterey Bay, Calif. Many believe this is only a subspecies of Xantus' Murrelet.

ANCIENT MURRELET (*Synthliboramphus antiquum*)

Appearance: Small (9½–10½ in.), with medium gray back, wings, and tail (darker and brownish on wings). Head, neck, and flanks are sooty black, and a rather broad, jagged white line extends from the rear of the eye almost to the back of the head. The rest of the plumage is white, some of this extending up the side of the neck almost to the white stripe of the head. Just behind the white on the neck is a patch of rather fine black-and-white horizontal barring. The short but sturdy bill is bluish white, darker at the base; the legs and feet are pale bluish gray. In fall and winter the white streak behind the eye and the black-and-white-barred patch at the side of the neck become sooty black, and the white of the underparts extends up almost to the base of the bill. Immature birds resemble the adults in winter.

Voice: A soft but shrill whistle while at sea; at breeding colonies, low whistles and chirps.

Range and status: Breeds on coasts and offshore islands from the Komandorskie Is. and the Aleutians to Korea, the Kuriles, and the Queen Charlotte Is., B.C.; casually to nw. Wash. Winters south to China, Formosa, and n. Baja Calif. Has straggled accidentally inland to B.C., Ore., Nev., Idaho, Minn., Wis., Ohio, s. Ont., and s. Que. Common.

Habitat: Open seas, deep sounds, and bays, coming to islets mainly for nesting.

Marbled Murrelet

Seasonal movements: Moves north Mar.–Apr.; leaves nesting islands Aug.–Sept.

Biology: Nest: Sometimes a burrow, perhaps appropriated from another species; more often no nest except a natural hollow or crevice in rock. Eggs: 1–2, usually 2; more than 2 are products of more than 1 female; whitish, tinged with blue, yellow, or brown, blotched or speckled with irregular spots of varying shades of brown and gray, somewhat heavier at larger end. Incubation period unknown. Age at 1st flight unknown; 2–4 days after hatching the parents gather at the water's edge during the night and call young, which scramble from burrows and nest sites and plunge without hesitation into the surf to join their elders. Apparently the adults tend the young until they are able to fend for themselves without returning to the islet or land. Food: Apparently small surface-feeding marine invertebrates.

Suggested reading: A. C. Bent, *Life Histories of North American Diving Birds,* Dover, N.Y. (reprint of U.S. Nat. Mus. Bull. 107, 1919), 1963, pp. 132–140.

CASSIN'S AUKLET (*Ptychoramphus aleutica*)

Appearance: Small (8–9 in.), with dark gray head, neck, back, rump, wings, and tail; throat, breast, and flanks are lighter gray, and it has a small white eyebrow. The remainder of the plumage is whitish. The iris of the eye is white, the legs and feet are bluish or brownish gray, and the short, stout bill is blackish with a yellowish or flesh-colored spot at the base of the lower mandible. There is almost no age or seasonal change in plumage.

Voice: Apparently silent at sea; at colonies a repeated rasping *creek-a-reek, creek-a-reek.*

The Parakeet Auklet wears its white facial plumes only during the breeding season.

Range and status: Breeds on islands and coasts from s. Alaska to w.-c. Baja Calif. Winters from Vancouver I., B.C., to Baja Calif. Most common of auklets and murrelets off Pacific Coast of U.S.

Habitat: Marine coastal islands and islets for nesting; open seas in nonbreeding seasons.

Seasonal movements: Mainly sedentary; only a movement to sea and a retreat from more northerly nesting range; nesting season mid-Mar.–Nov.

Biology: Nest: A burrow or crevice in rocks. Eggs: 1; unmarked, whitish, some with bluish or greenish tinge.

Incubation: At least 37 days. Age at 1st flight: More than 40 days; young remain in burrow until fully fledged. Food: Almost entirely small surface-feeding marine invertebrates.

Suggested reading: A. C. Thoresen, "The Breeding Behavior of the Cassin Auklet," *Condor*, vol. 66, pp. 456–476, 1964.

PARAKEET AUKLET (*Cyclorrhynchus psittacula*)

Appearance: Small (ca. 10 in.); sooty black above, including head and neck, and white below, with rather mottled barring of sooty black and brownish from sides of breast to flank. Long, thin, white plumes originate below the eye and extend behind the head. It also has a small white eyebrow. The short, stout, upturned, turgid-looking bill is bright red, except for black around the nostril; legs and feet are gray. In fall and winter it lacks the white head plumes and barring along the side and flank; the white of the underparts then extends almost to the base of the bill. The young are similar to the winter adults, but their bills have a duller color.

Voice: A trilling whistle.

Range and status: Breeds on rocky islands and coasts from ne. Siberia, and islands in the Bering Sea south to the Komandorskie and Aleutian Is. Winters from adjacent seas to Sakhalin I., n. Japan, and Calif. Rare close to shore and along coast from Wash. to Calif.

Habitat: Sea cliffs, rocky isles for nesting; open seas.

Seasonal movements: Breeding season May–July; records for Calif. all later than mid-Dec.

Biology: Nest: In unlined crevices of rocky cliffs or on bare ground of isles. Eggs: 1; unmarked, whitish or pale bluish. Incubation and age at 1st flight unknown. Food: Small marine crustaceans and other surface-feeding marine invertebrates.

Suggested reading: A. C. Bent, *Life Histories of North American Diving Birds*, Dover, N.Y. (reprint of U.S. Nat. Mus. Bull. 107, 1919), 1963, pp. 116–120.

CRESTED AUKLET (*Aethia cristatella*)

Small (ca. 9½ in.); all gray, dark above and medium below, with a prominent long crest curling forward from the cap just above the eye. Long, thin white plumes extend backward from just behind the eye. It has a white iris. Bright red wattles extend around the base and over much of the short, stout yellowish bill. Legs and feet are gray. In fall and winter the crest is much shorter, and there are no red wattles. Immature birds lack crest, plumes, and wattles. Breeds on coasts of ne. Siberia, islands in the Bering Sea, Sakhalin I., c. Kurile Is., the Aleutians, and Shumagin I., Alaska. Winters from Bering Sea to c. Japan. Accidental in interior of Alaska and off Iceland. Habitat and biology similar to that of Parakeet Auklet.

LEAST AUKLET (*Aethia pusilla*)

Smallest (ca. 6 in.) of the family; sooty black above, with a white throat, a blackish band across the upper breast, and the rest of the underparts whitish mottled with dark gray, more heavily on the sides and flanks. The forehead is faintly streaked with whitish, and there is a plume of white extending backward from just below the eye. The swollen bill is bright red with a whitish tip, and the legs and feet are gray. In fall and winter the throat and entire underparts are white, the bill is smaller and gray, and a patch of white on the inner edge of the wing shows as a horizontal white slash when the bird is on water. Breeds coastally from ne. Siberia, the Diomede Is., and Cape Lisburne, Alaska, south to the Aleutian and Shumagin Is. Winters from the Bering Sea to Sakhalin I., and n. Japan. Straggles along Arctic coast of Alaska and nw. Mack. Common. Habitat and biology similar to that of Parakeet Auklet.

WHISKERED AUKLET (*Aethia pygmaea*)

Somewhat larger (ca. 7 in.) than the Least Auklet. Plumage similar to that of the Crested Auklet, but forehead plume is longer and thinner, white-tipped bill is without wattles, and it has 2 long white plumes originating at base of bill and extending backward, 1 above and 1 below the eye. In winter the bill has a duller color. The immature is like the immature Crested Auklet, but it has a white eye and a faint white streak behind and another beneath the eye. It is resident of coasts, islands, and adjacent open seas of the Komandorskie Is., s. Kurile Is., and c. Aleutians. Biology similar to that of Parakeet Auklet.

RHINOCEROS AUKLET (*Cerorhinca monocerata*)

Appearance: Largest (14–15½ in.) of the auklets and murrelets; brownish black above, white below, with medium gray throat, upper breast, and sides. It has 2 long, rearward-sweeping white plumes, 1 originating just above the eye and the other at the base of the lower bill; the bill is yellowish. A single conical-shaped whitish "horn" projects upward from the base of the upper beak, from which both common and scientific names are derived; in fall and winter the horn is replaced by a rather slight swelling. Legs and feet are pale yellow. Immature birds lack both plumes and horn.

Voice: At breeding colonies, various growls, barks, and raucous shrieks.

Range and status: Breeds on coasts, offshore islets, and islands from s. Sakhalin I. and s. Kuriles Is. south to Korea and n. Japan, and from se. Alaska to nw. Wash.; formerly on the Farallon Is. off c. Calif., nonbreeders wandering to s. Calif. Retreats from more northerly parts of range in winter. Common.

Habitat: Open seas, deep bays with strong tidal flow; breeding isles and localities with some soil.

Seasonal movements: Apr.–May and Sept.–Oct.

Biology: Nest: A small accumulation of grasses, sticks, leaves, and feathers in chamber at end of 8–20-ft.-long burrows in soil. Eggs: 1; whitish, often faintly spotted with grays and dull browns, sometimes heavily spotted with dark browns. Incubation: 31–33 days, by both sexes. Age at 1st flight: 5–6 weeks; young apparently leave burrows and enter sea before able to fly. Food: Marine crustaceans at or near surface of sea and small fish.

Suggested reading: F. Richardson, "Breeding Behavior of the Rhinoceros Auklet on Protection Island, Washington," *Condor*, vol. 63, pp. 456–473, 1961.

Whiskered Auklet

Horned Puffin

COMMON PUFFIN (*Fratercula arctica*)

Appearance: Rather small (11½–13 in.); blackish above (including head and neck) and white below, with a large white face patch covering the entire side of the head and the upper throat. The yellowish eye has a short vertical streak of black above and a small spot of red below. The grotesque, laterally flattened, parrotlike bill is bright reddish orange at the tip half and has a yellow-bordered patch of blue at the rear half, all combining to give the bird a harlequinesque appearance; the bill is additionally sculptured with rounded ridges and grooves. Legs and feet are dark pinkish, almost red. In fall and winter the base of the bill is somewhat less swollen and looks discolored. The front part of the white face patch is then edged with brownish gray, fading to whitish at the rear of the patch. Immature birds are like the adults in winter, but colors are duller, and bill is smaller, without ridges and grooves.

Voice: A deep, slowly rising groan *a-a-awe;* in flight near nests, a low *purr-la-la-la,* growling notes, and wailing yelps (of nestling).

Range and status: Breeds along coasts and on islands from n. Lab., w.-c. and e.-c. Greenland, Jan Mayen, Spitsbergen, and n. Novaya Zemlya south to Anticosti I., the Magdalen Is., s. N.B., e. Maine, Nfld., Iceland, Ireland, nw. France, n. Scandinavia, and n. Russia; in winter in open water of Atlantic Ocean south to N.J. and w. Mediterranean. Accidental inland. Common in parts of range, but tameness allows it to be collected too easily for food, so rare near areas populated by man.

Habitat: Rocky seacoasts and open seas.

Seasonal movements: Sedentary in parts of range. Moves north Mar.–May and south Sept.–Nov.

Biology: Nest: A mass of grasses and feathers in a burrow 2–5 ft. long in loose soil at top of cliffs or islets, in soft rocks of cliffsides, rarely in rock crevices. Eggs: Almost always 1 (2 eggs probably indicate 2nd pair of birds); whitish, sometimes spotted with dull browns. Incubation: 40–43 days. Age at 1st flight: 49–51 days; young are untended in burrows last few days, then leave shortly after dusk and flutter off cliff into sea. Food: Mostly small fish and marine invertebrates, usually taken at or near surface of sea.

Suggested reading: D. A. Bannerman, *Birds of the British Isles,* Oliver and Boyd, Edinburgh, 1963, vol. 12, pp. 153–171. R. M. Lockley, *Puffins,* Devin-Adair, N.Y., 1953.

HORNED PUFFIN (*Fratercula corniculata*)

Appearance: Somewhat larger (ca. 14½ in.) than the Common Puffin and very similar to it in all plumages. It has a fleshy "horn" over each eye. The basal half of the bill is entirely yellow in spring and summer, gray in fall and winter. The top of the head is gray, and the white face patch in fall and winter is almost completely gray.

Voice: Low growling and grunting noises made at breeding grounds; loud quarrelsome growls from burrows.

Range and status: Breeds on coasts and islands from ne. Siberia, Diomede Is., nw. Alaska, and islands of the Bering Sea south to Sakhalin I., the n. Kurile Is., Komandorskie Is., the Aleutians, and coasts and offshore islands of s. Alaska. Winters from open waters of Bering Sea south to Ore.; casually to n. Japan and Calif. Common.

Habitat: Rocky coasts and open ocean, cliffs and isles with covering of soil or debris.

Seasonal movements: Moves north Apr.–June and returns Sept.–Nov.

Biology: Nest: In burrow or rock crevice; similar to that of Common Puffin. Eggs: 1; whitish, usually with faint spots and scrawls. Incubation period and age at 1st flight unknown. Food: Small fish and marine invertebrates.

Suggested reading: A. C. Bent, *Life Histories of North American Diving Birds,* Dover, N.Y. (reprint of U. S. Nat. Mus. Bull. 107, 1919), 1963, pp. 97–103.

TUFTED PUFFIN (*Lunda cirrhata*)

Appearance: A little larger (14½–15½ in.) than the Horned Puffin; plumage entirely black, except for the white face. Its face lacks the black and red marks of the other puffins but sports long, backward-curving yellow plumes that droop down the neck to the back. The typical puffin bill is bright red except for the basal part, which is yellowish green; legs and feet are red. In fall and winter the head, neck, and upperparts are brownish black, and the underparts are mottled with medium and light grays. There is a small patch of light gray about the eye, there are no tufts, and the basal third of the bill is blackish. Immature birds are like the adults in winter, but the bill is smaller and yellowish, and the underparts are a lighter, less-mottled gray.

Voice: Soft grunts and growls in colonies.

Range and status: Breeds on shores and islands of Bering Sea south to Sakhalin I., n. Japan, the Aleutians, and the Santa Barbara Is. off s. Calif. Winters from open water of Bering Sea to c. Japan and n. Baja Calif. Fairly common.

Habitat: Rocky shores and open seas.

Seasonal movements: Mainly sedentary; breeding season mid-Apr.–July (early in s. part, later in n. part).

Biology: Nest: In burrows, sometimes crevices in rocks. Eggs: 1; whitish, with faint gray or brownish markings. Incubation and age at 1st flight unknown. Food: Small fish and marine invertebrates.

Suggested reading: A. C. Bent, *Life Histories of North American Diving Birds,* Dover, N.Y. (reprint of U.S. Nat. Mus. Bull. 107, 1919), 1963, pp. 82–89.

PIGEONS AND DOVES (COLUMBIDAE)

Pigeons and doves are small to medium-sized (6–33 in.) land birds; the well-known Domestic Pigeon, or Rock Dove, is typical of this group. All American pigeons are small (6–17 in.); the largest is the Crowned Pigeon of New Guinea. The extinct flightless dodos of the Mascarene Is. were relatives of the pigeons. There are about 290 species, some of which are found in every part of the world except the polar regions, the subarctic area, and some oceanic islands. In America, there are 17 species; if the attempts to introduce them had been successful, Hawaii would boast another 11 species. Many species are at least partially migratory. Their plumage is soft and thick and comes in a great variety of colors; many species have barred or "scaled" patterns, and most of them have some metallic or iridescent glossing. A few species are crested. Their wings are pointed and range from short (on the more terrestrial species) to long. In most species the body is plump, the head rather small, and the neck somewhat short. The tail may be long or medium long, pointed or square. The bill, slender in some species and stout in others, is usually a bit shorter than the head, and there is a waxy-looking plate called a "cere" at the base of the upper mandible. The feet are sturdy and range from short to long. There is no seasonal change in plumage coloration, and the sexes are alike, except that the female is usually somewhat duller in color. Most species are excellent fliers. Sounds emitted consist of a variety of coos, also hissing, grunting, and whistling. These birds occupy a variety of habitats from scrub desert to woodland areas. Some species are gregarious, others are solitary. Courtship by males is usually a strutting, feather-displaying parade before the female. Most species build a simple platform nest of twigs and sticks in trees or on ledges; some build in three cavities, in burrows, or on the ground. The 1–3, most commonly 2, eggs are usually white or buffy. Incubation and care of young are by both sexes; the young are downy or almost naked at hatching and remain in the nest until fledging time. At first they are fed pigeon "milk," a substance secreted in the crops of the adults; later on, partially digested food is regurgitated by the parents. Most pigeons feed on seeds, fruits, and other vegetable matter; others eat a variety of insects and other small invertebrates. There is no technical difference between a pigeon and a dove; the 2 terms are synonymous.

WHITE-CROWNED PIGEON (*Columba leucocephala*)

About the size (13½ in.) of the Rock Dove (the common Domestic Pigeon of city parks), with the entire top of the head from forehead to nape pure white and the rest of the plumage dark, mostly a slate gray. A "cape" at the back of the neck is dark metallic green, and each feather is edged in black, giving it a scaly appearance. The bill is yellow, with a bright red base; legs and feet are red, as are the eyelids. The eye is light yellow. Resident throughout the W. Indies (except the s. Lesser Antilles) and into the s. Fla. Keys; casually into s. peninsular Fla.

SCALY-NAPED PIGEON (*Columba squamosa*)

Larger (ca. 15 in.) than the Rock Dove, with head, front of neck, and chest a reddish purple; the "scaly" cape is metallic purple, and the rest of the plumage is dark gray. The eyelids are bright red in the male and yellow in the female; the legs and feet are red, and the yellow bill has a red base. It is resident in the Greater and Lesser Antilles and has straggled to Key West, Fla.

BAND-TAILED PIGEON (*Columba fasciata*)

Appearance: Larger (14–15½ in.) than the Rock Dove; head, foreneck, and entire breast are a pinkish medium gray. A distinct narrow white bar separates the head from the cape of metallic, black-edged yellowish green that fades into a greenish gray back. It has a gray rump and gray wings, with dark, almost black, flight feathers. The greenish gray tail is centrally barred with dark gray, and the belly and undertail plumage is white. The bill is yellow with a black tip; legs and feet are yellow, and the red-rimmed eye is yellow.

Voice: A repeated, rather haunting *hoo-oo-hoo* and a long buzzy note during courtship flight.

Range and status: Breeds from sw. B.C. to mountains of n. Baja Calif., from Utah and n.-c. Colo. to El

Wise management is restoring the numbers of the once overhunted Band-tailed Pigeon.

Salvador and n. Nicaragua, and in the mountains of s. Baja Calif.; winters from Calif., c. Ariz., and N.Mex. south, casually north to s. B.C. Has straggled to Okla. and N.Dak. Only casual in Nev. and Idaho. Decimated by hunting pressure almost to the danger point, but sound game laws have allowed it to recover so that it is again fairly common.

Habitat: Oak forests, particularly in mountains, foothills, and canyons, during breeding season and into other types of forests in winter.

Seasonal movements: Gathers in large flocks in fall and disperses over wider area; only a scattered few remain in n. part of breeding range. Moves north Mar.–May and returns Sept.–Oct.

Biology: Nest: Sometimes in small "colonial" groups; a rather flimsy platform of sticks and twigs in the lower limbs of a fir or similar tree, generally near the bole. Eggs: 1–2, normally 1, white. Incubation: About 19 days. Age at 1st flight: About 30 days; possibly 2 broods in s. part of range. Food: Nuts (many acorns), berries, fruit, flowers, grain, and other seeds and vegetable matter.

Suggested reading: J. A. Neff and R. J. Neidrach, "Nesting of the Band-tailed Pigeon in Colorado," *Condor,* vol. 48, pp. 72–75, 1946.

RED-BILLED PIGEON (*Columba flavirostris*)

Same size (13–14 in.) as the Rock Dove, with a purplish gray head, neck, back, breast, and wing "shoulders"; bluish gray rump, tail, belly, and wing. It has a red-

rimmed yellow eye, yellow-tipped red bill, and red legs and feet. It occurs from w.-c., n.-c., and ne. Mexico and southernmost Texas south to Costa Rica. It is not common in Texas, being found only in the lower Rio Grande Valley. Its habits and biology are rather similar to those of the Band-tailed Pigeon.

ROCK DOVE (Domestic Pigeon) (*Columba livia*)

Appearance: Size 13–14 in.; color pattern variable, but the more feral bird is generally gray with a purple tinge, especially on head, neck, and breast; it has a white rump patch, a rather broad terminal bar of black on the tail, and a patch of iridescent green or bronze at the side of the neck.

Voice: To urbanites, the familiar bubbling *coo-a-roo*.

Range and status: The natural range includes much of w. and s. Europe, sw. and s.-c. Siberia, w.-c. and ne. China south to n.-c. Africa, Arabia, s. India, Ceylon, and s. Burma. Now established from escaped domestic stock, particularly in the larger cities, over most of the world, including Hawaii. From the urban centers it spreads over the countryside, but is not truly established as a wild bird, since it is dependent on man to a great extent.

Habitat: Cities and farms; in natural habitat of Eurasia found mainly at cliff sites.

Seasonal movements: Less frequently encountered in open country during winter, then preferring citified areas and the more immediate vicinity of farm buildings.

Biology: Nest: In America, building ledges, etc.; within natural range, cliff ledges and in caves, where it builds a flimsy, rather messy platform of sticks, twigs,

Wild ancestors of the familiar Rock Dove nested on rocky cliffs in Europe and Asia.

and grasses. Eggs: 1–2, normally 2, white. Several broods raised each year. Incubation: 17–19 days. Age at 1st flight: 35–37 days. Food: Various seeds and grain, other vegetable matter, and some animal food, such as insects, spiders, and remains in garbage.

Suggested reading: D. A. Bannerman, *Birds of the British Isles*, Oliver and Boyd, Edinburgh, 1959, vol. 8, pp. 349–360.

ZENAIDA DOVE (*Zenaida aurita*)

Smaller (9–11 in.) than the Rock Dove; brown above, purplish gray below, iridescent purple at the side of the neck. The black-barred square tail has white tips on the outer feathers; the white tips on the ends of the inner flight feathers show as a white bar. It ranges throughout most of the W. Indies, formerly to the Fla. Keys.

WHITE-WINGED DOVE (*Zenaida asiatica*)

Appearance: Smaller (11–12½ in.) than the Rock Dove; plumage largely a buffy brown, sometimes tinged with purple, especially about the head. There is a large white patch on the wing, the flight feathers of which are almost black. White corner patches are evident on the slightly rounded tail. It has a small black spot below and behind the orange eye; the bill is black, and the legs and feet are red.

Voice: A gruff *who-cooks-for-you* cooing call, sometimes tiresomely repeated, and a more multisyllabled, gentler cooing call.

Range and status: Resident, although numbers somewhat reduced in more northerly parts during winter months, from se. Calif., c. Ariz., s. N.Mex., and southernmost Tex. south to w. Panama; through the Bahamas and Greater Antilles (except Puerto Rico); and from sw. Ecuador to n. Chile. Has straggled to Wash., Colo., La., Miss., Ala., Fla., Maine, N.Y., B.C., Ont., and Puerto Rico. Common.

Zenaida Dove

Habitat: Forests at river edges, thickets, desert oases, and near human habitations and communities.

Seasonal movements: Arrives in numbers late-Apr.–mid-May and retires mid-Sept.–Oct. Individuals banded in Texas have been recovered in El Salvador.

Biology: Nests: 10–25 ft. above ground in trees or shrubs; a frail platform of twigs and sticks; many nests in 1 area. Eggs: 1–3, normally 2; yellowish white or very pale buff. Incubation: 17–19 days. Age at 1st flight: Between 3 and 4 weeks. Food: Fruit of trees, shrubs, and cactus; grain and other vegetable matter.

Suggested reading: L. W. Arnold, *The Western White-winged Dove in Arizona*, Ariz. Game and Fish Comm., Phoenix, 1943, 103 pp.

MOURNING DOVE (*Zenaidura macroura*)

Appearance: As long (11–13 in.) as the Rock Dove, but appears smaller and much slimmer, since the tail is proportionally longer. Plumage is a buffy brown with a metallic purplish sheen at the side of the neck and with a small black spot below and behind the dark eye; the slim, wedge-shaped tail has white tips to all but the elongated central feathers. The wings are usually a purple-tinged gray, darker on the flight feathers, and the back is sometimes sparsely spotted with very dark brown.

Voice: A mournful, drawn-out *oooo-cooo-cooo-coo*, repeated monotonously, and squeaky whistled noises when flushed.

Range and status: Breeds from se. Alaska, s. B.C., Alta., Sask., Man., s. Ont., s. Que., Maine, and s. N.B. south to w. Panama, the Greater Antilles, and the Bahamas. In winter it retreats south of s. B.C. and the n. tier of the U.S. Common.

Habitat: Almost any type but dense woods, alpine areas, and tundra.

Seasonal movements: Returns in larger numbers to northerly areas Mar.–mid-May and leaves Oct.–Nov.

Biology: Nest: A frail platform of twigs, on the ground or up to 50 ft. high in trees or shrubs (generally close to trunk on horizontal branch when in trees). Eggs: 1–4, but other than 2 very rare; white. Incubation: 13–15 days, by male in daytime and by female at night, early morning, and late afternoon. Age at 1st flight: About 2 weeks. Food: Almost entirely seeds, mainly of weeds; very little other vegetable matter.

Suggested reading: M. M. Nice, "A Study of the Nesting of Mourning Doves," *Auk*, vol. 39, pp. 457–474, 1922; vol. 40, pp. 37–58, 1923.

PASSENGER PIGEON (*Ectopistes migratorius*)

Appearance: Extinct. Larger (15–17 in.) than the Rock Dove; bluish gray above, including entire head and central feathers of long, web-shaped tail. Breast, including lower throat and sides of neck, was tawny; abdomen

The wide-ranging Mourning Dove is North America's commonest native dove.

and undertail feathers were white. Flight feathers of wing were blackish, and outer tail feathers white; the smaller feathers on the wing and back were sparsely spotted with black. The eyelids, eyes, legs, and feet were red; the bill was black.

Voice: Loud croaking, chattering, and clucking noises.

Range and status: Formerly bred east of the Rockies from c. Mont., N.Dak., s. Man., Minn., Wis., Mich., c. Ont., s. Que., N.B., and N.S. south to Okla., Miss., and Ga.; wintered from Ark., Mo., Tenn., and N.C. south to Tex., the Gulf Coast, and c. Fla. Straggled farther north and west; European records were probably escaped captives. Last bird known to science died in Cincinnati Zoo on Sept. 1, 1914; in colonial days population was probably in billions! Species such as this are still included in natural history books to remind us of lessons in conservation learned the "hard way" in the past.

Habitat: Mainly dense deciduous forests.

Seasonal movements: Tremendous flocks moved northward Mar.–Apr. and returned Sept.–Oct.

Biology: Colonial; last known nesting area included over 100,000 acres and yielded 1½ million birds for the market; there were often more than 100 nests in a single tree! Nest: A flimsy platform of twigs and sticks on branches of trees. Eggs: 1–2, very rarely more than 1; white. Incubation: About 14 days. Age at 1st flight: About 18 days. Food: Acorns, chestnuts, beechnuts, and other fruits of trees.

Suggested reading: A. W. Schorger, *The Passenger Pigeon*, Univ. of Wisconsin Press, Madison, 1955, 424 pp.

SPOTTED DOVE (*Streptopelia chinensis*)

About the size (13 in.) of the Rock Dove; a grayish brown above, lighter below (to white on the lower breast and belly), with a white-spotted black cape. The outer feathers of the rounded tail are black, broadly tipped with white. The bill is black; legs and feet are dark pink with black claws. Ranges from China to India, Ceylon, Burma, and n. Indonesia. Introduced in Los Angeles, Calif.; spreading into sw. Calif. and in Hawaii, where it is fairly common.

RINGED TURTLE DOVE (*Streptopelia risoria*)

Slightly smaller (12 in.) than the Rock Dove; pale brown above; lighter, almost yellowish white, below, with a narrow black cape at the rear of the neck and whitish corners on the tail. A widely domesticated dove of unknown origin (possibly from the very similar-looking *Streptopelia roseogrisea* of C. Africa and Arabia). Established locally in city parks of Los Angeles, Calif.

Passenger
Pigeon

BARRED DOVE (*Geopelia striata*)

Small (ca. 8 in.), with a pale gray head, upper neck, upper breast, and upper back. Back and wings are brown; rump and tail are medium gray. The rest of the plumage is white, including the outer tail feathers. It is barred with thin, wavy black lines on the back, wings, and sides. The bill is black; legs and feet are dull yellow. Native to Malaya, Indonesia, the Philippines, New Guinea, and Australia; introduced in Hawaii, where it is common on all main islands.

Suggested reading: C. W. and E. R. Schwartz, "Breeding Habits of the Barred Dove in Hawaii," *Condor*, vol. 52, pp. 241–246, 1950.

GROUND DOVE (*Columbigallina passerina*)

Appearance: Small (6–7 in.), with gray head, neck, back, and breast; becoming brownish and darker to the tip of the tail and on the inner half of the wing, somewhat lighter below. The outer half of the wing is bright brownish red, the flight feathers are tipped with black, and the outer tail feathers are black with a small white spot at each corner of the tail. The feathers of the back of the head, neck, and breast are edged with dark brown, giving a scaly effect to the plumage. There are some dark brown spots on the back and wings. The dusky-tipped bill is red or orange-red; legs and feet are pink.

Voice: A much reiterated, mournful cooing.

Range and status: Resident from s. Calif., c. Ariz., s. N.Mex., s. Tex., the Gulf Coast, s. Ga., S.C., and Bermuda south to Costa Rica, the Bahamas, the Greater and Lesser Antilles, and islands in the Caribbean, and from Colombia and Venezuela to Ecuador and Brazil. Has straggled north to c. Calif., Iowa, Pa., and N.Y. Locally common and even abundant in some places; rare in other localities.

Habitat: Farmlands, grasslands, gardens, dirt roads, open woodlands, beaches; generally drier situations.

Seasonal movements: There is some shifting of populations after breeding season.

Biology: Nest: A very frail structure of twigs on ground, in bushes, or in low trees. Eggs: 2–3, normally 2, white. Incubation: About 13 days. Age at 1st flight unknown. Food: Small seeds, berries, and a few insects.

Suggested reading: D. J. Nicholson, "Notes on the Breeding of the Ground Dove in Florida," *Wils. Bull.*, vol. 49, pp. 101–114, 1937.

INCA DOVE (*Scardafella inca*)

Appearance: Small (7½–8 in.); grayish buff above, with scaled effect, and whitish below; the flight feathers of the wing close to the body are bluish gray, and the outer, black-tipped flight feathers are brownish red. The white outer feathers are separated from the brownish

The Barred Dove, an introduced species, is common throughout Hawaii.

The Ground Dove builds its fragile nest on the ground or in shrubs and low trees.

Notably tolerant of humans, the Inca Dove thrives near homes and in city parks.

central feathers of the tail by a black streak. The bill is blackish, and the legs and feet are pink.

Voice: An oft-repeated bottle-whistle cooing of 2 notes on same pitch.

Range and status: Resident from s. Ariz., s. N.Mex., and s. Tex. south through the coastal lowlands of e. and w. Mexico to Costa Rica and Nicaragua. Extending its range northward and becoming more common.

Habitat: A ground dove of sparsely vegetated, semiarid regions, adapting itself readily to small urban areas and city parks.

Seasonal movements: None.

Biology: Nest: In low trees, bushes, cactus, or on man-made structures; a frail platform of twigs and straw. Eggs: 2, white or light buff. Incubation: About 14 days. Age at 1st flight: About 12 days. Food: Weed and other seeds.

Suggested reading: R. F. Johnston, "Behavior of the Inca Dove," *Condor*, vol. 62, pp. 7–24, 1960.

WHITE-FRONTED DOVE (*Leptotila verreauxi*)

Somewhat smaller (11–12 in.) than the Rock Dove; generally brownish above, fading to light purplish brown on the neck and upper breast and to gray on the crown; the breast color fades to white on the belly and undertail feathers. The forehead and throat are white, as are the tips of the outer tail feathers. The bill is black, the legs and feet are purplish red, and the eye color ranges from light yellow to orange-red. It is resident from c. Sonora and southernmost Texas south through the tropical lowlands to n. Argentina and Uruguay and on islands off the n. coast of S. America. Not common in n. part of range; it is difficult to see because of its rather secretive habits and haunts.

KEY WEST QUAIL-DOVE (*Geotrygon chrysia*)

Larger (10–11½ in.) than the Ground Dove; variable iridescent colors above (mainly greenish on the head and back of the neck, brownish red on rest of upperparts) and white below, with a horizontal streak of white running from the base of the bill to the lower rear quarter of the head just beneath the eye. The iris and the black-tipped bill are red; legs and feet are flesh-colored. It is resident in the Bahamas, Cuba, Hispaniola, and Puerto Rico; possibly casually or formerly at Key West, Fla.

RUDDY QUAIL-DOVE (*Geotrygon montana*)

Smaller (8–12 in.) than the Rock Dove; chestnut above (lighter at head and neck) and pinkish buff below, with a streak of buff below the eye. The bill is dark red, the eye is yellow, and the legs and feet are purplish red. It is resident in the tropical lowlands from s. Sonora and Tamaulipas in Mexico south to Bolivia, Paraguay, and Brazil, and through the Greater Antilles, Grenada, and Trinidad. It has straggled to Key West, Fla.

PARROTS, PARAKEETS, AND MACAWS (PSITTACIDAE)

These are small to medium-sized (4–40 in.) land birds; their general characteristics are usually well known to Americans, as they are very popular cage birds. There are about 315 species occurring in the tropics and subtropics of the N. Hemisphere and through most of the S. Hemisphere except Antarctica, the more remote oceanic islands, and the s. tip of Africa. Formerly occurred farther north into the temperate region of N. America. There were 4 American species; the only true native is now extinct, 1 species is a rare straggler, and 2 are established through introduction or escape from cages. Very few species are even partially migratory. Their feathers are usually stiff, glossy, and brightly colored; some species are crested. The strong wings are pointed or slightly rounded; the tail varies from long to short, and it may be square, rounded, pointed, or even racquet-tipped. The sturdy bill is short, strongly decurved, and hooked. The head is relatively large, and the neck is rather short. The legs are short and thick. The birds characteristically perch and climb with 2 toes forward and 2 to the rear; the bill is also used in climbing. The sexes are usually alike. Their voices are commonly raucous screams, shrieks, whistles, and grunts. Most parrots are arboreal and prefer woodlands, but some are found in semiarid scrub areas. Many parrots are gregarious, and some are colonial. Their nests are often unlined hollows in trees, rocks, or banks; some nest on the ground, and a few build nests of sticks and twigs in tree branches. Their eggs are almost always white, and any number from 1–12 constitutes a clutch; incubation may be by both sexes or by the females alone. The young are naked on hatching and shortly acquire a coat of down; both parents share in rearing the nestlings. A great variety of vegetable produce is eaten, including fruit, nuts, and grain; some species also eat some animal matter.

CAROLINA PARAKEET (*Conuropsis carolinensis*)

Appearance: Extinct. Small (11–13 in.); green, with a yellow head and orange forehead and face. There was some yellow and dark blue on the wing; the tail was long and graduated. The bill was pale yellow or buffy, the legs and feet light pink or flesh-colored. Recently fledged young had green heads with tawny or orange foreheads.

Voice: Loud, cacophonous screams in flight.

Range and status: Formerly found (apparently resident, but status uncertain) from N.Dak., Nebr., Iowa, s. Wis., Ohio, and c. N.Y. south to the Gulf Coast and s.-c. Fla. The bird was a pest around farms and was easily killed, since the flocks would merely flush and circle the spot where some of their members had been shot, then settle down again at the same place if food was still available. It was also in demand as a pet, and for food and millinery items.

Habitat: Forests, forest edges, coppices, and wooded river bottoms and ravines in plains areas.

Seasonal movements: None recorded.

Biology: Nest: Unlined hollow in trees. Eggs: 2–3, white. Incubation: 19–20 days (1 record). Age at 1st flight unknown. Food: In the wild, and before tempted by the abundance of cultivated grains and fruit, it apparently subsisted largely on the seeds of trees (including conifers) and weeds and on wild fruits.

Suggested reading: D. McKinley, "The Carolina Parakeet in Pioneer Missouri," *Wils. Bull.*, vol. 72, pp. 274–287, 1960.

THICK-BILLED PARROT (*Rhynchopsitta pachyrhyncha*)

A medium-sized (15–17 in.) green parrot with a red forehead, red at the bend of the wing, and red on the lower thigh; the bill, legs, and feet are black. It breeds only in the mountains of Chihuahua and Durango in Mexico and disperses over much of n.-c. and n. Mexico, even occasionally and abundantly to s.-c. and se. Ariz. and sw. N.Mex.; however, it has not been recorded north of the Mexican border since 1922.

Suggested reading: A. Wetmore, "The Thick-billed Parrot in Southern Arizona," *Condor*, vol. 37, pp. 18–21, 1935.

Carolina Parakeet

PALE-HEADED PARAKEET (*Platycercus adscitus*)

A small (11–12 in.) white-headed, dark-backed, and dark-tailed parrot. Breast and abdomen are finely barred blue and white; undertail feathers are red; rump is white. Native to se. Australia; introduced in Hawaii and apparently established on Maui I.

BUDGERIGAR (*Melopsittacus undulatus*)

This small (6½–7½ in.) parakeet is the most common of the small caged parrots; sometimes erroneously called "love bird." Intensively bred for the pet bird market through many years, with a great variety of plumage colors being developed. The wild ancestor, a native of much of Australia, is green with a blue tail, a yellow face, a mottling of black above from the crown to the rump and on to the wings, and flesh-colored bill, legs, and feet. Through the escape of caged birds, it has become fairly well established in s. Fla. and possibly in Hawaii.

The colorful Thick-billed Parrot has not been sighted north of Mexico since 1922.

CUCKOOS, ROADRUNNERS, AND ANIS (CUCULIDAE)

These are small to medium-sized (6–27½ in.), slender, long-tailed land birds. Their nearest relatives are the touracos and plantain eaters, restricted to Africa. There are 127 species, 7 of which have been recorded or occur regularly in America. They are cosmopolitan in distribution, except for the polar regions, the more remote oceanic islands, and the higher latitudes of N. America and Asia. Most species of the temperate zones are migratory; the majority, which occur in the tropical regions, are sedentary. They are found most commonly in forested regions, but some occur in sparsely vegetated areas. Browns, grays, black, and white plumages predominate, but there are some species with bright blues, purples, and greens in evidence. Many species are streaked and/or barred. The feathers are rather loose and in some species wiry. The bill, commonly long (never longer than the head), slender, and slightly decurved, is stout and heavy in some species. The legs are short except in the ground-dwelling species; 2 of the toes are directed to the rear and 2 forward. The pointed wings are medium to long; most species are excellent fliers, although some very rarely fly. A common habit of walking along tree branches, especially where foliage is dense, reminds one of the actions of squirrels. Sexes are alike in most species. Vocal efforts are usually loud, unmusical, much reiterated calls. Quite a few species are parasitic, laying their eggs in the nests of other species. They are mainly solitary, but the anis share nests with each other in community effort. Most nests are simple platforms of sticks and grasses, but some are domed structures with side entrances. The eggs are plain white, blue, greens, reds, and browns, or sometimes spotted. In nonparasitic species incubation is by both sexes, which also share in raising young. The young are hatched naked and acquire down quickly. Most species are insectivorous, but other invertebrates, small vertebrates, and fruit are also consumed.

ORIENTAL CUCKOO (*Cuculus saturatus*)

Medium-sized (13–15 in.); gray above, including head, neck, and upper breast; white below. Each white feather is tipped with black, giving the underparts a wavy-barred effect. The underside of the tail is black, spotted and tipped with white. Immature birds, and some females throughout their lives, are tawny above and white below, including neck and throat, with both underside and upper side patterned with wavy bars. The legs, feet, eyes, and base of the black bill are yellow. It breeds from c. Russia across n.-c. Siberia to Kamchatka south to the Himalayas, Burma, s. China, Formosa, and s. Japan. Winters from s. Asia through Indonesia to Australia and the Solomon Is. It has straggled to Alaska (St. Lawrence I., Seward Peninsula, the Pribilofs, and the Aleutians).

MANGROVE CUCKOO (Black-eared Cuckoo) (*Coccyzus minor*)

Small (12–13 in.); light grayish brown above and pale yellow below. The 2 black outer tail feathers on each side are tipped with white, and there is a broad streak of black extending from the base of the bill through the eye to the region of the ear. The upper bill is black, and the lower is yellow tipped with black. It is resident from n.-c. Mexico and s. Fla. through C. America and the W. Indies to n. S. America. Its voice is a low, guttural *gaw-gaw-gaw-gaw*, slower in cadence than that of the Yellow-billed Cuckoo, which occurs in the same areas. It is rather rare in Fla., where it is restricted to mangrove thickets along the sw. coast and in the Keys.

YELLOW-BILLED CUCKOO (*Coccyzus americanus*)

Appearance: Small (11–12½ in.); a silky grayish brown above and white below. The graduated outer tail feathers are black tipped with white; when the tail is folded while the bird is perching, the entire underside looks black, with 3 pairs of large white spots over its length. In flight the tawny bases of the larger flight feathers in the wing are exposed. The eyelids are yellow, and the legs and feet are black; the upper bill is black, and the lower bill is yellow tipped with black.

Voice: A rather rapid series of wooden-whistle *cuc*'s, the cadence slowing near the end and the notes becoming longer.

Range and status: Breeds from sw. Canada, n.-c.

U.S., and se. Canada south to s. Baja Calif., s.-c. Mexico, and through the W. Indies. Winters from n. S. America to Ecuador, c. Argentina, and Uruguay. It has straggled to Europe. Common, but solitary and secretive.

Habitat: Prefers damp, 2nd-growth wooded areas, thickets near river and swamps, and brush-grown deserted farmlands.

Seasonal movements: Arrives Mar.–mid-May and departs Sept.–Oct.

Biology: Nest: Usually low in bushes, shrubbery, thickets, or well-leaved trees, but some as high as 20 ft.; a frail saucer of twigs thinly lined with finer materials. Eggs: 1–5, usually 3–4, pale bluish green; occasionally laid in nests of Black-billed and even more rarely in nests of other birds. The eggs are laid at intervals of 2–3 days, and incubation begins with 1st egg. Incubation: About 14(?) days by both parents. Age at 1st flight unknown; young are able to climb about branches when only 7–9 days old. Food: Almost entirely insects; the Yellow-billed's apparent fondness for hairy caterpillars, such as the tent caterpillar, is a trait shared by few other birds.

Suggested reading: N. A. Preble, "The Nesting Habits of the Yellow-billed Cuckoo," *Amer. Midland Naturalist*, vol. 57, pp. 474–482, 1957.

BLACK-BILLED CUCKOO (*Coccyzus erythropthalmus*)

Appearance: About the same size (11–12 in.) as the Yellow-billed Cuckoo, and very similar in coloration. Grayish brown above and white below; the tail is grayish brown above and below, and the graduated feathers are narrowly tipped with white. The Black-bill's tail from beneath therefore has 3 whitish bands and a narrow white tip. The bill is entirely black, as are the legs and feet; the eyelids are red. It has no tawny color on the wings.

Voice: Tone rather similar to that of the Yellow-billed, but no slowing of cadence toward end of song, nor lengthening of notes; sometimes a run-together series of 3 notes alternating with more widely spaced *cuk*'s. Often sings at night. Sometimes called the "rain crow," as its notes seem to presage rainfall.

Range and status: Breeds east of the Rockies from s. Canada to se. Wyo., Nebr., nw. Ark., e. Kans., c. Tenn., and S.C. Winters in nw. S. America. Has straggled to Greenland and Europe. Sometimes and in places more common than the Yellow-billed; other times and places, where range overlaps, it is rarer.

The Black-billed Cuckoo's nest is a flimsy saucer of twigs.

Habitat: Forest edges, thickets, and groves of trees along rivers.

Seasonal movements: Arrives Apr.–mid-May and leaves Sept.–late Oct.

Biology: Nest: 2–10 ft. above the ground in low bush or tree; a frail saucer of twigs sparsely lined with finer materials. Eggs: 2–5, usually 2–3; a slightly darker blue-green than those of the Yellow-billed. Eggs occasionally laid in nests of Yellow-billed and other bird species. Incubation: About 14(?) days. Age at 1st flight unknown. Young climb expertly through and among branches of nesting shrub or tree when 7–10 days old. Food: Insects; like the Yellow-billed, it eats hairy caterpillars.

Suggested reading: O. R. Spencer, "Nesting Habits of the Black-billed Cuckoo," *Wils. Bull.,* vol. 55, pp. 11–22, 1943.

ROADRUNNER (*Geococcyx californianus*)

Appearance: Large (20–24 in.), with a tail nearly as long as the body, a heavy, strong bill nearly as long as the head, and long legs. The tail acts as a balance as the bird races over the ground and, with the aid of the wings, also acts as a rudder when the bird makes running turns; in the air wings and tail are just about adequate for short, last-resort escape flights. It is dark above and whitish below; the rough crest is black, spotted with white. The dark feathers of the wings are edged with light buff, and there are streaks of white in the upper part of the greenish brown back. The throat and breast are streaked with black. The outer feathers of the greenish brown tail are tipped with white; the forehalf of a long streak behind the eye is pale blue, and the rear half is red. The bill is black, and the legs and feet are pale blue. Top running speed is about 15 miles per hour.

Voice: Various purring and clucking sounds; in spring a series of *coo*'s that start higher but end in about the same tone as a Mourning Dove's. Ratchetlike rattles are made by "rolling" or clicking the mandibles together.

Range and status: Resident from n.-c. Calif., Nev., s. Utah, Colo., sw. Kans., e. Okla., w. Ark., and nw. La. south to s. Baja Calif., Michoacan, Puebla, and Vera Cruz. Not so common as it might be, since its comical aspect and amusing antics have led to its being chased by man, boy, and dog. It has thus been plagued away from populated areas.

Habitat: Semiarid and other dry, open areas with scattered cover, such as brush, piñon, juniper, stones, etc.

Seasonal movements: None.

Biology: Nest: In low tree, shrub, or cactus 3–15 ft. above the ground; made of sticks lined with leaves, grasses, feathers, roots, and any available material. Eggs:

The ungainly-looking Roadrunner can run as fast as 15 miles an hour.

2–8, usually 3–5; white, sometimes acquiring a yellow tinge. Incubation: 18(?) days, by female alone(?). Starts incubation with laying of 1st egg; the last egg laid may therefore hatch quite a few days after the 1st. Age at 1st flight unknown, but young are able to run after and capture their own food when about 3 weeks old. Food: Insects, lizards, snakes, scorpions, spiders (including the tarantulas), small rodents, small birds and their young and eggs, also various fruits and seeds. Live animals are seized in the bill and thumped violently against nearby rocks until dead or senseless before they are swallowed. Hunters will often kill Roadrunners on sight, believing that these birds kill too many game birds; this is rather poor pay for the benefits received from the other feeding activities of the Roadrunner.

Suggested reading: G. M. Sutton, "Titania and Oberon," in *Birds in the Wilderness,* Macmillan, N.Y., 1936, chap. 3, pp. 7–31.

SMOOTH-BILLED ANI (*Crotophaga ani*)

Medium-sized (12–14 in.), all-black bird, with a very stout bill almost as big as the head; the upper mandible is deeply curved like a parrot's, and the tail is as long as the body. The actions of the wings and tail as the bird climbs through a thicket almost convinces one that these appendages have not been fastened properly to the body. It is resident from Panama to s. Brazil, n. Argentina, and Ecuador, and throughout most of the W. Indies; it has become established in s. Fla. and has straggled to La., N.J., and N.C. Anis have developed a communal nesting habit; several females will each lay 3–4 pale blue eggs in 1 bulky nest of sticks and twigs lined with green leaves. Three pairs of parents to each nest is about the limit. The eggs hatch in about 14 days. Food is mainly larger insects; some fruit and seeds are eaten. The bird often lands on cattle and eats the ticks found there.

GROOVE-BILLED ANI (*Crotophaga sulcirostris*)

Smaller (11½–12 in.) than the Smooth-billed and differing mainly in the bill, which has several very distinct grooves in the upper mandible running parallel to the curve of the ridge. It is resident from s. Sonora, the n.-c. Mexican plateau, and the Rio Grande delta in s. Tex. south to Peru and Guyana; formerly in s. Baja Calif. It has straggled to Ariz., La., Miss., Minn., Nebr.,

Groove-billed Ani

Kans., Okla., Ark., and Fla.; may be extending its range farther north and east. Biology like that of the Smooth-billed.

Suggested reading: A. Skutch, "Life History of the Groove-billed Ani," *Auk,* vol. 76, pp. 281–317, 1959.

THE BARN OWLS (TYTONIDAE)

Barn owls are small to medium-sized (12–21 in.) nocturnal birds of prey, differing from typical owls in that the facial disk is white, long, and heart-shaped. The strongly hooked bill is almost concealed in the feathers of the face, the forward-directed eyes are comparatively small, the legs and rounded wings are long, and the claw on the middle toe is pectinate, having a comblike edge. There are 11 species found all over the world, except for the polar regions, Hawaii, New Zealand, some islands in Indonesia, and some remote oceanic islands; only 1 species occurs in America. Most species are sedentary. The sexes are alike, but the female may be slightly larger. Flight is strong but silent. They make a variety of noises, including high-pitched screams, snores, clucks, hisses, and clicks. Food is seized in the talons and is usually swallowed entire; the bones, fur, and feathers form pellets that are regurgitated. Barn owls are found in a great variety of habitats from forests to fields, cliffs, semiarid areas, cities, and about farms. The biology of all species is very similar to that described under the Barn Owl below.

BARN OWL (*Tyto alba*)

Appearance: A fairly large (14–20 in.) owl with light tawny and gray patterns, spotted with white and black above. It is white below, sparsely spotted with black or gray, including the long, completely feathered legs and feet. In some areas it is buffy or very light tawny below. The white heart-shaped facial disk is edged with gray or black; the rather small eyes are fairly close together and appear to be sunken in brownish red pits. In flight at night it looks large-headed and ghostly white.

Voice: Highly variable; a shrill, weird screech is common; also high, rattling hisses, raucous sneezes, and snoring noises.

Range and status: In America from s. B.C., N.Dak., s. Minn., s. Wis., s. Mich., s. Ont., s. Que., and Mass. south through all lands and archipelagoes to s. S. America; it ranges casually farther north, and in winter some individuals migrate south short distances. It is also resident from the British Isles, the Baltic Region, s. Russia, India, and n. Burma south to s. Africa, Madagascar, Ceylon, Indonesia, Australia, and the Society Is. Rather rare.

Habitat: Almost anywhere; most common near open areas. In woodlands it hunts along roadways and in clearings.

Seasonal movements: None; individuals moving south are generally the young of the year, possibly searching out new territory.

Biology: Throughout the U.S. eggs have been recorded from every month of the year. Nest: In barns, belfries, hollow trees, deserted animal burrows, caves, and holes in banks; no nesting material is added, but debris is allowed to accumulate. Eggs: 5–11, usually 5–7; white. Incubation: 32–34 days, apparently by female alone. Age at 1st flight: More than 6–7 weeks. The male helps feed and guard the young. Food: Almost entirely rodents and other small mammals; only occasionally are birds and insects eaten.

Suggested reading: P. A. Stewart, "Dispersal, Breeding Behavior, and Longevity of Banded Barn Owls in North America," *Auk*, vol. 69, pp. 227–245, 1952.

The valuable Barn Owl preys primarily on voles, mice, and other small mammals.

THE TYPICAL OWLS (STRIGIDAE)

Typical owls are small to medium-sized (5–33 in.) nocturnal birds of prey more closely related to the cuckoos and parrots than they are to the hawks and eagles. They are absent only from Antarctica and some remote oceanic islands. There are 123 species, 17 of which occur in America. Many species are quite common; very few are even partially migratory. Most species are found in forested areas, but many have adapted to plains, tundra, or even desert habitats. Their feathers are long and soft, most commonly in browns, grays, black, and white, with barred, streaked, and spotted patterns predominating. Many species have "ears" or "horns," which are long tufts of feathers on the head generally above the eyes. Their wings may be short or long, but they are usually broad and rounded, with the larger flight feathers at the leading edge of the wing fringed, thus enabling the birds to fly without making the whistling or fluttering noises caused by straight-edged primaries. Their tails are short to long and very commonly barred. The sturdy hooked bill is short and has a cere at the base. The legs are short to medium, never very long; the toes are strong and bear sharp, well-curved claws. The outer toe is reversible so that an owl may perch with 2 toes forward and 2 back, or 3 forward and 1 back. The large eyes are directed forward, and in most species they are adapted for night life. The ears are even more remarkable than the eyes: set deep in the soft plumage, which opens at the will of the owl to form an inward-directed funnel over each ear, they are receptive to the softest sounds made by rodents scurrying through the night. Many owls hunt by sound more than by sight. The sexes are alike in most species, although the female is larger; many species occur in light, dark, or differently colored phases. Besides the hoots usually associated with these birds, a variety of trills, mews, barks, and whistles are heard, and almost all species make clicking and snapping noises with their bills. Very few species are colonial, but at some seasons a few species are gregarious. Their nests are commonly made in hollow trees, in old, deserted eagles', crows', or hawks' nests; some may be constructed on the ground, in burrows, or in buildings, and seldom is even the smallest amount of material used or added. Eggs are almost spherical in some species, and nearly always white; any number from 1–10 (usually up to 7) makes a full clutch. In at least some species, more eggs are laid when food is plentiful than when it is scarce. Incubation is by the female alone in the majority of species. The hatchlings are covered with down; they are cared for and fed by both parents. Almost all kinds of animal life are eaten; there are even fish-eating owls, and some consume large numbers of crabs. Prey is generally swallowed whole; the indigestible parts, such as hair and bones, are regurgitated as "pellets."

SCREECH OWL (*Otus asio*)

Appearance: Small (7–10 in.), with prominent ear tufts. The gray phase is pale gray all over with a fine barring of darker gray, except on the completely feathered legs and feet, and except for the face, throat, and upper breast. In the dark phase the plumage is streaked with black, and the sides of the face are edged with black. The bill and claws are black; the eyes are bright yellow. The red, or rufous, phase is brownish red above and white below (including the legs and feet). The eyebrows are white. The brownish red of the back extends onto the sides of the breast, and there is a streak of white on the wing. The face is light reddish buff, and the flanks are streaked with reddish buff. The sides of the face are limned with black; the breast and most of the brownish red feathers above are streaked with black. There are many intermediate phases, and variation in colors, streaking, and size have led to the recognition of 20 geographic races known as subspecies. West of the Rockies, only the gray phase is known, although individuals intermediate between the 2 have been taken. The ratio of red to gray in the easternmost subspecies is almost 1 to 1, with many intermediates.

Voice: There is some variation from 1 part of America to another; in the East it is a hollow-toned, quavering whistle, rising and then lowering in pitch; the cadence increases almost to a whinny at the end. In the West it is almost a monotoned series of mournful whistles, starting out slowly and running together at the end. It also snaps its bill. It comes quite readily even to rough imitations of its call.

The 10-inch-long Screech Owl is the smallest of our "eared" owls.

Range and status: Resident from se. Alaska, s.-c. B.C., s. Man., s. Ont., s. Que., and Maine south to s. Baja Calif., c. Mexico, the Gulf Coast, and s. Fla. It is not found in the higher parts of the Rockies or Sierra Nevadas.

Habitat: Seldom far from trees; forests, wooded canyons, and groves of trees on farms, in villages, along rivers, etc.

Seasonal movements: Some individuals of more northerly subspecies wander south in winter.

Biology: Nest: In tree cavity or woodpecker nesting hole; no lining is added. Eggs: 3–8, usually 4–5; white, oval to almost spherical in shape. Incubation: 26(?) days; mostly by female, but male hunts for both, even if he takes no direct part in incubation. Age at 1st flight: About 28–30 days. Food: It will consume almost any available form of animal life from worms to small mammals; when mice are abundant, its diet includes many of these rodents. When small birds are numerous, many are captured, so it is a valuable natural population control. It is voracious; evidence shows that it actively hunts even fish and amphibians.

Suggested reading: Althea Sherman, "Nest Life of the Screech Owl," *Auk*, vol. 28, pp. 155–168, 1911.

WHISKERED OWL (*Otus trichopsis*)

Slightly smaller (6½–8 in.) than the very similar Screech Owl, but with rows of white spots on the smaller feathers of the wing near the body; these spots are difficult to see unless the bird is in hand. Sometimes called the Spotted Screech Owl. Its voice is distinctive; a rather rapidly repeated series of *boot-boot-boot*'s, sometimes with a 3-and-1 cadence, as *boot-boot-boot, boot*, sometimes slowing toward end, and sometimes a *choo-yoo, coo-coo*. It is resident in the mountains from se. Ariz. and sw. N.Mex. to Honduras, where it is found in the same sort of habitat as the Screech Owl. Its biology is probably very similar to that of the Screech Owl.

FLAMMULATED OWL (Flammulated Screech Owl) (*Otus flammeolus*)

Appearance: Smaller (6–7 in.) than the Screech Owl, but separated readily from it only when one is close enough to see that the eyes are a dark, deep brown rather than bright yellow like the Screech Owl's. Its ear tufts are shorter than the Screech Owl's; when held close to the head, it may be mistaken for one of the smaller "earless" owls.

Voice: Only 2 notes: *boo-boot*, the second the louder, but repeated so often and close together that the hollow, mournful tones become ventriloquistic. Also clucking and a weak screech.

Range and status: Resident in the mountains, except the Coast Ranges, from s. B.C., Idaho, Colo., and w. Tex. south to Mexico and Guatemala. Common in higher coniferous forests.

Habitat: Most common in ponderosa pine areas; found in open pine and fir forests.

Seasonal movements: None; possibly moves down mountains during worst of winter.

Biology: Nest: In hollow of tree or woodpecker hole. Eggs: 3–4, white. Incubation and age at 1st flight unknown. Food: Almost entirely larger insects and spiders.

Suggested reading: J. T. Marshall, Jr., "Territorial Behavior of the Flammulated Screech Owl," *Condor*, vol. 41, pp. 71–78, 1939.

GREAT HORNED OWL (*Bubo virginianus*)

Appearance: Large (18–25 in.), with prominent ear tufts. Very variable; there are 16 geographic subspecies. Those in the Northwest tend to be very dark; in the Southeast they are rather light. In general it is brown, spotted with darker browns and black both above and on the wing. It is light below, rather finely barred with dark brown or black. The upper breast, or bib, is whitish or light-colored, the eye disks are reddish, and in some parts of the range it has white eyebrows. The eyes are bright yellow.

Voice: A series of loud, penetrating hoots, only rarely less than 3 or more than 8. A common cadence from the males is *hoo, hoo-hoo-ooo, hoot, hoot;* the lower-pitched answering call of the female is a *hoot, hoot-hoot-hoot,* *hoo-oot, hoo-oot.* It has been reported making a hawk-like scream; when disturbed, it utters a drawn-out, wailing hoot.

Range and status: Resident in the Americas from the n. tree limit to the Strait of Magellan, except for the W. Indies. Common.

Habitat: All types of forests, thickets, scrub areas, plains, canyons, cliffsides, river bottoms, and deserts.

Seasonal movements: There is considerable southward movement from more northerly parts of range in winter.

Biology: Nest: Starts nesting while snow is still on ground, as early as Feb. Eggs have been found in nest in mid-May; in old nests of hawks, herons, or crows in trees, on cliff ledges, and even on ground. Eggs: 1–5, commonly 2–3; white. Incubation: Reported in some works as 26–30 days, but closely related Eagle-owl of Eurasia takes 34–36 days. Both sexes participate. Age at 1st

The Great Horned Owl is so powerful that it captures even rabbits and skunks.

flight: 9–10 weeks. Food: Voracious, eating any form of animal life; like most predators, usually feeds on the animal form most common in the area it ranges. A partial list to show variety: rats, squirrels, rabbits, skunks, cats, ducks, grouse, weasels, even fish and insects.

Suggested reading: P. L. Errington, F. Hamerstrom, and F. N. Hamerstrom, Jr., *The Great Horned Owl and Its Prey in the North-central United States,* Iowa State Coll. Agric. and Mech. Arts Research Bull. 277, pp. 758–850, 1940.

SNOWY OWL (*Nyctea scandiaca*)

Appearance: Large (20–27 in.), without ear tufts, and predominantly white. Some individuals are almost immaculate, but most have varying amounts of wavy, dark brown barring, particularly on top of the head and back. Generally the older individuals have less barring. The female is usually more heavily barred. The young are uniformly dark brown, with paler legs and feet. The bill and claws are black, the eyes bright yellow.

Voice: Silent most of the year, except for clicks and snaps of the bill to express annoyance. During the breeding season a harsh 3-part shriek, followed by a single low note; also a yelping *rick-rick-rick,* a croak, a booming *ho,* a whinnying note by the female when the nest is threatened, a grunt, and a low *kroo, kroo* by the male when approaching the nest with food.

Range and status: Resident throughout the Arctic where land is not covered by permanent ice and snow, north of the tree limit. In winter, populations irregularly move south somewhat, when nesting has been successful, owing perhaps to abundant food supply, and particularly if the population is large. There are mass movements south to B.C., Alta., Sask., N.Dak., Minn., Ont., N.Y., s. Que., s. Lab., Nfld., British Isles, c. Europe, Turkestan; in America to s. Calif., Nev., Utah, Colo., Okla., c. Tex., La., Tenn., Ga., and S.C. Has straggled to Bermuda, France, the Azores, Iran, w. Pakistan, India, and Japan. Common.

Habitat: Tundra; in nonbreeding seasons open fields, prairies, marshes, sandy beaches.

Seasonal movements: The southward movements in winter are irregular, although almost every year brings some individuals to s. Canada and n. U.S.; the "mass" invasions may come as frequently as every 3–4 years or as far apart as 7–8 years.

Biology: Active day and night, usually hunting from rather low perches, such as fences, posts, or hummocks, at edges of fields. Nest: On the ground, generally atop a mound or ridge of tundra; usually the female scrapes a hollow 3–4 in. deep in mound. Lining is very sparse or lacking; accumulated pellets and droppings make mound higher with each year's use and enrich the soil so that many nesting sites may be recognized by rich vegetation

In winter, the Snowy Owl occasionally invades the United States.

growing about them. Eggs: 4–10, commonly 6–7; white. When food is abundant, more eggs are laid than in other years. Incubation: 32–33 days; by female alone, the male hunting for both. The young remain sightless until 4–5 days old. Age at 1st flight: 56–60 days. Food: In the Arctic, lemmings are principal food; besides these, other small rodents, hares, rabbits, squirrels, and shrews are readily eaten. When live game is scarce, it will consume carrion. It has taken sea ducks and other birds.

Suggested reading: A. O. Gross, "Food of the Snowy Owl," *Auk*, vol. 61, pp. 1–18, 1944.

HAWK OWL (*Surnia ulula*)

Appearance: Medium-sized (14½–17½ in.) hawk-like owl without ear tufts. The face is less flattened than that of other owls. It is blackish brown above, spotted and marked with white; white below, with wavy barring of blackish brown from the lower breast to the tail, which is broadly barred with white and blackish brown. The face and eyebrows are white; the legs and feet are grayish, finely barred with dark gray; the claws and bill are black; the eyes are yellow. The young are dark sooty brown above and light gray below, with a broad band of blackish brown across the chest.

Voice: In courtship the male utters a tremulous whistled *wita-wita-wita-wita;* both sexes give a quavering, rattling *kre-e-e-ee-eep* or hawklike *ki-ki-ki-ki* call and various other rather musical notes.

Range and status: Generally resident from the n. limit of coniferous forests in N. America and Eurasia south to n. B.C., n. Alta., c. Sask., n. Mich., c. Ont., s. Que., and N.B. to c. Russia, w.-c., c., and se. Siberia, ne.

China, n. Sakhalin I., and s. Kamchatka, with isolated breeding areas in the Alaska Peninsula and se. Siberia, possibly in Nfld. In winter some birds are seen regularly south as far as the n. U.S., Scotland, and c. and se. Europe. There are irregular irruptions during which the species ranges farther south, especially in winter.

Habitat: Fairly thick coniferous forests and less commonly in similar more open woods; rather conspicuous where it occurs, as it hunts days as well as nights from high, prominent perches.

Seasonal movements: Wintering individuals may appear in n. U.S. as early as mid-Oct. and depart as late as Apr.

Biology: Nest: In tree hollows, abandoned woodpecker holes, and deserted, twig-built nests of crows and birds of prey. Eggs: 3–7, usually 5–6, but as many as 9 and 13 have been recorded; white. Incubation and age at 1st flight unknown, but duties are shared by both parents. Food: Smaller mammals, principally rodents, also insects and birds.

Suggested reading: A. C. Bent, "American Hawk Owl," *Life Histories of North American Birds of Prey,* part 2, Dover, N.Y. (reprint of U.S. Nat. Mus. Bull. 170, 1938), 1961, pp. 375–384.

PYGMY OWL (*Glaucidium gnoma*)

Appearance: Small (7–7½ in.), without ear tufts, brownish gray above and on the sides of the chest; spotted with white, particularly on the crown, wings, and chest sides. White below, streaked (especially on the flanks) with dark brownish gray. There is a rather prominent black bar on the nape; the tail, which is often held at an angle to the body, is blackish, with narrow white bars. There are brown and rufescent phases. The eyes are bright yellow.

Voice: Musical, dovelike *coo*'s repeated at intervals of 2–3 seconds, a more rapid rolling series slowing to 2 or 3 distinct and emphatic *took-took-took*'s, and a long, hollow whistle followed by a series of *cuck*'s.

Range and status: Resident in w. N. America from se. Alaska, n. B.C., and w. Alta. south to s. Baja Calif., s. Mexico, and Guatemala. Common.

Habitat: More open, mixed and coniferous forests; in arid regions found in wooded canyons.

Seasonal movements: None.

Biology: Nest: Unlined tree hollows and woodpecker holes. Eggs: 3–4 (1 record of 8); white. Incubation period unknown; apparently by female only. Age at 1st flight: About 4 weeks; young cared for by both parents. Food: Small vertebrates and large insects.

FERRUGINOUS OWL (*Glaucidium brasilianum*)

Appearance: Small (6½–7 in.) and very much like the Pygmy Owl, except that it is more reddish brown above. The streaks on the flanks are brown rather than blackish, and the crown has small light streaks rather than spots. The tail is twitched spasmodically. There are grayish brown and rufescent phases.

Ferruginous Owl

The Elf Owl, a native of the arid Southwest, often nests in deserted woodpecker holes.

Voice: A rapid, but not rolling, series of *took*'s; generally heard at night, but sometimes during the day.

Range and status: Resident from s. Ariz. and s. Tex. south through the lowlands to s. S. America. Rare along n. edge of range.

Habitat: Riparian woodlands and brushy thickets in semiarid regions.

Seasonal movements: None.

Biology: What little is known is very similar to that of the Pygmy Owl.

ELF OWL (*Micrathene whitneyi*)

Appearance: A tiny (5–6 in.), small-headed owl without ear tufts. Light above, spotted grayish brown; white below, striped with dull rusty brown, and with white "eyebrows." There are gray and brown phases with intermediates.

Voice: A high-pitched yelping, starting and ending in a rapid cadence, becoming a chatter in the middle. May rise and fall in pitch.

Range and status: Arid and semiarid areas from se. Calif., s. Ariz., s. N.Mex., and s. Tex. south to Revilla Gigedo Is. (off w. Mexico), s. Baja Calif., and c. Mexico. Winters mainly south of the U.S., very rarely in the U.S.; often locally common elsewhere.

Habitat: Giant cactus (saguaro) deserts, scrub oak, and wooded canyons in arid regions.

Seasonal movements: Schedule uncertain, but very few remain north of the U.S. border during winter.

Biology: Nest: In deserted woodpecker hole in tree or cactus. Eggs: 2–5, commonly 3; white. Incubation:

14(?) days by both sexes. Age at 1st flight unknown. Food: Almost entirely large insects; very rarely small birds.

Suggested reading: P. James and A. Hayse, "Elf Owl Rediscovered in Lower Rio Grande Delta of Texas," *Wils. Bull.*, vol. 75, pp. 179–182, 1963.

BURROWING OWL (*Speotyto cunicularia*)

Appearance: A small (9–11 in.) owl without ear tufts, brown above, profusely spotted with buff and dull white; whitish below, heavily barred with brown along the flanks. These bars merge into buff-spotted patches of brown at the sides of the breast. The eyebrows, lower half of the face, and the bib are white; the irises are yellow. The white-feathered legs are very long for an owl.

Voice: A rapid cackle or chatter of alarm: *cack-cack-cack;* mainly at night, a rapid cooing, higher in pitch than the notes of the Mourning Dove.

Range and status: Largely resident, except in the n. Great Basin and n. Great Plains, from s. B.C., s. Alta., c. Sask., and s.-c. Man. south to s. S. America; in c. and s. Fla., the Bahamas, Hispaniola, and some of the n. Lesser Antilles. In winter and during migration it is found in s. La., s. Miss., and w. Fla. It has straggled to Ind., Mich., s. Ont., N.H., Mass., N.Y., and Va. Common.

Habitat: Prairies, plains, deserts, and other open areas.

Like other owls, the Barred Owl can be lured from hiding by imitation of its call.

Seasonal movements: Returns to more northerly areas late Mar.–mid-Apr. and departs Oct.–mid-Dec.

Biology: Nest: Usually a deserted burrow of some mammal, such as the prairie dog, woodchuck, skunk, etc., or dug in softer soil by the owl. May be lined with dried horse and cattle droppings, feathers, grasses, or debris. They often form colonies, especially when using burrows of gregarious animals like the prairie dog. There is mutual toleration between the prairie dogs and the owl, but the owl will no doubt feed on an occasional small pup, and the rodents will enrich their diet with an owl's egg or two. The rattlesnake is in the burrows only for food or shelter and is certainly not welcomed by either bird or mammal. Eggs: 6–11, usually 7–9; white. Incubation: About 3 weeks. Age at 1st flight unknown. Food: Large insects and small mammals, principally rodents; rarely small birds.

Suggested reading: A. Sprunt, Jr., "A Feathered Miner," *Aud. Mag.*, vol. 47, pp. 359–362, 1945.

BARRED OWL (*Strix varia*)

Appearance: Medium-sized (17–24 in.), with a large-looking round head. The head, neck, chest, back, and rump are barred with pale buff or whitish and dark brown. The light bars are broader on the underparts, and the dark bars are broader on the upperparts. The wings and tail are dark brown above, with spots and bands of buff or tan on the wings and bands of light brown on the tail. The rest of the underparts are pale gray, streaked with dark brown; the underside of the tail is broadly banded with whitish and medium brownish gray. The face is very pale gray, with the dark brown eyes central in concentric rings of light brownish gray.

Voice: This owl hoots; sometimes the hoots sound like the barking of a dog, but they are usually given in 2 closely spaced, rather rapid series of 4 notes, with the last hoot trailing off as a *hooo-aw;* also makes a loud, rasping, laughlike call and a rather loud, tremolo *who-oo-oo-oo.*

Range and status: Resident, although many individuals move south in winter, from n. B.C., n. Alta., c. Man., Ont., s. Que., and N.S. south, generally east of the Rockies, to the Gulf Coast and through the mountains and highlands of Mexico to Guatemala and Honduras. Rather common.

Habitat: Forests; most common in riparian woodlands.

Seasonal movements: Some n. breeders have been taken as far south as La. Occasionally in spring and fall they have been reported in sizable flocks.

Biology: Nest: Preferably in tree cavity; often in abandoned hawk's or crow's nest; no lining, except accumulated debris. Eggs: 2–3, rarely 4; white. Incubation: 21(?)–28 days, possibly by both parents. Age at 1st flight: More than 6 weeks. Food: Hunts actively during cloudy days as well as during dawn and dusk. Rodents, other small mammals, birds, amphibians, reptiles, insects, crayfish, fish, and spiders; often actively pursues, captures, and eats smaller owls.

Suggested reading: R. D. Tyron, "Our 'Minnesota' Barred Owls," *Aud. Mag.*, vol. 59, pp. 10–11, 1957.

SPOTTED OWL (*Strix occidentalis*)

Appearance: Medium-sized (16½–19 in.); very similar to the Barred Owl, but more spotted and less barred on head and back; the underparts are completely barred, with no streaks. The eyes are very dark brown.

Voice: Series of 3–4 hoots, somewhat higher-pitched than those of the Barred Owl; also a long chain of rapid, almost staccato hoots, gradually rising in pitch.

Range and status: Resident from sw. B.C., Wash., Calif., n. Ariz., se. Utah, and c. Colo. south to n. Mexico, exclusive of Baja Calif. Rare.

Habitat: Dense coniferous and mixed woodlands; forested canyons.

Seasonal movements: None.

Biology: Nest: In tree cavities, on floors of caves, and in natural cliffside cavities; eggs are surrounded by only a few feathers and other accumulated debris. Eggs: 2–3, very rarely 4; white. Incubation and age at 1st flight unknown; possibly similar to those of Barred Owl. Food: Rodents, other small mammals (including bats), and a few birds.

Suggested reading: J. T. Marshall, Jr., "Food and Habitat of the Spotted Owl," *Condor*, vol. 44, pp. 66–67, 1942.

GREAT GRAY OWL (*Strix nebulosa*)

Appearance: Largest (24–33 in.) of the owls. It has no ear tufts; the thick, soft plumage is marked by variegated patterns of rather dingy light and dark gray; it is lighter below, with darker streakings, and darker above, with lighter streaks and bars. The tail is finely barred with light and medium gray and has 2–3 broad bars of darker gray. The face is a series of alternating light and medium gray rings, ending in the center at the rather small, light yellow eyes. The tail is comparatively long; the talons are black, and the bill is yellowish.

Voice: A low, loud, and resonant *hoo-hoo-hooo* and similar single hoots.

Range and status: Resident from the n. limits of dense coniferous forests of ne. Europe, n. Asia, c. Alaska, n. Yuk., and w. Mack. south to c. Poland, c. Russia, across c. Siberia to n. Sakhalin I., the Sierra Nevada of Calif., n. Idaho, w. Wyo., w. Mont., Alta., Sask., Man., n. Minn., and Ont. Irregular irruptions, probably due to shortages of food, have sent the species farther south in winter to c. Europe, Wis., Mich., N.Y., and Mass.; very rarely to Nebr., Iowa, Ind., Ohio, and N.J. Rare.

Thick, insulative plumage enables the Great Gray Owl to survive in cold northern forests.

Light gray inner edges accentuate the Long-eared Owl's prominent "ears."

Habitat: Dense coniferous forests with large, tall trees, and in America in mixed woodlands bordering such forests.

Seasonal movements: None, except for irregular irruptions.

Biology: Nest: Usually in abandoned nests of large hawks high in conifers, sometimes in such nests on rocky walls; only debris is added. Eggs: 2–3, very rarely 4 or 5; dull white. Incubation and age at 1st flight unknown. Food: Small and medium-sized mammals and birds.

Suggested reading: H. M. S. Blair, "Studies of Less Familiar Birds: 119—Great Gray Owl," *British Birds,* vol. 55, pp. 414–417, 1962.

LONG-EARED OWL (*Asio otus*)

Appearance: Medium-sized (13–16 in.), with long ear tufts; gray or brownish gray above, streaked and spotted with blackish and with some spots of tawny. The flight feathers of the wing are broadly barred with tawny or rufous. It is pale buff below, streaked with black on the throat, chest, and flanks. The facial disk is tawny, with a central white X formed by the eyebrows and "mustaches." The eyes are bright yellow; the "ears" are blackish, edged with light gray on the inner sides.

Voice: An extensive repertoire for an owl, including hoots, whistles, squeals, mews, and bill clicking. Most common are a soft, mournful *quoo-quoo-quoo*, a catlike *mie-e-ew* (sometimes prolonged), a whistled *whee-you*, and a series of 6–20 low hoots.

Range and status: Breeds from c. B.C., s. Mack., s. Man., w. and s. Ont., s. Que., N.B., and N.S. south to nw. Baja Calif., s. Ariz., N.Mex., w. Tex., n. Okla., Ark., and Va.; also from British Isles and c. Siberia south to nw. Africa, Sicily, Israel, n. Iraq, n. Iran, nw. India, nw. and ne. China, and s.-c. Japan. Winters from s. Canada to n. Mexico, the Gulf Coast, s. Fla., and Bermuda; in Eurasia south to Egypt, n. India, and s. China. Common.

Habitat: Dense forests or more open forests of all types; copses, wooded parks, suburban areas, etc., where there are heavy woody growths or thickets.

Seasonal movements: Largely sedentary; some withdrawal from more northerly parts of range and a slight extension of range to south, but this is apparently dependent on food supply and therefore irregular. Often forms communal roosts in the North during winter.

Biology: Nest: Commonly in evergreens 12–50 ft. above the ground; in those made of sticks and twigs by other birds, such as hawks and crows; no lining is added except fortuitously. Eggs: 3–8, commonly 4–5; white. Incubation: About 28 days; shared by both parents. Age at 1st flight: 23–24 days. Food: Mainly rodents and other small mammals, some small birds and large insects.

Suggested reading: W. H. Armstrong, *Nesting and Food Habits of the Long-eared Owl in Michigan,* Mich. State Univ. Biol. Series 1, pp. 63–96, 1958.

SHORT-EARED OWL (*Asio flammeus*)

Appearance: Medium-sized (13–17 in.), with ear tufts so short as to be visible only under best of conditions. Color varies from 1 part of extensive range to another; usually any shade between tawny and buff above and on head and chest, with central part of each feather streaked with dark brown. There is also some barring of brown on wing and tail. Generally immaculate white or very pale buff below, with some streaking of brown on upper flanks. Eyebrows, chin, and throat are dull white; the feathers just about the yellow eyes are blackish. There are thin streaks of dark brown radiating out from the eyes across the remainder of the dull white facial disk.

Voice: A *yak-yak-yak* repeated 8 or more times, sounding like the barking of a puppy; a wheezy, staccato *key-ow* or *ki-yi;* a noise like a short burst of escaping steam; hisses; and clicks.

Range and status: Breeds from n. Alaska, n. Mack., Baffin I., c. Greenland, Iceland, and n. Eurasia south to Calif., Utah, Colo., Kans., Mo., Va., s. France, n. Italy, Bulgaria, the Caucasus, s. Siberia, and ne. China; also in nw. and s. S. America, the Falklands, Hispaniola, Puerto Rico, the Galápagos, Ponape, the Caroline Is., and Hawaii. Winters from s. Canada, c. Europe, and s. Siberia to n. Mexico, the Gulf Coast, s. Fla., c. Africa, s. Asia, and Borneo; resident in other areas. Locally common; cultivation of fields and drainage of marshes is restricting its range.

Habitat: Tundra, grasslands of all kinds, marshes, dunes, clearings in forests, bushy areas, and, in S. America, mountain clearings and meadows.

Seasonal movements: Sedentary in tropical parts of range; elsewhere a rather irregular migrant. Extent and direction of migration dependent on food supply and number of owls; they may be encountered during migration or winter in flocks of 4–100 birds.

Biology: Sometimes nests in small colonies. Nest: On the ground among high grasses; a shallow depression sparsely lined with straws, stubble, and feathers. Eggs: Usually 4–7, but as few as 3 and as many as 14 have been recorded; white. Incubation: 21–23(?) days, by hen alone. Age at 1st flight: 31–36 days. Food: Small rodents and other small animals, including birds, that frequent open fields. Occasionally hunts during day.

Suggested reading: H. L. Short and L. C. Drew, "Observations Concerning Behavior, Feeding, and Pellets of Short-eared Owls," *Amer. Midland Naturalist,* vol. 67, pp. 424–433, 1962.

BOREAL OWL (Richardson's Owl) (*Aegolius funereus*)

Appearance: Small (8½–12 in.), earless, with a relatively large head. Dark brown above, with many small round spots of white on the crown, nape, and back. The rump has larger white or pale buffy spots, and the tail is crossed by 4–5 bands of almost contiguous white spots. The wing bears even larger whitish spots arranged in bar patterns. It is white or very pale buff below, with jagged streaks of grayish brown running down the breast and flanks from the edge of the white throat. The black-edged white facial disk is streaked with dull light brown in a radial pattern from the bright yellow eyes. The flight feathers of the wing and tail of immature birds are like those of the adults, but above they are plain dark brown, toward the head almost black, and below they are a richer, somewhat lighter brown, becoming mixed with buffy near the tail.

Voice: A far-carrying, but somewhat subdued, series of 5–8 liquid whistles with little variation in pitch; may be heard occasionally in daytime during height of breeding season. Also a sharp, harsh *kep-kep-kep* of annoyance or alarm.

Range and status: Resident of dense coniferous forests from n. Scandinavia, n. Russia, n.-c. Siberia, c. Alaska, n. Yuk., s. Mack., c. Sask., n. Man., c. Ont., s. Que., s. Lab., and Nfld. south to c. and se. Europe, s. Siberia, n. B.C., n. Alta., s. Man., s. Ont., s. Que., and N.B. Winter dispersal extends south to Spain, Turkey, and n. U.S.; very rare and irregular irruptions have

The Short-eared Owl's ear tufts are so short that they are seldom conspicuous.

Boreal Owl

reached farther south, in U.S. to s. Ore., Idaho, Colo., Nebr., Ill., Pa., N.Y., Conn., and R.I. Rather rare.

Habitat: Dense coniferous forests (favoring spruce) and mixed edges of such forests.

Seasonal movements: None regular; see above.

Biology: Nest: Small tree holes, deserted woodpecker holes; no lining added. Eggs: 3–8, most commonly 6; white. Incubation: 26–27 days, by female only. Age at 1st flight: 4–5 weeks; the male hunts for the incubating female and the young. Food: Small mammals, birds, insects.

Suggested reading: A. C. Bent, "Richardson's Owl," *Life Histories of North American Birds of Prey,* part 2, Dover, N.Y. (reprint of U.S. Nat. Mus. Bull. 170, 1938), 1961, pp. 220–228.

SAW-WHET OWL (*Aegolius acadicus*)

Appearance: Small (7–8½ in.); very similar to the closely related Boreal Owl, but the dark brown upperparts are less heavily spotted with whitish, the crown is finely streaked with white (not spotted), the facial disk lacks the black edging, the jagged streaks on the breast and flanks are more reddish brown, and the underparts are whiter. The immature is a lighter brown above and a more reddish brown below than the immature Boreal Owl.

Voice: A quavering, rapid, almost tremolo *too-too-too-too;* the cadence is too fast to count, and the call seems endless. During the breeding season it makes the name-originating saw-sharpening call described as a series of 3 ringing, metallic *skreigh-aw*'s. They are rather tame for owls and come readily to even crude imitations of their calls.

Range and status: Resident from s. Alaska, c. B.C., c. Alta., s. Sask., s. Man., n. Ont., c. Que., and N.S. south through the mountains to s. Calif., s. Ariz., s. Mexico, Okla., c. Mo., Ohio, W.Va., and Md. In winter it extends into the lowlands of sw. U.S. and to La., n. Fla., and Ga.; it has straggled to Nfld. and Bermuda. Common.

Habitat: All types of forests, groves, and copses.

Seasonal movements: Irregular, generally due to food shortages, storms, and local climatic changes. For example, tends to move from interior woodlands of New England to coastal areas in winter.

Biology: Nest: Small cavity in tree or abandoned woodpecker nest. Eggs: 4–7, usually 5–6; white. Incubation: more than 26 days, almost entirely by female. Age at 1st flight: 27–34 days. Food: Mainly small rodents and other small mammals and birds, plus large insects.

Suggested reading: L. McI. Terrill, "Nesting of the Saw-whet Owl in the Montreal District," *Auk,* vol. 48, pp. 169–174, 1931.

Dark, mottled plumage effectively camouflages the nesting Chuck-will's-widow.

GOATSUCKERS, WHIP-POOR-WILLS, AND NIGHTHAWKS (CAPRIMULGIDAE)

These small (7–13 in.) crepuscular to nocturnal, insectivorous birds are obviously closely related to the potoos, frogmouths, and oilbirds and rather distantly related to the hummingbirds, swifts, and trogons. They are worldwide except in the polar regions, the cooler parts of the temperate zones, and New Zealand and most of the oceanic islands. There are 67 species, 7 of which occur in America; most of the American species are migratory. They range over a wide variety of habitats. Because of their extraordinarily large mouths, many of the species were referred to as goatsuckers by country folk who once believed the birds milked goats during the night. The feathers are soft, commonly in browns, black, white, and grays in patches and in mottled, spotted, and vermiculate patterns. Some extralimital species have very long tail feathers (not included in length above), and 2–3 others have elongate flight feathers in the wing. The wings and tail are medium to long; the wings are pointed or rounded. The bill is short and weak, but the mouth is so broad that the gape is almost as wide as the head.

Hairlike feathers at the side of the mouth, called rictal bristles by ornithologists, aid in "netting" airborne insect prey. The legs are very short, and the nail, or claw, of the middle toe has a comblike edge. The eyes are large. In most species the sexes are not alike, but in the American species the difference is slight. Voice varies through purrs, rasps, and whistles; most calls are loud and distinctive. These birds are usually solitary in habit, although several species migrate in large flocks. They usually perch lengthwise along the limbs of trees. There is no nest; most eggs are laid on the ground. The protectively colored eggs are incubated largely by females, very rarely by both sexes; usually only 1–2 make up the clutch, very rarely 3. The downy young, cared for by both parents until they are able to fly, can crawl from the vicinity of the nest shortly after hatching. The food, almost entirely insects obtained while the birds course the night air with mouths agape, is sometimes more actively pursued and captured.

CHUCK-WILL'S-WIDOW (*Caprimulgus carolinensis*)

Appearance: Large (11–13 in.), generally brown and gray with spots, streaks, and bars of black above the fine irregular barring of black and brownish red below. The throat is brownish red, faintly and narrowly barred with dark brown and separated from the breast by a narrow edging of buff or whitish; the outer feathers of the tail are rufous with some barring of dark brown near the root; near the middle feathers there are 1–2 whitish

feathers, and the central feathers are grayish brown with irregular bands of blackish. There is no white in the wing. The female is tan or dark buffy where the male is white.

Voice: The well-known *chuck-will's-wid-ow* call is loud and emphatic, somewhat slower in cadence than the call of the Whip-poor-will, and given only while perched on ground, tree limb, or roof.

Range and status: Breeds from e. Kans., Mo., s. Ill., s. Ind., s. Ohio, s. Md., and s. N.J. south to c. Tex., the

White areas on its wings and near the tip of its tail identify the White-winged Dove, a common species in states along our Mexican border.

The secretive Yellow-billed Cuckoo usually lurks in the dense foliage of thickets and brushy areas. It feeds mainly on insects and seems to be especially fond of caterpillars.

Gulf Coast, and s. Fla. Winters from the Gulf Coast through e. Mexico and C. America to Colombia and throughout the Bahamas and Greater Antilles. Has straggled to Iowa, Ont., Conn., Mass., N.B., and N.S. Fairly common.

Habitat: Mixed oak and pine woodlands and along roads and edges of clearings in such forests.

Seasonal movements: Arrives mid-Feb.–Apr. and departs Sept.–Oct.

Biology: No nest; eggs are laid among dead leaves on forest floor. Eggs: Usually 2; pinkish cream or buff, marbled, blotched, and spotted with various shades of brown and gray. Incubation: More than 20 days, by female alone. Age at 1st flight: At 17 days the young are able to fly about 150 ft. Young are cared for solely by the female. Food: Large insects such as beetles and moths, many other insects, and in one or two cases even small birds. The open mouth is about 2 in. wide.

Suggested reading: A. F. Ganier, "The Alleged Transportation of Its Eggs or Young by the Chuck-will's-widow," *Wils. Bull.*, vol. 76, pp. 18–27, 1964.

RIDGWAY'S WHIP-POOR-WILL (Cookacheea) (*Caprimulgus ridgwayi*)

Somewhat smaller (8½–9 in.) than the Whip-poor-will and otherwise differing from that species in having a dark buffy or rufous collar on the hind neck (it is sometimes known as the Buff-collared Nightjar) and in its call, which is a *cuk-cuk-cuk-cuk-cuk-cuk-cuk-cukacheea* (Peterson), about the tone and quality of a katydid song. Found in the lowlands and foothills of Mexico; only recently discovered, probably breeding, in extreme sw. N.Mex.

WHIP-POOR-WILL (*Caprimulgus vociferus*)

Appearance: About Robin size (9–10 in.); when flushed in daytime it flits silently away on rounded wings, the male showing the white outer tail feathers and possibly the narrow white crescent at the lower edge of the dark brown, almost black throat, the female seeming entirely brown as she lacks the white patches. The plumage appears to be a uniform dark brown, but it is the usual mixture of gray on the crown with dark brown edges and median streaks; medium brown back, barred, streaked, and scaled with blackish, with a few streaks of rufous on the edges; and a rufous eye streak above the dark brown cheek and throat.

Voice: Best identified by the loud, rapid, much reiterated, and emphatic whistling of its name during the spring and summer nights. The call is made from some perch (which may be shifted once in a while) and probably never in flight. It also squeaks, makes clicking noises, and, in alarm or for recognition purposes, gives 1–2 *whip* calls.

Range and status: Breeds from c. Ariz., s. N.Mex.,

w. Tex., c. Sask., s. Man., c. Ont., s. Que., n. Maine, N.B., and N.S. south to mountains of n.-c. Mexico and east of the Great Plains to ne. Tex., n. La., n. Miss., c. Ala. n. Ga., nw. S.C., e.-c. N.C., and e. Va. Winters from nw. Mexico, s. Tex., the Gulf Coast, and S.C. south to Costa Rica and Cuba. Rather common.

Habitat: Deciduous and mixed forests and wooded canyons; particularly those with occasional clearings and in hilly areas.

Seasonal movements: Probably entirely at night. Moves north mid-Mar.–early May and returns mid-Sept.–early Nov.

Biology: No nest; eggs are laid on ground among leaf litter near edge of woods. Eggs: 2; white or cream-colored with spots and occasional blotches of grays over-laid with small spots of brown; a few are spotless. Incubation: More than 19 days; probably by female alone. Age at 1st flight: The young are able to leave "nest" area when 4–5 days old and are probably able to fly at about 20 days. Food: Moths, grasshoppers, ants, and other insects captured in midair or, very rarely, picked from ground.

Suggested reading: G. S. Raynor, "The Nesting Habits of the Whip-poor-will," *Bird-banding*, vol. 12, pp. 98–104, 1941.

POOR-WILL (*Phalaenoptilus nuttallii*)

Appearance: Smaller (7–8½ in.) than the Whip-poor-will and generally grayer; the outer tail feathers of the male are black and broadly tipped with white, while the female's are only narrowly tipped with white. There is a black eye patch, and the throat is black, crossed centrally by a white necklace. The wings are rounded.

Voice: When calling nearby at night, a harsh, 3-part *poor-will-it* which loses the 3rd note with distance; sometimes a soft *poor-will-uck*. It calls through most of the spring and summer, even into Oct.

Poor-will

Range and status: Breeds from s.-c. B.C., sw. Mont., nw. S.Dak., Nebr., and sw. Iowa south to s. Baja Calif. and c. Mexico. Winters from c. Calif., s. Ariz., and Tex. south to c. Mexico. Recorded as hibernating in Calif. and Ariz. Fairly common.

Habitat: Open semideserts; dry, rocky hills; areas of scattered, scrubby piñon and juniper and sparse brush.

Seasonal movements: Least migratory of American goatsuckers; moves north Feb.–May and returns Sept.–Oct. Cold spells in n. parts of winter range are passed in state of torpor, akin to hibernation, deep in rock crevices.

Biology: Nest: Reported to be barest scrape in ground, usually partly shaded by bush; most often not even a scrape. Eggs: 2, white or pale cream. Incubation: By both parents; period not known. Age at 1st flight unknown. Food: Moths, beetles, chinch bugs, locusts, and other insects, mainly night fliers and some insects gleaned from ground.

Suggested reading: E. C. Jaeger, "Poorwill Sleeps Away the Winter," *Nat. Geog. Mag.*, vol. 103, pp. 273–280, 1953.

PAURAQUE (*Nyctidromus albicollis*)

Larger (10–12 in.) than the Common Nighthawk or Whip-poor-will, with rounded wings marked with a white band like the Nighthawk's but nearer the tip. The outermost tail feathers are black and the next 2–3 are white (in the female the white is restricted to small spots near the tip of the tail); the chin is white. The voice is a rather harsh, throaty, whistled *per-weeeeeeeee*, sometimes led by a few short *per* notes. Resident from nw. Mexico and s. Tex. through continental areas (and some offshore islands of Mexico) to Peru, Bolivia, Paraguay, ne. Argentina, and se. Brazil. Common throughout most of its Latin American range.

COMMON NIGHTHAWK (*Chordeiles minor*)

Appearance: About the size (8½–10 in.) of the Whip-poor-will, but with pointed blackish wings crossed ⅓ of the way from the tip by a white band; the throat is white. Plumage is narrowly barred dark brown and buffy below, and brown marked with darker brown above. On the brown and blackish barred tail, the terminal blackish bar is broadest; the subterminal band on the tail of the male is white. The white bar on the wing of the female is smaller than that of the male.

Voice: Heard most commonly at dusk; a much repeated, nasal *peeent*. This should be a very familiar sound to urbanites, as large flocks fill the evening air with the sound as they course over the cities and suburbs, hawking the insects attracted by the city lights.

Range and status: Breeds from s. Yuk., w. Mack., n.

In cities, the Common Nighthawk sometimes nests on flat graveled roofs.

Sask., n. Man., n. Ont., and s. Que. south to s. Calif., c. Nev., Ariz., ne. Sonora, n.-c. Mexico, Jamaica, Puerto Rico, and the Bahamas. Winters from n. S. America to c. Argentina. Has straggled to Alaska, Melville I., Lab., Greenland, Bermuda, and Europe. Common.

Habitat: Plains, mountains, open woods, cities, and suburbs.

Seasonal movements: Arrives late Mar.–early Apr. and departs Sept.–Oct.

Biology: Nest: None; eggs are laid on bare ground in sparsely vegetated areas, burned-over spots, and graveled places including rooftops. Eggs: 2; cream-colored or pale greenish gray, speckled with browns and grays. Incubation: 19–20 days; if the male assists in this task at all, it must be very rare. He does at times assist in feeding the incubating female and later the young. Age at 1st flight: About 3 weeks. Food: Entirely insects, usually caught on the wing.

Suggested reading: H. J. Rust, "Migration and Nesting of Nighthawks in Northern Idaho," *Condor*, vol. 49, pp. 177–188, 1947. C. A. Sutherland, "Notes on the Behavior of Common Nighthawks in Florida," *The Living Bird*, pp. 31–39, 1963.

LESSER NIGHTHAWK (*Chordeiles acutipennis*)

Appearance: Slightly smaller (8–9 in.) than the Common Nighthawk, which it resembles very closely except that the light bar on the wing is nearer the tip. This species commonly flies very close to the ground, never so high as the Common Nighthawk.

Voice: A low *chuck-chuck* and a rather soft, toadlike trill, sometimes resembling the purring of a distant gasoline engine.

Range and status: Breeds from c. Calif., s. Nev., w. and c. Ariz., s. N.Mex., and sw. and s. Tex. south through Mexico and C. America to n. Chile, n. and e. Bolivia, and s. Brazil (but not through most of ne. S. America). Winters from s. Baja Calif. and n. Mexico southward. Common.

Habitat: Open arid areas, dry fields, open lowlands, and regions of scattered, scrubby growth.

Seasonal movements: Arrives in U.S. Mar.–early May and departs Sept.–early Nov.

Biology: Nest: None; eggs are laid on bare, usually gravelly ground. Eggs: 2; white, creamy, or pinkish, speckled with grays and browns; more variable than those of the Common Nighthawk. Incubation period not known, but probably the same as that of the Common Nighthawk; incubation by female alone. Age at 1st flight: The young are able to crawl over ground when only 2 days old and probably fly as early as 3rd week. Food: Insects; moths, grasshoppers, beetles, etc., of type that generally fly close to ground.

Suggested reading: G. Pickwell and E. Smith, "The Texas Nighthawk in Its Summer Home," *Condor*, vol. 40, pp. 193–215, 1938.

These nearly full-grown Chimney Swifts cling to the wall beside their nest.

THE SWIFTS (APODIDAE)

Swifts are small (3½–9 in.), diurnal, aerial, insectivorous birds, probably most closely related to the hummingbirds. There are about 75 species of almost worldwide distribution (missing only from n. N. America, n. Eurasia, s. S. America, and some oceanic islands), but only 4 occur regularly in America and only 2 others have straggled from Asia. All the American species are migratory. Plumage is normal but dull-colored, with grays and browns predominating and in a few species bluish black and whitish. The wing is long and pointed, the tail (specialized with spine tips in some species) short to long and forked. The bill is tiny, but the mouth is large. The legs are very short and feathered even to the toes in some species; the small feet are strong, and swifts are capable of turning the hind toe so that all toes are directed forward. They do not perch on tree branches but cling to vertical surfaces. The sexes are alike. Flight is very speedy; these are probably the fastest of all birds. And they are probably the most aerial of all birds. They are apparently airborne most of their adult lives, coursing the skies even at night in never-ending search for food or pure delight in flying. At the approach of low weather depressions signifying coming storms, they are known to fly several hundred miles, possibly to escape the bad flying conditions associated with such disturbances. They return when the storm has passed, little affected by the distances involved. Even copulation is performed in flight. Insects are caught in midair. Voice is confined to rasping notes and rapid twittering calls. Most species are gregarious, some colonial. Nests are mostly of natural materials such as twigs glued together with a special gelatinous saliva or, in a few Asiatic species, made entirely of such liquids. There are 1–6 eggs in a clutch, invariably white; they are incubated by both parents. The young, naked at hatching, are fed by both sexes. Fully feathered nestlings survive extended cold, damp periods when food is scarce or when the adults are driven off by storms, as their temperature control adapts to cold-blooded (poikilothermic) reactions. In this torpid state (similar to hibernation) they require much less food and live off the fat reserves stored from days when food was plentiful.

BLACK SWIFT (*Cypseloides niger*)

Appearance: Large (7–7½ in.) for a swift and completely black except for a small spot of white at the forehead; the tail is moderately long and slightly forked except when spread.

Voice: A smooth, clicking, chattering *plik-plik-plik;* usually silent.

Range and status: Breeds from se. Alaska, B.C., and s. Alta. to Costa Rica and into the Greater and Lesser Antilles and Guyana. Winter range not certainly known, but in tropical Americas. Rather rare.

Habitat: Airborne along sea cliffs and in mountains.

Seasonal movements: Arrives late Apr.–early June, departs Sept.–early Oct.

Biology: Nests: Made of mosses and algae; found in

small colonies (not discovered until 1901) in crevice of sea cliff or mountainside, sometimes behind small waterfalls. Eggs: 1, white. Incubation period not known. Age at 1st flight unknown; the young are fed partially digested, regurgitated insects by both parents. Food: A great variety of flying insects.

Suggested reading: O. A. Knorr, "The Geographical and Ecological Distribution of the Black Swift in Colorado," *Wils. Bull.*, vol. 73, pp. 155–170, 1961.

CHIMNEY SWIFT (*Chaetura pelagica*)

Appearance: Small (4½–5½ in.), entirely a rather dark sooty gray, somewhat lighter at the throat, with a short spine-tipped tail. In flight, on sickled wings, it has been called a "flying cigar."

Voice: A metallic twittering or rapid ticking; in courtship flights, a whistling tick. The nestlings at first make a squealing note and when older a rapid *cheh-cheh-cheh*.

Range and status: Breeds from se. Sask., s. Man., Ont., s. Que., and N.S. south to the Gulf Coast and c. Fla. Winters certainly in upper Amazon Basin of ne. Peru and probably in the rest of the upper basin. In migration, passes through e. Mexico and C. America and possibly the Greater Antilles. Has straggled to Mont., N.Mex., Utah, Bermuda, Nfld., and Greenland. Common.

Habitat: Open air over all types of terrain so long as chimneys and other suitable man-made structures can be found. Earlier, hollow trees were used for nesting sites.

Seasonal movements: Generally in large flocks; arrives late Mar.–mid-May and departs late Aug.–Oct.

Biology: Nest: Solitary, not colonial; glued to inside

Vaux's Swift

of chimney, outhouse, little-used barn, etc., with sticky saliva; a frail, rather skimpy-looking platform of twigs, with other twigs glued in an arching design to the support above the nest. The bird, in full flight, breaks the twigs off the ends of dead tree branches by the impact of its feet and transfers them to the bill just before reaching the nest. Late spring or early summer chills, causing fires to be built in fireplaces or the automatic furnace to start up, bring the householder the problem of young swifts dumped, complete with heat-loosened nest, into his living room or furnace. Canned dog or cat meat, rather moist, may nourish them until they are able to fly after their own food, if they are more than a few days old. Eggs: 2–7, usually 4–5; white. Incubation: 19–21 days, by both sexes. Age at 1st flight: 30 days. Young are fed by regurgitation the first 3 days, then small pellets of tiny insects from crops of both parents. Food: All sorts of small flying insects apparently "vacuumed" from the air.

Suggested reading: R. B. Fischer, *The Breeding Biology of the Chimney Swift*, N.Y.S. Mus. Bull. 368, Albany, N.Y., 141 pp., 1958.

VAUX'S SWIFT (*Chaetura vauxi*)

Appearance: Smaller (4–4½ in.) than the Chimney Swift and resembling it so closely (a lighter gray, but only discernible in direct comparison of specimens) that best means of identification is on geographic bases and possibly voice.

Voice: Similar to that of Chimney Swift but weaker and of slower cadence.

Range and status: Breeds from se. Alaska, n. B.C., and w. Mont. (probably) south to C. America and from e. Panama to n. Venezuela. Winters from c. Calif. and s. La. south. Common.

Habitat: Open air; primarily over forests and openings in forests.

Seasonal movements: Arrives in U.S. mid-Apr.–mid-May and departs Sept.–early Oct.; usually in big flocks, using chimneys as stopover resting places.

Biology: Nest: Only occasionally in chimneys; mainly in hollow trees in woodlands, where twigs are glued inside in manner described under the Chimney Swift. Eggs: 3–6, most commonly 4–6; white. Incubation: More than 12 days; probably about 19 days. Age at 1st flight: 20–21 days. Food: Small flying insects hawked from midair.

Suggested reading: P. H. Baldwin and N. K. Zaczkowski, "Breeding Biology of the Vaux Swift," *Condor*, vol. 65, pp. 400–406, 1963.

WHITE-RUMPED SWIFT (*Apus pacificus*)

About the size (6½–7½ in.) of the Black Swift. Blackish above, except for a white bar across the rump, and brownish below, with a narrow white tip to each feather giving a scaly effect; the throat is white. It breeds throughout most of e. Asia, with n. populations wintering in the Australian region. It has straggled to St. George I., Alaska.

COMMON SWIFT (*Apus apus*)

Almost twice as large (6–7 in.) as the Chimney Swift, with a moderately forked tail; blackish above, somewhat lighter below, with a white throat. It is "common" only in Eurasia. It breeds from n. Eurasia south to n. Africa, n. Mesopotamia, n. India, and ne. China; winters in Africa and Madagascar. It has straggled to the Pribilof Is. of Alaska.

WHITE-THROATED SWIFT (*Aëronautes saxatalis*)

Appearance: Smaller (6–7 in.) than the Black Swift and generally sooty black with a white face and throat. White extends in a broad streak down the center of the chest to the abdomen, and there are white patches on the rear end of the side, extending under the wing; the leading and trailing edges of the half of the wing nearer the body are also white. The tail is slightly forked.

Voice: A shrill *he-he-he-he-he* giggle; about the nesting grounds, a shrill *tee-dee-dee-dee,* usually lowering gradually in scale.

Range and status: Breeds from s. B.C., s. Alta., Mont., and nw. S.Dak. south to Guatemala and El Salvador; winters from c. Calif., c. Ariz., and sw. N.Mex. south. Common.

Habitat: Open air over all types of terrain, but in summer over mountains, canyons, etc.

Seasonal movements: Arrives Mar.–mid-May and departs Sept.–early Oct.

White-throated Swift

Biology: Probably the fastest-flying American bird. Nest: Made of feathers glued together; found in cracks and crevices of seaside cliffs and mountain precipices, where gathering of data on life history is difficult. Eggs: 3–6, commonly 4; white. Incubation and age at 1st flight unknown. Food: Flying insects.

THE HUMMINGBIRDS (TROCHILIDAE)

Hummingbirds are small (2¼–8½ in.), diurnal, aerial land birds closely related to the swifts and more distantly to the trogons and nighthawks. The smallest known bird in the world is the Bee Hummingbird of Cuba. There are about 320 species ranging through the New World tropics, subtropics, and warm temperate zones; 17 have been recorded in the U.S. and Canada. Most species are sedentary, but many, including almost all forms in our area, are migratory. The majority favor wooded areas. The plumage is fairly compact, and the most common colors are greens, browns, grays, black, and white; many species have a variety of bright metallic or iridescent hues, especially in the head region of the males. Some are crested; others have raquet-shaped tails or long, slender tail feathers, although the tail is more often short. The bill is commonly long, straight, and round in cross-section, but many species have long decurved bills and some have upcurved bills. The wings are comparatively very long and narrow, the legs short, and the feet tiny. The wings beat so rapidly that they become a blur of motion, and the wing joints allow a variety of positions so that the birds are in complete control of speed and direction. They hover in 1 spot, move straight up or down, and move backward. In backward movement, the body is held in such a position that the tail follows the body in direction of movement and the feathers are unruffled. Most species feed by hovering at the source of food and pumping the liquid food up the cylindrical bill. Small insects are caught on the wing. The males are more brightly colored than the females in most species, with brilliant, iridescent throats, or gorgets. The immature birds resemble the female at first; the males gradually acquire the brighter colors. Hummingbirds are solitary and pugnacious. Courtship often involves spectacular aerial dances and displays. The nest, composed of plant down and spider webbing, is saddled on a tree limb and camouflaged with lichens, placed in the fork of a small branch, or attached to the underside of a pendant leaf. There are almost invariably 2 eggs (never more) usually wedged into the deep cup of springy material. In only 1 species, an extralimital one, is the male known to assist in incubation or care of young. The hatchlings are naked, with only a trace of down.

Suggested reading: C. H. Greenewalt, *Hummingbirds*, Amer. Mus. Nat. Hist. and Doubleday, N.Y., 1960, 250 pp.

LUCIFER HUMMINGBIRD (*Calothorax lucifer*)

A small (3¾ in.) hummingbird. The male is metallic green above, white below, with a large iridescent violet-magenta to cobalt gorget; it has a long, slightly decurved black bill and a moderately forked blue-black tail. The female is the same color above, but her throat, breast, and flanks are buffy and her unforked tail is green centrally, with the outer feathers banded rufous, black, then white on the tip. It is resident in the mountains of e. and c. Mexico, moving in summer casually north to w. Tex.; it was taken once in s. Ariz.

RUBY-THROATED HUMMINGBIRD (*Archilochus colubris*)

Appearance: Small (3–4 in.). The male has metallic green upperparts and a moderately forked black tail; it is white below, with greenish gray flanks and a ruby-red to dark red (appearing black in some lights) metallic

A female Ruby-throated Hummingbird, sunning herself, displays her slender, pointed wings.

gorget. The female is entirely grayish below, and her unforked black tail has prominent white spots on the tips of the 3 outer feathers. The straight bill is moderately long.

Voice: Besides the pronounced hum of the wings, it makes high, easily unnoticed, squeaky notes.

Range and status: Breeds from c. Alta., c. Sask., s. Man., s. Ont., s. Que., N.B., P.E.I., and c. N.S. south, east of the Great Plains, to the Gulf Coast and s. Fla. Winters from n.-c. Mexico, s. Texas, s. Ala., and s. Fla. south to Costa Rica, casually w. Panama. Straggles to Alaska, n. Ont., Lab., Cuba, the Bahamas, and Bermuda. Common.

Habitat: Flower gardens, flowering deciduous forests of the East and Midwest, mixed woodlands.

Seasonal movements: Generally dependent on appearance of suitable flowers; arrives mid-Mar.–May and departs Sept.–Oct.

Biology: In courtship display the male swings slowly back and forth before the female in a "pendulum flight" with spread gorget and increased, regular, and persistent hum. Nest: Saddled on a limb 5–20 feet above the ground or surface of water. Compactly made, with a deep cup of plant down and spider webbing neatly camouflaged with lichens and mosses; outer circumference is seldom bigger than a half-dollar. Eggs: 2, white. Incubation: 16 days; erroneously and persistently reported as less. Age at 1st flight: 19–20 days. Food: Nectar of flowers and the tiny insects that feed on such nectar. In areas where the sapsuckers drill their regimented, shallow holes, the hummingbird will often be found waiting patiently nearby until the larger bird has brought the sap to the surface for a repast and departed.

Suggested reading: A. L. Pickens, "Notes on Nesting Ruby-throated Hummingbirds," *Wils. Bull.*, vol. 48, pp. 80–85, 1936.

BLACK-CHINNED HUMMINGBIRD (*Archilochus alexandri*)

Appearance: Small (3¼–3¾ in.). The male is bright metallic green above and white below, with a black chin merging with a dark magenta-cobalt-black iridescence; the moderately forked tail is dark blue-black. The female is entirely white below, except for greenish gray flanks, and has white-tipped outer feathers on her black tail. The black bill is fairly straight.

Voice: A soft, very high-pitched warble and similar chipping notes and a pleasant, sad, quavering, liquid "song" during courtship.

Range and status: Breeds from sw. B.C. and nw. Mont. south to n. Baja Calif., n.-c. Mexico, and s.-c. and sw. Tex. Winters from n. Baja Calif., se. Calif., and n. Mexico south to s. Mexico. Has straggled to La. Fairly common.

Habitat: Dry, scrub country near water, riparian groves, wooded canyons, and suburbs in such areas.

Seasonal movements: Arrives Mar.–May and departs mid-Aug.–early Nov.

Biology: Aerial dance of courtship is a shallow, back-and-forth swooping accompanied by a whirring noise. Nest: A neat cup of light tan felt saddled on a branch of a tree or shrub. Eggs: 2, white. Incubation period unknown (reported as 13 days, probably erroneously). Age at 1st flight: 3 weeks. Food: Nectar of flowers and small insects from same plants.

Suggested reading: F. Bené, "The Role of Learning in the Feeding Behavior of the Black-chinned Hummingbirds," *Condor*, vol. 47, pp. 3–22, 1945.

COSTA'S HUMMINGBIRD (*Calypte costae*)

Appearance: Small (3–3½ in.). The male is white below and bright metallic green above; it has a short, slightly forked black tail and a metallic, iridescent violet to blue to green crown and gorget. The feathers of the gorget on the side of the throat are elongated and, when spread, extend past the back of the neck. The straight bill is black. The female is bright green above and white below, with pale greenish gray flanks and white-tipped black outer tail feathers. It is virtually impossible to separate the females of this species and the Ruby-throated and Black-chinned Hummingbirds in the field.

Voice: 2–3 soft, high whistled notes, a soft *chik*, and hissing notes. The first call is probably too high-pitched for many human ears.

Range and status: Breeds from c. Calif., s. Nev., and sw. Utah south, including nearshore islands, to s. Baja Calif., s. Ariz., w.-c. Mexico, and sw. N.Mex. Winters south from s. Calif. and sw. Ariz. Fairly common.

Like all its kin, the immature Anna's Hummingbird has a long, slender bill.

Habitat: Hot, dry, scrubby, semiarid foothills.

Seasonal movements: A relatively short withdrawal in winter.

Biology: The aerial courtship dance is a U-shaped swing. Nest: A feltlike cup in bush or scrubby tree, well adorned with lichens and bits of leaves. Eggs: 2, white. Incubation period unknown, probably 16–18 days. Age at 1st flight: About 23 days. Food: Small insects and nectar.

ANNA'S HUMMINGBIRD (*Calypte anna*)

Appearance: Small (3½–4 in.). Bright metallic green above and white below, with pale greenish flanks, a slightly forked tail, and iridescent red cap and gorget; the red feathers on the side of the neck are somewhat elongated and reach nearly to the back of the neck. The black bill is faintly decurved. The female is green above and white below, with pale green flanks, a spot of bright red on the throat, and white tips on the outer tail feathers.

Voice: A series of rather harsh squeaks, a *chick* noise while feeding, and a popping noise by the male during the courtship flight.

Range and status: Breeds west of the Sierra Nevadas in Calif. south to n. Baja Calif. and adjacent islands. In winter, ranges to nw. Calif., c. Baja Calif., and east to s. Ariz. and n. Sonora. Has been taken in w. Tex. Common.

Habitat: Gardens, open woodlands, chaparral.

Seasonal movements: Best described as dispersal after breeding, with no regular schedule.

Biology: At the bottom of the pendulum courtship flight, the male makes a peculiar popping noise. Nest: A tiny, lichen-covered, cottony cup in bush or small tree. Eggs: 2, white. Incubation: 16–17 days. Age at 1st flight: About 21 days. Food: Nectar from flowers and tiny insects; many of the insects are caught in midair.

BROAD-TAILED HUMMINGBIRD (*Selasphorus platycercus*)

Appearance: Small (4–4½ in.). Shiny, dark green above and white below, with grayish green flanks and an iridescent red gorget; unforked green tail has 3 black outer feathers on each side. The black bill is straight. Male and female are very similar counterparts to Ruby-throated Hummingbirds.

Voice: A faint, squeaky song and several staccato *chip* notes. In flight, the male makes a loud, trilling "screech" with his wings.

Range and status: Breeds from Calif., n. Nev., n. Wyo., and sw. Tex. south to s. Mexico and the highlands of Guatemala. Winters southward from c. Mexico. Has straggled to Idaho, Mont., and Nebr. Common.

Habitat: Mountain woodlands, glades, etc.; common on edges of dense coniferous forests where there are some deciduous trees.

Seasonal movements: Arrives late Mar.–early May and departs late Aug.–early Oct.

Biology: Male's courtship flight is a series of U-shaped swoops. Nest: 4–15 feet high in bush or tree; a typical, neat cottony cup saddled on a branch and covered with lichens. Eggs: 2, white. Incubation: 16 days. Age at 1st flight unknown; probably about 3 weeks. Food: More insects, gathered from branches of coniferous forests, than nectar; birds make frequent long sorties into forests after insects.

The Broad-tailed Hummingbird usually nests in or near coniferous trees.

A young male Rufous Hummingbird probes a thistle, probably for tiny insects.

Suggested reading: A. C. Bent, "Broad-tailed Hummingbird," *Life Histories of North American Cuckoos, Goatsuckers, Hummingbirds, and Their Allies*, Dover, N.Y. (reprint of U.S. Nat. Mus. Bull. 176, 1940), 1964, pp. 387–396.

RUFOUS HUMMINGBIRD (*Selasphorus rufus*)

Appearance: Small (3½–4 in.). The male is dark tawny above, with a metallic-looking bronze cap. The tail is more rufous, becoming darker at the tip, and the flank and undertail feathers are light rufous; the gorget is bright metallic red, and the rest of the underparts are white. The female is metallic green above and white below, with pale rufous sides; the rounded tail is green centrally, and the outer feathers are rufous, then black, and finally tipped with white. The straight bill is black, and the wings are blackish.

Voice: A light chipping sound, high-pitched buzzes, a low *chewp-chewp*, and a twittering during courtship. The males make a whining sound with their wings and a loud, stuttering *ch-ch-ch-chut-churr*.

Range and status: Breeds from se. Alaska, s. Yuk., e.-c. B.C., sw. Alta., and w. Mont. south to nw. Calif. and s. Idaho. Winters in n. Mexico. Has straggled to Sask., Nebr., Okla., Tex., La., S.C., and Fla. Common at higher altitudes.

Habitat: Forest edges and mountain meadows; lowlands in migration.

Seasonal movements: Moves northward mid-Feb.–mid-May and returns Sept.–Oct.

Biology: The courtship flight is a complete oval with a long, slanted axis. Nest: A tiny, neat cup of felt covered with lichens, saddled on the branch of a bush or tree. Eggs: 2, white. Incubation period unknown; reports of 12–14 days erroneous. Age at 1st flight: About 20 days. Food: Nectar and tiny insects.

Suggested reading: A. D. DuBois, "Observations at a Rufous Hummingbird's Nest," *Auk*, vol. 55, pp. 629–641, 1938.

ALLEN'S HUMMINGBIRD (*Selasphorus sasin*)

Appearance: Slightly smaller (3¼–3½ in.) than the Rufous Hummingbird, which it resembles closely except that its back, nape, crown, and smaller wing feathers are metallic green. It has a broad eye band of bronzy brown, the tail and flanks are rufous, the gorget is bright metallic red, and the remainder of the underparts are white. The females are indistinguishable except in hand.

Voice: Similar to Rufous Hummingbird's, a light chipping. During courtship the male makes a buzzing during a short, shallow pendulum flight, and at nadir of long aerial dive that follows this, it gives a loud, cloth-tearing noise; the buzz is produced by the tail feathers.

Range and status: Breeds in coastal areas from sw. Ore. to sw. Calif.; resident on Santa Barbara Is. off s. Calif. In migration, ranges through Ariz. and Baja Calif. Winters in nw. Mexico. Has straggled to Wash. Common in coastal areas.

Habitat: Wooded humid and semihumid coastal districts, canyons, garden areas, and mountain grasslands.

Seasonal movements: Arrives Feb.–Mar. and departs Sept.

Biology: In courtship, male climbs into air about 100 ft. and makes "dive-bombing" swoop toward female at conclusion of pendulum dance. Nest: As with other hummers, a neat, lichened felt cup set on twigs or among vines, etc. Eggs: 2, white. Incubation: 17 days. Age at 1st flight: 22 days. Food: Nectar and tiny insects.

Suggested reading: E. C. Aldrich, "Nesting of the Allen Hummingbird," *Condor*, vol. 47, pp. 137–148, 1945.

HELOISE'S HUMMINGBIRD (*Atthis heloisa*)

A small (2¾ in.), straight-billed hummer, green above and white below, with rufous flanks and a widespreading, long-feathered magenta gorget. The female is very similar to the female Allen's Hummingbird. A resident of the Mexican highlands that has straggled into se. Ariz.

CALLIOPE HUMMINGBIRD (*Stellula calliope*)

Appearance: Smallest (2¾–3½ in.) bird found regularly in America. The male is metallic green above and white below, with grayish green flanks and a straight

The Calliope Hummingbird, like all its relatives, lines its delicate nest with soft down.

the shoulders), and white feathers on the legs. The female is metallic green above and gray below, with white "corners" on the square tail. The rather long bill is black.

Voice: A short, high *chip*.

Range and status: Breeds in the mountains from s. Ariz. and sw. N.Mex. to El Salvador and Nicaragua. Winters from n. Mexico southward. Rare in U.S.

Habitat: High wooded mountains and canyons.

Seasonal movements: Mainly sedentary.

Biology: Details unknown, but probably similar to others described above.

BLUE-THROATED HUMMINGBIRD (*Lampornis clemenciae*)

Appearance: A trifle larger (4½–5¼ in.) than Rivoli's Hummingbird. Metallic green above and bluish gray below, with metallic cobalt gorget, blackish wings, and a broad blackish tail with white-tipped outer feathers. The female lacks the gorget and is a drabber gray below. The long black bill is slightly decurved.

Voice: A far-carrying, strident *seep*.

Range and status: Mountains from s. Ariz., s. N.Mex., and sw. Tex. to s.-c. Mexico. Winters in Mexico. Fairly common locally.

Habitat: Lower, more humid, wooded mountain streams.

Seasonal movements: Mainly sedentary.

Biology: Nest: Uses same materials as other hummingbirds, but each year adds to old nest and prefers vertical supports, such as vines, near water. Eggs: 2, white. Incubation period and age at 1st flight unknown. Food: Nectar and insects.

RIEFFER'S HUMMINGBIRD (*Amazilia tzacatl*)

Small (3½–3¾ in.). Metallic, greenish bronze above, with a brilliant lime-colored gorget, bronzy flanks, gray abdomen, and chestnut rump, undertail feathers, and tail; the tail is edged with ultramarine-violet. The red bill is tipped with dark brown. The green feathers of the female's gorget are somewhat edged with white. It ranges from s. and e.-c. Mexico to nw. S. America and has straggled to s. Tex.

BUFF-BELLIED HUMMINGBIRD (*Amazilia yucatanensis*)

Larger (4–4½ in.) than the Ruby-throated Hummingbird. Metallic green above and buffy below, with an emerald green gorget, a dark-tipped scarlet-orange bill, and a slightly forked tawny tail. The sexes are alike. It makes shrill squeaks. Occurs from n.-c. Mexico and s. Tex. to n. Guatemala and British Honduras. A rare winterer in Tex. Found in woodlands, thickets, gardens,

black bill; it has a "peppermint candy" gorget of long, slender, bright metallic, dark magenta feathers with white bases overlying shorter white throat feathers. When the bird has brought the red feathers closer together, they make a dark V on the white throat. The female is almost identical to the female Rufous Hummingbird, but much smaller.

Voice: An apologetic *tsip* and light chips and squeaks. Near the bottom of its courtship flights the male makes a short *pfft*, like a stifled sneeze.

Range and status: Breeds in mountains from c. B.C. and sw. Alta. to n. Baja Calif., Utah, and w. Colo. Winters in Mexico. Has straggled to Sask., e. Colo., and Tex. Rather rare.

Habitat: High forest edges, especially of conifers, and canyons and copses.

Seasonal movements: Moves north Mar.–May and returns Aug.–mid-Sept.

Biology: Aerial courtship acrobatics are rather flat U-shaped swoops. Nest: The usual lichen-covered felt cup on branch, twig, or other slender support; sometimes built on remains of previous season's nest. Eggs: 2, white. Incubation: 15(?) days. Age at 1st flight: About 20 days. Food: Nectar, small insects, and some insects caught on the wing.

RIVOLI'S HUMMINGBIRD (*Eugenes fulgens*)

Appearance: A large (4½–5 in.), dark hummingbird with a light violet cap, a bright metallic lime-green gorget, black undersides with blackish green above and on the slightly forked tail (with some brighter green at

Buff-bellied Hummingbird

and farms. Its biology is much like that of the other hummingbirds.

VIOLET-CROWNED HUMMINGBIRD (*Amazilia verticalis*)

Somewhat larger (3¾–4¼ in.) than the Ruby-throated Hummingbird. Greenish above, with a metallic violet crown, and entirely white below; it has a black-tipped scarlet-orange bill. The crown of the female is greenish blue. Resident from nw. and n.-c. Mexico to s. Mexico, it has straggled to s. Ariz.

WHITE-EARED HUMMINGBIRD (*Hylocharis leucotis*)

Appearance: Small (3½ in.). Almost entirely metallic green, including the short, square tail, except for the iridescent violet crown and chin and the white streak (or ear) behind the eye. The scarlet-orange bill is dark-tipped. The female resembles the male, but is whitish below, including the chin and throat, with metallic green flanks and black and white corners to the tail.

Voice: A *tink-tink-tink* somewhat like the sound

produced by wind-brushed crystal prisms, a clanking rattle, and hums.

Range and status: Occurs in summer from s. Ariz. through the Mexican highlands to El Salvador, Honduras, and Nicaragua. Winters from n.-c. Mexico southward.

Habitat: Riparian pine-oak woodlands; generally smaller streams.

Seasonal movements: Apparently absent from U.S. Sept.–Apr.

Biology: Nest: A neat cup of down decorated with mosses and lichens, among the slender branches of vines or shrubs. **Eggs:** 2, white. Incubation period and age at 1st flight unknown. **Food:** Nectar and small insects.

Suggested reading: R. T. Moore, "Habits of the White-eared Hummingbird in Northwestern Mexico," *Auk*, vol. 56, pp. 442–445, 1939.

BROAD-BILLED HUMMINGBIRD (*Cynanthus latirostris*)

Appearance: Small (3¼–4 in.). Metallic yellowish green above, with a bluish green cap; a somewhat lighter metallic yellowish green below, with a turquoise throat that blends with the green on the breast. The tail is forked, and the orange bill is tipped with blackish. The female is metallic green above and green-tinged gray below; the square tail is blackish on the lower end, and the outer 2–3 feathers have small white tips.

Voice: A high-pitched chatter; the hum made by the male during the courtship pendulum flight has been described by many as like the zing of a rifle bullet (probably the ricochet's whine is more accurate).

Range and status: Breeds from nw. Mexico, s.-c. Ariz., sw. N.Mex., and ne. Mexico south to s.-c. Mexico; winters from n. Mexico southward.

Habitat: Desert brush areas and sparsely wooded canyons in semiarid areas.

Seasonal movements: Absent from U.S. apparently from mid-Sept.–mid-Mar.

Biology: Nest: Somewhat rougher in construction and materials than those of most other hummingbirds of comparable size, but a neat cup ornamented with leaves and bits of bark, placed on stalk of vine or shrub. **Eggs:** 2, white. Incubation period and age at 1st flight unknown. **Food:** Nectar and small insects.

Suggested reading: R. T. Moore, "The Arizona Broad-billed Hummingbird," *Auk*, vol. 56, pp. 313–319, 1939.

THE TROGONS (TROGONIDAE)

Trogons, small (9–13½ in.) arboreal birds, are probably most closely related to the hummingbirds, swifts, and goatsuckers. There are 34 species, but only 1, the Coppery-tailed Trogon, is found in America. Trogons are found throughout the tropical and subtropical woodlands of the world except for those in Indonesia and Australia. They are solitary and, except for some local movements, nonmigratory. The plumage is fluffy and thick; most species have metallic green, at least on the back and tail, and blues, reds, oranges, yellows, browns, grays, black, and white in distinctive patterns. In 1 species, the Quetzal of Mexico and C. America, the feathers of the rump are greatly elongated, forming a train as in the Peafowl. The wings are short and rounded, the tail almost as long as the body and usually square-tipped. The bill is wide, rather short, bright-colored, and notched near the tip. The legs are short and the feet small; 2 toes are directed permanently forward while 1 toe is reversible and may be turned in either direction. The eye is large, an adaptation to life in the dim forests. These birds are very rarely seen on the ground, generally feeding by flitting off perches after insects or climbing about trees after fruit. They usually perch in erect position. The voice is usually uncomplicated calls. The sexes are dissimilar. Courtship performances have not been observed. Trogons nest in tree hollows, tree stumps, or insect nests; most species add no lining. The 2–4 eggs are unmarked and are generally white, pale brownish, or very light blue-green. In most species, incubation and care of the young are performed by both parents. The hatchlings are naked and acquire down later. Food is largely insects and small fruits, with some small reptiles and amphibians also being eaten.

The handsome Coppery-tailed Trogon is the only trogon found in the United States.

COPPERY-TAILED TROGON (*Trogon elegans*)

Appearance: A large (11–12 in.) trogon. Dark metallic green above from the head (including throat, neck, and upper breast) to the rump; the top of the black-tipped tail is a bright coppery color; below, a collar of white separates the green of the upper breast from the bright ruby that extends to the light-gray-barred, black-tipped white tail. The female is brown where the male is green and has a small white patch behind the eye; her breast below the white collar is light tawny, becoming whitish in the center; the remainder of the underparts are pink. Her tail is browner above and less coppery in color. The dark eyes are ringed by scarlet eyelids, and the bill is bright yellow.

Voice: A loud, hoarse *kóa-kóa-kóa-kóa* and a turkey-like *cowm-cowm-cowm.*

Range and status: Breeds from s. Ariz. and n. Mexico south to nw. Costa Rica. Winters from n. Mexico south. Straggles to the lower Rio Grande Valley in Tex. Rare to rather common.

Habitat: Wooded mountain slopes and canyons.

Seasonal movements: Absent from U.S. in winter, but no schedule established.

Biology: Nest: Lined with grasses, feathers, and trash; a cavity in tree, usually large woodpecker holes or sometimes holes in banks. Eggs: 3–4, white. Incubation period and age at 1st flight unknown. Food: Small fruits, also grasshoppers and similar insects.

Two breast stripes identify this Belted Kingfisher as a female.

THE KINGFISHERS (ALCEDINIDAE)

Small- to medium-sized (4–18 in.) land birds, most species of kingfishers are adapted to catching small fish. They are related to the hornbills, motomots, rollers, and bee-eaters. There are 87 species in the family, found throughout the world except for the polar regions, the northernmost parts of America and Eurasia, and some oceanic islands; only 3 species occur in America. Species found in the temperate regions are migratory or partially so. Habitat is variable from semiarid areas to humid tropics. Plumage occurs in purple, greens, blues, browns, grays, and white, with some barring and/or spotting; a few species are crested. Most species have short, rounded wings; the tails range from short to long, some having elongated, racquet-tipped central feathers. The bills are commonly bright-colored, large, pointed, and strong. The legs are short, and the feet are small, with 3–4 toes; the outer toes are fused for some part of their length to the central toe. The sexes are alike in some species. Kingfishers fly strongly, but seldom for long distances. They capture food by diving into water, pouncing on prey, or flying from perches. The voice is characterized by loud, sharp cries and rattles. These birds are solitary in habit; courtship is usually restricted to aerial displays or acrobatics. Nests are burrows in banks, holes in termite nests, or hollows in trees and are usually unlined. There are 2–7 white eggs. Incubation and care of the young (hatched naked) are by both parents. The young are probably fed on regurgitated, partially digested food for the first few days. The adults eat fish, insects, crustaceans, small amphibians and reptiles, and rarely small mammals and birds.

BELTED KINGFISHER (*Megaceryle alcyon*)

Appearance: A large (11–14½ in.), ragged-crested kingfisher, blue-gray above and white below, with a collar of white extending around the back of the neck from the throat and a broad necklace of blue-gray across the breast. The flight feathers of the wing are blackish brown, the tail is barred pale gray and light gray below, the eye is dark, and the large bill is blackish. The female differs from the male in having a band of brownish red extending from the similarly colored flanks across the lower breast below the blue-gray chest belt and separated from it by a broad band of white.

Voice: A raucous, chattering rattle.

Range and status: Breeds from c. Alaska, s. Yuk., sw. Mack., c. Alta., c. Sask., c. Man., Ont., Que., c. Lab., and Nfld. south to the s. U.S. Winters from sw. Canada and n. U.S. south to Panama, Dutch W. Indies, W. Indies, and Trinidad; more or less regular in Bermuda during winter. Has straggled to Greenland, Iceland, Europe, and the Azores. Common.

Habitat: Freshwater and saltwater shores.

Seasonal movements: Returns to n. limits of range Feb.–Mar. and leaves Sept.–mid-Dec.

Biology: Nest: An unlined burrow in riverbank or sandbank usually 3–6 ft. deep, recorded up to 15 ft. deep; very rarely hollows in trees. Eggs: 5–8, usually 6–7; white. Incubation: 23–24 days. Age at 1st flight is unknown, but more than 23 days. Food: Small fish, crayfish, insects, and small rodents; rarely fruit.

Suggested reading: H. Mousley, "A Study of the Home Life of the Eastern Belted Kingfisher," *Wils. Bull.*, vol. 50, pp. 3–12, 1938.

RINGED KINGFISHER (*Megaceryle torquata*)

A large (15–16 in.) crested kingfisher, blue-gray above, with a white collar running around the neck from the white throat and with a rufous abdomen and breast. The female has a blue-gray band across the breast. Ranges along Atlantic and Pacific coasts from n.-c. Mexico to s. S. America and in the Lesser Antilles; has straggled to s. Tex.

GREEN KINGFISHER (Texas Kingfisher) (*Chloroceryle americana*)

Appearance: A small (7–8½ in.), uncrested, large-billed kingfisher with dark green back wings and tail; the upper half of the head is greenish black. The bird is white below (including lower half of head) and has a brownish red chest and large green spots along the flank. The wings are spotted with white. The female's breast is almost solid with large green spots. The eye is dark, and the bill black.

Voice: A ticking, rattling *tic-tic-tic* and a sharp squeak.

Range and status: Resident from nw. and c. Mexico and c. Tex. to Peru, Bolivia, c. Argentina, and Uruguay;

Green Kingfisher

has straggled to s. Ariz. and ne. Tex. Fairly common within regular range.

Habitat: Small ponds, streams, and rivers.

Seasonal movements: None.

Biology: Nest: An unlined burrow 2–3 ft. deep in loose soil or sandy bank. Eggs: 4–6, white. Incubation period and age at 1st flight unknown. Food: Insects caught in midair in the manner of the flycatchers; also small fish.

WOODPECKERS AND WRYNECKS (PICIDAE)

Woodpeckers and wrynecks are small- to medium-sized (3½–22 in.) arboreal birds related to the toucans, honeyguides, hornbills, puffbirds, and barbets. There are 210 species; 23 of these are found in America. The family ranges throughout the world except for the polar regions, New Guinea, Australia, New Zealand, and most of Oceania. They are solitary in habit, and most species are sedentary. They are seldom found away from trees or large plants. Plumage colors are predominantly black and white, with many species having red or yellow on the head and some having green, brown, red, and yellow in plumage. The sturdy wings are usually rounded; the tail is wedge-shaped or rounded and has stiff, strong shafts that serve as props when the birds use their bills as chisels while clinging to the boles of the trees. The bill is long to short, but usually very strong and flattened laterally at the tip into a chisel edge. The legs are short and strong; most species have two sturdily clawed toes directed forward and two backward; some have two forward and only one backward. The head is large, and the neck rather slim. The tongue is barbed and very long; the roots, providing the extra extension, curve to the back of the head and over the rear of the skull to the crown. Woodpeckers and wrynecks fly well, usually in undulating flight. Most species chisel into the wood of trees or into soil and insect nests and hills after food. The sexes are mostly dissimilar. The voice is usually characterized by loud, harsh, ringing cries or laughs; drumming with the bill on sounding stumps or boards replaces voice in courtship functions. Courtship usually consists of devious pursuit flights. Most species drill nesting holes into dead tree stumps or earthen banks at varying heights above the ground; these are generally dug fresh each year and are unlined. Eggs commonly number 2–8 and are almost invariably a glossy white; they are incubated by both sexes. The hatchlings are naked or, in very few species, sparsely covered with down; at first they are fed by both parents through regurgitation, then are brought entire insects. Food of the adults of most species consists of tree-boring insects; others eat acorns, berries, nuts, other fruit, sap, ants, termites, or insects caught in midflight or picked off ground or trees.

WRYNECK (*Jynx torquilla*)

A small (6½–7 in.), soft-feathered, rather weak-billed bird only vaguely resembling woodpeckers. Mottled and vermiculate patterns of browns, grays, and black above; pale grayish or brownish below, finely barred with dark gray. Its frequent twisting neck motions led to common name. Breeds from n. Eurasia to nw. Africa, se. Europe, sw. Siberia, n. India, c. China, and Japan; winters south to c. Africa and s. Asia. Straggled once to Alaska.

YELLOW-SHAFTED FLICKER (*Colaptes auratus*)

Appearance: Medium-sized (12–14 in.). Back and smaller nonflight feathers of wing are buffy brown, barred with black; the cap and back of the neck are medium gray, with a scarlet crescent across the nape; the rest of the head and neck are buffy brown, with a black "mustache" on the male and unmarked on the female. The rump is white, and the tail and flight feathers of the wing are black above and orange-yellow below. The rest of the underparts are white washed with buffy on the

Like all woodpeckers, the Yellow-shafted Flicker has a stout chisellike bill.

270

flanks; they bear roundish black spots and are separated from the throat by a large black crescentic bib. The black bill is about as long as the head and is sturdy, though not quite so strong as those of other woodpeckers. The legs and feet are dusky brown.

Voice: In spring and into early summer, a long series of sharp, penetrating *wick-wick-wick* or *yuck-yuck-yuck* notes and a series of softer *hic-up, hic-up, hic-up* calls; also gurgling notes and guttural yodels, and a *flicka-flicka-flicka* series. Drumming with the bill on a resonant stump or even a tin roof is part of the springtime courtship activities.

Range and status: Breeds from the n. tree limit of N. America to c. B.C. and east of the Rockies to s. Tex., the Gulf Coast, the Fla. Keys, Cuba, and Grand Cayman I. Withdraws somewhat from more northerly limits of range in winter, but a common winterer from n. U.S. south, reaching s. Calif. and s. Ariz. at this time. Has straggled to England. Very common.

Habitat: More open woods, farmlands, suburbs, riparian forests.

Seasonal movements: Reaches more northerly parts of range Mar.–Apr. and departs Oct.–Nov.

Biology: Courtship consists of bowing, dancing, and chasing around boles of trees as well as aerial pursuit antics. Nest: A hole dug in tree, side of building, or post; often high and prominent (in some areas the bird is called a high-holer). Eggs: 5–10, white. Incubation: 11–12 days. Age at 1st flight: 25–28 days. Food: Almost 50% of the food by bulk is ants, another 20% other insects, and 30–40% wild fruits, berries, and seeds.

Suggested reading: A. Sherman, "At the Sign of the Northern Flicker," *Wils. Bull.*, vol. 22, pp. 135–171, 1910. L. Kilham, "Early Reproductive Behavior of Flickers," *Wils. Bull.*, vol. 71 (4), pp. 323–336, 1959.

RED-SHAFTED FLICKER (*Colaptes cafer*)

Appearance: Same size (12½–14 in.) as the Yellow-shafted Flicker, which it resembles very closely except that the cap and back of the neck are buffy brown without the red crescent, the face and throat are light gray, the male has a scarlet mustache (the female has no mustache), and the undersides of the tail and wing are scarlet-orange or scarlet.

Voice: Hardly separable from that of the Yellow-shafted Flicker.

Range and status: Breeds from se. Alaska, c. B.C., s. Alta., sw. Sask., and c. N.Dak. south to n. Baja Calif. and s. Mexico ranging through the w. Great Plains, where it intergrades with the Yellow-shafted Flicker. Hybrids between the two have occurred as far east as New England. Resident through most of range, but many individuals move south in winter; east of the Rockies, it is seldom found as far north as Mont. and S.Dak. Straggles farther east. Common.

Habitat: Same as Yellow-shafted Flicker.

Seasonal movements: Large numbers move north Mar.–Apr. and return Oct.–early Dec.

Biology: Except for the unproven report that the entrance to the nesting holes of this species is more oval than that of the Yellow-shafted Flicker, their biology is almost identical.

GILDED FLICKER (*Colaptes chrysoïdes*)

Appearance: Smaller (10–12 in.) than the other flickers; almost a feather-for-feather duplicate of the Red-shafted Flicker except that the undersides of the wing and tail are an orange-yellow.

Voice: Like that of other flickers but higher-pitched.

Range and status: Resident from se. Calif. and se. Ariz. to s. Baja Calif. and n. Sinaloa in w. Mexico. Fairly common.

Habitat: Saguaro groves and riparian woodlands in arid and semiarid areas.

Seasonal movements: None.

Biology: Nest: Hole is usually dug in saguaro or other thick, treelike cactus and occasionally in cottonwoods. Eggs: 3–5, white. Incubation and age at 1st flight unknown. Food: Ants and other insects and fruits.

PILEATED WOODPECKER (*Dryocopus pileatus*)

Appearance: Large (16–19½ in.), sooty black, crested woodpecker. The male's long-feathered scarlet cap is separated from the black eye streak by a narrow white streak; a white line runs from the base of the upper bill, under the eye streak, and down the side of the neck to join the large patch of white on the underside of the wing. The chin and a streaky patch on the upper side of the wing are also white, and a scarlet mustache extends more than half the length of the head from the base of the lower bill. In the female only the rear half of the crested crown is scarlet, the forehead being brownish gray to blackish, and a black streak replaces the red mustache. The bill, legs, and feet are black, and the eye is yellow. The young resemble the adults but are duller-colored. The typical undulating woodpecker flight and the white patches should separate it easily from the similar-sized black crow in flight.

Voice: A ringing *yucka-yucka-yucka* much like that of the flickers, but louder and slower; in flight a loud *cac-cac-cac;* loud, cackling *chuck-chuck-chuck-chuck* notes often extend to a somewhat derisive laughing call. Drumming is slower and heavier than the flickers'.

Range and status: Resident of forest areas from c. and ne. B.C., s. Mack., s. Man., n. Ont., s. Que., N.B., and N.S. south to c. Calif., c. Tex., the Gulf Coast, and s. Fla. Population was low in the 1920s and 1930s but increasing since. The bird does considerable damage to wooden power poles, and some control measures may be

The crow-sized Pileated Woodpecker is often confused with the rare Ivory-billed Woodpecker.

necessary, but widespread killing is never allowed. Continuing research will soon develop inexpensive means of keeping the bird off power poles and individual trees, so we may look forward to keeping this valuable species with us.

Habitat: More mature coniferous and mixed forests.

Seasonal movements: Mainly resident, but some individuals move south in winter.

Biology: Nest: Unlined holes dug mainly in dead trees 15–70 ft. above the ground in denser parts of forest. Eggs: 3–5, usually 4; white. Incubation period unknown. Age at 1st flight: 22–26 days. Food: Forest insects, particularly borers and especially carpenter ants and relatives; some wild fruits and acorns. The large feeding holes after insects inhabiting the heartwood of trees are dug primarily in winter when other insects, closer to the surface and easier to obtain, are scarce.

Suggested reading: L. Kilham, "Behavior and Methods of Communication of Pileated Woodpeckers," *Condor,* vol. 62, pp. 377–387, 1959.

RED-BELLIED WOODPECKER (*Centurus carolinus*)

Appearance: Small (9–10½ in.) and not at all well named, as it is pale gray below and only very faintly tinged on the belly with pink almost impossible to see in the field. The rump, face, throat, and front of the neck are pale gray; the back and wings are zebra-patterned black and white; the tail is pale gray with dark gray bars and medium gray tip; and the top of the head and nape from the bill to the back is bright red. The female has red only on the rear half of the crown and on the nape; the rest of her crown is pale gray, and the feathers at the base of the upper bill are tawny.

Voice: A rather soft, querulous *chuh-chuh, chuh* or *cherr, cherr-cherr;* a loud, ratchety *crer-r-r-r-r-r-r-r;* and a loud, drawn-out *pu-er-r-r-r-r-r-r,* rolling the R's like a Castilian.

Range and status: Resident from se. Minn., s. Wis., s. Mich., s. Ont., w. N.Y., e. Ky., W.Va., Md., and Del. south to s. Tex., the Gulf Coast, and the Fla. Keys. Has straggled to Colo. Common.

Habitat: Forests, copses, orchards, and suburban and cultivated areas.

Seasonal movements: None.

Biology: Nest: Digs own hole in dead tree or stump or occupies deserted nesting holes of other woodpeckers.

Despite its name, the Red-bellied Woodpecker's underparts are not red at all.

Eggs: 4–5, white. Incubation: 14(?) days. Age at 1st flight: Certainly more than 16 days; probably more than 20. Food: Various insects and fruits of all sorts; it actively stores nuts and other vegetable food in deep crevices for future use.

Suggested reading: L. Kilham, "Reproductive Behavior of Red-bellied Woodpeckers," *Wils. Bull.*, vol. 73, pp. 237–254, 1961. L. Kilham, "Food Storing of Red-bellied Woodpeckers," *Wils. Bull.*, vol. 75, pp. 227–234, 1963.

GOLDEN-FRONTED WOODPECKER (*Centurus aurifrons*)

Appearance: About the same size (8½–10½ in.) as the Red-bellied Woodpecker, which it resembles. However, it has a scarlet cap separated from the scarlet-orange nape patch by an extension of the pale gray of the undersides and face; there is a tuft of golden yellow feathers at the forehead; the rump and a patch on the wing are pure white; and the tail is black above. Instead of the red cap, the female has pale gray.

Voice: A *cher-r-r-r* like the Red-bellied Woodpecker's and long series of flickerlike *kek-kek-kek-kek* notes.

Range and status: Resident from n.-c. Mexico, sw. Oklahoma, and c. Tex. to n. Nicaragua including islands off e. coast. Common, often abundant.

Habitat: Riparian woodlands and open areas with scattered groves and mesquite.

Seasonal movements: None.

Biology: Nest: Hole in tree or post. Eggs: 4–5, white. Incubation: 14(?) days. Age at 1st flight unknown. Food: Insects and about an equal amount of acorns, nuts, berries, and other wild fruit.

GILA WOODPECKER (*Centurus uropygialis*)

Appearance: About the same size (8–10 in.) as the Golden-fronted Woodpecker and same general appearance, but head of immatures and females is entirely pale buffy gray, and the male has a small scarlet cap; the rump and tail are zebra-patterned black and white.

Voice: A hard, loud, explosive *dchir-dchir-dchir* often drawn out and rolling at the end of each note, and a shrill *huit* repeated 2–3 times.

Range and status: Resident from se. Calif., sw. Nev., s. Ariz., and sw. N.Mex. south to s. Baja Calif. and w.-c. and c. Mexico. Abundant.

Habitat: Saguaro deserts, river woods, and cottonwood groves.

Seasonal movements: None.

Biology: Nest: Dug in saguaro, mesquite, or tree boles and stumps. Eggs: 3–5, white. Incubation: 14(?) days. Age at 1st flight unknown. Food: Insects, various fruits and berries; occasionally eggs of smaller birds.

The Red-headed Woodpecker's stiff tail serves as a prop when it climbs tree trunks.

RED-HEADED WOODPECKER (*Melanerpes erythrocephalus*)

Appearance: Small (8½–9½ in.); head, neck, and upper breast are bright red; rump, underparts, and smaller flight feathers of wing (secondaries) are pure white; tail, back, and remainder of wing are blue-black. The sexes are alike. Immature birds have a buffy brown head and neck, lighter on the throat and lower half of the head, streaked with blackish; the back and wings are barred and mottled buffy brown and blackish, and the white secondaries have two bars of blackish brown.

Voice: A loud *tchur-tchur* and a shrill *cherr-cherr* or a *kweerr-kweerr* and a harsh rattling note of alarm.

Range and status: Resident from s. Sask., s. Man., sw. and s. Ont., N.Y., and s. N.H. south to n. N.Mex., c.

Tex., the Gulf Coast, and s. Fla. (not on the Keys or Cape Sable); has straggled to Alta., Utah, Ariz., s. Que., and the Maritime Provinces of Canada. Common west of the Appalachians; much reduced in numbers east of these mountains and north of Md.

Habitat: More open forests; farmlands and open fields where there are groves and scatterings of trees; towns and suburbs.

Seasonal movements: Moves south in severe winters; in mild winters most of the population is sedentary.

Biology: Nest is dug in telephone poles, fence posts, and dead stumps of trees at varying heights. Eggs: 4–7, commonly 5; white. Incubation: 14(?) days. Age at 1st flight unknown. Reported by some to raise two broods each season at least in parts of range. Food: Insects, spiders, other small invertebrates, corn, wild berries, various fruits, acorns, and nuts.

Suggested reading: A. C. Bent, "Red-headed Woodpecker," *Life Histories of North American Woodpeckers,* Dover, N.Y. (reprint of U.S. Nat. Mus. Bull. 174, 1939), 1964, pp. 195–211.

ACORN WOODPECKER (California Woodpecker) (*Melanerpes formicivorus*)

Appearance: Small (8–9½ in.); tail, head, neck, back, breast, and wings are sooty black; the rump, rest of the underparts, the forehead, a U-shaped bib on the throat, and a line joining the upper arms of the U to the forehead are pure white; and the cap from the forehead almost to the back of the head is bright red. The flanks are streaked with sooty black, and there are white streaks on the sides of the breast and a small white patch on the wing. The white forehead of the female is separated from the scarlet cap by a black band. The eye is yellow, the legs and feet black.

Voice: A series of raucous, hiccuping *ja-cob, ja-cob, ja-cob* calls, a resounding *cleep-up-cleep-up-cleep-up,* and a harsh *chak-a-chak-a-chak.*

Range and status: Resident from sw. Ore., Calif. west of the Sierra Nevadas, Ariz., N.Mex., and w.-c. Tex. south through the highlands to s. Baja Calif. and w. Panama. Of local distribution in Ore., but generally common to abundant.

Habitat: Oak and mixed forests; dense stands, copses, canyons, and foothills.

Seasonal movements: None.

Biology: Nest: Hole dug in tree or pole. Eggs: 4–6, most often 4–5; white. Incubation: 14(?) days. Age at 1st flight unknown. Food: The scientific name of the species means "anteater," whereas the common name refers to its most prominent feeding activity, at least in oak forests. Using natural crevices in the bark or drilling tailored holes, it stores acorns in great numbers in the boles of trees and poles; it was once estimated that one tree held over 50,000 acorns. Besides a large number of acorns and other nuts, it eats wild berries and fruit as well as ants, beetles, other insects, and tree sap.

Suggested reading: A. C. Bent, *Life Histories of North American Woodpeckers,* Dover, N.Y. (reprint of U.S. Nat. Mus. Bull. 174, 1939), 1964, pp. 211–226.

LEWIS' WOODPECKER (*Asyndesmus lewis*)

Appearance: Medium-sized (10½–11½ in.); the cheeks, forehead, and throat form a brownish red patch in a sooty black head; the breast and a collar extending from it around the back of the neck are pale gray; the rest of the underparts are a pale rose; and the tail, wing, rump, and back are solid sooty black. The female is not always distinguishable, but sometimes the gray of the breast is mottled with brownish. Flight is rather crowlike. The bill, legs, and feet are black, and the eye is dark.

Although nuts seem to be its favorite, the Acorn Woodpecker eats other foods as well.

Voice: Most silent of the woodpeckers. Twittering notes, a shrill *huit-huit* of alarm, and a series of strident *chirr* or *chee-ur* calls.

Range and status: Breeds from s. B.C. (and Vancouver I.), w. Alta., Mont., and sw. S.Dak. south to s. Calif., c. Ariz., s. N.Mex., and nw. Nebr. Winters from n. Ore. to n. Baja Calif., n. Sonora, and s. Ariz. and from c. Colo. and s.-c. Nebr. to s. N.Mex. and w. Tex.; casually farther north. It has straggled to Sask., Man., Iowa, Kans., Okla., Ill., and R.I. Fairly common.

Habitat: More open forests or areas with scattered groves and burned or lumbered woodlands.

Seasonal movements: Migration not extensive or pronounced: Apr.–mid-May and Oct.–Nov.

Biology: Nest: Usually dug in dead, fire-scorched tree stump. Eggs: 5–9, usually 6–7; white. Incubation: 14(?) days. Age at 1st flight unknown. Food: Insects (very frequently caught on the wing), acorns, wild berries, and other fruit.

Suggested reading: A. C. Bent, *Life Histories of North American Woodpeckers*, Dover, N.Y. (reprint of U.S. Nat. Mus. Bull. 174, 1939), 1964, pp. 226–237.

YELLOW-BELLIED SAPSUCKER (*Sphyrapicus varius*)

Appearance: Small (8–9 in.) and highly variable, as indicated by specific name. The most common variety has a scarlet cap interrupted near the back by a black streak originating at the bill and passing just above the eye, a narrow white streak starting behind the eye and near the back of the head curving down the side of the neck, and, paralleling this, a broader black streak, then another white streak, and finally a narrow black streak that joins the black bib, thus enclosing the scarlet throat; the rest of the underparts are straw-yellow with fuscous streaking on the flank. The rump and a patch on the wing are white; the tail is black, with white barring on the central feathers; the back is barred black and white; and the wing is black, with narrow white barring on the flight feathers. At the other extreme is the so-called Red-breasted Sapsucker, whose head, neck, throat, and breast are entirely scarlet. In the more common variety the female's chin and throat are red rather than white; the female "Red-breasted" is indistinguishable from the male. The immature birds are like the adults except that the head, neck, back, throat, and breast are brownish barred with buffy on the back and breast and darker on the cap. The immature "Red-breasted" has reddish brown head, neck, throat, and breast.

Voice: A high, snarling mew: *che-err* of alarm, a *yew-ik-yew-ik* call at nesting hole, a nasal *hoih-hoih;* and a dead *tuck-tuck.* The drumming is several rapid beats, then a drastic slowing down like a ratchet coming to a halt.

Range and status: Breeds from se. Alaska, ne. B.C., c. Mack., c. Alta., n. Man., n. Ont., s. Que., s. Lab., and Nfld. south to the mountains of s. Calif., c. Ariz., n. N.Mex., se. S.Dak., e. Mo., c. Ill., nw. Ind., n. Ohio, n. Ga., n. N.Y., and c. New England. Winters from se. Alaska, s. B.C., Mo., the Ohio Valley, and n. N.J. south to n. Baja Calif., w. Panama, the Gulf Coast, and Fla.; casually to the Greater Antilles and the Bahamas. Has straggled to Greenland and Bermuda. Common.

Habitat: Forests, groves, and orchards.

Seasonal movements: Mainly sedentary, but arrives in n. parts of range late Mar.–early May and departs Sept.–Oct.

Biology: Nest: Hole dug in dead trees or stumps. Eggs: 4–7, commonly 5–6; white. Incubation: About 14 days. Age at 1st flight: 24–26 days. Food: Tree sap and cambium layer of trees beneath bark obtained through small (about ¼ in. in diameter), shallow holes drilled in

Lewis' Woodpecker

smooth-barked trees in a series of close parallel rows around bole. The trees usually survive such treatment, but it must be admitted that they are thus more exposed to attack by fungus and other tree diseases. In addition, the Yellow-bellied Sapsucker eats berries and other fruit as well as various insects such as ants and wood borers.

Suggested reading: T. R. Howell, "Natural History and Differentiation in the Yellow-bellied Sapsucker," *Condor,* vol. 54, pp. 237–282, 1952. L. Kilham, "Breeding Behavior of Yellow-bellied Sapsuckers," *Auk,* vol. 79, pp. 31–43, 1962.

WILLIAMSON'S SAPSUCKER (*Sphyrapicus thyroideus*)

Appearance: Slightly larger (9½ in.) than the Yellow-bellied Sapsucker, with glossy green-black head, neck, breast, back, wings, and tail. The flank is chevron-barred black and white; the rump and a large wing patch are white; the flight feathers of the wing are barred with narrow white; a narrow white streak runs from the back of the eye to the back of the head, and another starts at the base of the upper bill and continues to the rear of the cheek region; the chin and upper throat are scarlet; and the belly and undertail feathers are yellow. The female's rump is white; belly and undertail feathers are yellow; head, neck, and throat are brownish; and the rest of her plumage is barred black and white. The young are duller-colored replicas of the adults.

Voice: An explosive, shrill *che-eeer* like the scream of a Red-tailed Hawk, rolling *k-r-r-r-r-r*'s, and a wheezy *whang.* Drumming like that of Yellow-bellied, a series of rapid knocks followed by 3–4 slow, heavier knocks.

Range and status: Resident in mountains from s. B.C., w. Mont., Wyo., and Colo. south to s. Calif., s. Nev., c. Ariz., and n. N.Mex. Winters at lower elevations and south to n. Baja Calif., nw. Mexico, and w. Tex. Casual in w. Calif. and Nebr. Reportedly rare, but possibly not often seen because it inhabits more remote areas.

Habitat: Montane coniferous forests.

Seasonal movements: Moves to higher elevations and northward in Apr. and returns Sept.–Nov.

Biology: Nest: Hole dug in tree or dead stub. Eggs: 3–7, white. Incubation and age at 1st flight unknown. Food: Cambium layer of trees and sap, as in the case of other sapsuckers, but proportionately more insects and much less fruit.

HAIRY WOODPECKER (*Dendrocopos villosus*)

Appearance: Small (8½–10½ in.); very variable but generally entirely white or very pale gray below, with a sooty black cap ending at the nape in a small scarlet patch; there is a white streak below the cap, then a black streak through the eye and flaring out behind it; below

this is another white streak ending in a crescentic flare at the back of the head and separated from the throat by a narrow black line. The back and rump are white; the nape, tail, and wings are black; the flight feathers and some of the smaller feathers of the wing are spotted with white. The central feathers of the tail are black, and the outer feathers white. The bill, which is almost as long as the head, is black, and the legs and feet are light gray. There are 21 geographical varieties, 12 in N. America. The female lacks the red patch at the back of the head.

Voice: A loud, sharp *hueet* call note and a sharp, hurried-up, kingfisherlike rattle. A rather rapid, even-cadenced drumming in spring.

Range and status: Resident from the tree limit of N. America south to n. Baja Calif., the highlands of s. Mexico, and C. America to w. Panama, the Gulf Coast, s. Fla., and the Bahamas. Common.

Habitat: All types of forested lands.

Seasonal movements: There is considerable southward movement in winter, but within the total range.

Biology: Nest: Digs hole in dead stub of tree 5–30 ft. or more above the ground. Eggs: 3–6, commonly 4; white. Incubation and age at 1st flight unknown. Food: Almost 80% insects, spiders, etc; some fruit and seeds.

Suggested reading: L. Kilham, "Courtship and Territorial Behavior of Hairy Woodpeckers," *Auk,* vol. 77, pp. 259–270, 1960.

Wings forward and tail spread, a Downy Woodpecker swoops in for a landing.

DOWNY WOODPECKER (*Dendrocopos pubescens*)

Appearance: Smaller (6–7 in.) than the Hairy Woodpecker but, in both sexes, an almost exact feather-for-feather duplication. The bill of the Downy is much shorter than the head and sharper, appearing to be almost buried in the feather tufts at the base of the bill.

Voice: An abrupt, low but far-carrying *tchick* call and a rapid whinnying series. Spring drumming only slightly faster and lighter than that of Hairy.

Range and status: Resident from se. Alaska, sw. Mack., n. Alta., c. Sask., n. Man., James Bay, s. Que., and Nfld. south to s. Calif., Ariz., n. N.Mex., s.-c. Tex., the Gulf Coast, and Fla. Has been taken in England. Generally more common than its larger relative, the Hairy Woodpecker.

Habitat: Scattered forests and those with many openings, orchards, groves, etc.; favors mixed forests.

Seasonal movements: Considerable southward drift, but within overall range.

Biology: Nest: Digs hole in dead stumps or stubs of trees or posts 3–50 ft. above the ground. Eggs: 3–6, usually 4–5; white. Incubation: 12 days. Age at 1st flight unknown. Food: Over 75% insects, largely beetles and wood-boring larvae; some berries and other fruit.

Suggested reading: L. Kilham, "Reproductive Behavior of Downy Woodpeckers," *Condor,* vol. 64, pp. 126–133, 1962.

LADDER-BACKED WOODPECKER (*Dendrocopos scalaris*)

Appearance: About the size (6–7½ in.) of the Downy Woodpecker. Red cap, streaked with blackish on the forehead; a black nape, rump, and tail (outer feathers barred with white); the back and wings barred black and white; entirely white below, with brownish streaks on the flank; a white face with an angular black line going straight back from the eye, then to the side of the throat, and then to the base of the lower bill. The forehead of the female is brownish, and the cap entirely black.

Voice: A very rapid, resounding, medium-high-pitched *chee-dee-dee-dee-dee-dee-dee-dee* series and a high-pitched *queep* or *queep-queep*. Drumming is very rapid.

Range and status: Resident from se. Calif., s. Nev., nw. Utah, and s. Colo. south to s. Baja Calif., s. Mexico, and British Honduras. Fairly common.

Habitat: Wooded canyons, cottonwood groves, prairie copses, and brushy areas of arid and semiarid regions.

Seasonal movements: None.

Biology: Nest: Hole dug in post, dead stub of tree, or large plants of arid regions such as agave and yucca.

Nuttall's Woodpecker

Eggs: 2–6, usually 4–5; white. Incubation and age at 1st flight unknown. Food: Almost entirely insects.

NUTTALL'S WOODPECKER (*Dendrocopos nuttallii*)

Appearance: About the same size (7–7½ in.) as the Ladder-backed Woodpecker, from which it differs in having heavier black areas on the nape and face. The black lines on the back and wings are broader than the white lines.

Voice: A higher-pitched rattle than that of the Ladder-backed Woodpecker and a loud, rolling *p-r-r-r-t.*

Range and status: Resident in Calif. west of the Sierra Nevadas and deserts south to nw. Baja Calif.; has straggled to Ariz. Common.

Habitat: Riparian woodlands, groves, orchards, and forested canyons and foothills.

Seasonal movements: None.

Biology: Nest: Hole dug in dead stub of tree. Eggs: 4–5, white. Incubation and age at 1st flight unknown. Food: Wood-boring insects and some wild berries and other fruit.

ARIZONA WOODPECKER (*Dendrocopos arizonae*)

Appearance: Small (7–8 in.), with fuscous nape, back, wing, rump, and tail. The tail becomes blackish toward the tip, and the outer feathers are barred black

The Arizona Woodpecker and other species can be attracted to homes with offerings of suet.

and white; there are some white bars on the larger flight feathers of the wing. The cap is black, with a small scarlet patch at the back of the head. The face is white, with a patch of fuscous and black just behind the eye and separated from the white throat by a narrow line of fuscous. The rest of the undersides are white, and fuscous spots on the breast and flanks become faint barring toward the tail. The female has no red on the head, the crown being all black.

Voice: A loud, harsh whinny and a high, insistent *tseek.*

Range and status: Mountains from s.-c. and se. Ariz. and sw. N.Mex. south to Colima, Michoacan, and Zacatecas in Mexico. Fairly common.

Habitat: Oak and oak-pine forests of mountains and canyons.

Seasonal movements: None.

Biology: Nest: Hole dug in dead branches or stubs of trees. Eggs: 3–4, white. Incubation and age at 1st flight unknown. Food: Insects, mainly wood borers, and some acorns and other fruits.

RED-COCKADED WOODPECKER (*Dendrocopos borealis*)

Appearance: Small (8½ in.), with black-and-white ladder back, wing, and rump; a black cap and nape; a large white cheek patch that includes the eye; and black "whiskers" from the bill to the shoulder. Plumage is white below, with medium gray spots on breast and flank; the black tail has white outer feathers. The small, bright red cockade, absent in the female, is at the base and toward the rear of the cap.

Voice: Harsh and discordant *yank-yank* and a querulous *s-srip.*

Range and status: Resident from e. Okla., s. Mo., e. Ky., s. Md., and se. Va. south to e. Tex., the Gulf Coast, and s. Fla. Has straggled to Pa. Locally common; reduced in numbers at one time.

Habitat: Open pine woods.

Seasonal movements: None.

Biology: Nest: In stumps or dead stubs of trees or in pines when core has begun to rot. Eggs: 3–5, white. Incubation and age at 1st flight unknown. Food: Insects, primarily wood borers, but including corn borers for which the birds make special trips to the cornfields; also some seeds, wild berries, and other fruit.

WHITE-HEADED WOODPECKER (*Dendrocopos albolarvatus*)

Appearance: Small (9 in.), with white crown, face, throat, and large patch on the wing. The rest of the plumage is a glossy black, duller on the wing, except that the male has a small scarlet patch at the back of the crown.

Voice: A rattle similar to that of the Downy, a single *cheep* sometimes prolonged *cheep-eep-eep-eep,* a shriller, slower *yip-yip-yip-yip-yip,* and a *wit-wit.*

Range and status: Resident from n.-c. Wash. and n. Idaho south to s. Calif. and w. Nev.; it has straggled to s. B.C. Locally common.

Habitat: Pine and other coniferous forests.

Seasonal movements: None.

Biology: Nest: Hole dug in dead stumps of pine 6–15 ft. high. Eggs: 3–7, usually 4–5; white, sometimes appearing to be spotted with black as the eggs become dotted with resin, or pitch, which then gets black with dirt from the parents' plumage. Incubation: 14(?) days. Age at 1st flight unknown. Food: Almost entirely wood borers and other insects picked from the bark of trees.

Suggested reading: J. L. Blackford, "Woodpecker of the Sequoias," *Aud. Mag.*, vol. 43, pp. 265–269, 1941.

BLACK-BACKED THREE-TOED WOODPECKER
(Arctic Three-toed Woodpecker) (*Picoïdes arcticus*)

Appearance: Small (9–10 in.); sooty black above and white below, with narrow white barring on the larger flight feathers of the wing and white outermost tail feathers. There is heavy black barring on the flank, a yellow crown, a narrow white streak behind the eye, and a broad irregular streak of white from the base of the lower bill to the shoulder. The cap of the female is entirely black. The legs, feet, and bill are black; the eye is dark. As the common name indicates, the bird has only 3 toes, 2 of which are directed forward.

Voice: A *tschuk* or *tik* sometimes in fairly long series and a rattling cry. Drumming low and in short bursts.

Range and status: Resident from c. Alaska, s. Mack., n. Man., n. Ont., n. Que., s. Lab., and Nfld. south to the Cascades and Sierra Nevadas in Calif., w. Nev., nw. Wyo., sw. S.Dak., n. Minn., ne. Wis., n. Mich., se. Ont., n. N.Y., Vt., N.H., and n. Maine. Casual in winter to Nebr., Ill., Ind., Ohio, Pa., and n. N.J. Locally common.

Habitat: N. forests, primarily coniferous.

Seasonal movements: Only irregular movements to south in some winters.

Biology: Nest: A hole dug 5–15 ft. high in dead stump of tree. Eggs: 2–6, usually 4; white. Incubation: 14(?) days. Age at 1st flight unknown. Food: Over 75% tree-dwelling and tree-boring insects; also other insects and spiders and some nuts, wild berries, and other fruit.

Suggested reading: E. G. England, "A Nest of the Arctic Three-toed Woodpecker," *Condor*, vol. 42, pp. 242–245, 1940.

NORTHERN THREE-TOED WOODPECKER (*Picoïdes tridactylus*)

Appearance: Somewhat smaller (8–9½ in.) than the Black-backed Three-toed Woodpecker, from which it otherwise differs in lacking the narrow white streak behind the eye and having a jagged white patch or black-and-white barring on the back. The female's crown is entirely black. The less distinct yellow crown of the male is shaded fore and aft by black streaking.

Voice: Hardly distinguishable from that of the Black-backed Three-toed Woodpecker. Drumming rather soft and in short, irregular bursts.

Range and status: Resident from the tree limit of n. Eurasia, n. Alaska, n. Yuk., Mack., Man., Que., n. Lab., and Nfld. south to the Alps, the mountains of c. Asia, S. Korea, n. Japan, s. Ore., e. Nev., c. Ariz., c. N.Mex.,

Lack of a yellow crown distinguishes the female Black-backed Three-toed Woodpecker from the male.

The Northern Three-toed Woodpecker is common in many northern coniferous forests.

nw. Mont., n. Minn., c. Ont., n. N.Y., n. Vt., n. N.H., and n. Maine. Casual in winter to s. Wis., Mich., s. Ont., s. N.Y., and Mass. Locally common.

Habitat: Coniferous forests.

Seasonal movements: None; irregular winter irruptions on small scale.

Biology: Nest: A hole dug in dead stump of conifer. Eggs: 4, white. Incubation: 14(?) days. Age at 1st flight unknown. Food: Forest insects, particularly wood borers, spiders, nuts, wild berries, and other fruit.

IVORY-BILLED WOODPECKER (*Campephilus principalis*)

Appearance: Large (20 in.); similar to the Pileated Woodpecker but readily separable. The bill, which is as long as the head, is the color of antique ivory; the plumage is black except for the large ruby crest originating behind the eye and completely dominating the rear half of the head. White stripes begin at the lower part of the back of the head and continue down the side of the neck and then down the back, forming a V at the rump. There are 2 large patches of white on the wing, 1 of which shows while the bird is perching and both while in flight. Seen overhead, the tips of the wings are black, and the broad white leading and trailing edges are separated by a broad black band. The crest of the female is black.

Voice: A single loud *toot* while foraging; also a sharp, tinny, nuthatchlike *kent* or *pait*.

Range and status: Resident formerly from ne. Tex., se. Okla., ne. Ark., se. Mo., se. Ill., s. Ind., and se. N.C. south to the Brazos River of Tex., the Gulf Coast, and s. Fla. Nearly extinct; the most recent reports indicate a few pairs survive in the Big Thicket region of e. Texas.

Habitat: Heavily forested riparian flood plains with the many dead and dying mature trees usually found in virgin woodlands. The bird may perhaps be saved from extinction only by strict conservation of such woodlands, unless it changes its diet.

Seasonal movements: None.

Biology: Nest: A hole dug in dead or near-dead trees, 15–70 ft. above the ground. Eggs: 1–5, usually 1–3; white. Incubation: Probably 20 days. Age at 1st flight unknown. Food: Almost entirely wood-boring insects and grubs; some fruits and nuts.

Suggested reading: J. T. Tanner, *The Ivory-billed Woodpecker*, Nat. Aud. Soc. Research Report, no. 1, 1942.

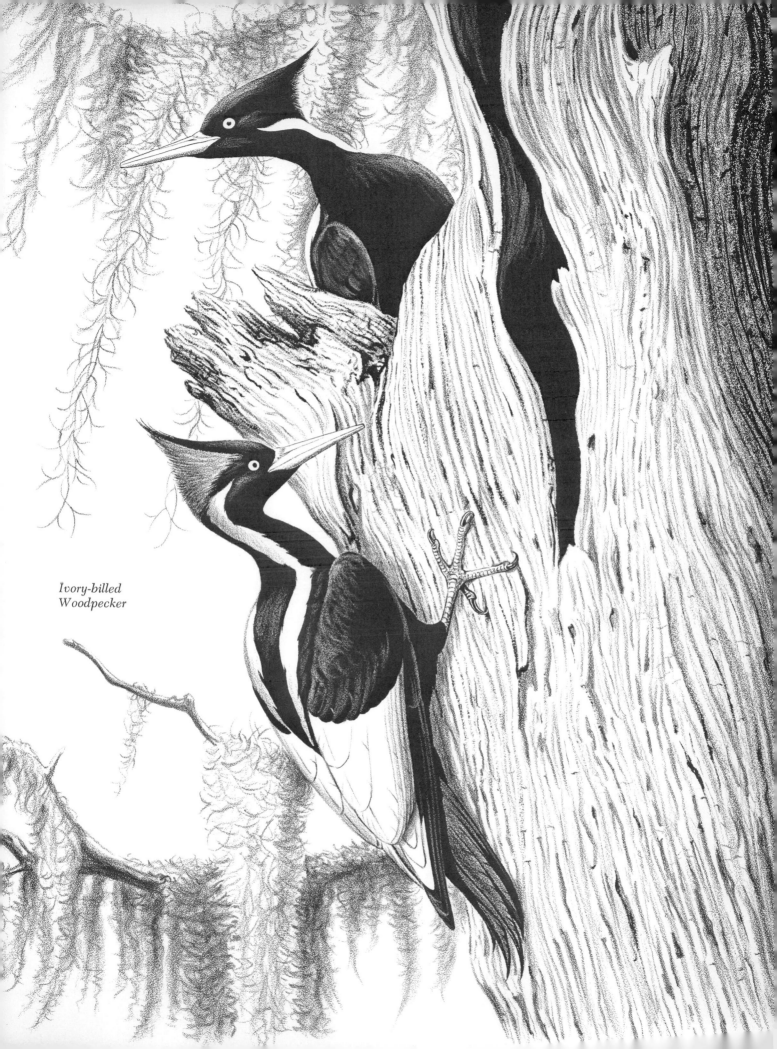

Ivory-billed
Woodpecker

THE COTINGAS (COTINGIDAE)

Cotingas are small- to medium-sized (3½–18 in.) birds of the New World tropics and subtropics; a few are adapted to the altitudinal temperate regions of the Andes. There are 90 recognized species, including umbrellabirds, cocks-of-the-rock, tityras, and becards; they are related to the manakins and tyrant flycatchers. The Rose-throated Becard is the only representative found north of Mexico. Plumage usually occurs in subdued grays and browns with some black and white patterns, but many species are in brilliant reds, oranges, blues, greens, and purples. Bizarre crests, caruncles, fleshy protuberances, and oddly shaped outer wing feathers adorn various members of the family. These birds are nonmigratory, and none are strong fliers. Their favored habitat is tropical rain forests; a few species are found in more arid, scrubby-growth forests. In many species the sexes look alike. Nests are made of twigs, other plant materials, and/or mud; they are built in tree hollows, on rock ledges, in caves, and on or suspended from branches. The 1–6 eggs are incubated by the female; the young, down-covered or naked on hatching, are cared for by both adults. Fruit and insects are the principal food items.

ROSE-THROATED BECARD (*Platypsaris aglaiae*)

Appearance: Small (6–7½ in.), big-headed, short-tailed, and similar to the flycatchers. The male is dark brownish gray above (including the tail) and pale gray below, with a patch of rose covering the throat and central upper breast. The female has a gray cap; the rest of her upperparts, including the tail, are dark reddish brown. She is buffy yellow below, with somewhat browner cheeks. The bill, legs, and feet are blackish, and the eye dark brown.

Voice: Chattering notes followed by a mournful whistle falling in pitch and volume; although never loud, it carries well.

Range and status: Resident from se. Ariz., sw. N.Mex., and southernmost Tex. south along the flanks of the Mexican plateau (rare or local on the plateau) through all of s. Mexico to n. Costa Rica. Rare and local in n. parts of range; fairly common in other parts.

Habitat: In N.Mex., "a mixture of elements characteristic of xeric [arid] scrublands and riparian woodland" (Johnson and Hardy, *Condor*, vol. 61, p. 207, 1959); also in tropical forests and agricultural areas.

Seasonal movements: Retires from northernmost parts of range in severe winters; scattered and solitary in nonbreeding seasons.

Biology: Nest: A bulky, somewhat pendulous mass of fibrous weed stems, lichens, spider webs, thistledown, etc., with entrance rather low on 1 side; built on drooping tree branch 15–50 ft. above the ground, often in same tree with nests of various orioles. Female does most building and all incubation. Eggs: 4–6; white or buffy, spotted with brown. Incubation and age at 1st flight unknown. Food: Fruit and insects.

Suggested reading: H. Brandt, *Arizona and Its Bird Life*, Bird Research Foundation, pp. 212–220, 1951. A. R. Phillips, "Nesting of the Rose-throated Becard in Arizona," *Condor*, vol. 51, pp. 137–139, 1949.

THE TYRANT FLYCATCHERS (TYRANNIDAE)

These small (3–16 in.), primarily arboreal, insectivorous birds are related to the manakins and cotingas of S. and C. America. There are 365 species; 32 are found in America, ranging from n. N. America through C. America and the W. Indies to s. S. America, in humid to dry and tropic to subarctic habitats. Many species, including most of those found north of Mexico, are migratory. The plumage colors are commonly grays, dull greens, and browns, but some species have black, white, yellow, red, and orange feathering. Some species wear prominent crests. Wings are short and rounded to long and pointed, and the tail is usually medium long and square-tipped; a few species have long tails, and some have forked ones. The bill is commonly rather broad and slightly hooked, with stiff, whiskerlike feathers called rictal bristles at the sides of the mouth. The legs and feet are relatively weak except in the very few terrestrial species. The sexes are alike in almost all species. Prey is commonly captured by short flying sorties from prominent perches. Although they are not technically songbirds, many have pleasant notes, calls, and uncomplicated songs. Most species are solitary, and none are colonial. Nests, usually made of plant material, are cuplike, domed, or pendant structures found on the ground, on tree branches, or in tree or ground cavities. The eggs are white or whitish and may be immaculate, spotted, or streaked. In most species the female does all the incubation, but the male generally helps feed and care for the nestlings. The hatchlings are naked below and downy above. In many species, more than 1 family is raised each year. The primary food of these birds is insects, but fruit and small vertebrates are also eaten.

The aggressive Eastern Kingbird attacks even crows if they intrude into its territory.

EASTERN KINGBIRD (*Tyrannus tyrannus*)

Appearance: Somewhat smaller (8–9 in.) than a Robin and dark gray, almost black, above and white below. The prominent dark tail is tipped with white. The crest is just noticeable, and the black-tipped orange crown feathers seldom show. The Eastern Kingbird usually perches in an almost erect position on power lines or prominent treetops where the flashing white breast advertises its presence and serves in identification.

Voice: High-pitched call notes, sometimes strident and accompanied by chattering, sometimes a nasal *tsip* or *tseep*. Song, reported only in very early morning, starts with a rolling note, then a low note followed by one much higher; may be repeated several times. The paired notes sound a bit like the calls of the Eastern Phoebe.

Range and status: Breeds from n. B.C., s.-c. Mack., c. Sask., c. Man., n. Ont., s. Que., and n. N.S. south to nw. Wash., e. Ore., ne. Calif., n. Nev., s. Idaho, n. Utah, Colo., ne. N.Mex., c. Tex., the Gulf Coast, and s. Fla. Winters in S. America from Peru to Bolivia; possibly farther north. Has wandered as far north as Alaska, Yuk., and s. Greenland and south to Cuba, the Isle of Pines, the Bahamas, and Guyana. Locally common.

Habitat: Open areas with occasional high shrub or tree; also along forest edges and hedgerows; rarely in forests where uneven growths furnish vantage points above general level of woods.

Seasonal movements: Migrates through e. Mex. and C. America; only rarely through w. Cuba. Arrives Apr.–mid-May and departs mid-Sept.–mid-Oct.

Biology: Courtship consists in part of aerial acrobatics and song; the male flies upward and then tumbles awkwardly a few feet while uttering a shrill cry or flies in zigzag, erratic patterns while making a harsh double-noted scream. Nest: Made of weed stalks, grasses, and mosses and lined with plant down; built from 2–60 ft., most often 15–20 ft., above the ground in extremities of tree limbs; very rarely built in hollow trees or in nests of other birds. Eggs: 3–5; white, spotted with chestnut. Incubation: Commonly reported as 13 days, but recent evidence indicates it may be as long as 16 days. Age at 1st flight: 13–14 days. Food: Insects; only about 10% of diet filled by fruit and seeds; it has been recorded as eating small vertebrates.

Suggested reading: C. Ogburn, Jr., "The Redoubtable Kingbird," *Aud. Mag.*, vol. 55, pp. 109–111, 1953.

GRAY KINGBIRD (*Tyrannus dominicensis*)

Appearance: Somewhat larger (9–9½ in.) than the Eastern Kingbird, which it resembles closely, but much paler gray above; the slightly notched tail is without the white tip, and the bill is conspicuously larger and more hooked.

Voice: Noisy; its notes are less shrill than those of

Perched on a branch, a Gray Kingbird patiently waits for passing insects.

the Eastern Kingbird, but chatters and calls rather constantly. Most common call described as *pe-cheer-y*.

Range and status: Coasts, from Ala. and S.C. to s. Fla. and through the W. Indies and Bahamas. May be locally common.

Habitat: Tropical and warm temperate coasts; most common in mangrove thickets.

Seasonal movements: Partially migratory, retiring in winter months as far south as the Lesser Antilles and n. S. America.

Biology: Nest: A loose structure of twigs, unlined; usually in a mangrove. Eggs: 3; pinkish, splotched with brown. Incubation and age at 1st flight unknown. Food: Almost 80% insects; the remainder consists of seeds and fruits, other small invertebrates, and some small vertebrates.

TROPICAL KINGBIRD (Couch's Kingbird) (*Tyrannus melancholicus*)

Appearance: About the size (8–9½ in.) of the Eastern Kingbird, with dusky brown wing and tail, a bluish, light gray cap, face, and nape, a greenish, light gray back and rump, and a white throat. The remainder of the underside is yellow, becoming tinged with green on the breast. The hidden crown is scarlet-orange.

Voice: A *pit-it-it-it-it* with a high, metallic tone rising in pitch and very rapid. Also a high, burry *queer* or *chi-queer* and a buzzy *b-re-e-e-er*.

Range and status: Breeds from se. Ariz., Sonora, Nuevo Leon, and s. Tex. to Bolivia and Argentina; winters from w.-c. Mexico, Nuevo Leon, and s. Tex. south. Has straggled to B.C., Wash., and Maine. Locally and sporadically common in s. Tex.

Habitat: Riparian forests, scattered groves, and open lowland woods.

Seasonal movements: Irregular; no schedule of arrival or departure.

Biology: Nest: Made of twigs and lined with moss; built on horizontal branches of tree or shrub. Eggs: 3–5; pinkish or buffy, blotched and spotted with browns. Incubation and age at 1st flight unknown. Food: Insects; some seeds and fruit.

WESTERN KINGBIRD (*Tyrannus verticalis*)

Appearance: Same size (8–9½ in.) as the Tropical Kingbird, which it resembles very closely except that the outer tail feathers are white and the breast is pale gray.

Voice: Noisy; squeaks, warbling twitters, and a shrill, metallic *ker-er-ip-ker-er-ip*, sometimes repeated several times; also a single *kip* or *quer-ich*.

Range and status: Breeds from nw. Ore., s.-c. B.C., s. Alta., s. Sask., s. Man., and w. Minn. south to n. Baja Calif., Sonora, nw. Chihuahua, s. N.Mex., w.-c. Tex., ne. Okla., and e.-c. Kans.; rarely from s. Wis., s. Mich., s.

Ont., and nw. Ohio to n.-c. Mo. Winters from s. Mexico to n. Nicaragua and in small numbers from coastal S.C. to Fla. Has reached N.B. and N.S. during migration. Fairly common to common.

Habitat: Farmlands and open country with scattered trees.

Seasonal movements: Arrives mid-Mar.–early May and departs late Aug.–Sept.

Biology: Nest: A compact structure of twigs, weeds, and plant fibers; built 5–40 ft. above the ground on limb or in crotch of bush or tree. Eggs: 3–6, usually 4; white, pinkish, or pale buffy, spotted and blotched with browns. Incubation: 12–14(?) days; probably longer. Age at 1st flight: About 14 days. Food: Over 90% insects and spiders; a few seeds, berries, and other fruit; occasionally a frog or other small vertebrate.

Suggested reading: A. C. Bent, *Life Histories of North American Flycatchers, Larks, Swallows, and Their Allies,* Dover, N.Y. (reprint of U.S. Nat. Mus. Bull. 179, 1942), 1963, pp. 57–70.

CASSIN'S KINGBIRD (*Tyrannus vociferans*)

Appearance: About the same size (8–9 in.) as the Western Kingbird, which it closely resembles. Its tail is a uniform dusky brown, it is a darker gray above and on the breast, and the white on the throat forms a larger, more distinct patch than in the Western Kingbird.

Cassin's Kingbird

Voice: A coarse, low-pitched *cherr—keh-deer,* a loud *che-beeu,* and a *kiddoo-kiddoo-kiddoo-kiddoo-kidduck* of alarm.

Range and status: Breeds from c. Calif., n. Ariz., s. Utah, Colo., e. Wyo., and se. Mont. south to s. Mexico, w. Tex., w. Okla., and sw. Kans. Winters from c. Calif. and nw. Mexico south to Guatemala. Has straggled to Ore., Nebr., and Ont. Locally common.

Habitat: Open pine-oak forests in mountains, open areas with scattered trees, and ranchland; generally more arid areas than Western Kingbird prefers.

Seasonal movements: Mar.–mid-May and Sept.–Oct.

Biology: Nest: A bulky but compact construction of twigs, weed stems, vegetable fiber, and wool; built on horizontal branch of tree, top of post, or fence rail. Eggs: 2–5, usually 3–4; white or creamy, spotted with browns in a wreath around larger end. Incubation: 12–14(?) days. Age at 1st flight: About 2 weeks. Food: About 80% insects and spiders; some berries and other fruit.

FORK-TAILED FLYCATCHER (*Muscivora tyrannus*)

Large (9–16 in.); gray above and white below (including the throat), with a black head and tail and a small, bright yellow crown. The long, streaming, forked tail is longer than the body and has white edging on the lower half of the outer feathers. It ranges from s. Mexico to Argentina, one of the relatively few birds that breed in the s. parts of their range and migrate northward in the winter period of the S. Hemisphere. It has straggled to or been reported from Pa., Maine, N.Y., N.J., Mass., Miss., Cuba, and Bermuda.

THICK-BILLED KINGBIRD (*Tyrannus crassirostris*)

About the size (9 in.) of the Eastern Kingbird and similar to it except that it is a medium brownish gray above and somewhat darker on the cap, wings, and square tail. It is whitish below but grayed on the breast to yellow-tinged on the belly. The black bill is conspicuously heavier and thicker, and the small hidden crown is bright yellow. A resident of w. and s. Mexico and w. Guatemala, with a small population recently discovered in extreme se. Ariz. and sw. N.Mex.

SCISSOR-TAILED FLYCATCHER (*Muscivora forficata*)

Appearance: Long (11–15 in.), but its tail accounts for almost ⅔ of its length. Head, nape, breast, and back are pale gray; throat is white, wing sooty black, and rump pinkish gray. Underparts range from pale fleshy pink at lower breast to fleshy pink of undertail feathers. A scarlet streak runs from the bill to the center of the crown and another from the shoulder to the flank. The central tail feathers are longest; each succeeding pair is

The Scissor-tailed Flycatcher prefers open areas with scattered shrubs and trees.

¼–⅓ shorter, with black tips overlapping above so the tail looks black above and buffy with black edgings below. The bill, legs, and feet are black, and the eye dark. Immature birds have not acquired the long tail and look like a pinkish Western Kingbird.

Voice: In flight, a much-repeated *ka-queee, ka-queee,* a loud, coarse *pup-pup-pup-pup-pup-pup-perlep,* and much squealing and scolding.

Range and status: Breeds from e. N.Mex., w. Okla., se. Colo., Nebr., Kans., w. Ark., and w. La. south to s. Tex. Winters from s. Mexico and Guatemala to w. Panama and casually in s. Fla. A confirmed wanderer; has straggled as far as Calif., Ariz., Man., Minn., Wis., Ont., Que., and N.B. and points between. Fairly common.

Habitat: Open and semiopen country with scattering of trees and high points such as buildings, and open spots in wooded areas.

Seasonal movements: Arrives Mar.–mid-Apr. and departs Sept.–mid-Nov.

Biology: Nest: A frail, sloppily built, shallow cup of twigs and grasses in tree or bush or on pole. Eggs: 4–6, commonly 5; white, buffy, or pinkish white, spotted and blotched with dark browns and grays; some are almost immaculate. Incubation: 12–14 days. Age at 1st flight: About 2 weeks. Food: Almost entirely insects; very rarely seeds, berries, and other fruit.

Suggested reading: F. W. Fitch, Jr., "Life History and Ecology of the Scissor-tailed Flycatcher," *Auk,* vol. 67, pp. 145–168, 1950.

KISKADEE FLYCATCHER (Derby Flycatcher) (*Pitangus sulphuratus*)

Larger (9–10½ in.) than the Eastern Kingbird, with a much bigger head and bill. A white stripe passes completely around the black head just above the eye. There is a patch of bright yellow in the center of the crown, and the white of the throat spreads to the center of the lower half of the head. The rest of the underparts are bright yellow, the back and rump are chestnut, and the wing and tail are brownish red. It is resident from nw. Mexico and s. Tex. to Uruguay and c. Argentina. Rare in U.S. except in lower Rio Grande Valley.

SULPHUR-BELLIED FLYCATCHER (*Myiodynastes luteiventris*)

Smaller (7½–8½ in.) than the Western Kingbird; smoke-gray above and pale yellow below, with dark brown streaking above and on breast and flank. There is a broad blackish streak through the eye, and the tail is brownish red. It breeds from se. Ariz. and n. Mexico south to Costa Rica and winters in w. and c. S. America. Rare in U.S.

GREAT CRESTED FLYCATCHER (Crested Flycatcher) (*Myiarchus crinitus*)

Appearance: About the size (8–9 in.) of the Eastern Kingbird. It is smoke-gray above (slightly darker on bulbous crest) and straw-yellow below, with whitish

The Saw-whet Owl, smallest of the northern species, is only 7 to 8½ inches long. It is so tame that even adults frequently can be captured by hand.

With its wings beating rapidly as it hovers in midair, the Black-chinned Hummingbird uses its long, slender bill to probe in blossoms for nectar and small insects.

throat, light gray breast, and light brownish red wing and tail. The bill is light gray, the legs and feet dark gray, and the eye dark brown.

Voice: A loud, rather clear, whistled *whip-whip-whip*, a pleasant but loud *wheep* or *queep* note of alarm, and a water-whistle song rising up and down on a much repeated *queedle-queedle-queedle*.

Range and status: Breeds from se. Sask., s. Man., c. Ont., sw. Que., n. Maine, and c. N.B. south to w. Okla., c. Tex., the Gulf Coast, and s. Fla.; winters from e. Mexico and s. Fla. through C. America to nw. S. America. Very rare in Cuba; has straggled to Alta., Mont., Wyo., Colo., Ariz., and N.S. Common.

Habitat: Woodlands, dense groves, and copses.

Seasonal movements: Arrives Mar.–May and departs Sept.–mid-Oct.

Biology: Nest: A bulky mass of twigs in a tree cavity or abandoned woodpecker hole. The nest very often includes the cast-off skin of a snake or, as a substitute for this, an occasional strip of cellophane or other shiny plastic. Eggs: 4–8, usually 5–6; yellowish white or pinkish white, scratched, streaked, and blobbed with dark browns and purples. Incubation: 13–15(?) days. Age at 1st flight: About 12–18 days. Food: Over 90% insects; the rest small wild fruits.

Suggested reading: H. Mousley, "A Study of the Home Life of the Northern Crested Flycatcher," *Auk*, vol. 51, pp. 207–216, 1934.

WIED'S CRESTED FLYCATCHER (*Myiarchus tyrannulus*)

Appearance: About the same size (8½–9½ in.) as the Great Crested Flycatcher and very similar, but a pale straw-yellow below, which grades evenly into a pale gray throat. The brown of the tail and wing is duller, closer to cinnamon.

Voice: A loud, clear *whit* and a low, trilling *p-r-reeer;* a dawn song of pleasant whistled *whit-will-do*'s alternating with *three for-you*'s.

Range and status: Resident from s. Nev., c. Ariz., sw. N.Mex., n.-c. Mexico, and s. Tex. south to Paraguay and n. Argentina; has straggled to Calif., Baja Calif., and s. Fla.

Habitat: Saguaro deserts, riparian woodlands, copses, and wooded canyons.

Seasonal movements: Some southward movement in winter by parts of population.

Biology: Nest: A cavity in tree or post or an abandoned woodpecker hole in tree or saguaro cactus. Eggs: 3–6, commonly 5; white, pinkish, or buffy, spotted, scratched, and streaked with browns and grays. Incubation period and age at 1st flight unknown. Food: Mainly insects; probably about same proportions as Great Crested Flycatcher.

ASH-THROATED FLYCATCHER (*Myiarchus cinerascens*)

Appearance: A smaller (7½–8½ in.) replica of the Wied's Crested Flycatcher, but with whiter throat and considerably paler yellow undersides.

Voice: A clear *huit-huit* repeated many times, a rolling *quir-r-r--quirp*, and a low *hip—ha-whip*.

Range and status: Breeds from sw. Ore., w. Wash., s. Idaho, sw. Wyo., Colo., and n. and c. Tex. south to s. Baja Calif. and sw. and ne. Mexico. Winters from n. Baja Calif., se. Calif., c. Ariz., and ne. Mexico to Guatemala and El Salvador; casually to Costa Rica. Has straggled to B.C., Mont., Kans., La., and Fla.

Habitat: Brushy deserts, open woods; mainly in semiarid areas.

Seasonal movements: Arrives in U.S. mid-Mar.–mid-May and departs Sept.–mid-Nov.

Biology: Nest: Hair and grasses in deserted woodpecker hole or natural cavity in tree, post, or large cactus. Eggs: 3–7, usually 4–5; pale yellowish white or pinkish white, streaked, splashed, and lined with browns and purples. Incubation: 15(?) days. Age at 1st flight: 16–17

The Great Crested Flycatcher often accepts nest boxes as a substitute for natural cavities.

days. Food: Over 90% insects and spiders; some berries and other small fruits.

OLIVACEOUS FLYCATCHER (*Myiarchus tuberculifer*)

Appearance: Rather small (6½–7 in.) and only slightly crested; entirely a brownish olive above, including tail; below, a pale gray at throat grading to a pale yellowish white at the undertail feathers. The bill, legs, and feet are blackish, and the eye dark brown.

Voice: A moaning, quavering, whistled *pi-ur-r-r.*

Range and status: Breeds from se. Ariz., sw. N.Mex., and n.-c. and ne. Mexico south to Argentina and s. Brazil; winters from n.-c. Mexico southward. Has straggled to Colo.

Habitat: Oak, pine-oak, and juniper forests of mountain slopes and canyons.

Seasonal movements: Arrives in U.S. in Apr. and departs in Sept.

Biology: Nest: Made of grasses lined with hair and finer grasses; built in natural cavity or deserted wood-

Ash-throated Flycatcher

The Eastern Phoebe frequently builds its bulky nest on ledges on barns and houses.

pecker hole in tree, post, or large cactus. Eggs: 3–5, usually 4–5; pale yellowish white, streaked with browns, purples, and grays. Incubation period and age at 1st flight unknown. Food: Probably, as for others of this genus, almost entirely insects.

EASTERN PHOEBE (*Sayornis phoebe*)

Appearance: Small (6¼–7¼ in.). Olive above, including wing and tail, and a pale buffy white below; whiter at the throat, and light olive at the shoulder and flank. The eye, bill, legs, and feet are black.

Voice: A rather husky but distinct *phoe-be* and sharp whistled *chip*'s.

Range and status: Breeds from c. Mack., n. Sask., n. Man., nw. and c. Ont., s. Que., and N.B. south to ne. B.C., s. Alta., se. Colo., e. N.Mex., c. and ne. Tex., Ark., ne. Miss., c. Ala., n. Ga., w. S.C., and N.C. Winters from n.-c. Mexico, the Gulf Coast, and coastal Va. south to s. Mexico; casually farther north. Has straggled to Calif., Baja Calif., Ariz., N.S., P.E.I., and Bermuda.

Habitat: Woodlands, farmlands, and urban and suburban areas, especially near streams.

Seasonal movements: Moves north Mar.–mid-May, often arriving before last of spring snows, and returns Sept.–early Nov.

Biology: Nest: A large but neatly made structure of mosses, grasses, and mud with a lining of fine fibers and hair; built on rock ledges in ravines, on shelflike projections under bridges and trestles, and on similar sites of man-made buildings. Eggs: 3–8, commonly 5; white, with a few bearing a few brown specks, mainly about larger end. Incubation: 16 days. Age at 1st flight: 15–16 days. Commonly 2 broods are raised. Food: 95% insects and spiders; some fruit and seeds.

Suggested reading: A. C. Bent, *Life Histories of North American Flycatchers, Larks, Swallows, and Their Allies*, Dover, N.Y. (reprint of U.S. Nat. Mus. Bull. 179, 1942), 1963, pp. 140–154.

BLACK PHOEBE (*Sayornis nigricans*)

Appearance: Small (6¼–7 in.); entirely sooty black above and on throat, breast, and flank. The rest of the underparts are white, and the eye, bill, legs, and feet are black.

Voice: A constantly repeated *tsip* or *chee* accompanied by a flick of the tail while the bird is perching; its song consists of 4 notes rapidly repeated, rising in pitch on the 1st pair and lowering in the 2nd *ti-wee, ti-wee*.

Range and status: Resident from Calif., s. Nev., sw. Utah, c. Ariz., s. N.Mex., and c. Tex. south through the highlands of C. America and S. America to n. Argentina. Has straggled to Ore. and B.C. Locally common.

Habitat: Near usually well-shaded stream, pond, or marsh; also shaded, brushy canyons, farmlands, and urban and suburban areas.

Seasonal movements: None.

Biology: Nest: Made of mud, grasses, shredded bark, and hairs; stuck to rough vertical surface of building, canyon wall, side of well or bridge, or on ledges in similar situations. Eggs: 3–6, white; usually immaculate, but some are spotted with reds or browns about larger end. Incubation: 15–17 days. Age at 1st flight: About 20 days; usually 2 broods raised in same nest each year. Food: Almost exclusively insects; very occasionally berries.

Suggested reading: G. Oberlander, "The History of a Family of Black Phoebes," *Condor*, vol. 41, pp. 133–151, 1939.

SAY'S PHOEBE (*Sayornis saya*)

Appearance: Larger (7–8 in.) than the Eastern and Black Phoebes. Say's Pheobe is a brownish olive above (darker on the wing and almost black on tail), with the light brownish olive of the breast becoming a pale gray at the chin. The rest of the underparts are tawny, and the eye, bill, legs, and feet are blackish.

Voice: A low, querulous *fee-yurr* accompanied by tail twitching and crest raising; in the mating season, a much-repeated, rapid *pit-tsee-ar* followed by a rough trill call while the bird flutters in air.

Range and status: Breeds from Alaska, c. Yuk., w. Mack., c. Alta., s. Sask., and sw. Man. south to c. Mexico. Winters from Calif., n. Ariz., c. and se. N.Mex.,

and s. Tex. south to s. Baja Calif. and s.-c. Mexico. It has straggled to Wis., Ill., Ind., N.Y., Conn., Mass., and Que. Fairly common.

Habitat: Open arid and semiarid areas, ranchlands, brushy plains, and generally around mouths of canyons.

Seasonal movements: Arrives in n. parts of range mid-Feb.–early May and departs mid-Aug.–early Nov.

Biology: Nest: Rather flat brackets made of weed stems, grasses, plant fibers, spider webbing, and wool; built on ledges of rock walls, bridges, and farm buildings, usually under overhanging shelter. Eggs: 3–6, usually 4–5; white, very seldom sparsely spotted with browns. Incubation: About 14(?) days. Age at 1st flight: 14–16 days; usually 2, sometimes 3 broods each year. Food: Insects; less than 1% seeds and berries.

YELLOW-BELLIED FLYCATCHER (*Empidonax flaviventris*)

Appearance: This and the following 8 species of the genus *Empidonax* are all so very similar that they may best be separated by voice, habits, habitat, and comparative measurements in hand. This species, like the others,

Say's Phoebe

The Yellow-bellied Flycatcher is difficult to identify by appearance alone.

is small (5–5¾ in.), brownish olive above (darker on wing and tail) and yellowish below, with smoke-gray running from the side of the breast down the flank. There is a whitish ring about the eye, and 2 whitish bars are visible on the wing while the bird is perching.

Voice: A monotonously repeated *chee-weep, chee-weep* or *phee-i, phee-i* and, in flight, a *killick-killick*.

Range and status: Breeds from n. B.C., n. Alta., s. Mack., c. Sask., c. Man., n. Ont., c. Que., s. Lab., and Nfld. south to n. N.Dak., n. Minn., n. Wis., s. Ont., ne. Pa., s. N.H., and Maine. Winters from c. and ne. Mexico to e. Panama. Has straggled to Greenland. Locally common.

Habitat: Coniferous forests, muskeg, alder thickets, and cold bogs.

Seasonal movements: Arrives in U.S. and Canada May–early June and departs Aug.–mid-Oct.

Biology: Nest: A deep cup of mosses lined with black rootlets, pine needles, and fine grasses, with green mosses covering the outside; built on or near ground in cavities among roots of fallen trees or dense sphagnum moss. Eggs: 3–5; white, sparsely speckled with browns. Incubation: 15 days. Age at 1st flight: 13 days. Food: 97% insects and spiders; some seeds and berries.

Suggested reading: L. H. Walkinshaw, "Yellow-bellied Flycatcher Nesting in Michigan," *Auk*, vol. 74, pp. 293–304, 1957.

ACADIAN FLYCATCHER (*Empidonax virescens*)

Appearance: Small (5½–6¾ in.); brownish olive above and whitish below, with smoke-gray flanks. It has a white eye-ring and 2 white wing bars (see other flycatchers of same genus).

Voice: A startling, sharp *ka-zeep* or *spit-chee*, higher at end, and a whispery *peet*.

Range and status: Poorly named as it never reaches Acadia (N.S.). Breeds from se. S.Dak., n. Iowa, s. Wis., s. Mich., s. Ont., s. N.Y., ne. Pa., and se. Conn. (casually to Vt. and Mass.) south to c. and se. Tex., the Gulf Coast, and c. Fla. Winters from Costa Rica to Ecuador and w. Venezuela. Rare in w. Cuba during migration; has straggled to the Bahamas. Fairly common, but inconspicuous; rare or becoming rare in ne. part of range. Deciduous woodlands and wooded swamps, common in beech forests.

Seasonal movements: Arrives in U.S. Apr.–mid-May and departs Sept.–early Oct.

Biology: Nest: A basket woven of plant stems and fibers, with some spider and insect webbing; suspended between two horizontally forked twigs near the end of a tree branch, usually fairly close to the ground and often over a stream. Eggs: 2–4, usually 3; white or buffy,

Masses of Spanish moss decorate the nest of a pair of Acadian Flycatchers.

This Traill's Flycatcher's nest is the cruder type, built of coarse plant material.

sparsely peppered at the larger end with browns. Incubation: 13–14 days. Age at 1st flight: About 13 days. Food: Almost entirely insects and spiders; less than 3% seeds and berries.

Suggested reading: D. L. Newman, "A Nesting of the Acadian Flycatcher," *Wils. Bull.*, vol. 70, pp. 130–144, 1958.

TRAILL'S FLYCATCHER (Alder Flycatcher) (*Empidonax traillii*)

Appearance: Small (5¼–6¾ in.); brownish olive above and whitish below, with smoke-gray on sides of breast and flanks. It has a whitish eye-ring and 2 whitish wing bars.

Voice: Somewhat variable, but breaks down into 2 different "songs," a sneezy *fitz-bew* and a *fee-bee-o;* also a *pip* and husky *weep* notes. There is some question as to whether or not there are 2 very similar species concerned, since overlapping but separate geographic ranges may be plotted for the major songs and there seem to be 2 kinds of nests made.

Range and status: Breeds from c. Alaska, c. Yuk., nw. Mack., ne. Alta., n. Sask., n. Man., n. Ont., Que., and Nfld. south to n. Baja Calif., s. Ariz., sw. N.Mex., ne. Okla., Ark., s. Ill., s. Ind., Ohio, W.Va., se. Pa., and n. N.J. Winters from s. Mexico to n. Argentina. Has straggled to Bermuda. Fairly common.

Habitat: Brushy swamps and thickets generally near water.

Seasonal movements: Arrives in U.S. and Canada in May and departs Aug.–mid-Oct.

Biology: Nest: A rather loose structure of weed stems and grasses in a fork of a bush, or a more compact nest of finer grasses and plant material with fine fibers and cottony material added. Eggs: 2–4; white or pale buffy, wreathed about larger end with brown or purplish spots. Incubation: 12–14 days. Age at 1st flight: 13–14 days. Food: Almost exclusively insects; a few spiders and millipedes and less than 4% berries and seeds.

Suggested reading: R. C. Stein, *Two Populations of the Alder Flycatcher*, N.Y.S. Mus. and Sci. Serv. Bull. 371, 63 pp., 1958. J. R. King, "Notes on the Life History of Traill's Flycatcher," *Auk*, vol. 72, pp. 148–173, 1955.

LEAST FLYCATCHER (*Empidonax minimus*)

Appearance: Small (5–5¾ in.); brownish olive above and whitish below, with smoke-gray on side of breast and flank, white eye-ring, and 2 white wing bars. It is somewhat more grayish above and whiter below than other members of the genus, but direct comparison is needed to be sure of identification.

Voice: A monotonously repeated, vigorous *chebec* with accent on final syllable; not loud, but far-carrying. Also a short *whit* of alarm.

Least Flycatcher

Range and status: Breeds from sw. Yuk., c. Mack., ne. Alta., n. Sask., c. Man., n. Ont., c. Que., P.E.I., and N.S. south to ne. B.C., east of the Rockies to sw. Mo., c. Ill., s.-c. Ind., n. Ohio, W. Va., and the Appalachians to n. Ga., se. Pa., and n. N.J. Winters from c. Mexico (including Yucatan Peninsula) south to Panama. Common; locally abundant.

Habitat: Open woodlands, orchards, suburbs, and groves.

Seasonal movements: Arrives in U.S. and Canada late Mar.–late May and departs Aug.–Oct.

Biology: Nest: Compact and well made, with deep cup, of shreds of bark, weed stems, and grasses and lined with thistledown, other plant fibers, and feathers; firmly set in crotch or fastened to horizontal limb of tree 2–60 ft. above the ground, generally below 20 ft. Eggs: 3–6,

commonly 4; cream-white. Incubation: 13–16 days. Age at 1st flight: 13–14 days. Food: Insects and spiders; less than 3% seeds, berries, and other vegetable matter.

Suggested reading: D. E. Davis, "'The Breeding Flycatchers," *Wils. Bull.*, vol. 71, pp. 73–85, 1959. M. M. Nice and N. E. Collias, "A Nesting of the Least Flycatcher," *Auk*, vol. 78, pp. 145–149, 1961.

HAMMOND'S FLYCATCHER (*Empidonax hammondii*)

Appearance: Small (5–5½ in.); grayed brownish olive above and whitish below, with smoke-gray on the side of the breast and down the flank. It has a whitish eye-ring and 2 whitish wing bars.

Voice: Apparently there is some confusion as to how distinct the song of this species and that of the Dusky Flycatcher really are. This species' song is a low, weak *se-put, tsur-r-r-p, tseep;* the rough-trilled central phrase is said to be distinctive, but some say the Dusky occasionally makes this note. Voice includes a *pee-eet* and a faint *quip.*

Range and status: Breeds from s. Alaska, s. Yuk., B.C., w.-c. Alta., s.-c. Mont., and nw. Wyo. south to nw. and e.-c. Calif., nw. Nev., Utah, w. Colo., and n.-c. N.Mex. Winters from se. Ariz. and ne. Mexico south to Nicaragua. Has straggled to Okla. and Tex. Locally common.

Habitat: Coniferous forests in mountains; during migration, other woodlands and thickets.

Seasonal movements: Data confused; apparently reaches breeding areas late Apr.–mid-May and departs late Aug.–Sept.

Biology: Nest: A neat, compact structure of fine grasses and vegetable fiber lined with finer grasses, hair, and feathers; saddled on horizontal limb 15–50 ft. above the ground. Eggs: 3–4; white, very rarely spotted with browns. Incubation: 15 days. Age at 1st flight: 17 days. Food: Little known; probably almost entirely insects.

Suggested reading: D. E. Davis, "The Breeding Biology of Hammond's Flycatcher," *Auk*, vol. 71, pp. 164–171, 1954.

DUSKY FLYCATCHER (Wright's Flycatcher) (*Empidonax oberholseri*)

Appearance: Small (5¼–6 in.); grayed brownish olive above and whitish below, with smoke-gray on the side of the breast and down the flank. It has a whitish eye-ring and 2 whitish wing bars.

Voice: Song, transliterated as *pusek-pitic-squizik, sitick-chitick-suewhit, pssit-pewic-pusee,* is supposedly milder and less sharply accented than the song of Hammond's Flycatcher. Voice includes a *tsee-wick* and a soft *pit.*

Range and status: Breeds from s. Yuk., nw. and c. B.C., sw. Alta., sw. Sask., and Wyo. south to s. Calif., s.

Nev., Utah, c. Colo., c. Ariz. and n. N.Mex. Winters from se. Ariz. and n.-c. and ne. Mexico south to s. Mexico. Straggles to Baja Calif., Kans., and Tex.; also to coastal Wash. and Ore. Fairly common locally.

Habitat: Favors chaparral with scattering of trees, also brush on mountain slopes and open coniferous forest of foothills and s. mountains.

Seasonal movements: Arrives in U.S. and Canada mid-Apr.–May and departs mid-Aug.–Sept.

Biology: Nest: A neat, deep-cupped structure of fine grasses, weed bark, plant down, spider webbing, and hair; built in the crotch of a bush or low sapling 2–18 ft. above the ground. Eggs: 2–4, commonly 3–4; white, very seldom spotted with browns. Incubation: 12–15(?) days. Age at 1st flight: About 18 days. Food: Probably almost entirely insects.

GRAY FLYCATCHER (*Empidonax wrightii*)

Appearance: Small (5½ in.); very little olive in the medium gray above. It is whitish below (smoky gray at side of breast and down flank) and has a whitish eye-ring and 2 white wing bars. There is hardly any yellow tinge on the breast. The rear half of lower bill is flesh-colored.

Voice: A vigorous *tu-wheet* by the male and a weak *tseet* by the female; also notes described as *hesick-pitick*.

Range and status: Breeds from c. Ore., sw. Idaho, sw. Wyo., ne. Utah, and c. Colo. south to e.-c. Calif., s. Nev., c. Ariz., and w.-c. N.Mex. Winters from s. Calif., c. Ariz., and n.-c. and ne. Mexico south to s. Baja Calif. and s.-c. Mexico. In migration, ranges to w. Tex. Fairly common locally.

Habitat: Semiarid sagebrush and piñon-juniper areas; in winter, also brushy areas and willow thickets.

Seasonal movements: Moves north in Apr. and south in Sept.

Biology: Nest: A neat, deep-cupped structure of fine grasses, shredded weed stems, hairs, plant fibers, and feathers, of looser construction than nests of 2 species above; built in dead thornbush, sagebrush, or small tree. Eggs: 3–4, white. Incubation: 14 days. Age at 1st flight: 16 days. Food: Almost entirely insects.

Suggested reading: H. N. Russell, Jr., and A. M. Woodbury, "Nesting of the Gray Flycatcher," *Auk*, vol. 58, pp. 28–37, 1941.

WESTERN FLYCATCHER (*Empidonax difficilis*)

Appearance: Small (5½–6 in.); brownish olive above and pale yellowish below, with greenish smoke-gray at side of breast and down flank. It has a whitish eye-ring and 2 whitish wing bars.

Voice: A wheezy *pee-ist*, a 3-syllable song of variable arrangements, as *pseet-trip-seet*, and a low *whit*.

Range and status: Breeds from se. Alaska, s. B.C., w.-c. Mont., n. Wyo., and sw. S.Dak. through the moun-

Shady crevices and rock ledges are the Western Flycatcher's preferred nesting sites.

tains to Baja Calif., Honduras, and w. Tex. Retreats south of Mexican border in winter. Fairly common, but not conspicuous.

Habitat: Damp woodlands, mixed or coniferous; requires shade and water. Deciduous groves and forested canyons also favored.

Seasonal movements: Arrives in U.S. mid-Mar.–mid-May and departs Sept.–mid-Oct.

Biology: Nest: A neat cup of mosses and rootlets lined with fine grasses, shredded bark, hair, and plant down; built in shady place on rock ledge, log, side of cabin, or crotch of small tree. Eggs: 3–5, usually 3–4; white, spotted and blotched with browns and purples chiefly at the larger end. Incubation: 14–15 days. Age at 1st flight unknown. Food: Insects and spiders; less than 1% berries and other vegetable matter.

Suggested reading: J. Davis, G. F. Fisler, and B. S. Davis, "The Breeding Biology of the Western Flycatcher," *Condor,* vol. 65, pp. 337–382, 1963.

BUFF-BREASTED FLYCATCHER (*Empidonax fulvifrons*)

Appearance: Smallest (4½–5 in.) of the *Empidonax* flycatchers. It is brownish olive above and buffy below

The inconspicuous Eastern Wood Pewee often reveals its presence with its haunting whistle.

(richer on breast), with smoke-gray side of breast and flank, white eye-ring, and 2 white wing bars.

Voice: A soft *pit-pit* by female and a somewhat louder, more emphatic *chicky-whew* by the male; also a *quit-quit* or *quit-quit-quirrr* of alarm.

Range and status: Breeds from c. and se. Ariz. and w.-c. N.Mex. south through w. Mexico to El Salvador and Honduras. In winter retires south of Mexican border and to lower altitudes. Rare in U.S.

Habitat: Wooded canyons and montane oak-pine forests.

Seasonal movements: Arrives in U.S. in Apr. and leaves Aug.–mid-Oct.

Biology: Nest: On the branch of a tree, a deep-cupped structure of grasses, vegetable fibers, feathers, and spider webbing disguised with lichens on the outside. Eggs: 3–4, light cream. Incubation period and age at 1st flight unknown. Food: Probably almost entirely insects and spiders.

COUES' FLYCATCHER (*Contopus pertinax*)

Appearance: Larger (7–7¾ in.) than the Eastern Phoebe. All medium gray, slightly darker above, except for white from the mid-belly to the undertail feathers and light gray throat. It has a bushy crest and a rather long, slightly forked tail. The lower bill is yellowish, the rest of the bill and the legs, feet, and eyes are blackish. It has very indistinct light wing bars.

Voice: A querulous whistled *ho-say, ray-ah* or *ho-say, ma-ray-ah,* earning it the nickname José María; also a loud and rather musical *pe-wee-ee* and *pip-pip* notes.

Range and status: Breeds from c. and se. Ariz., sw. N.Mex., and n.-c. Mexico south to n. Nicaragua. Retreats from U.S. in winter; has straggled to Calif. and Tex. Fairly common locally in U.S.

Habitat: Pine and pine-oak woodlands, sycamore groves, and groves of tall trees.

Seasonal movements: Arrives in U.S. Mar.–Apr. and leaves in Sept.

Biology: Nest: Saddled on horizontal tree limb 10–50 ft. high; made of fine grasses, slender weed stems, and dry leaves held together with spider webbing and plant fibers; the deep cup is lined with fine yellow grass stems, and the outside camouflaged with lichens. Eggs: 3–4; very pale cream, sparingly marked with spots and dots mainly about larger end. Incubation period and age at 1st flight unknown. Food: Probably almost entirely insects.

EASTERN WOOD PEWEE (*Contopus virens*)

Appearance: Small (6–6¾ in.); olive above and a grayish straw-yellow below, with a wash of olive on the side of the breast and down the flank. There are 2 distinct white wing bars. The legs, feet, upper bill, and eyes are blackish, and the lower bill is straw-yellow, becoming blackish at the tip.

Voice: A hauntingly whistled *pee-a-wee* repeated over and over, usually alternating with a *pee-wee* in remarkable, even cadence. Also a squeaky *wee-chuttle-chuttle*, *wee-chuttle* and a soft, low *shee* call note.

Range and status: Breeds from s. Man., w. and c. Ont., s. Que., n. Maine, c. N.B., P.E.I., and N.S. south along the w. edge of the Great Plains to c. and se. Tex., the Gulf Coast, and c. Fla. Winters from Costa Rica to Peru, Ecuador, Colombia, and Venezuela; in migration, casually to Colo. and Cuba. Has straggled to Lab. and Bermuda. Common.

Habitat: Forests, riparian woodlands, and groves; most abundant in mature deciduous forests.

Seasonal movements: Arrives at breeding grounds Apr.–May and departs Sept.–Oct., sometimes lingering until Nov.

Biology: Nest: A neat, shallow, thick-walled cup made of grasses, weed stems, plant fibers, and hair, lined with finer materials of same sort, and camouflaged with lichens; built on a horizontal lichen-covered tree limb 15–50 ft. above the ground. Eggs: 2–4, usually 3; creamy white, irregularly wreathed about larger end with blotches and spots of browns. Incubation: 13 days. Age at 1st flight: 15–18 days. Food: Insects and spiders; less than 1% berries and seeds.

Suggested reading: W. Craig, *The Song of the Wood Pewee*, N.Y.S. Mus. Bull. 334, 186 pp., 1943.

WESTERN WOOD PEWEE (*Contopus sordidulus*)

Appearance: About the same size (6–6½ in.) as the Eastern Wood Pewee. Olive above and whitish below, with light olive crossing the breast and extending down the flank. There are 2 whitish wing bars. The bill, legs, feet, and eyes are blackish; the lower bill is somewhat yellowish at the base.

Voice: A *tswee-tee-teet,* shorter and harsher than that of the Eastern, repeated twice and followed by a down-slurring *bzew.* Also a gurgling *ahee-up, chee-up,* a *pip-pip-pip-pip-pee-a,* and a *pit-pit-pit* call in flight.

Range and status: Breeds from e.-c. Alaska, s. Yuk., s. Mack., e.-c. Sask., and c. Man. south through the mountains to Guatemala, possibly to Costa Rica or Colombia. Winters from c. Panama to Peru, Bolivia, and Venezuela. Common.

Habitat: A variety of forests, including pine-oak and open coniferous woodlands and riparian groves.

Seasonal movements: Arrives Apr.–May and departs Sept.–mid-Oct.

Biology: Nest: A shallow lichen-covered cup fashioned of grasses, shredded bark, fine weed stems, and plant fibers, usually lined with fine yellow grass; built 15–75 ft. above the ground on horizontal tree limb, occa-

sionally in crotch. Eggs: 2–4, usually 3; creamy white, wreathed about larger end with spots and blotches of browns. Incubation: 12(?) days. Age at 1st flight unknown. Food: Insects and some spiders; less than 1% seeds and berries.

OLIVE-SIDED FLYCATCHER (*Nuttallornis borealis*)

Appearance: Larger (7–8 in.) than the Wood Pewees, but similarly colored. Olive above, more blackish brown on wing and tail, and white below with olive sides from the shoulder to the flanks. The feathers near the back just under the wing are white and sometimes show as a white patch when the bird is perching. The lower bill is straw-yellow, and the upper bill, legs, feet, and eyes are blackish.

Voice: A series of short, emphatic, high-pitched *pip-pip-pip*'s used as alarm or warning and a "bibulous" *hic-three-beers* trailing off on the last note from the higher middle note.

Range and status: Breeds from n. Alaska, Yuk., s. Mack., ne. Alta., n. Sask., n.-c. Man., n. Ont., c. Que., and c. Nfld. south to n. Baja Calif., c. Nev., c. Ariz., n. N.Mex., c. Sask., s. Man., ne. N.Dak., c. Minn., n. Wis., n. Mich., s. Ont., ne. Ohio, through the Appalachians to

The Western Wood Pewee is nearly identical to its eastern counterpart.

e. Tenn. and w. N.C. and Mass. Winters from Colombia and n. Venezuela to Peru and n. Brazil. Migrates through Mexico and C. America; has straggled to Greenland and Bermuda. Locally common, but generally rather rare.

Habitat: Coniferous forests, lumbering burns; mixed forests and others in migration; eucalyptus groves in Calif.

Seasonal movements: Arrives late Mar.–May and departs Aug.–mid-Oct.

Biology: Nest: 15–50 ft. above the ground on horizontal tree limb; made of grasses, mosses, rootlets, and pine needles, with a base of interlaced twigs; the lining is of the same but finer materials. Eggs: 3–4, usually 3; creamy white, buffy, or pinkish, lightly spotted and blotched with browns and grays, mainly in a loose wreath around the larger end. Incubation: 14(?) days. Age at 1st flight: 23 days. Food: Insects of the type taken on the wing; very few other insects and spiders and almost no vegetable matter.

Suggested reading: A. C. Bent, *Life Histories of North American Flycatchers, Larks, Swallows, and Their Allies*, Dover, N.Y. (reprint of U.S. Nat. Mus. Bull. 179, 1942), 1963, pp. 288–302.

VERMILION FLYCATCHER (*Pyrocephalus rubinus*)

Appearance: Small (5½–6½ in.). The male's nape, back, rump, wing, tail, and a line from the bill through the eye to the nape are sooty black, and the rest of the plumage is scarlet. The bill, legs, and feet are blackish. The female is buffy brown above, darker (almost black) on wing and tail, and white below streaked with buffy brown. She is tinged with pinkish on the flank, lower belly, and undertail feathers. The immature birds resemble the female.

Voice: A *ching-tink-a-le-tink* flight song during courtship, and a phoebelike *peet-peet* or *peet-ter-weet*.

Range and status: Breeds from se. Calif., s. Nev., sw. Utah, c. Ariz., sw. N.Mex., and w. and c. Tex. south to Guatemala and Honduras and in S. America from the Galápagos Is., Colombia, and Venezuela to c. Chile and s. Argentina. Bulk of population winters south of Mexican border, but some wander north in Tex. and east to w. Fla. Has straggled to Colo., Ont., and Nebr. Locally common.

Habitat: Willow and cottonwood groves, mesquite areas; in arid and semiarid regions, near water.

Seasonal movements: Starts arriving at breeding areas in Mar. and departs Sept.–Oct.

Biology: Nest: A shallow platform of sticks and twigs lined with a few grasses, 8–40 ft. above the ground in branches of mesquite or other trees. Eggs: 2–4, usually 3; white or creamy, heavily marked with spots and blotches of browns and grays. Incubation: 12(?) days. Age at 1st flight: 14–16 days. Food: Probably entirely insects.

Suggested reading: A. C. Bent, *Life Histories of North American Flycatchers, Larks, Swallows, and Their Allies*, Dover, N.Y. (reprint of U.S. Nat. Mus. Bull. 179, 1942), 1963, pp. 302–308.

BEARDLESS FLYCATCHER (*Camptostoma imberbe*)

Appearance: Small (4½ in.). Brownish olive above and white below, with smoke-gray throat and breast and 2 indistinct wing bars of smoke-gray. The upper bill is blackish, the lower bill straw-yellow, and the legs and feet black.

Voice: Call notes described as *pier-pier-pier-pier*, starting high and falling a full note at each call, and as soft *ee-ee-ee-ee-ee* notes; also a *peeeee-yuk* call and a *yoop-yoop-yoope-deedledeee*.

Range and status: Breeds from s.-c. and se. Ariz. and s. Tex. south to nw. Costa Rica. Winters from se. Ariz. and n.-c. and ne. Mexico south. Probably resident many years throughout range. Rather rare.

Habitat: Scrubby forests, thickets near streams, mesquite areas, and semiarid brush areas.

Seasonal movements: Not enough data to set a schedule.

Biology: Often acts like vireos, warblers, or kinglets. Nest: A roughly globular mass of plant fiber and fur, with entrance on side sloping upward to interior; built at almost any height in tree or shrub. Eggs: 2–3; white, sparsely peppered with browns, mainly about larger end. Incubation period and age at 1st flight unknown. Food: Insects gleaned from foliage in the manner of warblers and vireos; no vegetable matter found in the few stomachs examined.

THE LARKS (ALAUDIDAE)

Larks are small (4½–9 in.) terrestrial birds distantly related to the swallows, thrushes, and blackbirds. There are 76 species, some of which are found in every part of the world except for the polar regions, New Zealand, Oceania, and S. America; 1 species reaches extreme nw. S. America. Only 1 species occurs naturally in America; 2 have been introduced in Hawaii, and 1 in N. America. Our single native species is partially migratory. Most species are found in open, grassy, and otherwise treeless regions. Most are primarily brown, streaked with darker browns, with lighter browns below; many species have yellow, black, and/or white in the plumage, and several are crested or bear tiny plumes on the head. The wings are comparatively long and generally pointed, and tails vary from short to medium. The bill may be short and stout or fairly long and curved. The legs range from short to long. The claw of the hind toe is as long as or longer than the toe, usually straight and very sharp. In most species the sexes are alike. Food is commonly sought on the ground. Many species are noted singers; technically, they are considered songbirds. Some species sing pleasing, elaborate songs during aerial courtship performances. Larks are often gregarious, never colonial. Nests, mainly of grasses, are built on the ground; some are roofed. The 2–6 whitish eggs, with spots and peppering of browns, are incubated by the female alone in most species. The hatchlings are covered with down above, sometimes also below, and are tended by both parents. Incubation periods are usually less than 14 days; as is the case with the majority of ground-nesting flying birds, the young are fledged in the rather short period of less than 14 days. They eat seeds, insects, and small invertebrates.

MONGOLIAN LARK (*Melanocorypha mongolica*)

Small (7¾–8¼ in.); brown above, streaked with black, and white below, with chestnut crown and neck. There is a white streak above the eye and a buffy yellow bar on the nape. Native from se. Siberia to n. China; introduced in Hawaii and established on Kauai I.

SKYLARK (*Alauda arvensis*)

Appearance: Between Robin and House Sparrow in size (7–7½ in.). The Skylark is brown above, streaked with black and darker brown; the tail has 2 white outer tail feathers on each side. The breast and flanks are light buffy brown, streaked and spotted with dark brown, and the rest of the underparts are white. The bill, legs, and feet are yellowish, and the eyes dark brown.

Voice: The song, which has been the subject of much poetry, is delivered while the bird is poised on pulsing wings well above the ground; it is a long, beautiful song replete with trills and cadenzas at a rather high pitch. Its note outside the courtship season is a loud, clear, bubbly *chir-r-r-up.*

Range and status: Native of Europe, n. and c. Asia, and n. Africa. Introduced and established in Hawaii and on Vancouver I., B.C., where it is resident; not successful on Long I., N.Y., where it was last recorded in 1913. Locally common.

The Old World Skylark has become established in Hawaii and on Vancouver Island.

Habitat: Open fields and cultivated land.

Seasonal movements: None in America.

Biology: Nest: A grass-lined hollow on ground in fields. Eggs: 3–4; whitish ground color nearly hidden by spots of brown and gray. Incubation: 11–12 days; 13–14 in incubator. Age at 1st flight: 9–10 days. Food: Weed seeds and grain; almost 50% insects and small invertebrates.

Suggested reading: G. D. Sprot, "Notes on the Introduced Skylark in the Victoria District of Vancouver Island," *Condor*, vol. 39, pp. 24–30, 1937.

The Horned Lark's head plumes are so small that they are seldom conspicuous.

HORNED LARK (*Eremophila alpestris*)

Appearance: Smaller (7–8 in.) than the Robin; generally cinnamon above and whitish below, with light cinnamon flanks, a yellow face, forehead, and throat, and a black half-moon below the throat. A thin streak of black curves down from the eye, and a narrow black line starts at the forehead, running above the eye and terminating in a small tuft of feathers, which look like small horns, at the back quarter of the head. The outer feathers of the tail are white, the legs and feet are black, and the bill is black above and straw-yellow below. Some birds are yellowish below, but the intensity and extent of this coloring vary from 1 part of the range to another. The immature birds lack the "horns" and are generally whitish below, and the black feathers of the head and breast show only as shadows if at all.

Voice: Courtship flight song, on soaring wings several hundred feet in air, starts with a few introductory high notes, then a series of squeals and trills "like distant sleigh bells" (G. B. Pickwell) and creaking gates. Also a shrill *tsee* or *tsee-de-ree* and a sharp, double-tongued *ti-sick*.

Range and status: Breeds in tundra of n. Eurasia, in mountains, tablelands, and stony deserts of nw. Africa, se. Europe, and sw. and c. Asia; in N. America from n. Alaska and the s. Canadian Arctic Archipelago (except for the Pacific Coast from se. Alaska to sw. B.C.) south to Baja Calif., s. Mexico, s. Tex., sw. La., n. Miss., n. Ga., and N.C.; also in the Bogotá Savanna of Colombia. Retreats from more northerly parts of range and from higher elevations; in America, from s. Canada and Nfld. southward (rarely to Fla.). Rare in Europe, where it travels in small bands; in America it is common and gathers in very large flocks. There are 40 geographical varieties or subspecies in the world, 21 occurring in the Americas.

Habitat: Tundra, all kinds of grasslands, meadows, prairies, and stony deserts.

Seasonal movements: Follows the heels of retreating winter so closely that schedules are difficult to arrive at; nesting often starts before snow is completely off the ground.

Biology: Nest: A shallow cup of fine grasses, sometimes lined with feathers, in hollow in ground. Eggs: 3–5, commonly 4; pale gray, blotched and speckled with pale browns. Incubation: 11–14 days. Age at 1st flight: 10–12 days; commonly 2 broods each year. Food: In summer mainly insects and small invertebrates; in winter mainly grass seeds and weed seeds.

Suggested reading: G. B. Pickwell, "The Prairie Horned Lark," *Trans. Acad. Sci. St. Louis*, vol. 27, 160 pp., 1931.

Even at rest, the great length of the Violet-green Swallow's wings is obvious.

THE SWALLOWS (HIRUNDINIDAE)

Small (3½–9 in.), svelte land birds, swallows are the most completely aerial of the perching birds. Although dissimilar from them externally, they are probably most closely related anatomically to the larks, thrushes, and weaver birds. There are 79 species distributed throughout the world except for the polar regions and some oceanic islands; 11 species have been listed for America, and 1 other, the House Martin of Europe, has been recorded in Greenland. They are usually a common and prominent part of the avifauna; most species are migratory. They range over a great variety of habitats. Their feathering is commonly black, browns, blue, dark greens, and white; some species are streaked, some have metallic sheens, and some have chestnut or brownish red coloring. Sexes are alike, or nearly so, in most species. The wings are long and pointed; the tail may be long or moderately long and deeply forked or square-tipped. The legs are short, and the feet rather weak. The bill is short and much flattened, with a very wide gape. Flight is swift and strong; most food is captured in the air. These birds spend almost as much time on the wing as the swifts, but often perch on trees, wires, ledges, and buildings—the swifts never perch, but cling to the sides of rough, vertical surfaces. Some swallows sing melodic songs or pleasant notes; most species make twittering or high-pitched squeaks. Most swallows are colonial nesters or at least nest in loose groups; they usually congregate in large flocks when not nesting. In most species, courtship is almost entirely aerial pursuit involving graceful maneuvers. Nests are made in hollows of trees, in cavities in rocks, or in burrows dug in banks or level ground or are made of mud plastered against rough vertical surfaces or on ledges. The 3–7 white eggs are peppered or spotted in some species. In many species incubation is by the female alone; in others, both parents participate. The hatchlings are naked but for a little down above and are cared for by male and female together. Insects captured in midair form the main food item; many species supplement this diet with a few berries, and some species subsist over fairly long periods on meals of berries.

BAHAMA SWALLOW (*Callichelidon cyaneoviridis*)

Small (6 in.); metallic green and blue-green above and white below, with blackish wings and moderately forked tail. Resident in the Bahama Is.; has been recorded twice in Fla.

VIOLET-GREEN SWALLOW (*Tachycineta thalassina*)

Appearance: Small (5–5½ in.); metallic bronze-green to violet-green above and white below, with the white extending to behind the eye and onto the sides of the rump. The tail is slightly forked.

301

Like all its kind, the Tree Swallow is an invaluable destroyer of insect pests.

Voice: In the predawn dark during courtship flights, 2–3 notes, rapidly repeated in a high whispery tone, as *tsip-tseet-tsip;* regular call is a rapid twitter.

Range and status: Breeds from Alaska, sw. Yuk., B.C., sw. Alta., c. Mont., and sw. S.Dak. south to s. Baja Calif., nw. and c. Mexico, and w. Tex. Winters from c. coastal and s. Calif. and nw. and n.-c. Mexico south to El Salvador and Honduras. Has straggled to Ill. Common to abundant.

Habitat: Open forests of all types of terrain and urban areas in breeding season; at other seasons over a great variety of habitats.

Seasonal movements: Arrival in spring is not on a regular schedule; arrives at breeding places late Feb.–early May and departs Aug.–Oct.

Biology: Nest: A mass of weed stems and grasses lined with feathers, built in deserted woodpecker holes, in natural cavities in trees or cliffs, on ledges in buildings, or in birdhouses. Eggs: 4–6, usually 4–5; white. Incubation: 13–14 days. Age at 1st flight: Less than 23 days. Only 1 brood each year as a rule. Food: Insects caught on the wing; no vegetable matter reported.

Suggested reading: C. R. B. Combellack, "A Nesting of Violet-green Swallows," *Auk,* vol. 71, pp. 435–442, 1954.

TREE SWALLOW (*Iridoprocne bicolor*)

Appearance: Small (5–6¼ in.); metallic blue-black or green-black above and pure white below, with slightly forked tail. Immature birds are dusky brown above, with smoke-gray at the sides of the breast on the otherwise pure white undersides.

Voice: A pleasing, sibilant *silip* repeated rapidly, sometimes prolonged into a chatter or trill, and a loud, shrill whistle of alarm.

Range and status: Breeds from c. Alaska, sw. Yuk., w.-c. and s. Mack., n. Sask., n. Man., n. Ont., n. Que., s. Lab., and Nfld. south to s. Calif., Nev., Idaho, Utah, Colo., se. Wyo., s. N.Dak., e. Nebr., s.-c. Mo., nw. Tenn., s. Ill., c. Ind., c. Ohio, n. W.Va., Va., c. Md., ne. Pa., se. N.Y., n. Conn., Mass., and R.I.; casually farther south. Winters from s. Calif., sw. Ariz., n. Mexico, the Gulf Coast, and se. Va. (casually to e. Mass. and se. N.Y.) south to s. Baja Calif., Guatemala, Honduras, and Cuba. Accidental in Greenland, England, and Colombia. Common to abundant.

Habitat: Open areas near water, preferably with tall dead tree stubs.

Seasonal movements: Arrives late Feb.–Apr. and departs late Aug.–early Nov.; in fall Tree Swallows gather in flocks of hundreds and thousands before starting south.

Biology: Nest: Grasses and straws lined with feathers, with a marked preference for white chicken feathers, in a natural tree cavity, deserted woodpecker

The tunnel leading to the Bank Swallow's nest may be more than 6 feet long.

hole, nest box, rural mailbox, or ledge in building. Eggs: 4–6, white. Incubation: 13–16 days. Age at 1st flight: 16–24 days; the 8-day spread said to be the result of abundance or lack of food. Food: 80% insects caught on the wing; bayberries consumed in winter months make up most of vegetable food consumed; some seeds and other berries are eaten.

Suggested reading: L. B. Chapman, "Studies of a Tree Swallow Colony," *Bird-banding*, vol. 6, pp. 45–57, 1935; vol. 10, pp. 61–72, 1939; and vol. 26, pp. 45–70, 1955.

BANK SWALLOW (*Riparia riparia*)

Appearance: Smaller (4½–5½ in.) than the Tree Swallow; sepia above and white below, with a band of dull sepia across the breast. The tail is slightly forked. Immature birds are duller-colored, with undersides a very pale brownish gray.

Voice: A much-repeated, gentle, and subdued *speedz-sweet, speedz-sweet* and a trilling *tri-tri-tri.*

Range and status: Breeds from the tree limits of Eurasia and N. America (s. Que., s. Lab., and sw. Nfld. in e. N. America) south to s. Europe, ne. Africa, Mesopotamia, n. India, c. and se. China, and n. Japan; east of the Coast Ranges except in Calif. to s. Calif., w. Nev., n. Utah, Colo., Okla., Tex., Ark., n. Ala., c. W.Va., and e. Va.; casually to S.C. Winters in e. and s. Africa, s. Asia, and S. America. Common.

Habitat: A wide variety of open areas, mainly grasslands, usually near fresh water and not at high altitudes; abundance governed by availability of proper nesting sites.

Seasonal movements: Reaches breeding areas Apr.–mid-May and departs mid-Aug.–mid-Oct.

Biology: Nest: Of grasses at the end of a burrow dug 9 in. to 6 ft. deep in steep banks of sand, clay, or loam; in rather dense colonies where possible. Eggs: 4–5, white. Incubation: 14–16 days, by both sexes. Age at 1st flight: 20–30 days. Only 1 brood each year. Food: Almost entirely insects caught during flight.

Suggested reading: D. Stoner, "Studies on the Bank Swallow," *Roosevelt Wildlife Ann.*, vol. 9, pp. 122–233, 1936. A. J. Peterson, "The Breeding Cycle in the Bank Swallow," *Wils. Bull.*, vol. 67, pp. 235–286, 1955.

ROUGH-WINGED SWALLOW (*Stelgidopteryx ruficollis*)

Appearance: About the size (5–5¾ in.) of the Bank Swallow. Buffy brown above and white below, with smoke-gray throat and upper breast. Tail is slightly forked.

Voice: Rather silent. A buzzy *quiz-z-z-zeep, quiz-z-z-zeep* near nest and a low, faint twittering during flight.

Range and status: Breeds from B.C., s. Alta., sw.

Rough-winged Swallow

Sask., se. Man., w. and s. Ont., sw. Que., c. Vt., and N.H. south to Peru, Bolivia, Paraguay, and Argentina. Winters from s. U.S. south. Rather rare compared with other swallows.

Habitat: A variety of open areas, including more open woodlands near fresh water; rarely seasides.

Seasonal movements: Arrives at breeding areas late Feb.–Apr. and departs Sept.–Oct.

Biology: Nest: A solitary burrow 9 in. to 6 ft. deep in banks of sand, clay, or gravel, usually dug by the birds themselves; terminal chamber is lined with chips of bark and grasses. Sometimes made in cavities of trees or on ledges of rock or wood or in drain tiles in bank. Eggs: 4–8, usually 6–7; white. Incubation: 12(?)–16 days. Age at 1st flight: 20–30 days. Food: Insects and spiders; mainly captured in air.

Suggested reading: W. A. Lunk, *The Rough-winged Swallow*, Publ. Nuttall Ornith. Club, no. 4, 155 pp., 1962.

BARN SWALLOW (*Hirundo rustica*)

Appearance: Small (5¾–7¾ in.); metallic blue-black above and light flesh color below, with light brownish red throat and forehead and deeply forked tail. The immature birds are duller-colored, and there is considerable variation in the intensity of the brownish red and flesh colors below.

Voice: A pleasant quick metallic *kvik-kvik-vit-vit* clicking and a harsh *keet* of alarm or annoyance near nest.

Range and status: Breeds from n.-c. Alaska, s. Yuk., s. Mack., s. Ont., s. Que., and Nfld. south to n. Baja Calif., s.-c. Mexico, w. Tex., Okla., n. Ark., n. Ala., nw. N.C., c. Va., and locally to se. Ga.; also from n. Europe and n.-c. Asia south to n. Africa, Mesopotamia, s. Iran, n. India, s. China, Formosa, and Japan. Winters from w. Panama to s. America, throughout Africa, and from s. Asia and the Philippines to Ceylon, Indonesia, New Guinea, and Micronesia. Common to abundant.

Habitat: More open forests of all types, farmlands, suburban areas, and in mountain areas to tree line.

Seasonal movements: Reaches breeding range mid-Feb.–mid-May and departs late Aug.–Oct.; often migrates in large flocks, especially in fall.

Biology: Nest: A sturdy cup constructed of mud or clay pellets and lined with grasses and feathers; built on ledges of wood, rock, or other natural material in caves, along cliffs, or in farm buildings. In U.S. and Canada barns furnish the most commonly used nesting sites. Eggs: 4–7, usually 4–5; white, spotted and peppered with browns. Incubation: About 15 days, by both sexes. Age at 1st flight: 18–23 days. There are 2 broods each year in warmer parts of range. Food: Insects, predominantly those caught in air.

Suggested reading: E. M. Davis, "Observations on Nesting Barn Swallows," *Bird-banding*, vol. 8, pp. 66–73, 1937.

CLIFF SWALLOW (*Petrochelidon pyrrhonota*)

Appearance: Of Tree Swallow size (5–6 in.). Wings, back, and square-tipped tail are sooty black, rump and forehead buffy yellow, cap metallic blue-black, and throat and face brownish red. The undersides are light smoke-gray, with a line of this separating the nape and back. Immature birds are much duller-colored, with buffy gray replacing much of the brownish red.

Voice: A low, rapid twittering or chatter, a throaty *chur-rr*, and a loud, high *keer* of alarm. Notes are not so pleasant as those of the Barn Swallow.

Range and status: Breeds from c. Alaska, c. Yuk., w. and c. Mack., Sask., s. Man., c. Ont., s. Que., P.E.I., and N.S. south to c. Mexico, w.-c. Tex., c. Mo., c. Tenn., n. Ala., w. N.C., Va., and Del. Winters from c. Brazil to c. Chile and c. Argentina. Migrates through Mexico and C. America. Locally common.

Habitat: Open country and more open forests and agricultural lands with cliffs, canyons, and fresh water.

Seasonal movements: This is the swallow reputed to arrive each spring on Mar. 19 at San Juan Capistrano Mission in Calif.; it is not always on schedule. Arrives at breeding places Mar.–mid-May and departs mid-Aug.–early Oct.

Biology: Nest: Gourd-shaped structures of mud and clay with entrances on open side, cemented to sides of farm building under eaves or to sides of cliffs in sheltered places or to the sides of big trees; the chambers are sparsely lined with grasses and feathers. Hundreds of

*The sleek Barn Swallow is characterized by a
deeply forked tail.*

nests may occupy 1 side of a barn. Eggs: 3–6, usually
4–5; white or creamy, peppered and spotted with
browns, grays, and purples. Incubation: 16 days. Age at
1st flight: 23 days. Food: Insects and spiders, mainly
taken in air; occasionally a few berries.

Suggested reading: J. T. Emlen, Jr., "Social Behavior in Nesting Cliff Swallows," *Condor,* vol. 54, pp.
177–199, 1952.

CAVE SWALLOW (*Petrochelidon fulva*)

Same size (5–6 in.) as the Cliff Swallow, differing from
it in having a brownish red forehead and a buffy yellow
throat. Nests in caves from se. N.Mex., s.-c. Tex., and the
Greater Antilles south through c. and e. Mexico to Costa
Rica, Yucatan, and the Isle of Pines. Accidental in Fla.

PURPLE MARTIN (*Progne subis*)

Appearance: The largest (7¼–8½ in.) swallow.
Glossy, purplish black all over, with a fairly long, moderately forked tail. The female is duller, less purplish
black above and light gray below, with a light gray forehead. The immature birds resemble the female.

Voice: A loud, much-repeated, somewhat musical
pew-pew-pew, a series of guttural trills, a low-toned
kroop followed by several throaty notes then a stuttering
trill, and a loud *kerp* of alarm. A house colony produces a
constant, pleasing refrain.

Range and status: West of the Cascade and Sierra

Nevada Ranges from s. B.C. and w. Wash. to Baja Calif.
and nw. Mexico; east of the Rockies from ne. B.C., c.
Alta., c. Sask., s. Man., w. Ont., n. Minn., n. Wis., s.
Ont., s. Que., N.B., and c. N.S. south to the Gulf Coast
and s. Fla. Winters from Venezuela, Guyana, and Surinam to s. Brazil. Has straggled to Alaska, Bermuda, and
Ireland. Migrates through the W. Indies, Mexico, and C.
America. Locally common; in some areas has been driven
out by starlings and other birds, which usurp its nesting
holes.

Habitat: Open areas, more open woodlands, lumber
burns, saguaro deserts, farmlands; preferably near freshwater lake or pond.

Seasonal movements: Arrives in U.S. and Canada
late Jan.–Apr. and departs Sept.–mid-Oct.; disperses
over wide area during migration.

Biology: Nest: Formerly and now occasionally in
natural cavities of caves and trees. To attract martins to
their villages, Indians set up poles on which hung clus-
ters of hollowed gourds with holes of proper size in the
sides. Many rural and suburban communities of the U.S.
and Canada now have their multiple-chambered martin
houses set on poles in the village squares or near the
village pond. There the birds build their nests of grasses,
leaves, twigs, feathers, papers, string, and debris. Green
leaves are commonly placed in the nest for unknown
reasons. Eggs: 3–8, usually 4–5; white. Incubation: 15–
16 days. Age at 1st flight: 24–28 days; said to be 6
weeks by 1 author. Despite conflicting information in
frequent published articles, only 1 brood is raised each
year. Food: Insects, mainly those caught on the wing.
Members of the fly family make up 16% of diet.

Suggested reading: S. M. Richmond, "The Attrac-
tion of Purple Martins to an Urban Location in Western
Oregon," *Condor,* vol. 55, pp. 225–249, 1953. R. W.
Allen and M. M. Nice, "A Study of the Breeding Biology
of the Purple Martin," *Amer. Midland Naturalist,* vol. 47,
pp. 606–665, 1952.

CUBAN MARTIN (*Progne cryptoleuca*)

Same size (7½ in.) and appearance as Purple Martin,
but a broad, practically concealed band of white crosses
the lower abdomen. It breeds in Cuba and the Isle of
Pines and in winter has been taken in Jamaica, Guatemala, and British Honduras. It has straggled to s. Fla.

GRAY-BREASTED MARTIN (*Progne chalybea*)

Same size (7 in.) as Purple Martin and very much like
the female of that species except that the crown, back,
rump, and tail are glossy blue-black, the belly is white,
and the forehead is a darker gray. It is resident from c.
Mexico south through C. America to Peru, Bolivia, and c.
Argentina; wanders north in summer occasionally to
southernmost Tex.

CROWS, JAYS, AND MAGPIES (CORVIDAE)

These small- to medium-sized (7–27½ in.) songbirds are most closely related anatomically to the birds-of-paradise, bowerbirds, titmice and chickadees, and Old World orioles. There are 103 species, some of which are found in every part of the world except polar regions and some oceanic islands; 17 have been recorded from America, and 2, the Rook and Hooded Crow of Eurasia, have reached Greenland. They are usually conspicuous and common in the avifauna where they occur; most species are sedentary. Crows are rather large and predominantly black, jays are usually brightly colored, and magpies have prominent long tails. They occupy almost all kinds of habitats. They are reputed to be the most intelligent of birds, and for that reason many consider them the highest of the families. Plumage commonly occurs in black, white, grays, blues, purples, greens, yellows, and browns. The strong wings vary in shape from group to group, as does the tail. The bills are sturdy, with the nostrils hidden by bristlelike feathers rising from the forehead. The legs are fairly long and thick, the feet usually big and strong. Most species are gregarious, and some are colonial. Flight is strong, usually a steady flapping with comparatively little soaring. Very few species have anything approaching a melodious song; most have rather harsh or monotonous calls. Courtship is probably simple; it certainly is not conspicuous. Nests are usually built of sticks, twigs, grasses, etc., in trees or bushes; only a few are covered, and some are built on ledges, on the ground, or in cavities in trees. The 3–10 eggs are commonly white or light green, spotted and otherwise marked with browns, greens, and grays. Incubation, in most species by the female only, ranges from 15–21 days, and the young fledge in about 3 weeks. The hatchlings are naked or only very sparsely downed and are fed and otherwise cared for by both parents. The family may be described only as omnivorous.

The Gray Jay is a common resident of northern and western coniferous forests.

GRAY JAY (Canada Jay) (*Perisoreus canadensis*)

Appearance: Slightly larger (10–13 in.) than the Robin. The back, rump, wing, and tail are medium gray; nape and line from eye are blackish gray; forehead, most of crown, face, and undersides are pale gray. The bill, legs, and feet are blackish; eyes are dark. Young are medium to dark gray above and below, with blackish gray head and wing and light gray "whiskers" from the base of the bill down the side of the throat.

Voice: A great variety of shrill, penetrating notes, including a "hawk-like whistle" (Wm. Brewster), a short series of mellow whistles of the kind produced by blowing across the neck of a small bottle, and longer, loud *cla-cla-cla-cla-cla* notes as well as a querulous *quee-ah-wah*.

Range and status: Resident from n.-c. Alaska, n. Yuk., w. Mack., sw. Keewatin, n. Man., n. Ont., n. Que., n. Lab., and Nfld. south to n. Calif., c. Ariz., sw. Colo., n. N.Mex., S.Dak., n. Minn., n. Wis., n. Mich., s.-c. Ont., ne. N.Y., and n. New England. In winter moves down mountains to lower altitudes and casually south to Nebr., Pa., and Mass. Common.

Habitat: Coniferous woodlands; attracted to camps of hunters and trappers to the extent of earning such names as whisky-jack, camp-robber, meatbird, lumberjack, etc.

Near its nest, the noisy Blue Jay usually becomes silent and unobtrusive.

Seasonal movements: Mainly altitudinal in severe winters.

Biology: Nest: Made of strips of bark, sticks, twigs, and mosses lined with pine needles and feathers; built 4–30 ft., commonly 6–8 ft., up on branch of tree. Nesting starts in late winter, Feb.–Mar. Eggs: 2–5, usually 3–4; pale gray to pale greenish, evenly spotted and peppered with dark grayish green. Incubation: 16–18 days, by female alone. Age at 1st flight: About 15 days. Food: Reputed to eat almost anything; insects, small vertebrates, birds' eggs and young, garbage, seeds, fruit, and dead animals.

Suggested reading: L. deK. Lawrence, "Five Days with a Pair of Nesting Canada Jays," *Canadian Field Naturalist,* vol. 61, pp. 1–12, 1947.

BLUE JAY (*Cyanocitta cristata*)

Appearance: Slightly larger (11–12½ in.) than the Robin. The prominent crest, nape, back, and rump are a light purplish blue, and the tail and wing are a light cobalt, with wavy bars of black. The round-tipped tail has white-tipped outer feathers, and the wing has a narrow white bar near the shoulder and small white patches near the tip. Face and undersides are pale gray to whitish, with a small black patch before the eye and a prominent, gracefully curving necklace of black outlining

the throat and face. The bill, legs, feet, and eyes are blackish.

Voice: The loud, familiar *jay-jay* or *jeer-jeer,* the less familiar anvil call *tull-ul* of bell-like quality, and the "pulley call" *whee-oodle-oodle* are but the more common calls of a large repertoire; it also has a spring-song olio of low whistles, pleasant notes, and squeals as well as other calls, possibly imitations of songs and notes of other species.

Range and status: Resident from c. Alta., c. Sask., s. Man., c. Ont., s. Que., and Nfld. south, east of the Rockies, to se. Tex., the Gulf Coast, and s. Fla. Accidental in Bermuda. Common to abundant.

Habitat: Forests, groves, suburbs, and farmlands.

Seasonal movements: Particularly in fall they move about in large flocks, sometimes silent and unnoticed; also some retreat from higher altitudes.

Biology: Nest: Made of twigs, barks, mosses, leaves, and grasses, lined with fine rootlets and pine needles; built 5–50 ft. but usually less than 20 ft. high in branches of trees. Eggs: 3–6, usually 4–5; gray-green to buffy or bluish, with scattered spots of dark browns and grays. Incubation: 17–18 days; male shares in incubation in at least some cases. Age at 1st flight: 17–21 days. Food: Omnivorous; will eat any available food, animal or vegetable; holds nuts with feet while cracking the shell with the bill. It robs nests of other birds to a considerable extent, but probably makes up for this somewhat by actively warning all within hearing of the presence of hawks, cats, and other enemies.

Suggested reading: A. R. Laskey, "Blue Jays at Nashville, Tennessee: Movements, Nesting, Age," *Bird-banding,* vol. 29, pp. 211–218, 1958. J. W. Hardy, *Studies in Behavior and Phylogeny of Certain New World Jays,* Univ. Kans. Sci. Bull., vol. 42, no. 2, 149 pp., 1961.

Prominent crest and brilliant coloration identify the handsome Steller's Jay.

STELLER'S JAY (*Cyanocitta stelleri*)

Appearance: Larger (12–13½ in.) than the Blue Jay. The front half of the body, including the very prominent crest, is sooty black. The rest of the body is cobalt, slightly more purplish on wing and tail, which are somewhat ripple-barred with black. There are 2–3 thin, stuttering lines of light blue above the eye in the front half of the crest. The bill, legs, and feet are blackish gray, and the eye is dark. Immature birds are duller, and their blues are more greenish.

Voice: A harsh, staccato, often-repeated *shaack-shaack-shaack,* a mellow *clook-clook-clook,* and a loud scream resembling that of the Red-tailed Hawk (perhaps mimicking).

Range and status: Resident from s. Alaska, w. and s. B.C., sw. Alta., w. Mont., Wyo., sw. S.Dak., and w. Nebr. south to El Salvador, Nicaragua, and sw. Tex. Has straggled to Que. Fairly common.

Habitat: Coniferous and pine-oak woodlands, most common in edges of forests.

Seasonal movements: None.

Biology: Nest: Made of dead leaves and twigs, lined with rootlets; 8–40 ft., usually 20–25 ft., high in branches. Eggs: 3–5, usually 4; pale blue or pale greenish blue, sparsely spotted or peppered with dark browns. Incubation period and age at 1st flight unknown. Food: Insects, small vertebrates, grain, fruit, and other available vegetable and animal matter; this species is also a well-known camp-robber and is very familiar around picnic groves in the West.

Suggested reading: A. C. Bent, *Life Histories of North American Jays, Crows, and Titmice,* Dover, N.Y. (reprint of U.S. Nat. Mus. Bull. 191, 1947), 1964, pp. 56–77.

SCRUB JAY (California Jay) (*Aphelocoma coerulescens*)

Appearance: About Blue Jay size (11–13 in.); highly variable in shades of color and patterns (there are 13 subspecies in U.S. and Canada). Crestless; cobalt above, including wing and tail, with the center of the back a smoke-gray; pale gray below. The throat is streaked with white and bordered at the lower sides with cobalt. A mask of black passes through the eye, flaring out near the back of the head. The bill, legs, and feet are blackish gray, and the eye is dark. Immature birds are grayer.

Voice: A loud, long, rapid *quay-quay-quay-quay,* a harsh *chek-chek-chek* repeated many times, and a rather shrill *ker-week* call. The voice is almost as variable as color and pattern.

Range and status: Resident from sw. Wash., Ore., n. Nev., se. Idaho, n. Utah, sw. Wyo., Colo., and c. Tex. south to s. Baja Calif. and s. Mexico; also in c. Fla. Fairly common.

*Like all its kin, the Mexican Jay samples almost
any kind of food it finds.*

wak, a low, mournful *coot-coot-coot,* and a loud, harsh *weent-weenk-weenk* call note.

Range and status: Resident from c. Ariz., sw. N.Mex., n.c. Mexico, and sw. Tex. south through the mountains to s.-c. Mexico. Has straggled to Kans. Rather common.

Habitat: Open oak forests, mixed oak and pine forests, and scrub forests of semiarid regions.

Seasonal movements: None.

Biology: Nest: A deep saucer of sticks, twigs, rootlets, and fine grasses, 10–25 ft. high in scrub oaks and occasionally in pines. Eggs: 3–7, commonly 4–5; unmarked grayish green. Incubation: 18 days. Age at 1st flight: 24–25 days. Food: Insects, particularly grasshoppers, and acorns; also other fruits and animal matter.

Suggested reading: A. O. Gross, "Nesting of the Mexican Jay in the Santa Rita Mountains, Arizona," *Condor,* vol. 51, pp. 241–249, 1949. J. W. Hardy, *Studies in Behavior and Phylogeny of Certain New World Jays,*" Univ. Kans. Sci. Bull., vol. 42, no. 2, 149 pp., 1961.

GREEN JAY (*Cyanocorax yncas*)

Appearance: Slightly larger (10–12 in.) than the Robin. Back, rump, wing, and tail are green, the outer feathers of the tail are yellow, and the head is a light cobalt-ultramarine. The throat, a streak through the eye, and a broad line joining the rear of this streak to the throat are black. The rest of the undersides are pale

*In the United States, the Green Jay is found
only in southernmost Texas.*

Habitat: Scrubby forests, brushland, riparian forests, and oak-chaparral, piñon, and juniper areas.

Seasonal movements: None.

Biology: Nest: A rather bulky bowl of twigs, grasses, and mosses lined with rootlets; usually in low trees or bushes. Eggs: 2–7, usually 4–6; ground color highly variable: pale greens, blues, and reds, some darker colors, freckled and peppered with dark reds and browns. Incubation: About 16 days; by female with some assistance from male. Age at 1st flight: 18 days. Food: Seeds, berries, nuts, and other fruit make up about 70% of diet; insects, spiders, small invertebrates, small vertebrates, and birds' eggs and nestlings make up remainder.

Suggested reading: A. C. Bent, *Life Histories of North American Jays, Crows, and Titmice,* Dover, N.Y. (reprint of U.S. Nat. Mus. Bull. 191, 1947), 1964, pp. 77–118.

MEXICAN JAY (Arizona Jay) (*Aphelocoma ultramarina*)

Appearance: About the size (11½–13 in.) of the Scrub Jay; generally grayish blue above and light gray below. The back is a somewhat grayer blue, and a patch of blackish gray runs from the bill through the eye and covers the cheek.

Voice: An insistent, much-repeated *wak-wak-wak-*

Like all magpies, the Black-billed Magpie has an exceptionally long tail.

green. The bill, legs, and feet are blackish, and the eyes are dark.

Voice: A series of rapid *cheh-cheh-cheh*'s; also rattles, squeals, and musical whistles.

Range and status: Resident from c. Mexico and southernmost Tex. to n. Honduras and from Colombia and Venezuela to Ecuador, Peru, and Bolivia.

Habitat: More open woods and brushy areas.

Seasonal movements: None.

Biology: Nest: Made of sticks and twigs, lined with rootlets, mosses, grasses, and leaves; 5–30 ft. from ground in bushes or low trees. Eggs: 3–5, commonly 4; whitish, greenish, or yellowish, spotted and blotched with browns, grays, and purples. Incubation and age at 1st flight unknown. Food: Insects, seeds, berries, and other fruit.

SAN BLAS JAY (*Cissilopha san-blasiana*)

Larger (12–13½ in.) than the Robin. Head, neck, and underparts are black; wing, tail, back, and rump are turquoise. Bill, legs, and feet are blackish gray, and eyes are dark. Resident in w. Mexico; has reached Ariz.

BLACK-BILLED MAGPIE (*Pica pica*)

Appearance: Slightly longer (17½–22 in.) than the Common Crow, but a bit more than half of this is tail.

Head, neck, upper breast, a broad streak down the center of the back, and the lower rump are black. The larger flight feathers of the wing are white, edged and broadly tipped with black; the rest of the wing is bluish black, except for a fairly large white patch near the back. The rest of the underparts are white. The central feathers of the green-glossed black tail are longest, and the outermost feathers are shortest. The bill, legs, and feet are blackish gray, the eye dark brown. Immature birds are duller, with gray on the breast and dull brownish on the flank.

Voice: A high, grating *cack-cack*, a shrill cackling *ca-ca-ca-ca-ca*, and a lower, more musical *kay-e-ehk-kay*.

Range and status: Resident from n. Europe, w.-c., c., and se. Siberia (also ne. Siberia including Kamchatka) south to nw. Africa, Turkey, Mesopotamia, n. W. Pakistan, nw. China, n. Burma, Laos, Hainan I., Formosa, and s. S. Korea and in America from s. Alaska, s. Yuk., c. Alta., nw. and e.-c. Sask., and w. Man. south to e.-c. Calif., w. Nev., s. Idaho, c. and ne. Utah, ne. Ariz., n. N.Mex., w. Okla., and w. Kans. It has straggled east of the Mississippi River and farther north and east in Canada. Fairly common.

Habitat: More open forests of foothills, ranchland, sagebrush, riparian woodlands, prairie brush, and brushy coastland.

Seasonal movements: None.

Biology: Nest: Often in small, loose colonies; large masses of sticks, some more than 6 ft. in each direction, with an entrance on 1 side to a chamber with a heavy cup of mud lined with rootlets, grasses, and hair. Nest is often on the ground near a stream, but may be in bushes, preferably thorny, and low trees. Other species often build their nests in or among the debris of a magpie's nest. Eggs: 4–8, commonly 5–7; greenish gray, blotched with browns, which sometimes obscure the ground color. Incubation: 16–18 days. Age at 1st flight unknown; brood just able to fly at 5 weeks. Food: Over 90% of nestling's diet is animal matter, mostly large insects; the adults eat more than 80% animal matter. Vegetable matter such as grain and fruit is definitely 2nd choice. Consumption of nestlings and eggs of other birds is relatively low.

Suggested reading: J. M. Linsdale, "The Natural History of Magpies," *Pacific Coast Avifauna*, no. 25, 234 pp., 1937.

YELLOW-BILLED MAGPIE (*Pica nuttalli*)

Appearance: Smaller (16–18 in.) than the Black-billed Magpie, which it closely resembles otherwise except for its yellow bill and a small patch of bare yellow skin just below and slightly to the rear of the eye.

Voice: A series of 2–6 raucous, rapid *qua*'s, a single querulous *quack*, and a weak *kek*.

Range and status: Resident in the lower foothills

Yellow-billed Magpie

edging the Central Valley of Calif. Locally rather common.

Habitat: Groves along rivers and streams, scattered woodlands of oak, agricultural lands, and parklands, particularly picnic areas.

Seasonal movements: Occasional local movements within range.

Biology: Nest: Sometimes in loose colonies like the Black-billed, but nests closer together and almost always far out on the limb of a tree, almost never in low bushes or bushy trees. The nests are smaller and resemble large clumps of mistletoe, made of sticks, twigs, and leaves with side entrance to an interior chamber lined with mud and grasses. Eggs: 5–8, usually 6–7; grayish yellow or pale grayish browns and grayish greens. Incubation period and age at 1st flight unknown; probably similar to those of the Black-billed. Food: Large insects, carrion, and other animal matter make up about 70% of diet; fruit, acorns, and other seeds are also eaten.

Suggested reading: J. M. Linsdale, "The Natural History of Magpies," *Pacific Coast Avifauna*, no. 25, 234 pp., 1937.

COMMON RAVEN (*Corvus corax*)

Appearance: Largest (21½–27 in.) of the crows; plumage entirely glossy black with purple cast. Throat feathers are stiffer and appear shaggier than those of the Common Crow, the tip of the tail is more wedge-shaped, and the black bill somewhat heavier. The legs and feet are black, and the eyes dark brown. Frequently glides on flattened wings, which is seldom done by the Common Crow.

Voice: A *cr-r-ra-ack* or *cr-r-r-uck* croak, a metallic *croang-croang*, and various buzzing and gargling sounds.

Range and status: Resident from n. Alaska, n. Yuk., Prince Patrick I., Ellesmere I., n. Greenland, Iceland, n. Europe, n. Asia (except ne. Siberia), and Wrangell I. south to s. Baja Calif., the Revilla Gigedo Is., Nicaragua, Minn., Wis., n. Mich., s. Ont., s. Que., Maine, s. N.S., in the Appalachian Mountains to nw. Ga., the Canary Is., the n. third of Africa, s. Arabia, s. Iran, nw. India, Tibet, Nepal, n. China, se. Siberia, and n. Japan. Casual farther south during winters in e. U.S. Distribution local, missing as regular resident in c. Europe; may be locally common.

Habitat: Mountains, plains, deserts, and seacoasts; coniferous, mixed, and deciduous forests; and tropics to arctic regions.

Seasonal movements: Local and sporadic only.

Biology: Nest: Made of sticks and twigs, lined with grasses, mosses, seaweed, and hair; built in trees or on cliff ledges. Eggs: 3–8, usually 4–6; gray, greenish gray, or light green, spotted, splotched, and scrawled with dark, dull browns and greens. Incubation: 20–21 days, by female alone. Age at 1st flight: 5–6 weeks; only 1 brood raised each year. Food: Very varied; all kinds of

The omnivorous Common Raven often includes carrion in its diet.

White-necked Raven

building sometimes as high as 40 ft. above the ground in trees, commonly in scrubby trees and mesquite 9–10 ft. high, and sometimes on crossbars of power poles. The nest is a large, almost spherical mass of sticks, twigs, and debris, with an egg bowl of grasses, rootlets, paper, leaves, and hair. Eggs: 3–8, usually 5–7; pale green, grayish green, and light bluish green, spotted, blotched, and scrawled with browns; some are unmarked. Incubation: About 21 days, by both sexes. Age at 1st flight unknown. Food: An intensive study disclosed 288 different items of food. Insects such as grasshoppers and beetles made up the bulk of the food, and small mammals and carrion were important items, as were small invertebrates such as worms and snails; grain, wild fruit, and several cultivated crops form part of the diet.

Suggested reading: S. E. Aldous, *The White-necked Raven in Relation to Agriculture,* U.S. Fish and Wildlife Service Research Report, no. 5, 56 pp., 1942.

COMMON CROW (*Corvus brachyrhynchos*)

Appearance: Medium-sized (17–21 in.) and entirely black with a purple gloss. Even the bill, legs, and feet are black, and the eye is a blackish brown. The tail is square-tipped.

Voice: Besides the familiar *caw-caw* notes, highly variable in tempo, stress, and length of series, it makes a rather high-pitched, laughing *ha-a-a-a-a* and a throaty, gobbling *cow-cow-cow* as well as cooing notes during courtship.

Range and status: Breeds from n. B.C., sw. Mack., n. Sask., n. Man., n. Ont., c. Que., and s. Nfld. south to n. Baja Calif., c. Ariz., c. N.Mex., Colo., c. Tex., the Gulf Coast, and s. Fla. In winter retreats to s. Canada. Common.

Habitat: Forests, agricultural areas, parklands, groves, and shorelands.

Seasonal movements: Arrives at more northerly breeding areas late Mar.–mid-May and departs Sept.–Oct. In fall and winter the birds often gather in large numbers at favored roosting places from which they forage over the surrounding countryside during the daylight hours. Some of these rookeries have been estimated to contain hundreds of thousands of individuals.

Biology: Behavioral habits and intelligence have enabled the crow to compete successfully with man. Man's attempts to safeguard crops against the crow's depredations has had an annoying way of boomeranging through the increase of other crop pests usually controlled by the crow. Nest: Never in colonies, almost always in trees; a large, neatly woven basket of sticks and twigs with the finer materials in the lining. Eggs: 3–8, usually 4–6; pale bluish green and grayish green, blotched and spotted with browns and grays. Incubation: 18 days, by male and female. Age at 1st flight: 4–5 weeks. Food: Over 650 different items have been re-

animal matter from invertebrates, such as insects, shellfish, and echinoderms, to vertebrates and from fish to mammals, either as carrion or freshly killed by the raven. The small percentage of vegetable matter consumed includes mostly grains, acorns, and other nuts.

Suggested reading: W. B. Tyrrell, "A Study of the Northern Raven," *Auk,* vol. 62, pp. 1–7, 1945.

WHITE-NECKED RAVEN (*Corvus cryptoleucus*)

Appearance: About the size (19–21 in.) of a large Common Crow, but its bill is heavier and its tail more wedge-shaped. The feathers of the neck and breast are white at the bases only so that, unless these feathers are ruffled by the bird or wind, the bird's plumage looks completely sooty black.

Voice: A hoarse *quark-quark,* a little higher-pitched than the call of the Common Raven.

Range and status: Resident from se. Ariz., s. N.Mex., ne. Colo., s.-c. Nebr., and w. Kans. south to the s. edge of the Mexican plateau. Locally common.

Habitat: Arid and semiarid deserts and plains and rangelands.

Seasonal movements: None.

Biology: Nest: The bird is usually a solitary nester,

The adaptable, highly intelligent Common Crow is frequently kept as a pet.

corded in diet: about 30% animal matter, such as insects, spiders, crustaceans, snails, amphibians, reptiles, birds and their eggs, small mammals, and carrion; the 70% vegetable matter includes large amounts of corn and other cultivated crops as well as wild fruits and seeds.

Suggested reading: J. T. Emlen, Jr., "Notes on a Nesting Colony of Western Crows," *Bird-banding,* vol. 13, pp. 143–153, 1942.

NORTHWESTERN CROW (*Corvus caurinus*)

Appearance: A smaller (16–17 in.) replica of the Common Crow, best separated in the field by voice and geographic location.

Voice: The *caw* is lower-pitched and hoarser than that of the Common Crow.

Range and status: Resident along coasts and islands from Kodiak I. to w. Wash.; wanders inland in Wash. and Ore. Common.

Habitat: Marine coasts, brackish-water areas, and occasionally lower river valleys.

Seasonal movements: Starts gathering in large flocks and roosts as early as Aug.; some southward movement of flocks and individuals.

Biology: Nest: Often in small colonies; very similar to that of the Common Crow, but mud and bark used more frequently in lining. Eggs: 4–5; coloration same as eggs of Common Crow. Incubation period and age at 1st flight unknown, but probably same as those of Common Crow. Food: Shellfish, other invertebrates, offal, seashore carrion, insects, and some berries, seeds, etc.

Suggested reading: A. C. Bent, *Life Histories of North American Jays, Crows, and Titmice,* Dover, N.Y. (reprint of U.S. Nat. Mus. Bull. 191, 1947), 1964, pp. 269–275.

FISH CROW (*Corvus ossifragus*)

Appearance: Slightly smaller (16–20 in.) than the Common Crow and, like it, completely black. Since there is a large overlap in size, the best field identification is by voice.

Voice: A rasping, nasal *ca-r* or *ca* and sometimes an *ah-uk*.

Range and status: Resident coastally from R.I. to s. Fla. and west along the Gulf Coast to se. Tex. and inland along major waterways, but rarely beyond tide limits. Common.

Habitat: Marine and brackish-water shorelands and along lower river valleys.

Seasonal movements: Some southward movement in severe winters. Travels in small flocks most of year but merges into large flocks and roosts in fall and winter.

Biology: Nest: In small colonies; neat baskets of sticks and twigs lined with mosses, grasses, bark, pine needles, and hair. Eggs: 4–5; inseparable from those of the Common Crow. Incubation: 16–18 days. Age at 1st flight: More than 3 weeks. Food: Omnivorous, but primarily marine invertebrates, offal, and seashore carrion; birds' eggs, insects, berries, fruit, and seeds are also consumed.

Suggested reading: A. C. Bent, *Life Histories of North American Jays, Crows, and Titmice,* Dover, N.Y. (reprint of U.S. Nat. Mus. Bull. 191, 1947), 1964, pp. 275–283.

HAWAIIAN CROW (*Corvus tropicus*)

Appearance: Same size (21 in.) as a large Common Crow. Plumage is a dusky brown, with head and tail almost black, black bill, legs, and feet, and dark brown eyes.

Voice: A harsh *caw,* usually repeated rapidly.

Range and status: W. slopes of Hawaii I. Reduced in numbers over former years, but apparently not yet in danger of extinction.

Habitat: Dry forests.

Seasonal movements: None.

Biology: Very little known, especially about breeding habits. Food: Formerly mainly flowers and fruit of the ieie vine, but now, in addition, other fruits, berries, and carrion.

PIÑON JAY (*Gymnorhinus cyanocephalus*)

Appearance: A small, Robin-sized (9–11¾ in.) bird, dull grayish cobalt-blue, somewhat lighter below and darker on the head. The throat is streaked with pale blue. The bill, legs, and feet are black, and the eye dark brown; the tail is proportionately shorter than in true jays.

Voice: A shrill *why-ar-wak, why-ar-wak,* a mewing *kweh-a-eh,* chattering notes, and jaylike calls.

Range and status: Resident from c. Ore., e.-c. Mont., and w. S.Dak. south, through e. Calif. to n. Baja Calif., c. Nev., c. and e.-c. Ariz., c. N.Mex., and w. Okla. Wanders in nonbreeding seasons to Wash., n. Idaho, sw. Sask., Nebr., Kans., w. Calif., c. Tex., and n.-c. Mexico. Fairly common.

Habitat: Piñon pine and juniper forests and edges of sagebrush areas.

Seasonal movements: Gathers in large flocks in fall and wanders erratically outside breeding range.

Biology: Gregarious at all seasons. Nest: In large or small colonies, usually about 10–12 ft. above the ground in branches of piñon pine or juniper (rarely other kinds of trees); a large platform of sticks, twigs, and rootlets with a cup of matted dead grasses and leaves. Eggs: 3–6, usually 4–5; bluish white, greenish white, or grayish white, peppered and spotted and occasionally blotched with browns. Incubation: 16(?) days, by both sexes. Age at 1st flight: About 3 weeks. Food: Nut of the piñon pine, other wild nuts and fruit, some grain, and insects.

Suggested reading: A. C. Bent, *Life Histories of North American Jays, Crows, and Titmice,* Dover, N.Y. (reprint of U.S. Nat. Mus. Bull. 191, 1947), 1964, pp. 302–310.

CLARK'S NUTCRACKER (*Nucifraga columbiana*)

Appearance: Larger (12–13 in.) than the Robin. Predominantly gray, with white forehead, face, and throat fading into the pale gray of the body, which becomes a medium gray toward the tail. The central tail feathers are blackish gray, and the outer tail feathers white; the wings are black, with a distinct white patch on the central flight feathers. The rather long, pointed bill, the legs, and the feet are blackish gray; the eye is dark brown. Looks and acts like a cross between a woodpecker and a crow.

Voice: A throaty, squawking *chaar, char-r-r, chur-r-r, kra-a-a,* or *kar-r-ak,* repeating each note 2–3 times. Noisy.

Range and status: Resident from c. B.C., sw. Alta., w. and c. Mont., and w. and se. Wyo. south in the mountains to n. Baja Calif., e. Ariz., and w. N.Mex. Has wandered to Alaska, Yuk., Sask., sw. Man., S.Dak.,

The gregarious Piñon Jays almost always travel in small flocks.

Clark's Nutcracker lives in coniferous forests high in the western mountains.

Nebr., Kans., and Tex. and has straggled to Iowa, Minn., Wis., Ill., Mo., Ark., and ne. Mexico. Fairly common.

Habitat: Coniferous woodlands and groves near tree limit of high mountains.

Seasonal movements: A vagrant in the nonbreeding season, appearing almost anywhere within or near the nesting area.

Biology: Nest: A platform of sticks and twigs forms the base for a thick, deep cup of matted, finely shredded bark, plant down, and grasses; built near the end of a pine-tree branch 5–30 ft. above the ground at high alti-tudes. Snow is still on ground at start of nesting season. Eggs: 2–6, usually 2–3; pale green or gray-green, sparingly spotted with browns and grays. Incubation: 17–18 days, by both sexes. Age at 1st flight: 24–28 days. Food: Omnivorous, but primarily nuts of piñon pine and other nuts and pine seeds. Like the Gray Jay it is called a camp-robber, as it scavenges food from campsites; consumes many insects and is fond of the eggs and nestlings of other birds.

Suggested reading: L. R. Mewaldt, "Nesting Behavior of the Clark's Nutcracker," *Condor*, vol. 58, pp. 3–23, 1956.

THE MUDNEST-BUILDERS (GRALLINIDAE)

The mudnest-builders are small- to medium-sized (7–20 in.) terrestrial forest birds. They are now placed near the crows, but the exact relationships are obscure. There are 4 species native to Australia and New Guinea, 1 of which, the Magpie-lark, has been introduced into Hawaii. Plumage is in bold patterns of black and white or in dark bluish or brownish gray. The wings are short and rounded in some species and long and pointed in others, and the tail may be short and square-tipped or long and round-tipped. There are 2 species with long, slender, decurved bills; the other species have short, stout bills. The sexes are alike in 2 of the species. These birds are very gregarious, often nesting in small colonies. The nests are deep cups of mud lined with grasses and feathers and usually placed on a horizontal branch of a tree. The 3–8 white or pinkish eggs are incubated by both male and female; the hatchlings have some down and are tended by both sexes. Food is primarily insects, other small invertebrates, and seeds.

MAGPIE-LARK (*Grallina cyanoleuca*)

About Robin size (11 in.), with a glossy black cap, nape, back, throat, and breast. The large flight feathers of the wing, a streak from the base of the bill through the eye to the nape, and a broad terminal band on the tail are also black; the rest of the plumage is white. The bill, legs, and feet are dark gray. It is at home in all of Australia and has been introduced to Oahu and Hawaii Is. It prefers more open areas and forest edges and was imported to Hawaii as a possible control for mollusk pests brought in accidentally. It eats insects and other small invertebrates, but so do many of the native Hawaiian birds.

Magpie-lark

TITMICE AND CHICKADEES (PARIDAE)

Titmice and chickadees are small (3–8 in.) arboreal birds most closely related to the crows and nuthatches. There are 65 species in the family; 15 of these have been recorded from America. They range throughout N. America south to Guatemala and from n. Eurasia south to s. Africa, s. Asia, Ceylon, and Indonesia, and in Japan. Very few species are migratory, and most are restricted to forested areas. The long, soft plumage is usually in combinations of black, white, grays, browns, greens, blues, and yellows (brighter-colored species occur in Eurasia); no species are spotted or streaked. The wings are short and rounded, the tail rather long, the bill short and small but strong, and the legs and feet relatively long and thin. A number of species are crested. These birds are gregarious, very active, and quite communicative, with chattering, lisping, and whistled notes. Flight appears fluttery and weak. Food is generally obtained through various tricky arboreal acrobatics. Sexes are alike or nearly so in almost all species. Courtship consists of simple displays. Nests vary; there are bulky constructions of mosses, plant fibers, and furs; pendant structures similar to those of the Baltimore Oriole; spherical conglomerations of sticks, twigs, and thorns with a side entrance into a lined chamber; and holes and cavities in trees, rocks, banks, and cliffs. The 4–14 eggs have a light ground color and are either immaculate or heavily spotted. Incubation is almost always by the female alone, although she is fed during this period by the male, who also helps feed the young. The hatchlings may be naked or covered with down. The young of most species are fed almost exclusively on insects. Insects form the bulk of the adults' diet, but, especially in winter, fats, nuts, seeds, and berries are eaten in large quantities.

BLACK-CAPPED CHICKADEE (*Parus atricapillus*)

Appearance: Small (4¾–5¾ in.), with black forehead, nape, cap, and throat; the rest of the head is white. It is also white below, with smoke-gray flanks, and light gray above, including the rather long tail. The bill, legs, and feet are black, and the eye is dark brown.

Voice: Its call is a distinct, buzzy, happy-sounding *chick-a-dee-dee-dee* or *dee-dee-dee;* in spring its song is a clear, sweet whistled *fee-bee.*

Range and status: Resident from c. Alaska, s. Yuk., sw. Mack., c. Sask., c. Man., c. Ont., s. Que., and Nfld. south to nw. Calif., ne. Nev., c. Utah, n. N.Mex., c. Mo., c. Ind., s. Ohio, through the Appalachians to e. Tenn. and w. N.C., Pa., and n. N.J. Many ornithologists believe this is conspecific with the Willow Tit, *Parus montanus,* of Eurasia. Common to locally abundant. It is a favorite at feeding trays, thriving because of the abundant food.

Habitat: Deciduous and mixed forests, groves, and suburban areas.

Seasonal movements: Some, especially in winter, within regular range.

Biology: Nest: A hollow dug in the decaying stump of a birch or similar tree and lined with plant fibers, mosses, feathers, wool, and hair. Eggs: 5–10, usually 6–8; white, evenly spotted and dotted with browns;

Throughout its range, the Black-capped Chickadee is a familiar visitor at feeding trays.

sometimes the spots are heavier around the larger end. Incubation: 11–13 days. Age at 1st flight: 14–18 days. Food: In summer primarily insects, spiders, and other small invertebrates; in winter, besides the bounty of sunflower seeds at feeders, it eats insect eggs and larvae found in bark crevices and wild seeds and dried berries.

Suggested reading: E. P. Odum, "Annual Cycle of the Black-capped Chickadee," *Auk*, vol. 58, pp. 314–333, 518–535, 1941; vol. 59, pp. 499–531, 1942.

CAROLINA CHICKADEE (*Parus carolinensis*)

Appearance: Small (4¼–4¾ in.) and so much like the Black-capped Chickadee that voice and locality are better guides to identification than appearance. This species' wing is a more even-colored gray as it lacks the whitish edging to the smaller feathers.

Voice: *Chick-a-dee-dee-dee* at faster cadence and higher pitch than that of the Black-capped. Song is clear and sweet, but in 4 parts: *fee-bee-fee-bay.*

Range and status: Resident from se. Kans., sw. and e.-c. Mo., c. Ill., c. Ind., c. Ohio., sw. and se. Pa., and c. N.J. south to the Gulf Coast and c. Fla. Fairly common.

Habitat: Deciduous and mixed woodlands, groves, and parklands.

Seasonal movements: None.

Biology: Nest: Dug in rotting tree stump or deserted woodpecker hole; lined with plant fibers, mosses, feathers, wool, and hair. Eggs: 5–8, usually 6; white, peppered and spotted with reddish browns. Incubation: 11(?) days. Age at 1st flight unknown. Food: Insects, small invertebrates, seeds, berries, and other wild fruit; primarily insectivorous.

Suggested reading: R. Brewer, "Ecological and Reproductive Relationships of Black-capped and Carolina Chickadees," *Auk*, vol. 80, pp. 9–47, 1963.

MEXICAN CHICKADEE (*Parus sclateri*)

A small (5 in.) chickadee with gray flanks and a black bib that extends over the upper breast, but otherwise just like the Black-capped Chickadee. Its voice is a low, slow, explosive *dzay-dzee.* Resident from se. Ariz. and sw. N.Mex. south through the highlands to s.-c. Mexico.

MOUNTAIN CHICKADEE (*Parus gambeli*)

Appearance: About the size (5–5¾ in.) of the Black-capped. Light gray above, including wing and tail, and white below, with gray flank, black throat, white face, and a black cap. A white streak above the eye originates at the forehead.

Voice: Call similar to that of Black-capped, but *chick-a-dee-a-dee-a-dee;* also a buzzy *t-r-r-r-r-p.* Song is a clear whistled *fee-bee-bay.*

Range and status: Resident in the Coast Ranges, the

The Mountain Chickadee has a prominent white stripe above each eye.

Sierra Nevadas, and the Rockies from nw. B.C. and sw. Alta. south to n. Baja Calif., c. and se. Ariz., c. and se. N.Mex., and sw. Tex. Rather common.

Habitat: Coniferous and oak-pine forests of mountain areas; at lower altitudes and in mixed forests in winter.

Seasonal movements: Local only.

Biology: Nest: 2–80 ft. above the ground in natural cavity or old woodpecker hole in tree, though the bird sometimes digs its own hole in rotting stump; lined with mosses, hair, fur, and plant down. Eggs: 6–12, usually 8–9; white, some immaculate, others spotted with pale browns, and some spotted heavily with rich brownish reds. Incubation: 14 days. Age at 1st flight unknown. Food: Insects primarily, some berries, other fruit, and seeds.

Suggested reading: A. C. Bent, *Life Histories of North American Jays, Crows, and Titmice,* Dover, N.Y. (reprint of U.S. Nat. Mus. Bull. 191, 1947), 1964, pp. 357–368.

GRAY-HEADED CHICKADEE (*Parus cinctus*)

Appearance: Small (5½ in.); similar to the Black-capped Chickadee except that the cap is medium gray instead of black and the flank is only very slightly tinged with smoke-gray.

Voice: A *dee-deer, chee-ee,* or *pee-vee* with rather querulous accents.

Range and status: Resident from n. Eurasia, n. Alaska, n. Yuk., and nw. Mack. south to c. Scandinavia, n.-c. Russia, n.-c. and s. Siberia, c. Alaska, and n.-c. Yuk. Locally abundant in c. Yukon River Valley and lower Mackenzie River area.

Habitat: In America, riparian groves and woodlands; in Eurasia, the dense spruce-larch-cedar forests and deciduous woods along rivers in such areas.

Seasonal movements: None.

Biology: Nest: Natural tree cavities and abandoned woodpecker holes lined with mosses and fur. Eggs: 7–9; white, spotted with browns. Incubation period and age at 1st flight unknown. Food: Insects and seeds of conifers.

BOREAL CHICKADEE (Brown-capped Chickadee) (*Parus hudsonicus*)

Appearance: About the same size (5–5½ in.) and appearance as the Black-capped Chickadee, except that the cap and flank are buffy brown and the back and rump a grayish brown.

Voice: A rather slow-cadenced, husky *atser-day-day-*

day (O. L. Austin) and a higher-pitched *che-day-day;* the song is a brief melodious *o-phe-leoo* warble.

Range and status: Resident from the tree limit of N. America south to s. continental Alaska, n.-c. Wash., nw. Mont., c. Sask., c. Man., ne. Minn., n. Mich., c. Ont., ne. N.Y., n. Vt., n. N.H, Maine, and N.S.; irregularly south in winter to Wis., Ill., Ohio, Md., N.J., se. N.Y. and s. New England. Locally common.

Habitat: Coniferous forests.

Seasonal movements: None regular.

Biology: Nest: In natural tree cavity, deserted woodpecker hole, or chamber dug in rotting tree stump, lined with fur and feathers. Eggs: 4–9, usually 6–7; white, sparsely and irregularly peppered and spotted with browns. Incubation period and age at 1st flight not known. Food: Insects; in winter, the eggs, pupae, and wintering larvae of insects as well as various coniferous seeds.

Suggested reading: A. C. Bent, *Life Histories of North American Jays, Crows, and Titmice,* Dover, N.Y. (reprint of U.S. Nat. Mus. Bull. 191, 1947), 1964, pp. 371–384.

CHESTNUT-BACKED CHICKADEE (*Parus rufescens*)

Appearance: Slightly smaller (4½–5 in.) than the Black-capped Chickadee, which it resembles except that

The Boreal Chickadee inhabits northern forests from Nova Scotia all the way to Alaska.

The Yellow-bellied Sapsucker drinks sap that oozes from the small holes it drills in tree trunks but also feeds on berries and various insects.

The **Cliff Swallow** cements its gourd-shaped mud nest to the sides of cliffs and buildings and even against the trunks of large trees. It usually breeds in large colonies.

the back, rump, flank, and shoulders of the wing are light chestnut, with some dark brown in the center of the crown and nape.

Voice: A coarse, rather explosive *kiss-a-dee* and soft, conversational *tseek-a-dee-dee*'s. No whistled song.

Range and status: Resident along coasts and on coastal islands from s.-c. Alaska to s.-c. Calif. and inland south to se. Wash., n. Idaho, and nw. Mont. Common.

Habitat: Humid coniferous forests and bordering deciduous woodlands.

Seasonal movements: None.

Biology: Nest: Sometimes in loose colonies; 1–20 ft. above the ground, usually less than 10 ft., in natural cavity in tree, deserted woodpecker hole, or dug in rotting stub; packed and lined with mosses, plant fibers, and hair. Eggs: 5–9, usually 6–7; white, sparingly sprinkled with reddish brown spots, sometimes nearly immaculate. Incubation period and age at 1st flight unknown. Food: Forest insects in all developmental stages, spiders, fruit pulp, and seeds of coniferous trees.

Suggested reading: A. C. Bent, *Life Histories of North American Jays, Crows, and Titmice*, Dover, N.Y. (reprint of U.S. Nat. Mus. Bull. 191, 1947), 1964, pp. 384–393.

TUFTED TITMOUSE (*Parus bicolor*)

Appearance: Larger (6–6½ in.) than the Black-capped Chickadee; crested; medium gray above, including wing and tail, with black forehead. Below, it is white to pale gray, with pale flesh-colored flanks. There is a small patch of pale gray between the black bill and the dark brown eye. The legs and feet are a blackish gray.

Voice: A clear, piping, much-repeated *peter-peter-peter* or variations of this; also a peevish, buzzy *day-day-day-day*.

Range and status: Resident from se. Nebr., Iowa, se. Minn., s. Wis., s. Mich., s. Ont., c. N.Y., and s. New England south to se. Tex., the Gulf Coast, and c. Fla. Has straggled to Maine. Hybridizes in Tex. with the Black-crested Titmouse.

Habitat: Deciduous woodlands, orchards, suburbs, cypress swamps, pine woods, etc.

Seasonal movements: Wanders in small flocks during nonbreeding season.

Biology: Nest: Cavities in trees, deserted woodpecker holes, or holes dug in rotting stubs; padded and lined with leaves, strips of bark, grasses, mosses, vegetable fiber, and hair. Eggs: 4–8, usually 5–6; white to cream, more or less evenly spotted with browns. Incubation: 13 days. Age at 1st flight: 17–18 days. Food: Over 65% insects and spiders; also seeds, acorns, and other nuts.

Suggested reading: A. R. Laskey, "Some Tufted Titmouse Life History," *Bird-banding*, vol. 28, pp. 135–144, 1957.

Like many of its relatives, the Tufted Titmouse has a conspicuous crest.

BLACK-CRESTED TITMOUSE (*Parus atricristatus*)

Appearance: Smaller (5–6 in.) than the Tufted Titmouse, which it resembles except that the prominently crested crown starting at the pale gray forehead is black and the flank is light tawny.

Voice: *Peter-peter-peter* like the Tufted Titmouse, but lower and more abbreviated.

Range and status: Resident from n.-c. and ne. Mexico and Tex. south to c. and e.-c. Mexico. Common.

Habitat: Wooded river bottoms, groves, oak and cedar forests, orchards, and suburbs.

Seasonal movements: None.

Biology: Nest: In natural tree cavities, abandoned woodpecker holes, and holes dug in rotting stumps 3–22 ft. above the ground; packed and lined with leaves, mosses, rootlets, grasses, bark, fur, hair, and pieces of snakeskin. Eggs: 4–7, usually 5–7; white to pale cream, sparsely and evenly spotted with browns. Incubation period and age at 1st flight unknown. Food: Insects and spiders; seeds, nuts, berries, and other fruit.

Plain Titmouse

PLAIN TITMOUSE (*Parus inornatus*)

Appearance: Smaller (5–5½ in.) than the Tufted Titmouse; crested; medium gray above, including wing and tail, and completely pale gray below. Face and forehead are also pale gray. Bill, legs, and feet are black; the eye is dark brown.

Voice: A hissing, raspy *tsick-a-dee-dee* and a whistling *witee-witee-witee* or *ti-wee, ti-wee, ti-wee* spring song.

Range and status: Resident, mainly in the mountains, from s. Ore., Nev., se. Idaho, sw. Wyo., and s.-c. Colo. south to n. Baja Calif., c. and se. Ariz., sw. and c. N.Mex., and w. Tex.; also in s. Baja Calif. Common.

Habitat: Oak, piñon, and juniper woodlands, riparian groves, and tree-shaded suburbs.

Seasonal movements: None.

Biology: Nest: In natural cavities or old woodpecker holes in trees, in birdhouses, and in holes excavated in rotting stubs; padded and lined with grasses, mosses, weed stems, fur, and hair. Eggs: 6–8, usually 7; white, sometimes sparingly marked with pale browns. Incubation: 14–15 days. Age at 1st flight: 16–21 days. Food: About 40% insects and spiders and 60% seeds, acorns and other nuts, and fruit.

Suggested reading: K. L. Dixon, "Behavior of the Plain Titmouse," *Condor*, vol. 51, pp. 110–136, 1949.

BRIDLED TITMOUSE (*Parus wollweberi*)

Appearance: About the same size (4½–5 in.) as the Chestnut-backed Chickadee; crested. Light gray above

and a very pale gray below, with a white face. The gray cap and crest are edged with black. A black line through the eye angles down just before the black-edged gray nape and there curves forward to join the black throat. The bill, legs, and feet are black, and the eye is dark brown.

Voice: A coarse, squealing *chicka-dee-dee-dee*, the last notes rather cacophonic, and a very high-pitched *fee-bee* whistle repeated several times.

Range and status: Resident from c. and se. Ariz. and sw. N.Mex. south through the highlands to s. Mexico. Locally common.

Habitat: Pine-oak, oak, and sycamore forests in canyons and foothills.

Seasonal movements: None.

Biology: Nest: In natural cavities in trees 2–15 ft. above ground; padded and lined with leaves, grasses, and plant down. Eggs: 5–7, white. Incubation period and age at 1st flight unknown. Food: Probably insects, seeds, nuts, and fruit.

VARIED TIT (Yamagara) (*Parus varius*)

A small (5 in.), chickadeelike bird, with black throat, upper breast, cap, nape, and upper back. The forehead, face, side of neck, lower breast, belly, and undertail feathers are cream; the flanks and bar across the upper

The juvenile Bridled Titmouse's facial pattern is less marked than the adult's.

In semiarid areas, water holes are good places to watch for Verdins and other birds.

back are rufous. The rest of upperparts, wing, and tail are medium gray. The bill is black, the legs and feet blackish gray, and the eye dark brown. It is resident in Japan and the Korean peninsula, and has been established on Kauai and Oahu Is., Hawaii.

VERDIN (*Auriparus flaviceps*)

Appearance: Small (4–4½ in.); light smoke-gray above and pale smoke-gray below, with entire head and neck yellow. There is a patch of brownish red on the shoulder. Immature birds are plain smoke-gray above, including wing and tail, and pale smoke-gray below. The bill is buffy brown, and legs and feet are bluish gray.

Voice: A loud whistled *tswee-tswee-tswee-tsweet*, a buzzy *tsee-tu-tu*, and a long series of *tsit-tsit-tsit* notes often run together into a chatter.

Range and status: Resident from se. Calif., s. Nev., sw. Utah, s. and w. Ariz., s. N.Mex., and sw. and s.-c. Tex. south to Baja Calif. and w.-c. and c. Mexico. Common.

Habitat: Semiarid brushy and grassy areas, usually with mesquite and thorny scrub.

Seasonal movements: None.

Biology: Nest: A large, globular "hedgehog" of thorny twigs, with entrance on the side leading to a chamber lined with leaves, grasses, feathers, spider webbing, and plant down; 2–20 ft. above the ground. Eggs: 3–6, usually 4–5; pale greenish blue or bluish or greenish white, sparingly and irregularly spotted, sometimes blotched with reddish brown. Incubation: 10(?) days. Age at 1st flight: 21 days. Food: Insects and their larvae and eggs, berries, and other fruits.

COMMON BUSHTIT (*Psaltriparus minimus*)

Appearance: One of the smallest (3¾–4½ in.) of the family. Cap and nape a buffy brown, sides of head a smoke-gray, and undersides a pale smoke-gray. Back, rump, wing, and tail are medium gray. In Rocky Mountain form, the cap and nape are the same color as the back. Bill, legs, and feet are black; the eyes are yellow.

The Common Bushtit is dull and inconspicuous, but its nest is quite distinctive.

Voice: 1–5 sibilant notes followed by a long, shrill, trembling note: *tsit-tsit-tsit-sre-e-e-e-e;* a softer, calmer series of *tsit*'s; and a monotonous, trilling *sre-e-e-e-e.*

Range and status: Resident in Coast Ranges from sw. B.C. to s. Baja Calif. and in the interior from s. Ore., sw. Idaho, n.-c. Utah, w. Colo., w. Okla., and n. and c. Tex. to nw. Mexico. Common to locally abundant.

Habitat: Mixed woodlands or pure stands of scrub oak, chaparral, piñon, and juniper.

Seasonal movements: Moves about in flocks during nonbreeding seasons.

Biology: Nest: In trees 6–25 ft. above the ground; a hooded, pendant basket shaped like a summer squash, made of firmly woven fine twigs, grasses, mosses, lichens, leaves, insect webbing, rootlets, and plant fibers, and lined with downy feathers and fur; the entrance is usually on the side, near the top, and protected by the hood. Eggs: 5–13, commonly 5–7; white. Incubation: 12 days, by both sexes. Age at 1st flight: 14–15 days. Food: More than 80% insects and spiders; the rest seeds and some fruit.

Suggested reading: A. R. Addicott, "Behavior of the Bush-tit in the Breeding Season," *Condor,* vol. 40, pp. 49–62, 1938.

BLACK-EARED BUSHTIT (Lloyd's Bushtit) (*Psaltriparus melanotis*)

Small (4–4½ in.). Smoke-gray above, with a light gray cap and nape, and pale gray below, with a broad black mask running from the bill through the eye. In the female and young the area of the mask is smoke-gray, spotted with black. Its voice, habitat, and biology are very similar to those of the Common Bushtit. It is a resident from s. N.Mex. and w. Tex. south to Guatemala.

THE COMMON NUTHATCHES (SITTIDAE)

These small (3½–7½ in.) arboreal birds are related to the chickadees and creepers. There are 17 species, although some authorities include the Australian and Coral-billed Nuthatches and some genera of the creeper family for a total of 29 species. There are 4 species in America. The family ranges through N. America and Eurasia, the Celebes, Formosa, Japan, and the Philippines. Most species are sedentary and are usually common and conspicuous members of the avifauna. They are seldom found outside forested areas. The plumage usually occurs in grays, browns, black, and white, generally unstreaked, and most species have some white on the tail. The wing is somewhat long and pointed, the tail short and square-tipped, and the bill strong, slender, straight, and pointed. The legs are short; the toes are long, strong, and stout-clawed. Nuthatches fly in an up-and-down line like the woodpeckers and climb around tree boles, usually head down, in short, jerking hops. Food is picked from crevices in bark or wedges in cracks and hacked apart with the bill—"hatch" in Old English meant "to hack." Voice is generally a single, much-repeated note. Courtship is simple and usually consists of the male's posturing before the female and a feeding ritual. Nests are built in natural cavities in rocks and trees, with the entrance hole built up with mud and resin and the interior lined with twigs and leaves. The eggs, commonly 4–12, are white with brownish red spots; incubation is by the female, possibly helped by the male. The hatchlings are sparsely covered by long down. Food is insects, seeds, and various nuts.

The White-breasted Nuthatch ranges over most of the United States.

WHITE-BREASTED NUTHATCH (*Sitta carolinensis*)

Appearance: About the size (5–6 in.) of the House Sparrow. Cap and nape are black; back, rump, tail, and wing are bluish gray, with some black on wing and tail. It is bright white below, including the face, and there are white patches on each side of the end of the tail. The flanks are tawny. The black bill seems to be uptilted because the top edge is perfectly straight and the lower bill curves up. The legs and feet are blackish gray, and the eye is dark brown.

Voice: A resonant whistled *too-too-too* or *wat-wat-wat-wat* in long series and a nasal *yank-yank*, which increases in frequency, vigor, and tempo in spring.

Range and status: Resident from s. B.C., se. Alta., nw. and c. Mont., s. Man., s. Ont., s. Que., n. Maine, P.E.I., and n. N.S. south to s. Baja Calif., c. Mexico, w.-c. Tex., n. La., c. Miss., c. Ala., and c. Fla. Absent from most of the Great Plains. Common and conspicuous.

Habitat: Mixed and deciduous woodlands, riparian and scattered groves of trees.

Seasonal movements: None.

Biology: Nest: High in tree within natural cavity or old woodpecker hole; lined with strips and shreds of bark, twigs, grasses, rootlets, and fur. Eggs: 5–10, commonly 8; white, sprinkled, spotted, and dotted with brownish reds, purples, and grays. Incubation: 12 days, by both sexes. Age at 1st flight: About 2 weeks. Food: A

327

The Red-breasted Nuthatch destroys a great many insect larvae and eggs.

great variety of seeds and nuts; also many insects and spiders.

Suggested reading: A. A. Allen, *The Golden Plover and Other Birds,* Comstock, Ithaca, N.Y., 1939, pp. 95–104.

RED-BREASTED NUTHATCH (*Sitta canadensis*)

Appearance: Smaller (4½–4¾ in.) than the White-breasted Nuthatch and similar to it in general coloration, except that a black streak runs through the eye, parallel to the edge of the cap, and the undersides are a light tawny fading to whitish at the throat. In the female and immature birds the cap and eye streak are bluish gray, like the back.

Voice: A short, almost whispered *hit;* a whiny, tinny *ang-ang-ang* in series of varying length, and a reedy, rapid-cadenced *wa-wa-wa-wa-wa* "song."

Range and status: Resident from se. Alaska, s. Yuk., sw. Mack., c. Sask., s. Man., w. and n. Ont., s. Que., and Nfld. south to Guadalupe I. off nw. Baja Calif., s. Calif., se. Ariz., s.-c. Colo., sw. S.Dak., c. Minn., Wis., n. Mich., s. Ont., through the Appalachians to e. Tenn. and w. N.C., se. N.Y., and s. New England. Winters at lower altitudes and casually south to s. N.Mex., Tex., the Gulf Coast, and n. Fla. It has straggled to Bermuda. Some ornithologists consider it conspecific with the very similar nuthatches of Corsica and the Himalayan region. Common, at least locally.

Habitat: Coniferous woodlands and into mixed and deciduous forests during winters.

Seasonal movements: Altitudinal migrations rather regular; other movements irregular and erratic.

Biology: Nest: Excavates a cavity in rotting stump or stub or uses an old woodpecker's hole; lined with grasses, mosses, shredded bark, and plant fibers. Entrance to nest commonly marked by patches of resin or pitch. Eggs: 4–7, usually 5–6; white, peppered and spotted in varying degree with browns. Incubation: 12 days, by both sexes. Age at 1st flight: 18–21 days. Food: Pine seeds, insects and spiders, fruit, and nuts.

Suggested reading: L. deKiriline, "Red-breast Makes a Home," *Aud. Mag.,* vol. 54, pp. 16–21, 1952.

BROWN-HEADED NUTHATCH (*Sitta pusilla*)

Appearance: Smaller (4–5 in.) than the White-breasted Nuthatch; back, rump, wing, and tail bluish gray. Cap, which extends to level of eye, and nape are a dark buffy brown; entirely white below, with a spot of white in the brown of the nape where it meets the back. The bill is black, the legs and feet blackish gray, and the eye dark brown.

Voice: A high, rapidly repeated *pit-pit-pit-pit* or *cha-cha-cha-cha,* a lively, twittering *dee-dee-dee,* a chirping songlike *priu-deu-deu* in spring, and a *wik-wik-wee-eh-eh-wik-wicker-wicker* chatter.

Range and status: Resident from Ark., se. Okla., e. Tex., n. La., n. Miss., n. Ala., n. Ga., c. S.C., se. Va., se. Md., and s. Del. south to the Gulf Coast, s. Fla., and the Bahamas. Has straggled to Mo., Iowa, N.Y., and N.J. Locally common.

Habitat: Open pine forests.

Seasonal movements: None.

Biology: Nest: A hollow dug in rotting post or stump, a natural cavity in tree, and probably old woodpecker holes; lined with grasses, weed stems, mosses, shredded bark, hair, and feathers. Eggs: 3–9, usually 5–6; white, fairly heavily peppered, spotted, and blotched with browns. Incubation: About 14 days. Age at 1st flight: About 18 days. Food: Insects, spiders, pine seeds, other seeds, and nuts.

Suggested reading: R. A. Norris, *Comparative Biosystematics and Life History of the Nuthatches Sitta pygmaea and Sitta pusilla*, Univ. Calif. Publ. Zool., vol. 56, no. 2, pp. 119–300, 1958.

PYGMY NUTHATCH (*Sitta pygmaea*)

Appearance: Smallest (3¾–4½ in.) of our nuthatches. Back, rump, wing, and tail bluish gray; cap and nape (with an indistinct whitish spot where it meets the back) brownish olive, darker at the edge running through the eye; and entirely white below. The bill is bluish gray, darker at the tip, and the legs and feet are blackish gray; the eye is dark brown.

Voice: Noisy; an almost incessant, high, staccato *ti-di, ti-di, ti-di* becoming more vigorous in spring and often accompanied by a strong trill; in flight a soft *kit-kit-kit*, often high and piercing.

Range and status: Resident from s. B.C., n. Idaho, w. Mont., c. Wyo., and sw. S.Dak. south to n. Baja Calif. and through the highlands to s.-c. and e.-c. Mexico. Common.

Habitat: Pine forests, especially yellow pine, and Douglas fir areas in mountains and humid coastal regions.

Seasonal movements: Wanders about in small bands during nonbreeding seasons.

Biology: Nest: 8–50 ft. above the ground in a natural cavity, an old woodpecker hole, or a hole dug in

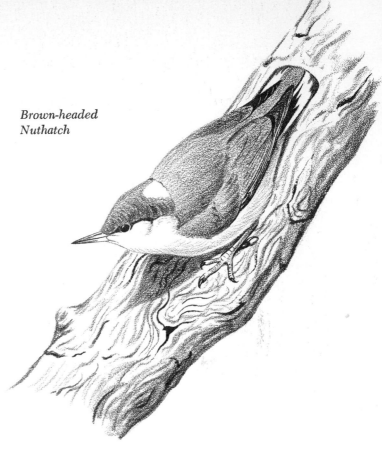

Brown-headed Nuthatch

rotting wood of pine stubs or stumps of other species of trees; lined with pine-cone scales, feathers, plant down, leaves, fur, and hair. Eggs: 4–9, usually 6–8; sparsely and unevenly peppered, sometimes more heavily spotted, with reddish browns. Incubation: 15½–16 days. Age at 1st flight: About 18 days. Food: Over 80% insects gleaned in pine forests and nearby; the remainder mainly seeds of coniferous trees.

Suggested reading: R. A. Norris, *Comparative Biosystematics and Life History of the Nuthatches Sitta pygmaea and Sitta pusilla*, Univ. Calif. Publ. Zool., vol. 56, no. 2, pp. 119–300, 1958.

The Brown Creeper's slender bill is ideal for picking insect prey from narrow crevices.

THE CREEPERS (CERTHIIDAE)

These small (4½–7 in.) arboreal songbirds are related most closely to the nuthatches and titmice. There are 17 species ranging throughout N. America, Eurasia, Africa, Japan, Indonesia, the Philippines, and Australia; only 1 species, the Brown Creeper, is found in America. Only a few species are migratory. The plumage commonly occurs in browns, black, white, grays, and buffs, most often in streaked or spotted patterns. There is only 1 species with red in the plumage. The wings are long and may be pointed or rounded; the tail is rather long, usually wedge-shaped, with stiff, pointed tips. The bill may be short, but is rather long and slender in most species and straight or well decurved. The legs are often slender but strong, with large feet, and the claws are long and sharp. The sexes are alike. Flight is strong and direct. None of the species is markedly gregarious, even in migration.

Most feed by creeping over vertical surfaces or around boles of trees, with head upward, searching crevices for food. Voice is variable, characterized commonly by cheeping and piping notes and clear songs. Courtship is an aerial display of great agility, with the birds weaving and twisting around and through trees at top speed. The nest is a crevice in a rock or under tree bark, padded with grasses and mosses or bark lined with hair, feathers, and plant down; a few extraterritorial species saddle their nests on tree branches. The 2–9, commonly 5–6, eggs are white or pinkish, spotted with browns. The female incubates with no help from the male in most species. The downy hatchlings are fed by both parents. Insects, spiders, and other small invertebrates make up the bulk of the food, although some seeds and fruit are eaten.

BROWN CREEPER (*Certhia familiaris*)

Appearance: Slightly smaller (5–5¾ in.) than the House Sparrow. Brown above (shades vary from 1 part of vast geographical range to another, with 7 subspecies in U.S. and Canada), streaked and spotted with darker browns, lighter browns, and grays. The tail is commonly unstreaked reddish brown. It is white below, including throat, with a white streak above the eye; the face is streaked with brown. The long, slender, sharp-pointed, decurved bill is blackish brown; the legs and feet are dusky brown.

Voice: A short, thin, high hissing *tss*, sometimes lengthened and strengthened to a *zi-i-i-it*; the song, delivered almost entirely during spring, is a high, softly whistled *see-tee-wee-tu-wee* with more sibilant variations.

Range and status: Resident from s.-c. and se. Alaska, B.C., c. Alta., c. Sask., s. Man., n. Ont., s. Que., and Nfld. south through the mountains to s. Calif., s. Nev., Nicaragua, s. Iowa, s. Wis., c. Mich., n. Ohio, through the Appalachians to e. Tenn. and w. N.C., se. N.Y., and Mass. In Eurasia from n. Europe and across c. Siberia to Sakhalin I. and Japan south to ne. Spain, Italy, Greece, Turkey, n. Iran, the Himalayas, and s. Japan. Distribution, especially in Eurasia, somewhat local and disconnected. Common but inconspicuous; perhaps unnoticed by many since its notes are too high for some ears to catch.

Habitat: Coniferous and mixed forests; usually in mountains, especially to the south.

Seasonal movements: Retreats to lower altitudes in winter; some southward movement during winter in Canada and U.S.

Biology: Nest: Built, behind loose slabs of bark still clinging in part to the tree, on a foundation of sticks and twigs; made of strips and shreds of bark and lined with feathers and finer-fibered bark shreds. Eggs: 4–8, commonly 5–6; white, sometimes creamy white, peppered and spotted with browns. Incubation: 14–15 days, by both sexes. Age at 1st flight: 14–15 days. Food: Insects and their larvae, pupae, and eggs searched out in bark crevices summer and winter; spiders and other small invertebrates and some seeds are also eaten.

Suggested reading: D. A. Bannerman, "Tree Creeper," *Birds of the British Isles*, Oliver and Boyd, Edinburgh, 1953, vol. 2, pp. 154–160.

THE WRENTIT (CHAMAEIDAE)

Since this family contains but a single species, details of range and biology are covered under the following species account. It is the only family of birds found solely in N. America, a dubious distinction, as many experts feel that it is only a member of the babblers (Timaliidae) that managed to find its way long ago, without the help of man, to w. N. America.

WRENTIT (*Chamaea fasciata*)

Appearance: About House Sparrow size (6–6½ in.). Fuscous above, including wing and relatively long, graduated tail; buffy brown below, with faint streaking of darker brown. There is a medium gray streak through the bright yellow eye; the bill, legs, and feet are a light buffy brown.

Voice: A series of loud, single-pitched, ringing whistles increasing in cadence to a trill at the end, as *pit—pit—pit-pit-pit-ptr-r-r-r,* and a similar but slower double-noted version; also soft *pr-r-r* notes.

Range and status: Resident in coastal regions of Ore., Calif., and nw. Baja Calif. and into the Central Valley of Calif. Fairly common.

Habitat: Brushy areas, chaparral, suburban gardens, and parks.

Seasonal movements: None.

Biology: Apparently practices lifetime monogamy. Individuals are seldom found more than 5–6 miles from birthplace. Nest: In bushes; usually at the edge of dense growth; a framework of spider webbing holds the bark-fiber cup together, with further reinforcing by webbing throughout structure, which has a deep cup, lined with finer bark fibers. Eggs: 3–5, usually 4; pale greenish blue. Incubation: 16 days, mainly by female. Age at 1st flight: 15–16 days. Food: Insects, berries, and other wild fruit.

Suggested reading: M. M. Erickson, *Territory, Annual Cycle, and Numbers in a Population of Wren-tits,* Univ. Calif. Publ. Zool., vol. 42, pp. 247–334, 1938.

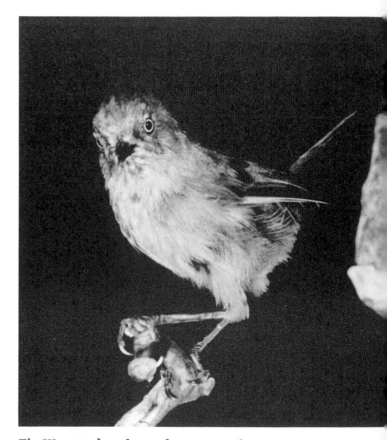

The Wrentit, the only member of its family, is closely related to the Old World babblers.

THE BABBLERS (TIMALIIDAE)

Babblers are small to medium-sized (3½–16 in.) arboreal, thrushlike songbirds related to the bulbuls, wrens, thrushes, and Old World flycatchers. There are 242 species ranging throughout Africa and from Mesopotamia, the Himalayan region, c. China, and the Philippines south to Madagascar, Ceylon, Indonesia, and Australia. Babblers are not native to America, but 3 species have been introduced successfully in Hawaii. Most species are sedentary forest dwellers. Plumage is soft and thick, in a variety of colors and patterns. The wings are short and rounded, the tail varies from short to long, the legs and feet are sturdy, and the bill is short and weak to long and strongly decurved. The sexes are alike. Flight is fluttery and seldom sustained. Various types of nests are built on the ground, in bushes or trees, and in cavities in trees, rocks, or ground. The 2–7 eggs are white, greenish, bluish, or pinkish; most are unspotted; incubation is by both sexes or by female alone. They eat insects, small animals, and fruit.

HWA-MEI (Chinese Thrush) (*Garrulax canorus*)

About Robin size (9 in.); a dark buffy brown above. Belly is pale gray, and rest of underparts are cinnamon from throat to flanks. The legs and bill are a dark buffy yellow. A white streak extends from the white ring about the eye to the rear of the head. This native of China and Formosa has been introduced on all main Hawaiian islands.

COLLARED THRUSH (Brown or Laughing Thrush) (*Garrulax albogularis*)

Slightly larger than the Robin (11½ in.); brownish olive above and light rufous below, with white throat and cheeks. Its outer tail feathers, like those of the American Robin, are tipped with white. A native of n. W. Pakistan, n. India, Nepal, Bhutan, s. China, and Formosa; introduced in Hawaii and established on Kauai and Oahu Is.

PEKO THRUSH (Black-throated Laughing Thrush) (*Garrulax chinensis*)

About the same size (11 in.) as the Collared Thrush. Olive above, with dark bluish gray cap and nape; cheeks are streaked black and white. Throat and upper breast are black, and the rest of the underparts are olive. The bill is black, and the legs and feet are buffy brown. Native of e. India, E. Pakistan, Burma, Thailand, Indochina, s. China, and Hainan I. Established on Kauai I., Hawaii.

RED-BILLED LEIOTHRIX (Hill Robin) (*Leiothrix lutea*)

Small (5–6 in.); olive above, with a black tip on the forked tail, a spot of scarlet-orange at the bend of the wing, and light greenish yellow about the eye. The throat and breast are orange-yellow, and the rest of the underparts are pale gray. The bill is scarlet-orange, and the legs and feet are a dark straw-yellow. It is native to n. W. Pakistan, n. India, n. Burma, Nepal, Bhutan, and s. China; it was introduced successfully and has since become abundant on the Hawaiian islands of Oahu, Maui, and Hawaii and locally on Molokai. It is characteristically found among the underbrush and in low scrubby growths.

THE BULBULS (PYCNONOTIDAE)

Bulbuls are small (6–11 in.) songbirds with relatively short necks, wings, and legs. There are 119 species ranging through Africa and s. Asia; only 1 species, the Red-whiskered Bulbul, has become naturalized in America. Most species are clad in rather dull plumages of browns, grays, greens, black, and white; some species are spruced up with patches of yellow or red, and many have prominent crests. A peculiarity of this family is a growth of hairlike feathers on the nape. The males are usually slightly larger than the females, but otherwise similar. Most species contrive pleasant, uncomplicated songs and calls. Persian literature, including the contributions of Omar Khayyám, often praises the beautiful songs of the garden-loving bulbuls, but the Persian "bulbul" intended is a thrush related to the Nightingale! Bulbuls are active, gregarious birds that do not shun human habitations, and they prefer the more open sunny spaces to the dense forests or jungles. Nests are usually fairly deep cups made of leaves, grasses, mosses, and bark and lined with rootlets and fine vegetable fibers; they are placed 5–15 ft. above the ground in trees or shrubs. The 2–5 eggs are of light ground color peppered and spotted with dark reds, purples, and black. Incubation is almost entirely by the female, but the male feeds his brooding mate and helps with the nestlings. In the warmer tropics 2 or 3 broods may be raised each year. Fruit forms the largest part of the diet, supplemented by flowers, insects, and other small animals.

RED-WHISKERED BULBUL (*Pycnonotus jocosus*)

Slightly smaller (8 in.) and slimmer than the Robin. The head is black except for a white throat and cheek patch and a bright red whisker patch behind and slightly below the eye. The bird is white below save for the red crissum at base of tail. Upperparts and white-tipped tail are buffy brown. It is a native of India, Burma, E. Pakistan, Thailand, and s. China, where it commonly travels about in large flocks through gardens, fields, and scrub jungles. It was found nesting near Miami, Fla., in 1962, probably a result of escaped or released cage birds. The song is short and rather dull, but the two-note calls of a traveling flock make pleasant listening. Nest is a cup made of leaves, grasses, and twigs molded compactly if untidily and placed rather low in a bush or shrub. The 2–4 pale pink eggs are peppered and spotted with dark reddish and purple. Diet includes a variety of fruits, flowers, insects, and seeds.

THE DIPPERS (CINCLIDAE)

These small (5½–8½ in.) aquatic songbirds are most closely related to the thrushes and wrens. There are only 4 species known; 1 species is found in America, and the others in the mountains of w. S. America, Europe, nw. Africa, and n.-c. and se. Asia to Formosa and Japan. Generally sedentary, they make some altitudinal movement in winter. Dippers are almost always found near water, preferably near mountain streams. Since all species have very similar habits and biology, the following account of the Dipper, or Water Ouzel, will serve as a guide to the family.

DIPPER (Water Ouzel) (*Cinclus mexicanus*)

Appearance: Smaller (7–8½ in.) than the Robin. Plumage entirely blackish gray, eyelid white, eye dark brown, bill black, and legs and feet straw-yellow. The plumage is thick, with a downy undercoat. The wings are short but pointed, the tail is short and square-tipped, and the bill is straight, slightly hooked and notched, and rather long and slender. The sexes are alike. On perches above water the Dipper continually bobs the whole body up and down. Flight is short and swift, with rapid wingbeats. The wings are used underwater, and the bird seems able to walk on the bottom of even the swiftest streams. It swims well on the surface even without webbed feet.

Voice: The song, heard throughout the year, partakes of the spirit of the mountain streams that are the bird's home; it is highest and fullest when these streams are at flood, lowest and weakest in the slack of dry seasons. A varied, melodic, bubbling, gurgling, trilling, Mockingbirdlike song. The alarm call is a double-noted *jigic-jigic;* other calls are a *zit-zit-zit* or an extended *bz-zee-zee-zee-zee-eet* and a metallic *ching-ching-ching-ching,* often in long series.

Range and status: Resident from the Aleutian Is., n.-c. Alaska, c. Yuk., nw. and c. Alta., n.-c. Mont., and sw. S.Dak. south to s. Calif., and through the highlands of Mexico and C. America to w. Panama. Fairly common.

Habitat: In and close to fast-flowing mountain streams; seldom near still water, and then only near streams.

Seasonal movements: Remains as long as the streams show open water, then merely moves downstream until open water is found again.

Biology: Nest: A large spherical mass of mosses, with entrance to the interior on the side; placed on rock ledges under low bridges or among roots of fallen trees, always near or practically in water. Many nests seem to be intentionally placed so that they are constantly showered by the mist and spray of small waterfalls. Eggs: 3–6, usually 4–5; white. Incubation: 15–17 days, by female only. Age at 1st flight: 24–25 days. Food: Aquatic insects and their larvae, which the bird obtains by "walking" along the bottom of a stream and searching them out from among the rocks and bottom debris; also small fish and other small invertebrates and a few aquatic plants.

Suggested reading: H. W. Hann, "Nesting Behavior of the American Dipper in Colorado," *Condor,* vol. 52, pp. 49–62, 1950. W. R. Goodge, "Locomotion and Other Behavior of the Dipper," *Condor,* vol. 61, pp. 4–17, 1959.

The Dipper goes underwater to glean insects from the bottoms of swift streams.

335

Like all its relatives, the House Wren is noted for its elaborate, melodic song.

THE WRENS (TROGLODYTIDAE)

Wrens are small (3½–8¾ in.) songbirds related to the dippers, mockingbirds, and thrushes. Of the 63 species, all but the Winter Wren are confined to the W. Hemisphere, ranging from n. N. America to n. Chile and n. Argentina and from n. Eurasia to nw. Africa, s. Europe, s. India, s. China, and Japan; 10 species occur in America. The more northerly species are migratory; they occupy a wide variety of habitats. Predominant plumage colors are browns, grays, black, and white, with streaked, barred, and spotted patterns very common. Wings are short and rounded; flight is generally rather weak. The tail, varying from short to long, is typically held erect. The bill is never short and may be as long as or slightly longer than the head; it is commonly slender and curved. The legs and feet are relatively big and strong, with long claws. The male and female are alike, or the difference is slight. Song is elaborate and complex, with well-coordinated duets between male and male or male and female. Several species are known to be polygamous. Courtship may be quite elaborate, including posturing and nest-site preparation by the male. Nests are built in crevices or cavities in rocks, trees, houses, or banks, or may be roofed globular structures of grasses, etc., in trees or shrubs. The males may build unlined nests, possibly used as nighttime roosts. The 2–10 eggs are white or some shade of brown and are immaculate or spotted with darker browns. Incubation is almost entirely by the female. The hatchlings have some down on the upper parts; in many species the male assists in feeding the young. Food is almost exclusively insects and spiders.

HOUSE WREN (*Troglodytes aedon*)

Appearance: Small (4½–5¼ in.); buffy brown above and smoke-gray below. The dark brown barring on the wing and tail and grayish brown barring along the flank become more prominent toward the tail. The eye streak of smoke-gray is rather obscure. The straw-yellow bill is black at the tip, the legs and feet are flesh-colored, and the eye is dark brown.

Voice: The song is a rapid, unnumbered cadence of notes. It varies considerably over the wide geographic range, and the song words used throughout are chattering, gurgling, stuttering, burbling, and trilling. A common variant starts with a medium-range chatter, switches suddenly to a higher-pitched chatter, and then goes through a series of slower notes in descending scale to a burbling final movement. In spring the songs seem to be incessant. The common alarm call is a cacophonic chatter.

Range and status: Breeds from s. and e.-c. B.C., Alta., s. Sask., s. Man., c. Ont., s. Que., Maine, and N.B. south to n. Baja Calif., se. Ariz., n. Tex., Ark., Tenn., and n. Ga. Winters from s. Calif., Ariz., N.Mex., c. Tex., s. Ark., n. Ala., nw. Ga., and s.-c. and se. Va. (farther north in small numbers) south to s. Baja Calif., s. Mexico, the Gulf Coast, and s. Fla. Common.

Habitat: More open forests, scrub-growth regions, suburban gardens, and city parks.

Seasonal movements: Arrives at breeding areas late Mar.–mid-May and departs late Aug.–mid-Nov. Younger adults arrive first in spring; females arrive about 9 days after males.

Biology: Nest: In a cavity in tree or stub and in birdhouses; as part of the courtship performance the male will fill several cavities or houses with sticks and twigs. One of these sites or another chosen by the female may be used, and the material gathered by the male may be unceremoniously ejected or used, as is, as the base for the actual nest, which is made of grasses, feathers, hair,

Winter Wren

wool, insect webbing, and plant fiber. Eggs: 5–12, commonly 6–8; pale pink, thickly peppered with brownish red, which may almost obscure the ground color. Incubation: About 15 days. Age at 1st flight: About 15 days; generally 2 broods are raised each season. Food: Grasshoppers, beetles, caterpillars, bugs, and other insects; spiders, and other small invertebrates. Any vegetable matter found in stomachs was probably ingested accidentally with animal food.

Suggested reading: E. P. Odum and D. W. Johnston, "The House Wren Breeding in Georgia," *Auk*, vol. 68, pp. 357–366, 1951.

BROWN-THROATED WREN (*Troglodytes brunneicollis*)

As small (4¼–5 in.) as the House Wren and very similar to it, but stripe over eye is buffer and more distinct. Somewhat darker above and lighter below, with spotty mottling at sides of breast. A keen ear may be able to separate this species' song from that of the House Wren, but the difference is apparently impossible to describe. Resident from se. Ariz. and n. Mexico to s. Mexico; fairly common. Habitat and biology similar to those of House Wren, with which many ornithologists believe it should be considered conspecific.

WINTER WREN (*Troglodytes troglodytes*)

Appearance: Smaller (4–4½ in.) than the House Wren and rather similar to it, but plumage, above and below, is in more reddish browns, and barring, especially on tail, flank, and to rear of body below, is darker. The tail is comparatively much shorter.

Voice: A fifelike, rollicking cadenza of warbles, trills, and rapid, tumbling notes usually ending on a sweet, high trill. The alarm or conversational call is an explosive *kip* or *kip-kip*.

Range and status: Breeds from the Pribilofs and Aleutian Is., s. Alaska, s. Yuk., s.-c. Mack., c. Sask., s. Man., n. Ont., c. Que., and Nfld. south to c. Calif., c. Idaho, nw. Wyo., n. Mont., the Great Lakes region, through the Appalachians to n. Ga., se. N.Y., w. Mass., Vt., N.H., Maine, N.B., and N.S.; from Iceland and n. Europe south to n. Africa, Palestine, Turkey, and w. and n. Iran; in the Tien Shan, Pamir, and Himalaya Mountains; and from se. Siberia, Sakhalin I., the Kurile Is., and the Commander Is. south to w.-c. and ne. China, Korea, Formosa, and s. Japan. There are 35 subspecies recognized in this range. Winters mainly within breeding areas, but at lower altitudes in mountains and scattered over vast continental areas from s. parts of breeding range south in U.S. to s. Calif., Ariz., c. Tex., the Gulf Coast, and s. Fla. Common.

Habitat: Varied; dense forests, especially those with thick undergrowth, woodland swamps, and along sea cliffs.

Seasonal movements: Moves north Mar.–Apr. and south Oct.–Nov. in America.

Biology: Nest: A somewhat spherical mass of twigs and mosses with a side entrance to the interior, which is lined with feathers, hair, fur, and plant down; built in cavities among exposed roots of forest trees, rock crevices, and holes in trees. Eggs: 4–7, usually 5–6; white, with small spots and pepperings of reddish and yellowish browns. Incubation: 14–16 days. Age at 1st flight: About 19 days. Food: Beetles, bugs, spiders, caterpillars, ants, and other insects and small invertebrates.

Suggested reading: E. A. Armstrong, *The Wren,* Macmillan, N.Y., 1955, 312 pp.

BEWICK'S WREN (*Thryomanes bewickii*)

Appearance: Slightly larger (5–5½ in.) than the House Wren. Dark tawny above, including the wing, which has dusky brown barring; a very pale smoke-gray below. A distinct white streak borders the cap just above the eye. The rather long, dark smoke-gray tail is barred and margined with black, all but the central feathers are tipped with white, and the outermost feathers are edged with white spots. The legs and feet are light buffy brown, and the black-tipped bill is buffy brown.

Voice: A common *plit* of alarm; a loud, pleasant rattle; and a *chip-chip-chip-te-da-a-te-de-e-e* song, sometimes with interspersed trills in a pleasant, melodic series.

Range and status: Largely resident from sw. B.C., c. Wash., Nev., s. Utah, sw. Wyo., c. Colo., se. Nebr., s. Iowa, s. Wisc., s. Mich., s. Ont., c. Pa., and Va. south to Guadalupe I., s. Baja Calif., c. Mexico, n. edges of the Gulf States, c. Ga., and c. S.C. Winters at lower altitudes and south to the Gulf Coast and s. Fla. Rather rare, but may be locally common; ousted from some areas by the House Wren.

Habitat: Brushy areas, gardens, juniper, piñon, chaparral, and open woodlands.

Seasonal movements: Moves north mid-Feb.–Apr. and south mid-Sept.–mid-Nov.

Biology: Nest: In almost any cavity or on any ledge and in birdhouses; a mass of sticks, leaves, and debris fills the crevice or hole, with a deep cup on top made of feathers, hair, and other soft materials. Eggs: 4–11, usually 5–7; white, irregularly spotted and dotted with browns, purples, and grays, sometimes nearly immaculate. Incubation: 14(?) days. Age at 1st flight: About 14 days. Food: Various insects, spiders, and other small invertebrates; less than 3% vegetable matter, which is probably swallowed with insect food.

Suggested reading: E. V. Miller, "Behavior of the Bewick Wren," *Condor,* vol. 43, pp. 81–99, 1941.

CAROLINA WREN (*Thryothorus ludovicianus*)

Appearance: Larger (5¼–6 in.) than the House Wren; brownish red above and tawny (grading to almost

Removal of a birdhouse roof reveals the bulky nest of a Bewick's Wren.

About 14 days. Age at 1st flight: 13–14 days. There are 2 broods each year. Food: Insects, a few other small invertebrates, and less than 6% seeds.

Suggested reading: M. M. Nice and R. H. Thomas, "A Nesting of the Carolina Wren." *Wils. Bull.*, vol. 60, pp. 139–158, 1948.

CACTUS WREN (*Campylorhynchus brunneicapillus*)

Appearance: Largest (7–8¾ in.) wren. Cap, nape, and back brownish red; rump, wing, and tail dark smoke-gray, with some white near the tip of the blackish outer tail feathers; wing and tail barred with blackish gray; and back streaked with white. There is a white streak just above the eye, from the forehead to the side of the nape. Below the streak a light flesh color grades into almost pure white at the throat, with the breast rather heavily spotted and the flank lightly spotted and streaked with black. The bill is a dusky straw-yellow, and the legs and feet are a dusky, light flesh.

Voice: A series of grating, accelerando whistles, as *chuh-chuh-chuh-chuh-chuh* in a monotone.

Range and status: Resident from s. Calif., s. Nev., sw. Utah, w. and s.-c. Ariz., s. N.Mex., and c. Tex. south to s. Baja Calif. and w.-c. and s.-c. Mexico. Common.

Habitat: Arid and semiarid areas of cactus, yucca, mesquite, or brush.

Even a canvas bag provides an acceptable nest site for the Carolina Wren.

The Cactus Wren's massive nest is built of twigs and straw.

white at the throat) below. A white streak runs from the forehead, just above the eye, almost to the nape; the tail and wing are barred with dusky brown. The black-tipped bill is smoke-gray, and the legs and feet are a dusky flesh.

Voice: The song is a rich, ringing, whistled *tea-kettle-tea-kettle-tea-kettle* or variations of this; other calls are rather short, rolling, scolding, clinking, metallic rattles and trills.

Range and status: Resident from se. Nebr., s. Iowa, s. Ill., se. Mich., s. Ont., s. Pa., se. N.Y., s. Conn., and se. Mass. south to n.-c. and ne. Mexico, the Gulf Coast, and s. Fla. Frequently farther north. Fairly common.

Habitat: Undergrowth-filled forests, shrubby areas, thickets, and the sides of brushy streams or lakes; prefers to be near water.

Seasonal movements: None.

Biology: Nest: Bulky masses of leaves, twigs, sticks, and debris, domed or with side entrance, lined with feathers and other soft materials; built in hole, cavity, or crotch of tree, in bird boxes, or in cavities among up-turned tree roots or stone walls. Eggs: 4–8, usually 5–6; white or pale pink, commonly heavily spotted with browns, but sometimes almost immaculate. Incubation:

Seasonal movements: None.

Biology: Nest: An ovoid mass of sticks, straw, and twigs, with entrance on side, near the top, into a chamber of felted feathers, webbing, and plant down; usually 2½–9 ft. above the ground in cactus or other desert scrub. Nest may be used several seasons; those not used as "nurseries" are used as "caravansaries." Eggs: 3–7, commonly 4–5; white to various shades of pink, rather evenly spotted and peppered with browns. Incubation: 16 days. Age at 1st flight: 19–23 days; may raise as many as 3 broods each year. Food: Insects, some spiders, and about 15% seeds and berries.

Suggested reading: A. H. Anderson and A. Anderson, "The Cactus Wrens on the Santa Rita Experimental Range, Arizona," *Condor*, vol. 66, pp. 344–351, 1965.

LONG-BILLED MARSH WREN (*Telmatodytes palustris*)

Appearance: About the size (4½–5½ in.) of the House Wren. Dark brownish red above and very pale smoke-gray below (darker on flank). A light buffy streak just above the eye; parallel black and white streaks cross the upper back. The wing and tail are barred with dusky brown. The bill, almost as long as the head, is dusky brown, and the legs and feet are dark straw-yellow.

Voice: Call note is a sibilant *tsuck* or a series, as *tsu-tsu-tsu-tsu-tsuck;* the song is a continuum of throaty, gurgling notes, a low bubbly trill, and a squeaky rattle, as *gug-gug-gug-dr-r-r-di-di-di-di-di.*

Range and status: Breeds from c. B.C., n. Alta., s.-c. Sask., s. Man., s. Ont., sw. Que., s. Maine, and e. N.B. south to n. Baja Calif., s.-c. Mexico, the Gulf Coast, and s. Fla. In winter seldom found north of the Gulf Coast states between the Rockies and Appalachians; elsewhere generally resident, but in reduced numbers to north. Locally common.

Habitat: Freshwater and brackish-water marshes with cattails, rushes, sedges, and reeds.

Seasonal movements: Moves north Mar.–mid-May and south mid-Sept.–mid-Nov.

Biology: Nest: A spherical construction of moist reed and grass leaves with side entrance to inner chamber, which is lined with finer materials and feathers; lashed to tall marsh plants such as cattails, bulrushes, and other reeds, 1–3 ft. above the water in marshes and marshy edges of ponds and rivers. While the female is raising the family in the nest, the male may build 5–6 incomplete dummy nests nearby. Eggs: 3–10, usually 5–6; the ground color is usually a dull brown, sometimes dull gray or pinkish, evenly sprinkled with small specks of darker browns, which may sometimes obscure the ground color or be gathered in a wreath about the larger end. Incubation: 13–16 days. Age at 1st flight: 11–16 days. Food: Almost entirely the varied kinds of insects found near marshes, sometimes caught in midair in the manner of flycatchers; the young are at first fed the softer-bodied types.

Suggested reading: J. Verner, "Breeding Biology of the Long-billed Marsh Wren," *Condor*, vol. 67, pp. 6–30, 1965.

SHORT-BILLED MARSH WREN (*Cistothorus platensis*)

Appearance: Smaller (4–4½ in.) than the House Wren, with bill a little less than half as long as the head. Cap, nape, back, and rump fuscous, wing brownish red, and tail buffy brown. The cap is streaked with buff, the back with black and white (less prominently than that of the Long-billed Marsh Wren), and the tail and wing are barred with dark browns. Below, it is a light tawny, almost white at the throat and center of the abdomen. The dark-tipped bill, legs, and feet are dusky, light flesh.

Voice: The song is a rather wooden, chattering trill, with gradually increasing cadence toward the end. The call note is a simple low *chap.*

Range and status: Breeds from se. Sask., s. Man., w. Ont., s. Que., s. Maine, and e. N.B. south to Ark., the n. edge of the Ohio River Valley, W.Va., and Va. and from n.-c. Mexico to s. S. America (exclusive of the Amazon Basin) and the Falkland Is. The American subspecies winters from s. Tex., the lower Mississippi Valley, the Gulf Coast, and coastal Md. south to ne. Mexico and s. Fla. Locally common.

Habitat: Grass and sedge marshes

Seasonal movements: Moves north through Apr. and early May and returns Aug.–mid-Oct.

Biology: Nest: A globular structure of dried and green grasses or sedges with entrance in a side to the chamber, which is lined with feathers and plant down; built close to ground or surface of water in taller grasses or sedges, never high in reeds. Eggs: 4–8, usually 7; white. Incubation: 12–14 days. Age at 1st flight: 12–14 days. Food: Insects in all forms, spiders, etc.

Suggested reading: L. H. Walkinshaw, "Studies of the Short-billed Marsh Wren in Michigan," *Auk*, vol. 52, pp. 362–369, 1935.

CAÑON WREN (*Catherpes mexicanus*)

Appearance: Larger (5½–5¾ in.) than the House Wren. Cap, nape, and cheeks fuscous; back, rump, tail, wing, belly, and feathers under tail brownish red; throat and breast white. There are some lines of faint white spots on the cap and nape and dark brown barring on the wing and tail. The blackish crescentic spots on the belly have some whitish on the concave side. The long bill is blackish above and straw-yellow below; the legs and feet are light dusky brown.

Voice: A loud, joyous rhapsody of pleasing slurred notes, as *peup-peup-peup-peup-peup* in descending scale. Also a harsh *peenk* call.

Range and status: Resident from n.-c. Calif. and (east of the Cascades and Sierra Nevadas) from s.-c. B.C., Idaho, se. Mont., and sw. S.Dak. south to s. Baja Calif., s. Mexico, and c. Tex. Locally common.

Habitat: Cliffsides, canyons, talus slopes, and stone buildings.

Seasonal movements: None.

Biology: Nest: Mosses, leaves, and spider webbing on a base of twigs, with a deep cup lined with felted wool, hair, and plant down; built on rock shelves and ledges. Eggs: 4–7, usually 5–6; white, sparingly spotted with browns or nearly immaculate. Incubation and age at 1st flight unknown. Food: Probably entirely insects.

ROCK WREN (*Salpinctes obsoletus*)

Appearance: Larger (5–6¼ in.) than the House Wren, with a rather large tail. Cap, nape, back, wing, and tail are smoke-gray (darker on cap); below, white at throat grades into light tawny on lower flank and beneath tail. There are some whitish or buffy spots near the tips of the outer tail feathers. There is a buffy streak just above the eye, some buffy and blackish spots and short streaks on crown and back, and dark, smoke-gray streaks on breast and partway down the flank. The rather long bill is blackish above and dark-tipped straw-yellow below, and the legs and feet are fuscous.

Voice: A harsh, grating, sometimes titillating chant or series of trills, as *tur-tur-tur-tur, keree-keree-keree-tr-r-r-r-r* or *ti-yu, ti-yu, ti-yu* and other variations; the calls

Even when it sings, the Cañon Wren is easily overlooked in its rocky habitat.

The Rock Wren usually lives in areas drier than those inhabited by the Cañon Wren.

are a rather raspy, monotonous trill and a loud *tick-ear*.

Range and status: Breeds from s.-c. B.C., s. Alta., s. Sask., nw. N.Dak., and s. S.Dak. south to the Revilla Gigedo Is. off Mexico, and through C. America to Costa Rica. Winters from n. Calif., s. Nev., s. Utah. n.-c. N.Mex., and s. Tex. southward. Locally common.

Habitat: High, dry plains, rocky mountain slopes, talus slopes, and cliffs; generally in drier areas than Cañon Wren.

Seasonal movements: Moves north late Mar.–early May and returns Sept.–Oct.

Biology: Nest: In crevices and holes in rock, under loose rocks, or in burrows (probably dug by other animals) in loam or clay banks; entrance usually paved with small, flat stones; nest is made of rootlets, plant stems, and finer material toward center, the lining of matted fur and feathers. Eggs: 4–10, usually 5–6; white, sparingly and irregularly marked with browns. Incubation and age at 1st flight unknown. Food: Insects, spiders, etc.

Suggested reading: A. C. Bent, *Life Histories of North American Nuthatches, Wrens, Thrashers, and Their Allies*, Dover, N.Y. (reprint of U.S. Nat. Mus. Bull. 195, 1948), 1964, pp. 284–294.

Large white wing patches are the Mockingbird's best field marks.

MOCKINGBIRDS, CATBIRDS, AND THRASHERS (MIMIDAE)

This family of small (8–13 in.) songbirds is probably most closely related to the wrens, thrushes, and robins. There are 31 species, 10 in America, ranging from s. Canada through C. America and the W. Indies to c. Chile and c. Argentina, where they are common and prominent members of the avifauna. Only those species of the cooler temperate regions are migratory. Most species are arboreal, but many feed on the ground. Plumage occurs in grays and browns above, usually white or lighter shades of grays or browns below; many species are spotted or streaked, especially below, and with some black. The sexes are alike, or almost so. The wings are relatively short and rounded, and the tail is nearly as long as the body. The legs are long and stout, the feet strong. The bill is fairly long and slightly to rather well decurved.

These birds fly well, but usually only for short distances. The voice is well developed, and the songs are complex; most species are noted mimics of other birds' songs, hence the family sobriquet, "mimic thrushes." Courtship is, most often, simply an aerial pursuit of female by male through the woods and underbrush, which is not courtship as we ordinarily think of it. The birds are very rarely seen in flocks, being rather solitary in habit except when spring brings them together in pairs. Nests are bulky structures in bushes or on the ground, with well-shaped cups. The 2–5 eggs are in pastel shades of buff, green, and blue. In some species the female alone incubates; in all species both sexes feed and care for the young. The hatchlings are naked except for a little down above. Insects, fruit, and seeds form the principal food items.

MOCKINGBIRD (*Mimus polyglottos*)

Appearance: Robin-sized (9–11 in.), but looks longer and slimmer because of the relatively longer tail. Medium gray above and very pale gray below; the central tail feathers, especially near the tip, are almost black, the outermost feather on each side is white, and the tips of the next 2–3 feathers from the outside are

white. There are 2 white bars on the wing, and in flight there is a large whitish patch near the tip of the wing. The nearly straight bill and the legs and feet are blackish gray; the eye is pale yellow.

Voice: A rich variety of musical notes and phrases, each usually repeated as many as 5–6 times before moving into the next cadenza with hardly a pause. Mockingbirds often sing at night, particularly in the spring, and in the daytime may mimic the calls of night birds such as Whip-poor-wills and owls. The call note is an emphatic *tchack* or *tchair*.

Range and status: Resident from n.-c. Calif., c. Nev., n. Utah, se. Wyo., s. S.Dak., c. Iowa, c. Ill., c. Ind., Ohio, W.Va., Md., and c. N.J. (locally and irregularly to Mass.) south to s. Baja Calif., s. Mexico, the Greater Antilles, the Virgin Is., and the Bahamas; introduced and established in Hawaii. In winter, may retreat somewhat from n. edges of range. Common.

Habitat: Open areas, gardens, agricultural lands, parklands, more open woodlands, and brushy regions; near streams in desert areas.

Seasonal movements: None measurable.

Biology: The so-called courtship dance is not that at all, but merely a jockeying for position in territorial flights. While on the ground or perching, the bird habitually flashes its wings by swiftly extending them upward and then drawing them back to the rest position. Nest: Made of short twigs and lined with grasses and rootlets; usually 3–10 ft. above the ground in a small tree or shrub or in climbing vines. Eggs: 3–6, usually 4–5; light to medium pastel shades of blue and green, commonly

Regular removal of membranous fecal sacs keeps the Catbird's nest clean.

heavily marked with browns. Incubation: 12–12½ days, by female alone. Age at 1st flight: 10½–12½ days. Food: Slightly over 50% vegetable matter, mainly wild berries, seeds, and other fruit (less than 4% cultivated fruit); insects make up the bulk of the animal food consumed, along with a few spiders and other small invertebrates and an occasional small vertebrate.

Suggested reading: A. R. Laskey, "Breeding Biology of Mockingbirds," *Auk,* vol. 79, pp. 596–606, 1962.

CATBIRD (*Dumetella carolinensis*)

Appearance: Smaller (8–9¼ in.) than the Robin. Cap and nape black; rump, back, wing, and tail dark to blackish gray; and undertail feathers tawny. Face and rest of underparts light to medium gray. The rather straight bill, legs, and feet are black; the eye is brown.

Voice: Song is very variable in pitch and content, but most commonly in rather high pitch; unlike song of Mockingbird or some thrashers in that each phrase is different and is not repeated in same song. The call is a distinctive catlike mewing; other common calls may only be described as squealing.

Range and status: Breeds from s. Canada south through e. Wash. and e. Ore. to n.-c. Utah, e.-c. Ariz., n.-c. N.Mex., Tex., c. La., c. Miss., c. Ala., and s. Ga., rarely to s. Fla. and Bermuda. Winters from s.-c. and ne. Mexico, se. Tex., se. Ark., c. Ala., c. Ga., c. S.C., e. N.C., and se. Va. south to Panama, and the W. Indies; casually north to S.Dak., s. Ont., and n. New England. Has straggled to Calif., Nev., w. Tex., Colombia, and Germany. Common.

Habitat: Forest undergrowth, shrubby areas, and gardens.

Seasonal movements: Moves north Mar.–mid-May and south Aug.–early Nov.

Biology: Nest: Made of twigs, sticks, grasses, leaves, and weed stems with a neat, deep cup lined with hair, rootlets, bark of grape vines, and other soft materials; built in dense thickets, vines, shrubs, or low, brushy trees. Eggs: 2–6, usually 4; a glossy, dark pastel greenish blue. Incubation: 12–15 days. Age at 1st flight: 9–15 days; commonly 2 broods each year. Food: About 55% vegetable matter, largely berries and other fruits and seeds; animal food is almost entirely insects, with a few spiders and other small invertebrates consumed.

Suggested reading: W. P. Nickell, "Habits, Territory, and Nesting of the Catbird," *Amer. Midland Naturalist,* vol. 73, pp. 433–478, 1965.

BROWN THRASHER (*Toxostoma rufum*)

Appearance: Slightly larger (10½–12 in.) than the Robin. Tawny above, including wing and long tail. White below, with smoke-gray cheeks and streak above the eye and with streaky spots of brown on the breast and flank. There are 2 whitish stripes on the wing. The long, noticeably decurved bill is fuscous above and fuscous-tipped straw-yellow below. The legs and feet are a dusky straw-yellow, and the eye is yellow.

Voice: The song is a series of loud, clear whistles in measured phrases often repeated 2–3 times in rapid succession; the repertoire is extensive and generally worth listening to. The call note is a loud, sibilant or buzzy *tee-o-la* or a harsh, slurred series, as *teea-teea-teea*. Its imitations are less frequent than those of the Catbird or Mockingbird, but competent.

Range and status: Breeds from se. Alta., s. Sask., s. Man., w. Ont., n. Minn., s. Ont., sw. Que., n. Vt., c. N.H., and sw. Maine south, east of the Rockies, to the Gulf Coast and s. Fla. Winters from e. Okla., Ark., s. Tenn., n. Ga., N.C., and s. Md. south to the Gulf Coast and s. Fla. Irregularly farther north in winter. Has straggled to Ore., Calif., Utah, Ariz., N.Mex., Bermuda, Cuba, and Germany. Common.

Habitat: Hedgerows, brushy fields, thickets, and brushy edges of woodlands.

Seasonal movements: Moves northward Mar.–mid-May and returns late Aug.–Oct.

Biology: Nest: Made of twigs, dry leaves, bark, and grasses, lined in deep cup with rootlets; built on the ground (mainly in the East), in a low brushy tree, or in a shrub. Eggs: 4–6, usually 4–5; pale bluish to almost white and evenly, often thickly, spotted and peppered with browns. Incubation: 12–14 days, by both sexes. Age at 1st flight: About 11 days. Food: Over 60% animal food, almost entirely insects and a few other small invertebrates; vegetable food is largely fruit, nuts, and seeds.

Suggested reading: W. G. Erwin, "Some Nesting Habits of the Brown Thrasher," *Journ. Tenn. Acad. Sci.,* vol. 10, pp. 179–204, 1935.

LONG-BILLED THRASHER (Sennett's Thrasher)
(Toxostoma longirostre)

Appearance: Same size (10–12 in.) as the Brown Thrasher, which it resembles closely except that it is buffy brown above (dark smoke-gray cap and nape), the cheeks are grayish, and the spots on the white breast are black. The bill is longer, more decurved, and black.

Voice: Very similar to Brown Thrasher's.

Range and status: Resident from s.-c. Tex. south to c. and e.-c. Mexico.

Like most of its relatives, the sleek Brown Thrasher is a notable mimic.

Bendire's Thrasher

Habitat: Open woodlands with undergrowth, mesquite.

Seasonal movements: None.

Biology: Probably very similar in all respects to that of the Brown Thrasher.

BENDIRE'S THRASHER (*Toxostoma bendirei*)

Appearance: Robin-sized (9–11 in.). Brownish olive above, including wing and tail. Smoke-gray below, with a whitish throat and faint streaking spots of darker smoke-gray on the breast and flank. The slightly decurved black bill is buffy brown at the base; the legs and feet are a dusky yellow. The eye is scarlet-orange.

Voice: Song is a continuous warble with no pauses; there is apparently much variation in theme, but execution is the same, including many burry double notes. The call note is a low *tee-up.*

Range and status: Breeds from se. Calif., nw. Ariz., s. Nev., s. Utah, and sw. N.Mex. south to w.-c. Mexico. Winters from s. Ariz. to Sinaloa. Locally fairly common.

Habitat: Arid and semiarid lands, agricultural lands, and brushlands.

Seasonal movements: Rather irregular.

Biology: Nest: Neatly and compactly built of twigs and lined with grasses and hair; built 1½–12 ft. above the ground in mesquite, cholla, or other low tree or bush. Eggs: 3–5, usually 3; pale bluish green, irregularly spotted and blotched with pale browns. Incubation and age at 1st flight unknown. Food: Mainly insects, probably some fruit and seeds.

CURVE-BILLED THRASHER (*Toxostoma curvirostre*)

Appearance: Slightly larger (9½–11½ in.) than Bendire's Thrasher, which it resembles, but slightly more reddish brown above, throat is not so whitish, and spotting on breast and flank is more obscure. The somewhat longer blackish bill is distinctly decurved. The eye is orange.

Voice: Song is a loud, clear, melodious carol, but somewhat slow and interrupted; the call notes are a loud, startling, whip-swishing trio and a softer, liquid *tee-dle-lah.*

Range and status: Resident from nw. and c. Ariz., N.Mex., and w. and s. Tex. south to s. Mexico. Locally common.

Habitat: Arid and semiarid brush.

Seasonal movements: None.

Biology: Nest: A loose weaving of thorny twigs, lined with rootlets, grasses, fine bark, hair, and feathers; built 3–6 ft. above the ground in cholla or other scrubby bushes. Eggs: 2–4, usually 3; pale bluish green, evenly peppered with pale browns. Incubation: About 13 days,

The Curve-billed Thrasher is a year-round resident of dry, bushy areas in the Southwest.

by both sexes. Age at 1st flight: 14–18 days. Food: Insects, berries, and other fruits.

CALIFORNIA THRASHER (*Toxostoma redivivum*)

Appearance: Larger (11–13 in.) than the Robin; dark brownish olive above, including wing and tail, and smoke-gray below, tinged with pinkish on the belly and undertail feathers. The cheek is streaked with brownish olive, the sharply decurved bill is dusky brown, the legs and feet are buffy brown, and the eye is brown.

Voice: Call notes are a dull, flat *chack* and a harsh scream of alarm; the song, not given so often as by other thrashers, is a long series of pleasant musical notes and phrases, interlarded with harsher notes and imitations of other birds, all at a rather leisurely pace.

Range and status: Resident from n. Calif. to n. Baja Calif. Fairly common.

Habitat: Semiarid brush (chaparral), brushy areas in foothills and valleys, parks, and suburban areas.

Seasonal movements: None.

Biology: Nest: Made of sticks and twigs, lined with rootlets, grasses, and fibers; built near ground in bush or shrubby tree. Eggs: 2–4, commonly 3; pale blues or blue greens, evenly spotted and flecked with pale browns. Incubation: 14 days, by both sexes. Age at 1st flight: 12–14 days. Food: Nearly 60% wild berries and other fruit; insects and other small invertebrates make up rest of diet.

Suggested reading: G. I. Sargent, "Observations on the Behavior of Color-banded California Thrashers," *Condor*, vol. 42, pp. 49–60, 1940.

LE CONTE'S THRASHER (*Toxostoma lecontei*)

Appearance: About the size (10–11 in.) of the Robin. Light brownish gray above and immaculate pale brownish gray to whitish below, with a long, decurved black bill, buffy brown legs and feet, and brown eyes.

Voice: Alarm note is a loud, sharp, much-repeated *whit* or *quit*, the most common call a low, whistled *hew-eep* or *hew-hew-eep;* the song, not heard so often as those of most other thrashers, is rather sweet and low, without much repetition of notes or phrases.

Range and status: Resident from c. Calif., s. Nev., sw. Utah, and w. and c. Ariz. south to c. Baja Calif. and nw. Sonora. Rather rare.

Habitat: Arid and semiarid flats with sparse scrub.

Seasonal movements: None.

Biology: Nest: Made of long twigs and grasses, with a neat, deep cup of felted leaves and scraps of paper; built in saltbush or other scrub. Eggs: 2–4, usually 3; pale greenish blues, decorated with small spots of pale browns. Incubation period unknown, but by both sexes. Age at 1st flight unknown. Food: Insects; probably also some berries and fruit.

The California Thrasher's bill is even more deeply curved than the Curve-billed Thrasher's.

Suggested reading: J. Grinnell, "The Le Conte Thrasher of San Joaquin," *Condor*, vol. 35, pp. 107–114, 1933.

CRISSAL THRASHER (*Toxostoma dorsale*)

Appearance: Slightly larger (10½–12½ in.) than the Robin. Brownish olive above and dark smoke-gray below, almost white at the throat, with tawny undertail feathers. The long, well-decurved bill is black, the legs and feet are sepia, and the eye is straw-yellow.

Voice: A more melodious, even-cadenced song than those of most thrashers; calls are a *queety-queety,* a scolding *cha*, and a solicitous *pichoory-pichoory* repeated 2–3 times.

Range and status: Resident from se. Calif., s. Nev., sw. Utah, n. Ariz., s. N.Mex., and w.-c. Tex. south to ne. Baja Calif. and nw. and s.-c. Mexico. Rather rare.

Habitat: Thickets and dense brushy growths along streams in desert areas and irrigated lands in semiarid regions.

Seasonal movements: None.

Biology: Nest: Made of sticks and thorny twigs with a deep, neat bowl of felted feathers and plant fiber; built in thick bushes or dense scrubby trees or shrubs. Eggs: 2–4, usually 2–3; immaculate pale blues. Incubation: 14 days, by male and female. Age at 1st flight: 16 days. Food: Insects, seeds, berries, and fruit; an occasional small lizard.

Despite its name, the Sage Thrasher is not limited to sagebrush areas.

SAGE THRASHER (*Oreoscoptes montanus*)

Appearance: Smaller (8–9 in.) than the Robin and most thrushlike of the thrashers in looks. Brownish olive above, including wing and tail, with a short and a long white wing bar and white-tipped outer tail feathers. Whitish below, with dark brown longish spots subjoined into long streaks almost the length of the undersides. The dark brown bill is rather short and straight and similar to the Robin's; the tail is relatively short; and the legs and feet are buffy brown. The eye is yellow.

Voice: Song is a continuous outpouring of clear-whistled warbles, mixed near the end with more intricate trills and burring notes. The most common calls are a *chuck-chuck* of alarm and a high, pleasant *wheurr.*

Range and status: Breeds from s.-c. B.C., c. Idaho, s.-c. Mont., and n. and se. Wyo. south, east of the Coast Ranges to s.-c. Calif., s. Nev., Utah, n.-c. N.Mex., nw. Tex., and w. Okla., with an isolated "colony" in sw. Sask. Winters from Calif., s. Nev., n. Ariz., s. N.Mex., and c. and s. Tex. south to s. Baja Calif. and n. Mexico; casually and irregularly farther north. Has straggled to N.Dak., S.Dak., Nebr., Kans., La., and N.Y. Common.

Habitat: Semiarid sagebrush and scrub areas, also brushy slopes and, in winter, deserts.

Seasonal movements: Moves north in Mar. and Apr. and returns Aug.–Nov.

Biology: Nest: A bulky platform of coarse sticks, twigs, plant stems, and sage bark with a cup of fine rootlets, sometimes hair, and fur; built on ground, in bushes such as sagebrush, or in brush piles. Eggs: 4–7, commonly 4–5; a rather deep blue or greenish blue, spotted and blotched with browns. Incubation period unknown; male certainly assists at least to some extent. Age at 1st flight unknown. Food: Insects and some berries and other wild fruit.

Suggested reading: A. C. Bent, *Life Histories of North American Nuthatches, Wrens, Thrashers, and Their Allies,* Dover, N.Y. (reprint of U.S. Nat. Mus. Bull. 195, 1948), 1964, pp. 427–437.

THRUSHES, ROBINS, BLUEBIRDS, AND SOLITAIRES (TURDIDAE)

This family of small (4½–13 in.) songbirds is related to the Old World warblers and to the flycatchers, as well as to the thrashers, wrens, and dippers. There are 306 species ranging throughout the world (except for the polar regions, n. New Zealand, and some oceanic islands); 23 species are found in America. These include the European Redwing and Blackbird, which have been recorded from Greenland; 6 species found in Hawaii; and 3 others, which have barely reached our shores. Most of the species are at least partially migratory. They are predominantly birds of the woodlands or field borders. Plumage is characteristically in muted combinations of browns, grays, blues, black, and white; a few exotic species have glossy plumage. Most of the immature birds and some of the adults are prominently spotted on the breast. The wings may be long and pointed or short and rounded. The tail is commonly short and square-tipped, but in many species it is long, and in a few species forked. The moderately long bill may be slender or stout, the sturdy legs are usually long (short in very few species), and the feet are strong. The sexes are alike or nearly so in most American species, being most unlike in the bluebirds. Songs are varied and commonly complex and pleasant. Courtship is rather simple, but is initiated by complex territorial-defense and sex-recognition behavior, indicating that when the sexes look alike they do not recognize each other except through behavioral differences. In such cases, the males arrive first at the breeding grounds and set up territories before the females arrive. Formerly the Hermit, Swainson's, and Gray-cheeked Thrushes and the Veery were included in the genus *Hylocichla* with the Wood Thrush, but pronounced behavioral differences between these thrushes and the Wood Thrush have led many ornithologists to place them in a separate genus, *Catharus*. Nests are commonly open cups of various plant materials, built on the ground, on tree branches, in natural cavities, in shrubbery, or on ledges. The 2–6 eggs are white or pastel hues, spotted or, rarely, immaculate. In many species the male assists in incubation, and in all species he helps feed the nestlings, which are covered with sparse down on hatching. Some species eat mostly animal food, others mostly vegetable food, and the majority eat various proportions of both.

ROBIN (*Turdus migratorius*)

Appearance: A large (9–11 in.) thrush. Brownish olive above, including wing and tail, but variable through range: in some areas more brownish, in others almost black, especially on head, wings, and tail. Light brownish red below, with white lower belly and undertail feathers and a black-streaked white throat. The dark-tipped bill is dusky straw-yellow; the legs and feet are buffy brown. In fall and winter the bird is duller, and the feathers below are tipped with whitish. The female may be generally duller. The immature birds are similar to the female, but only the upper breast and flank are light brownish red, the rest being whitish. All the underparts but the throat are rather heavily spotted with black.

Voice: Most common calls are a *tut-tut* of warning or alarm and a *skeet-skeet* with many variants, plus hissing and trilling notes. The most common rendering of the caroling song, sung over and over again, especially in morning and evenings of spring days, is *cheerup-cheerup-cheerup-cheerily*.

Range and status: Breeds from the tree limit of N. America (including Nfld.) south to s. Calif., s. Mexico, the Gulf Coast, and s. Ga. Winters regularly from sw. B.C., Wash., s. Idaho, Wyo., s. N.Dak., s. Minn., s. Wis., s. Ont., N.Y., Vt., N.H., s. Maine, and s. Nfld. south to s. Baja Calif., Guatemala, the Gulf Coast, and s. Fla.; casually farther north. Common.

Habitat: Towns, suburbs, open woodlands, and agricultural lands; in winter, areas where berries and other fruits cling to trees and shrubs.

Seasonal movements: The "first" Robin of spring is apt to be a bird emerging from the nearby berry-stocked, shrubby areas where it had wintered. Mass northward movements generally Mar.–Apr. and return flights Sept.–Oct.

Biology: The springtime pursuit flights, often described as courtship performances, are most likely done

This western Robin has a bit more white about its eyes than does the eastern subspecies.

in defense of territories. Although they result in recognition of the female by the male, it should not be said that the pursued female is being courted. Nest: A neat, deep cup made of mud and grasses and lined with fine grasses; on ground (rarely), in tree or shrub, or on almost any kind of ledge. Eggs: 3–6, usually 4; immaculate pastel blue so familiar that robin's-egg blue is a standard color. Incubation: 12½–13 days, almost entirely by female. Age at 1st flight: 14–16 days; usually at least 2 broods raised each year. Food: In woodlands and during winter in the North mainly berries and other fruits; all forms of insects and other small invertebrates; earthworms and insect grubs on our lawns in summer, as well as cultivated wild fruits and berries.

Suggested reading: H. Young, "Breeding Behavior and Nesting of the Eastern Robin," *Amer. Midland Naturalist*, vol. 53, pp. 329–352, 1955.

FIELDFARE (*Turdus pilaris*)

Robin-sized (10 in.) and Robinlike, with medium gray head and rump, chestnut back and wing, and dusky brown tail and wing tip. White below, with rufous breast and chevron-shaped blackish spots covering the breast and flank. The dark-tipped bill is straw-yellow, and the legs and feet are buffy brown. It ranges from Greenland, Iceland, n. Europe, and nw. Siberia south to the Mediterranean, n. Iran, and nw. India. It has straggled to Jens Munk I. off Baffin I. in the Canadian Archipelago.

VARIED THRUSH (*Ixoreus naevius*)

Appearance: Slightly smaller (9–10 in.) than the Robin. Blackish gray above, including the wing and tail; the throat, breast, 2 wing bars, and a streak from the eye to the back of the head are bright tawny. A band of blackish gray crosses the upper breast. The rest of the underparts and the tips of the outer tail feathers are white. The bill, legs, and feet are blackish. The female's breast bar is gray and that of the young is spotted with rufous; the young are spotted elsewhere below with dusky brown.

Voice: Song is a series of 5–6 long, haunting, vibrating, whistled notes of 5–6 different tones; each series, which may be higher or lower, is separated from the next by a slight pause. Call notes are a weak, sibilant *tschook* and a low, buzzy whistled *vwoooeee*.

Range and status: Breeds from n.-c. Alaska, c. Yuk., and nw. Mack. south to nw. Calif., n. Idaho, and nw. Mont. Winters from s. B.C. and n. Idaho south to w.-c. and s. Calif. and ne. Baja Calif. Has straggled to Alta., Mont., n. Alaska, and as far east as Que., Mass., and N.J. Common in mountains.

Habitat: Dense, humid, coniferous and mixed (rarer) forests; during winter, a variety of moist woodlands, thickets, and wooded canyons.

Seasonal movements: Much migration is from higher altitudes to lower; moves north Mar.–mid-May and south Sept.–mid-Nov.

Biology: Nest: In small trees; made of mosses reinforced with twigs and lined with fine grasses. Eggs: 2–5, usually 3–4; pale blue, evenly and sparsely spotted and dotted with dark browns. Incubation: About 2 weeks, by female alone. Age at 1st flight unknown; perhaps 2 broods are raised each year. Food: Berries, nuts, other seeds, and fruits; also insects and other small invertebrates.

Suggested reading: L. Sumner and J. S. Dixon, *Birds and Mammals of Sierra Nevada*, Univ. Calif. Press, Berkeley, 1953, pp. 171–172.

WOOD THRUSH (*Hylocichla mustelina*)

Appearance: Smaller (7½–8½ in.) than the Robin. Light brownish red above, grading to sepia on the rump, tail, and tip of the wing. White below, with prominent roundish black spots on the breast and flank. The bill, legs, and feet are buffy brown; the eye is dark brown.

Voice: There are 3 common calls: a short, soft whistled *tr-r-r-r*, an impatient *pit-pit-pit* when somewhat alarmed, and a more emphatic *quirt-quirt-quirt* when danger threatens. The song is a loud, ringing, well-separated series of phrases consisting of 7–10 notes, each of clear, bell-like quality, as *eeohlay—ayolee—ahleelee —ayleahlolah—ilolilee*.

Range and status: Breeds from se. S.Dak., c. Minn.,

c. Wis., n. Mich., s. Ont., s. Que., n. Vt., c. N.H., and sw. Maine south to the Gulf Coast and n. Fla.; casually farther north and west. Winters from s. Tex. south through e. Mexico and C. America to Panama; in migration to Cuba. Has straggled to Colo., the Bahamas, Bermuda, Curaçao, and Guyana. Common.

Habitat: Low, cool, humid deciduous forests.

Seasonal movements: Moves north Mar.–May and returns Sept.–Oct.

Biology: Nest: Like the Robin's, grasses and other plant material mixed with mud, forming a neat, deep cup lined with rootlets; 6–50 ft. above the ground, commonly low in sapling or shrub. Most Wood Thrushes incorporate white paper, birch bark, or broad leaves in foundation of nest. Eggs: 2–5, usually 3; immaculate pale blues or blue-greens. Incubation: 13–14 days, by female alone. Age at 1st flight: About 12–14 days; 2 broods each year. Food: Insects, worms, and other small invertebrates; about 33% plant food, such as berries and other wild fruit.

Suggested reading: J. Burroughs, "The Wood Thrush," *Bird Stories from Burroughs*, Houghton Mifflin, N.Y., 1911, pp. 83–90. H. Brackbill, "Nesting Behavior of the Wood Thrush," *Wils. Bull.*, vol. 70, pp. 70–89, 1958.

The Wood Thrush typically includes a few leaves or bits of paper in its bulky nest.

Like several of its relatives, the Hermit Thrush is noted for its melodious song.

HERMIT THRUSH (*Catharus guttata*)

Appearance: Small (6½–7¾ in.); grayish brown above, grading to a reddish brown rump and tail, and white below, with fine to medium streaky spots on the side of throat, breast, and flank. The relatively short bill is sepia, and the legs and feet are buffy brown. The eye is dark brown.

Voice: Calls a simple *quoit* or *chuck* when disturbed, but the song has been likened to that of the Nightingale in sweetness and musical quality. Some phrases of the song are too high for the average human ear. There are 8–12 notes in each phrase and 8–10 phrases in each song, with the tones, rather like those of a silver bell, strung together in pleasant ascending melody.

Range and status: Breeds from c. Alaska, s. Yuk., s. Mack., nw. Sask., s. Man., n. Ont., c. Que., s. Lab., and Nfld. south to mountains of s. Calif., n. N.Mex., c. Wis., n. Mich., c. Ont., ne. Ohio, w. Md., ne. Pa., se. N.Y., Conn., and Mass. Winters from sw. B.C., s. Ariz., w. and c. Tex., Ark., Ky., s. Ohio, n. Ga., c. N.C., c. Va., N.J., se. N.Y., and Conn. south to s. Baja Calif., Guatemala, the Gulf Coast, and s. Fla.; casually and irregularly farther north. Fairly common.

Habitat: Floors of coniferous or mixed forests; in winter any woods, thickets, or parks.

Seasonal movements: Moves north Mar.–early May and south Sept.–early Nov.

Biology: Nest: A compact construction of twigs, bark fibers, grasses, and ferns decorated externally with

Swainson's Thrush

mosses, the neat cup lined with pine needles, plant fibers, or rootlets. Eggs: 3–6, usually 3–4; very pale blue, commonly immaculate, but sometimes sparsely spotted with pale brown. Incubation: 12 days; probably by female only. Age at 1st flight: 12 days. Food: About 66% insects, spiders, snails, and other small invertebrates; vegetable matter consumed is mainly wild berries and fruit.

Suggested reading: John Burroughs, *Wake-Robin*, Houghton Mifflin, Boston, 1871, pp. 51–53.

SWAINSON'S THRUSH (Russet-backed Thrush, Olive-backed Thrush) (*Catharus ustulatus*)

Appearance: Same size (6½–7¾ in.) as the Hermit Thrush, which it resembles very closely, but entirely a buffy brown above and white below, with light buffy breast and flank. The eye is prominently ringed with buffy. The side of the throat and the breast are decorated with small blackish spots. The dark-tipped bill is straw-yellow, and the legs and feet are flesh-colored. Generally the populations in the West are slightly more reddish brown, and those in the East more grayish brown.

Voice: The call notes are a soft, liquid *whoit-whoit*, like 2 drops of water falling some distance into a half-filled bucket, and an abrupt, raspy *chee-ur-r-r*. This species' melodious whistled series of phrases, a typical thrush song, is more liquid than that of the Hermit Thrush, and the notes are not so clear. Each of the 3–8 phrases has 8–15 notes; usually the first 3 notes are the same, as *wheer-wheer-wheer-wheia-wheeia-wee-e-e*.

Range and status: Breeds from c. Alaska, n. Yuk., Mack., n. Man., n. Ont., c. Que., s. Lab., and Nfld. south to s. Alaska, Calif., Colo., s. Man., the n. Great Lakes region, through the Appalachians to W.Va., se. N.Y. (Catskills), s. Vt., and Maine. Winters from s. Mexico to Peru, nw. Argentina, w. Brazil, and Guyana; casually and irregularly farther north in Mexico. Has straggled to Bermuda and Europe. Fairly common.

Habitat: A bird of the n. spruce forest but also, especially in the West, of mixed-growth riparian woodlands, willow thickets, etc.

Seasonal movements: Moves north mid-Mar.–mid-May and returns Aug.–Nov.

Biology: Nest: Made of twigs, mosses, grasses, sedges, leaves, and rootlets, the neat cup lined with the finer materials; built in small trees or bushes 2–20 ft. above the ground. Eggs: 3–5, commonly 3–4; pale blues, generally evenly spotted and blotched with pale browns, some marked most heavily about the larger end. Incubation: 11–13 days, by female only. Age at 1st flight: 10–12 days. Food: Slightly more than 50% animal matter, such as insects and other small invertebrates, and seeds, berries, and other fruit.

Suggested reading: C. J. Stanwood, "The Olive-backed Thrush at His Summer Home," *Wils. Bull.*, vol. 25, pp. 118–137, 1913.

GRAY-CHEEKED THRUSH (Bicknell's Thrush) (*Catharus minimus*)

Appearance: Larger (7–8 in.) than the Hermit Thrush, but similar to it. Buffy brown or grayish brown above, including wing and tail, and white below, with a light buffy tinge on flank. Small blackish gray spots on side of throat and breast fade to light gray along flank. The cheek is grayish, and the eye-ring is dull and obscure. The bill is blackish gray above and flesh-colored below, and the eye is dark brown.

Voice: A variety of harsh or abrupt notes, as *what, chuck, pheu,* or *fee-ah;* the song is shorter than those of the previous 2 species, with liquid rolls and slurs. *Wee-oh, chee-chee-wee-oh, wee-oh* is a common transliteration.

Range and status: Breeds from ne. Siberia, n. Alaska, n. Mack., n. Man., n. Que., c. Lab., and Nfld. south to s. Alaska, ne. B.C., n. Sask., se. N.Y. (Catskills), nw. Mass., n. N.H., Maine, and s. N.S. The subspecies known as Bicknell's Thrush breeds in the mountains of N.Y., New England, and southeasternmost Canada. Winters from Nicaragua, Colombia, Venezuela, and Guyana to n. Peru, and nw. Brazil and in Hispaniola. In migration through s. Mexico and the Greater Antilles. Has straggled to Ariz., Greenland, and Europe. Fairly common.

Habitat: N. spruce-fir forests and scrub growth in tundra; in migration through the woodlands, groves, and farmlands of e. U.S. and Canada.

Seasonal movements: Moves north Mar.–early June and returns mid-Aug.–mid-Nov. The birds breeding in Siberia migrate through the Mississippi Valley.

Biology: Nest: Made of grasses mixed with a little mud and lined with finer grasses; built on the ground or up to 20 ft. high in low trees of scrub growth. Eggs: 3–6, usually 4; very pale blue or blue-green and very sparingly marked with pale brown dots and splotches. Incubation: 13–14 days, probably by female alone. Age at 1st flight: 11–13 days. Food: About 75% insects and other small invertebrates; plant food is mainly seeds and berries and other wild fruit.

Suggested reading: G. J. Wallace, "Bicknell's

Of all our thrushes, the Gray-cheeked Thrush travels farthest north to breed.

Thrush: Its Taxonomy, Distribution, and Life History," *Proc. Boston Soc. Nat. Hist.*, vol. 41, pp. 211–402, 1939.

VEERY (*Catharus fuscescens*)

Appearance: The same size (6½–7¾ in.) as the Hermit Thrush. Light brownish red or fuscous above, including wing and tail, and white below. Face, side of throat, and side of upper breast are reddish buff marked with small dark brown spots. The blackish-tipped bill is dusky straw-yellow, the legs and feet pale flesh, and the eye dark brown.

Voice: A clear whistled *hee-oo* and a low, guttural *whuck* of alarm are the commonest notes; the song is a series of 4–5 rolling, slurring, silvery, husky *whiree-u, whiree-u, whiree-u, whiree-u* phrases.

Range and status: Breeds from s. Canada (except sw. B.C.) and c. Nfld. south through the Rockies to ne. Ariz., s.-c. Colo., se. Wyo., ne. S.Dak., se. Minn., s. Wis.,

The Veery, common in moist woodlands, forages for insects on the forest floor.

the s. edge of the Great Lakes region, through the Appalachians to e. Tenn. and w. N.C., c. Va., c. Md., and c. N.J. Winters from C. America to Colombia, Venezuela, and c. and ne. Brazil. A very rare migrant in the Southwest; has straggled to Europe. Common.

Habitat: Moist deciduous forests and riparian and marshy woodlands.

Seasonal movements: Arrives at breeding grounds Apr.–mid-May and departs mid-Aug.–Oct.

Biology: Nest: Made on a heap of dead leaves of twigs, weed stalks, and leaves, with a lining of soft bark strips, rootlets, or grasses; built on or close to the ground, under or in a low tree or shrub. Eggs: 3–5, usually 4; immaculate light or pale blues, very rarely spotted with light browns. Incubation: 10–12 days. Age at 1st flight: 10(?) days. Food: Insects, spiders, snails, and other small invertebrates make up about 60% of the diet; berries and other wild fruit make up the rest.

Suggested reading: K. C. Day, "Home Life of the Veery," *Bird-banding*, vol. 24, pp. 100–106, 1953.

EASTERN BLUEBIRD (*Sialia sialis*)

Appearance: Smaller (6½–7½ in.) than the Robin. Light cobalt above, including tail and wing (the wing is almost black at the tip). The throat, breast, and flank are rufous, and the rest of the underparts are white. The female is a brownish blue on the head, nape, and back, and the ventral rufous is much paler. Immature birds have cobalt wings and tail, but the rest of the upperparts are bluish gray, as are the breast and flank, with heavy white spotting below and a scattering of white spots on the back. The bill, legs, and feet are black; the eye is dark brown.

Voice: Calls are a 2–3-syllabled, liquid *oola, aloo,* or *oolaloo* and a harsh *chat* or *chatat;* the song is a low, soft, gurgling *ayo-ala-looee—alee-ay-lalo-leeo.* John Burroughs claimed the Bluebird's song was *"Bermuda-Bermuda-Bermuda."*

Range and status: Breeds from s.-c. Ariz., s. Sask., s. Man., s. Ont., s. Que., N.B., and s. N.S. south to Nicaragua, the Gulf Coast, s. Fla., and Bermuda. Winters from s. Ariz., Nebr., Mo., the Ohio Valley, se. N.Y., and s. Mass. southward; casually and irregularly farther north. Was common, now almost rare. A. C. Bent, writing in 1949, remarked, "Bluebirds seem to have no human enemies; everybody loves the gentle birds and appreciates that they are very useful and harmless tenants in our orchards and about our farms and gardens." Today the Starling, introduced by man, usurps the nesting places of the Bluebird, and the sprays uncorked by man in even the smallest gardens have opened Pandora's box on the "gentle birds." The hole for Bluebird nest boxes should be no bigger than 1⅝ in. in diameter to bar the Starling and welcome back the Bluebird.

Habitat: Unpoisoned agricultural lands, open areas with scattered trees, gardens, and suburbs.

Over its extensive geographic range, the attractive Scrub Jay varies so much in pattern and color that it has been divided into thirteen subspecies in the United States and Canada.

The Long-billed Marsh Wren lashes its bulky nest to cattails and other marsh plants. The inside of the nest is lined with feathers and finer plant material.

Seasonal movements: Moves into more northerly areas late Feb.–Apr. and departs Sept.–Nov.

Biology: Nest: Made of twigs, weed stems, and grasses, lined with finer grasses; built in a cavity or hole in tree or post or in birdhouses 5–20 ft. above the ground, but 8–12 ft. preferred. Eggs: 3–7, usually 5–6; white or very pale blue. Incubation: 13–16 days (varies apparently with weather or latitude); the male has been known to assist. Age at 1st flight: 17–18 days; 2 broods commonly raised. Food: About **70%** insects and other small invertebrates and 30% plant food, mainly wild berries; most cultivated fruit eaten is taken in June and July.

Suggested reading: J. M. Hartshorne, "Behavior of the Eastern Bluebird at the Nest," *The Living Bird*, vol. 1, pp. 131–150, 1962.

WESTERN BLUEBIRD (*Sialia mexicana*)

Appearance: Somewhat smaller (6½–7 in.) than the Eastern Bluebird, which it resembles closely except that its throat and upper breast are light cobalt and the shoulder of the wing and the upper back are light chestnut. The female is like the female Eastern Bluebird except that the throat is white or pale grayish blue. Immature birds of the 2 species are hardly separable.

Voice: A few low *chu-chu-chu*'s pass as the song; the calls include 2–3 *miu*'s and a raspy, chattering phrase.

Range and status: Resident from s. B.C. and c. Mont. south through the mountains and highlands to n. Baja Calif. and s.-c. Mexico; in winter descends to lower altitudes. Fairly common.

Habitat: Open coniferous woodlands, agricultural lands, open areas with scattered trees; in winter also in deserts and scrub areas.

Seasonal movements: Reaches breeding areas in Mar. and departs in Oct.

Biology: Nest: Like that of the Eastern Bluebird, a hole or cavity in a tree or a bird box; made of loosely woven twigs, weed stems, and grasses and lined with finer grasses. Eggs: 3–8, commonly 4–6; very pale blue, occasionally white. Incubation period unknown; by female only. Age at 1st flight unknown; 2 broods each year. Food: More than 80% insects and other small invertebrates; plant matter consumed is mainly seeds and wild berries.

Suggested reading: F. F. Gander, "Western Bluebirds in My Garden," *Aud. Mag.*, vol. 62, pp. 70–71, 1960.

MOUNTAIN BLUEBIRD (*Sialia currucoides*)

Appearance: Slightly larger (6½–7¾ in.) than the Eastern Bluebird. Turquoise-cobalt above, with throat, breast, and flank a lighter shade of the same color. The abdomen and undertail feathers are white or bluish

Building birdhouses is a good way to attract the once common Eastern Bluebird.

white. The female is brownish gray above, with blue on the wing and tail, and whitish below, with smoke-gray on the breast and flank. The immature birds resemble the female, with light streaking on the back and pale spots on the breast. The bill, legs, and feet are black.

Voice: Rather silent; the seldom-heard song is a short, warbling *ku-ku-ku* or *keu-keu-keu;* the calls are a *tschuck* of alarm and a *pew* or *mew* note.

Range and status: Breeds from c. Alaska, s. Yuk., s. Mack., s. Sask., and sw. Man. south along e. slopes of Coast Ranges and through the mountains to nw. and s.-c. Calif., c. and se. Nev., n. Ariz., s. N.Mex., w. Okla., w. Nebr., S.Dak., and ne. N.Dak. Winters from s. B.C. and w. Mont. south to n. Baja Calif., n. Mexico, and s. Tex. Fairly common.

Habitat: Open areas with scattered trees and into treeless regions, especially in winter.

Seasonal movements: Moves into breeding latitudes and altitudes Mar.–Apr. and returns Sept.–early Nov.

Biology: Nest: As with other bluebirds, a loose structure of twigs and weed stems lined with grasses, in a hole or cavity in a tree or cliff or in a birdhouse. Eggs: 4–8, usually 5–6; pale blue. Incubation: 14 days; male assists. Age at 1st flight unknown. Food: More than 90% insects and other small invertebrates; also seeds, berries, and other fruit.

Suggested reading: F. W. Haecker, "A Nesting Study of the Mountain Bluebird in Wyoming," *Condor,* vol. 50, pp. 216–219, 1948.

HAWAIIAN THRUSH (Omao) (*Phaeornis obscurus*)

Appearance: Smaller (7–8 in.) than the Robin; sepia above, including wing and tail, and pale smoke-

This Wheatear carries a meal of insects to its nest.

gray below. The bill is brown, and the legs and feet are dark straw-yellow.

Voice: Song varies from island to island; in general a strong, emphatic *chup-wechew-chup,* often lengthened and melodious. Calls are a grating *mia* and a rolling *pr-r-reet.*

Range and status: Resident on the Hawaiian islands of Kauai, Molokai, Lanai, and Hawaii. Extirpated from Oahu I. Rare, but apparently in large numbers where they have not been eliminated by alterations of habitat.

Habitat: Mountain forests and neighboring scrub areas.

Seasonal movements: None; the bird flies, but the wings are remarkably short and weak.

Biology: Nest: Made of twigs, leaves, and rootlets, about 20–25 ft. above the ground in trees. Little else known of breeding. Food: Flowers, berries, fruit, insects, and other small invertebrates.

SMALL KAUAI THRUSH (Puaiohi) (*Phaeornis palmeri*)

Smaller (7 in.) than the very similar Hawaiian Thrush, but with flesh-colored legs and feet and a white spot over the eye. Once thought to be extinct on Kauai I., Hawaii, the only place from which it is known, it was reported in 1960 and possibly still exists in small numbers.

WHEATEAR (*Oenanthe oenanthe*)

Appearance: About the size (6¼ in.) of the House Sparrow; cinnamon or grayish cinnamon above, including wing, and light rufous below. The forehead, a small patch above and behind the eye, and the rump are white. The central tail feathers are black; the outer feathers are white, with broad black tips. A mask of black runs from the bill to behind the eye. In winter the black mask is replaced by dark cinnamon and the white on the head is obscure. The Robinlike bill, legs, and feet are black.

Voice: The call is a harsh *chak-chak* or *weet-chak-chak;* the song, not heard in U.S. (except Alaska), is a melodious warble.

Range and status: Breeds from s. Baffin I., nw. and ne. Greenland, Iceland, n. Eurasia, n.-c. and ne. Alaska, and n. Yuk. south to n. Que., s. Lab., nw. Africa, Crete, Turkey, Iran, the Himalayas, Mongolia, e.-c. Siberia, and s.-c. Alaska. In winter south to c. Africa, n. India, c. China, the Philippines, Japan, and the Pribilofs and Nunivak I. of Alaska; increasingly reported along Atlantic seaboard to se. N.Y. Has straggled to Colo., Pa., La., Cuba, and Bermuda. Locally common in the North.

Habitat: Open country; tundra, meadows, beaches, alpine fields, and deserts.

Seasonal movements: Not enough data to list a schedule; most of the birds breeding in America winter in Africa or Asia.

Biology: Nest: Made of grasses and lined with feathers, in crevices of rock, among stones on ground, in holes in ground, or on rock ledges. Eggs: 3–8, usually 5–6; pale blue, rarely with pale reddish brown specks. Incubation: 14 days, almost entirely by female. Age at 1st flight: About 15 days. Food: Small ground-dwelling insects, spiders, and other invertebrates; also seeds of grasses and other plants.

Suggested reading: G. M. Sutton and D. F. Parmelee, "Nesting of the Greenland Wheatear on Baffin Island," *Condor,* vol. 56, pp. 295–306, 1954.

BLUETHROAT (*Luscinia svecica*)

A small (5½ in.) Robinlike thrush. Buffy brown above, including wing and tail, with a buff eye streak. The outer tail feathers are brownish red or rufous, with buffy brown tips, and the black-bordered cobalt throat may have a white or tawny spot in the center. The rest of the underparts are white. The female is buffy brown above and white below, with a buff eye streak and a spotty sepia edging to the white throat. The species ranges through most of Eurasia and Africa and breeds in n. Alaska from Wales to Point Barrow and possibly south along the Colville River.

SIBERIAN RUBYTHROAT (*Luscinia calliope*)

Of House Sparrow size (6 in.). Brownish gray above, grading to almost white on the abdomen, with a white eye streak and "mustache" and a ruby-red throat. The female is duller, with less distinct eye streak and mustache, and has a plain white throat. The bill is black, and the legs and feet are a dusky straw-yellow. It breeds from n. Siberia to Sakhalin I. and the Kurile Is. It winters from s. China and the Philippines to c. India, Burma, Thailand, and S. Vietnam. Straggles occasionally to the w. Aleutian Is., Alaska.

JAPANESE RED ROBIN (*Luscinia akahige*)

Sparrow-sized (ca. 6 in.); reddish brown above and gray below, with a buffy brown neck and throat. A resident of Japan and a winter visitor to s. China and Formosa; introduced and established on Oahu I., Hawaii.

RYUKYU ROBIN (Korean Robin) (*Luscinia komadori*)

Small (ca. 6 in.) and very similar to the Japanese Red Robin, but with a black throat and breast. Resident of the Ryukyu Is. south of Japan; introduced successfully on Oahu I., Hawaii, but rather rare.

DYAL (*Copsychus saularis*)

Larger (ca. 7 in.) than the House Sparrow; black with a blue gloss above, including wing, tail, throat, and breast. It is white below and has a white patch on the

Townsend's Solitaire

wing and a white edge on the tail. The bill is dark brown, and the legs and feet are light gray. Resident from n. W. and E. Pakistan, n. India, and s. China south to Indonesia and the Philippines; introduced, possibly successfully, on Oahu I., Hawaii.

SHAMA (*Copsychus malabaricus*)

The size (ca. 9 in.) of a small Robin, with sooty black head, nape, throat, back, wing, and tail. The rump and the outer tail feathers are white, and it is rufous below.

The bill is black, and the legs and feet are straw-yellow. Its melodious, flutelike song is commonly heard at dusk. It is resident from c. India, Burma, and Hainan I. south to Indonesia and has been successfully established on the islands of Kauai and Oahu in Hawaii, where it frequents thickets and woodland undergrowth.

TOWNSEND'S SOLITAIRE (*Myadestes townsendi*)

Appearance: Smaller (8–9½ in.) than the Robin; smoke-gray above and below (somewhat lighter below). It has a white eye-ring, a dark brown wing with a flesh-colored patch, and a sooty black tail with white outer feathers. The bill, legs, and feet are black, and the eye is dark brown. It acts more like a flycatcher than a thrush.

Voice: The song is a long series of pleasant whistled warbles, each clear, sweet note on a different pitch from the last and repeated rapidly; a similar but more tinkling song is sung in flight. The call is a short, metallic *tink* or *peet.*

Range and status: Resident in discontinuous areas from e.-c. and se. Alaska, s. Yuk., sw. Mack., sw. Alta., w. and s. Mont., ne. Wyo., sw. S.Dak., and nw. Nebr. south to s. Calif. and n. Mexico. In winter descends to lower altitudes and south to Baja Calif. and nw. and w.-c. Mexico. Rather rare, but may be locally common.

Habitat: Forests, particularly coniferous, of mountainous regions; in winter into neighboring brushy areas, wooded canyons, and juniper forests.

Seasonal movements: Moves into breeding areas Mar.–Apr. and departs Oct.–Nov.

Biology: Nest: Made of sticks, twigs, pine needles, grasses, and rootlets on a platform of old plant debris, with a lining of fine grasses in the neat shallow cup; built on or close to the ground under overhang of tree branches, logs, or rocks. Eggs: 3–5, usually 4; dull white, very light blues, or pale pinks, rather evenly peppered and blotched with browns. Incubation and age at 1st flight unknown. Food: Wild fruit, berries, and seeds; about 40% insects and other small invertebrates.

Suggested reading: P. B. Peabody, "Rim Rock and Solitaire," *Wils. Bull.,* vol. 67, pp. 257–265, 1935.

KINGLETS AND OLD WORLD WARBLERS (SYLVIIDAE)

This family of small (3¼–11½ in.) songbirds is related to the thrushes, Old World flycatchers, and pipits and wagtails. There are 398 species distributed throughout the world, except for the polar regions, the s. half of S. America, and some oceanic islands. Only 8 species have been recorded from America, and 1 other, the Willow Warbler (*Phylloscopus trochilus*) has been recorded from Greenland. Most species are sedentary. They are most common in woodland or dense brushland habitats, but many Old World species occupy reeds and tall grass niches. Plumage colors are blendings of pale browns, grays, and greens, with spots of bright yellow or red in a few species; very few species have streaked or barred patterns. The bill is small but may be comparatively long. The medium-long wings are rounded. The tail varies from short to long and may be square, rounded, or graduated. The legs vary from slender to stout and are short or medium-long. The sexes are alike in most species. Some songs are complex and well developed, encompassing a wide variety of notes. Many species are gregarious, but none are colonial. Nests are neat cups, with or without domes, placed in trees, bushes, or marsh plants. The 3–12 eggs are generally white, pink, or buffy, spotted in most species. Incubation is by both sexes or by the female alone. Both sexes care for the nestlings, which hatch naked or with a little down. Food is primarily insects and other small invertebrates.

ARCTIC WARBLER (*Phylloscopus borealis*)

Appearance: Small (4¾ in.) and very similar to the Tennessee Warbler (an American wood warbler). Brownish olive above and whitish below, with smoke-gray along the flank and on the cheek, a thin streak of brownish olive through the eye, and a buff streak above the eye. The bill is blackish, and the feet are buffy yellow.

Voice: The song is a rattling repetition of a sibilant *tzik*, and the notes are a husky *tswee-ep* and a loud *sit-sit-sit-sit*.

Range and status: Breeds from the tree limit of n. Eurasia and w. Alaska south to n. Russia, across n.-c. Siberia, n. Mongolia, n. Manchuria, Korea, s. Japan, and sw. Alaska. In winter, south to the tropical lowlands of se. Asia, Indonesia, and the Philippines. Very rare in Alaska.

Habitat: Scrubby growth, mainly willows, but also birches, briars, and alders.

Seasonal movements: Apparently arrives in Alaska in June and departs Aug.–early Nov.

Biology: Nest: A neat, domed cup made of weed stems, mosses, and grasses, lined with finer grasses; built on the ground under shrub or hidden in tall grasses. Eggs: 5–7, usually 6; white with spots of reddish brown, heaviest in a wreath at larger end. Incubation period unknown, but by female alone. Age at 1st flight unknown. Food: Insects in all stages, mainly mosquitoes, wasps, beetles, and bugs.

MIDDENDORFF'S GRASSHOPPER WARBLER (*Locustella ochotensis*)

A small (5¼ in.) bird rather similar to the Arctic Warbler, but buffy brown above and very pale smoke-gray below (darker on flank). The central tail feathers of the graduated tail are longest, with each pair getting gradually shorter to the shortest outer tail feathers. It breeds from e. Siberia south to s. S. Korea and Japan and winters from the Philippines to Borneo and the Celebes. It has been recorded from Nunivak I., Alaska.

BLUE-GRAY GNATCATCHER (*Polioptila caerulea*)

Appearance: Small (4–5 in.); bluish gray above and very pale gray to white below, with the central tail feathers of the graduated tail almost black and the outer feathers white. The bluish gray of the cap becomes almost black at the very edge above the eye, and there is a distinct white eye-ring. The bill, legs, and feet are a dark bluish gray. The female is dark smoke-gray above, including wing and white-sided tail, fading to almost white below, especially at the throat and undertail feathers. Her flank is a pale dusky flesh color and the eye-ring is also white. The immature bird resembles the

In the East, the Blue-gray Gnatcatcher is slowly extending its range northward.

female, but the young male is slightly more bluish above and the young female is paler.

Voice: Call notes a buzzy *tzee* or a twangy *twee*; the song is a soft, squeaky, buzzy series of trills and warbles, difficult to hear even with acute ears.

Range and status: Breeds from n. Calif., c. Nev., s. Utah, Colo., e. Nebr., c. Minn., s. Wis., s. Mich., s. Ont., w. N.Y., n. N.J., se. N.Y. (Long I.), and Conn. south to s. Baja Calif., Guatemala, the Gulf Coast, c. Fla., and the Bahamas, extending its range northward. Winters from the s. U.S. to Cuba. Fairly common to locally common.

Habitat: Mixed forests, also oak woodlands, chaparral, and piñon and juniper areas of more open type. In winter into thickets and riparian groves.

Seasonal movements: Moves north mid-Mar.–mid-May and returns mid-Aug.–Oct.

Biology: Nest: A neat lichen-decorated cup of plant down, fine grasses, feathers, and hair, saddled on a horizontal limb or in a crotch of a tree, 3–80 ft. above the ground. Looks very much like a large hummingbird's nest. Eggs: 3–6, usually 4–5; very pale blue, sparsely and evenly spotted with reddish browns, sometimes immaculate and sometimes wreathed with spots about larger end. Incubation: About 13 days, probably by female alone. Age at 1st flight: 10–12 days. Food: Almost entirely insects, with a few other small invertebrates and some berries and seeds.

Suggested reading: M. M. Nice, "Observations on the Nesting of the Blue-gray Gnatcatcher," *Condor*, vol. 34, pp. 18–22, 1932.

BLACK-TAILED GNATCATCHER (Plumbeous Gnatcatcher) (*Polioptila melanura*)

Appearance: Same size (4½ in.) as the Blue-gray Gnatcatcher. The cap, nape, and white-edged tail are black; the back, rump, and wing are dark blue-tinged gray. Entirely white below. The female is light brownish gray above and white below, with a white-sided blackish tail and a rather prominent white eye-ring. The bill, legs, and feet are black.

Voice: Call notes *chee-chee-chee*; song a whispy *tsee-dee-dee-dee-dee.*

Range and status: Resident from s. Calif., s. Nev., Ariz., s. N.Mex., and s. Tex. south to s. Baja Calif. and the n. states of Mexico. Locally common.

Habitat: Arid and semiarid scrub, mesquite, and sage.

Seasonal movements: None.

Biology: Nest: A neat cup of quilted plant down, fibers, leaves, and insect webbing, lined with fine fibers and feathers; built in forks of smaller bushes 2–5 ft. off the ground. Eggs: 3–5, usually 4; green or pale blue, sparsely and evenly spotted with browns. Incubation: 14 days, by both parents. Age at 1st flight: 14–15 days. Food: Insects of all kinds and stages, spiders, and other small invertebrates; seeds and berries form bulk of a very small percentage of vegetable food.

GOLDEN-CROWNED KINGLET (*Regulus satrapa*)

Appearance: Tiny (3¼–4 in.); greenish gray above and paler below, grading to almost white at the throat. There is a whitish streak above the eye at the base of the black-sided golden crown. The female's crown is plain yellow; the male's is more orange, with a scarlet-orange center. There are 2 whitish wing bars. The bill, legs, and feet are black.

Voice: The call notes are series of high, hissing *see-see-see*'s; the song starts with a monotonous, high-pitched series of squeaks, followed by rapid, harsh, lower chattering notes, as *eee-teee-teee-teee-teee, chititatatutup*.

Range and status: Breeds from s. Alaska and B.C. south through the mountains to s. Calif., se. Ariz., and n.-c. N.Mex.; from n. Man., Ont., s. Que., and Nfld. south to e. Tenn. and w. N.C., c. Mass., and s. Maine; and in the highlands of s. Mexico and Guatemala. Winters from B.C. and c. Alta. south and from Colo., Nebr., Iowa, Ill., Ind., Ohio, c. N.Y., Mass., se. N.H., and s. Maine south to s. Tex., the Gulf Coast, and n. Fla.; casually and irregularly farther north. Common.

Habitat: Coniferous forests, and in winter also in mixed and deciduous woodlands.

Seasonal movements: Moves into breeding areas Mar.–mid-May and out Sept.–Oct; sometimes in sizable flocks.

Biology: Nest: A deep cup in a spherical mass of mosses and lichens, open above and lined with fine bark and rootlets; built 6–50 ft. above the ground in a conifer, usually near the top. Eggs: 5–10, usually 8–9; white to cream, marked, spotted, and blotched with browns and grays. Incubation period unknown; probably 14–15 days as in closely related European Firecrest. Age at 1st flight unknown. Food: Insects in their various forms and other small invertebrates; very few berries and seeds.

RUBY-CROWNED KINGLET (*Regulus calendula*)

Appearance: Slightly larger (3¾–4½ in.) than the Golden-crowned Kinglet; greenish gray above and somewhat lighter greenish gray below. The male has a bright patch of ruby on his crown. The bill, legs, and feet are black, and the eye is dark brown. The tail is slightly forked, and there are 2 rather indistinct whitish wing bars.

Voice: Call a low, buzzy *zhi-dit;* the variable song is in 3 distinct parts: 4–8 high-pitched squeaks, 5–10 lower-pitched notes, rapid chatter, and a 3–4-note musical phrase repeated 2–7 times, as *eee-tee-tee-tee-too-too-tu-tu-ti-ta-tidaweet-tidaweet-tidaweet* (A. A. Saunders).

Range and status: Breeds from nw. and c. Alaska, nw. Mack., n. Man., Ont., c. Que., s. Lab., and Nfld. south to Guadalupe I. off Baja Calif., c. Ariz., c. N.Mex.; and from c. Alta., s. Man., n. Mich., s. Ont., ne. N.Y., n. Maine, and N.S. Winters from s. B.C., Idaho, Nebr., s. Iowa, the Ohio River Valley, s. W.Va., Md., and N.J. south to s. Baja Calif., Guatemala, the Gulf Coast, and s. Fla. It has straggled to Greenland and Britain. Common.

Habitat: Coniferous woodlands and into thickets and other types of forests in winter.

Seasonal movements: Often travels in fairly large flocks. Moves north Mar.–mid-May and south late Aug.–mid-Nov.

Biology: Nest: Made of mosses, lichens, and plant down, the deep cup lined with feathers; built 2–100 ft. above the ground in conifers, usually spruce, and commonly seen hanging from branches. Eggs: 5–11, usually 7–9; they vary from white to buff, evenly spotted and peppered with browns, only rarely wreathed about large end. Incubation: 12(?) days, apparently by female

The female Ruby-crowned Kinglet lacks the male's red crown patch.

The rare Millerbird is now found only on Nihoa Island in Hawaii.

alone. Age at 1st flight: 12(?) days. Food: almost 95% insects, spiders, and other small invertebrates; also some fruit and seeds.

MILLERBIRD (*Acrocephalus familiaris*)

A small (5½ in.), plain, Old World warbler. Dark smoke-gray above, including wing and tail, and dusky, pale straw-yellow below. The bill is sepia above and straw-yellow below, and the legs and feet are buffy brown. No one seems to have described the voice. It is native to Nihoa I. and formerly Laysan I., Hawaii, but has been extirpated from the latter island. Rare. Frequents shrubby and grassy areas. Its nest, made of grass, plant down, and feathers, is usually placed in the top of a shrub. It commonly has 2 eggs; not much more seems to be known of its biology except that it eats insects of all types and probably other small invertebrates.

BUSH WARBLER (*Cettia diphone*)

About the size (5–5½ in.) of the Millerbird and very similar to it. Light brownish olive above and white below, with a distinct whitish streak above and a dark streak through the eye. The upper bill is dark brown, and the lower bill is buff; the legs and feet are buffy yellow. Its song, according to Peterson, is "a long, low whistle ending with an emphatic twist, *prrrrrrr-p'we-chew!* Also a stuttered trill followed by a decelerating *pe-chew, pechew, pe-chew . . . pe-chew . . . pe-chew.*" A native of e. Siberia and Japan south to e. China, Formosa, and the Philippines; introduced successfully on Oahu I., Hawaii, where it is now fairly common in the drier forests. Very little information is available about its biology.

OLD WORLD FLYCATCHERS (MUSCICAPIDAE)

These small (3½–9 in.) songbirds are somewhat like the American flycatchers in habits and general appearance. The Paradise Flycatcher of s. Asia, Africa, and Madagascar reaches a length of 22 in., but ¾ of this is tail. These birds are related to the thrushes, babblers, and Old World warblers; some ornithologists insist that these 3 groups, plus others, are but a single big family. The 328 species of this group are found throughout the E. Hemisphere except for northernmost Asia, and in Oceania east to Hawaii and the Marquesas. There are only 2 species in Hawaii, and 1 of these was introduced.

ELEPAIO (*Chasiempis sandwichensis*)

Appearance: Small (5½ in.) and variable from island to island. On Hawaii I. it is fuscous above, including wing and tail; the rump, 2 wing bars, and spots on the corners of the tail are white; the throat is black, spotted with white toward the breast and side; the breast and flank are tawny, and the rest of the underparts are white. On Oahu I. the crown, nape, and back are buffy brown, and the breast and flank are whitish. On Kauai I. the head, neck, back, and wing are dark smoke-gray, and it is entirely pale smoke-gray below. The bills, legs, and feet are dark brown. Immature birds are varying shades of brown above and whitish below, but have the dark brown tail and white rump. The females are similar to but duller than the males.

Voice: A loud, emphatic *wheet-feeoo* whistle or *el-e-pai-o;* also a strong *whit* or *whik-whik-whik-whik-whik.* The female makes a short *meow.*

Range and status: Kauai, Oahu, and Hawaii Is.; formerly also Laysan. Common.

Habitat: Forested mountain slopes.

Seasonal movements: None.

Biology: Nest: A neat cup made of the soft scales of a fern tree glued together with the bird's saliva, then bound more firmly with spider webbing; built in a low tree or shrub. Eggs: 2–3, white, evenly speckled with reddish brown. Incubation and age at 1st flight unknown. Food: Insects caught on wing or searched out among foliage; also spiders and other small arthropods.

BLUE NILTAVA (*Muscicapa cyanomelana*)

Small (5½–6 in.). Blue above (cobalt on head and greenish blue on back) and white below, with a black face, throat, and upper breast. The female is brown above and buffy white to white below. Breeds in ne. Asia and Japan and winters in Malaysia and Indonesia. Has been introduced, possibly successfully, from Japan into Oahu I., Hawaii.

Elepaio

ACCENTORS AND HEDGE-SPARROWS (PRUNELLIDAE)

Accentors and hedge-sparrows are small (5–7 in.), somewhat sparrowlike birds of uncertain relationships; in habitat and behavior they resemble the sparrows, and anatomically they show some affinity with the thrushes. There are 12 species ranging through Europe, n. Africa, and n. and c. Asia; the Mountain Accentor has straggled to Alaska. All species are migratory, although some only altitudinally. They live in brushlands, forest edges, alpine meadows, and barrens. Plumage is in grays, browns, black, white, and mixtures, commonly streaked above and plain or spotted below. The wing may be short and rounded or fairly long and pointed, the tail short to fairly long, and the bill of moderate length, sharply pointed and somewhat slender. Voice consists of loud, ringing calls, chatters, trills, and warbles. Flight is generally for short distances, but strong. These birds are commonly gregarious but not colonial. Their food, of insects, small invertebrates, berries, and seeds, is usually gleaned from or near the ground. The nest is an open cup of grasses and plant fragments on the ground or in a low shrub or tree. The 2–7 eggs are unspotted blue, rarely with some marks, and are incubated by both sexes, sometimes by the female alone. The hatchlings are downy; both parents feed and otherwise take care of the nestlings.

MOUNTAIN ACCENTOR (*Prunella montanella*)

Small (ca. 6 in.). Cap and nape are chestnut, and back and rump are buffy brown streaked with brownish red. Buffy yellow below. The tail is buffy brown above and light gray below. There is a streak of buffy yellow above the eye, a broad mask of dusky brown through the eye, and some cinnamon streaking on the flank. A bar of gray marks the side of the neck. The female and young are similar but duller. The dark-tipped bill and the legs and feet are straw-yellow. It breeds in the forests of Siberia, reaching n. China, s. S. Korea, and Japan in winter; it has been recorded on Nunivak and St. Lawrence Is., Alaska.

Mountain Accentor

WAGTAILS AND PIPITS (MOTACILLIDAE)

These small (5–8¾ in.) terrestrial songbirds are probably most closely related to the thrushes and Old World warblers. There are 54 species scattered about the world except for the polar regions and a few oceanic islands: 6 species have been recorded from America, and another, the Meadow Pipit (*Anthus pratensis*) of Europe and w. Siberia, breeds in e. Greenland and Iceland. Many species are migratory, at least to some extent. Most are ground dwellers, and some are found on the tundra and among scrub growth. The pointed wings are long, or moderately so, and the tail is long. The birds walk, rather than hop, about the ground on fairly long, long-toed legs; the hind toe is very long in many species. Plumage occurs generally in grays, browns, yellows, black, and whites, plain or broadly streaked and often in distinguishing patterns. Flight is fairly strong. The habit of many species of constantly pumping the tail up and down has given these birds the common name of "wagtail" in many lands and languages. In most species the sexes are alike or nearly so. Courtship commonly involves aerial pursuit of the female by the male and strutting and posturing before her on the ground. Nests are cup-shaped, sometimes domed structures on the ground or in a natural cavity of a tree, rock, or wall, and are usually built by both sexes. The 2–7 eggs are incubated by the female alone in most species. The nestlings, covered with down above on hatching, are cared for by both parents in the majority of the species and by the female alone in but a few. Insects and other small invertebrates form the bulk of the diet, with very little vegetable matter being eaten.

WHITE WAGTAIL (*Motacilla alba*)

A small (ca. 7 in.), variable, widespread species. In America the rear half of the cap, the nape, back, rump, throat, breast, central tail feathers, and a narrow streak through the eye are black. The wing is light gray, with a large patch of white (in some subspecies the back and rump are also light gray); the rest of the underparts, the broad forehead, the face, side of neck, and outer tail feathers are white. The bill, legs, and feet are black. The immature birds are light gray above and white below, with 2 white wing bars and a band of medium gray separating the throat and breast. It ranges throughout Eurasia and into Africa, Japan, and the Philippines; it has straggled to the w. Aleutian Is. of Alaska and to ne. Quebec.

YELLOW WAGTAIL (*Motacilla flava*)

Appearance: Small (6–7 in.). Medium gray above, including face, with a white streak above the eye and 2 indistinct white wing bars; yellow below, with a band of faint grayish streaks across the breast. The immature bird is darker gray above and white below, with a white streak above the eye and a necklace of blackish gray around the throat. The bill, legs, and feet are blackish.

Voice: Call notes a faint, frequently repeated *pe-weet*; songs a buzzy *tzee-zee-zee* and a rapid medley of tinkling notes during courtship flights described below.

Range and status: Breeds from n. England, n. Scandinavia, n. Russia, n. Asia, n. Alaska, and n. Yuk. south to nw. Africa, Sicily, Crete, c. Egypt, Israel, Mesopotamia, Iran, s.-c. Siberia, Mongolia, se. Siberia,

Yellow Wagtail

The Water Pipit spends most of its time on the ground in open, treeless areas.

Sakhalin I., n. Kuriles, and along the Alaskan coast to Nunivak I. In winter south to s. Africa, s. and se. Asia, and the Philippines. Common to abundant in Alaska.

Habitat: Marshy grasslands, tundra, and areas with tall grasses and reeds.

Seasonal movements: Schedule and route not known.

Biology: In courtship, flies almost straight up for 20–30 yd. then sings while volplaning down on stiffly arched wings with spread tail held erect. Nest: Built, under overhanging grasses, of grasses and mosses, and lined with hair and feathers. Eggs: 4–7, usually 5–6; white to greenish white, spotted with grays and browns. Incubation: 10–13(?) days. Age at 1st flight: 15–18 days. Food: Almost entirely insects.

WATER PIPIT (American Pipit) (*Anthus spinoletta*)

Appearance: Small (6–7 in.). Buffy brown above, including wing and white-sided tail, with some darker and lighter streaking on the breast and flank. The bill is buffy brown below and sepia above, and the legs and feet are sepia.

Voice: Call notes a series of 2–3 sharp *tsee-seep*'s;

the regular song is variable, often a long series of *see-see-see* or *swit-swit-swit* notes sometimes mixed with short trills. The courtship flight song is a simple *che-whee* repeated over and over on ascent and descent.

Range and status: Breeds along the coasts of Scandinavia, the British Isles, nw. France, and w. Greenland; in the mountains of Spain, s.-c. and se. Europe, the Caucasus, the Tien Shan and Altai Ranges of c. Asia, ne. Siberia, and the Kamchatka Peninsula; and Corsica, Sardinia, and the Kurile and Aleutian Is. Also from n. Alaska, n. Yuk., and Banks, Victoria, Bylot, and Baffin Is. south in the mountains to Ore., Idaho, Utah, Ariz., and n.-c. N.Mex.; and n. Mack., Keewatin, n. Ont., n. Que., along the coast of Lab. to the Gaspé Peninsula in Que., and Nfld. Winters along ice-free coasts and in the continental interiors from c. Europe, c. Asia, Japan, s. B.C., Ore., Nev., s. Utah, Tex., Ark., Tenn., W.Va., se. Pa., and s. N.J. south to n. Africa, Mesopotamia, Iran, n. India, se. Asia, s. Japan, s. Baja Calif., Guatemala, the Gulf Coast, and Fla.; irregularly farther north. Fairly common.

Habitat: Tundra, marshy alpine meadows, grasslands, open beaches, and marine coasts.

Seasonal movements: Migrates in flocks, moving north Mar.–May and returning Sept.–Nov.

Biology: Nest: Made of fine grasses, on bare ground or among grasses and mosses. Eggs: 4–7, usually 4–5; white to buffy white, rather thickly covered with dark brown spots and blotches and scrawled with black lines. Incubation: In Europe 13–14 days, 12 days according to Pickwell; by female alone. Age at 1st flight: About 13 days. Food: Insects, mollusks, crustaceans, small seeds, and berries.

Suggested reading: G. Pickwell, "The American Pipit in Its Arctic-Alpine Home," *Auk*, vol. 64, pp. 1–14, 1946.

PECHORA PIPIT (*Anthus gustavi*)

Slightly smaller (5¾ in.) than the Water Pipit, which it resembles closely except that it is somewhat grayer and paler and the spots on the side of the throat, breast, and flank are heavier and blacker. It breeds in ne. Russia and n. Siberia and winters from c. Asia to Indonesia, Formosa, and the Philippines; it has been recorded from St. Lawrence I., Alaska.

RED-THROATED PIPIT (*Anthus cervinus*)

Smaller (5¾ in.) than the Water Pipit and rather similar to it, but the entire head is suffused with pinkish so that the unmarked throat appears rather flesh-colored. The short streaks on the breast, side of the throat, and flank are darker. Breeds on the tundra of Eurasia; recorded in winter south to c. Africa and s. Asia. It has been taken several times in Alaska and once in Baja Calif.

Like its relatives, the Sprague's Pipit has an elaborate courtship flight song.

SPRAGUE'S PIPIT (*Anthus spragueii*)

Appearance: About the same size (6¼–7 in.) as the Water Pipit. Pale buffy brown above and below, except for the outer tail feathers, abdomen, throat, and 2 wing bars, which are white. The central tail feathers are dark brown toward the tip, and the cap, nape, back, rump, and wing are streaked and spotted with dark brown and blackish. The breast is faintly streaked with buffy brown. The dark-tipped bill, legs, and feet are a dusky, buffy yellow.

Voice: Calls are a chain-jangling *jingle-jingle-jingle-jingle,* beginning high and loud and fading in volume and pitch at the end, and a high *chip.* The courtship flight song is a series of high, musical, sleighbell-tinkling notes, separated by distinct pauses.

Range and status: Breeds from n. Alta., c. Sask., and c. Man. south to Mont., N.Dak., and nw. Minn. Winters from s. Ariz., Tex., s. La., and nw. Miss. south to s.-c. Mexico. It has straggled to Mich., S.C., Ga., and Fla. Locally common to rather rare.

Habitat: Plains and prairies where shorter grasses abound.

Seasonal movements: Moves north mid-Mar.–early May and returns Sept.–early Nov.

Biology: Courtship flight of male is an undulating circle 100–350 ft. above the nesting grounds. Nest: Made entirely of fine grasses, in a hollow in the ground among grasses. Eggs: 3–6, usually 4–5; grayish white, thickly blotched with purplish brown. Incubation period unknown; by female alone. Age at 1st flight: About 10–11 days. Food: Insects.

THE WAXWINGS (BOMBYCILLIDAE)

These small (6¼–8¾ in.) arboreal birds are closely related to the palmchats and silky flycatchers, but their affinities to other families are obscure. There are only 3 species found in the n. subarctic and temperate zones; 2 of these occur in America. All species are migratory. Waxwings are all so similar in appearance, habits, and biology that the following species accounts will serve very well as a guide to the family as a whole.

BOHEMIAN WAXWING (*Bombycilla garrulus*)

Appearance: Largest (7½–8¾ in.) of the waxwings. Generally a warm smoke-gray, including prominent pointed crest; paler and grayer below, with brownish red undertail feathers. The rump and tail are medium gray, grading to almost black near the orange-yellow tip. The throat and a streak starting at the base of the upper bill and running through the eye to the upper back of the head are black. The light rufous of the forehead and face grades into the rest of the plumage. The wing bears 2 white patches; the larger flight feathers are black, and those closer to the body have orange-yellow edges and tips (white on the female). The male has small plastic-like scarlet tips on the feathers above the flight feathers (this is the "wax" leading to the name). The young are duller, streaked with whitish on the upper back and flank, and lack a crest. The bill, legs, and feet are black.

Voice: A weak, high-pitched *zir-r-r-r* barely audible when made by 1 bird, but amply distinctive when produced by a large flock; also a somewhat louder, harsher *scree*.

Range and status: Breeds south of the tree limit and in coniferous forests in n. Norway, n. Sweden, Finland, n. Russia, n. and c. Siberia, and from c. Alaska, c. Yuk., n. and c. Mack., ne. Sask., and n. Man. south to c. Wash., n. Idaho, nw. Mont., and s. Alta. Winters from s. edges of breeding areas in Eurasia south to the British Isles, France, n. Italy, Turkey, n. Iran, s. Siberia, and Japan. In America from se. Alaska, sw. Mack., c. B.C., s. Alta., c. Sask., s. Man., s. Ont., s. Que., P.E.I., and N.S. south to s. Calif., s. Ariz., c. N.Mex., n. Tex., nw. Ark., s. Ill., c. Ind., c. Ohio, Pa., Conn., and Mass. Very rare in e. Canada and e. U.S. and common only in sw. Canada and nw. U.S. in winter. Very erratic in nesting locales and wintering areas; sometimes locally abundant.

Habitat: In summers generally in coniferous forests with dense undergrowths; into muskeg and brushy berry-producing regions in winter.

Seasonal movements: Erratic; movements apparently depend on berry crops.

Biology: Courtship consists of strutting, posturing, and display of raised crest and spread tail by male in presence of hen. Nest: Made of coniferous twigs, grasses,

Fruits and berries are the principal items in the Cedar Waxwing's diet.

and mosses, lined with finer grasses, mosses, and plant down; built on horizontal branches next to bole 20–40 ft. above the ground in evergreens. Eggs: 2–6, usually 4–6; pale grayish blue, profusely spotted and scrawled with blackish. Incubation: 14 days (in captivity), by female alone. The hatchlings are naked. Age at 1st flight: 13–14 days. Food: Mainly insects in summer and berries in winter.

Suggested reading: D. A. Bannerman, "Waxwing," *Birds of the British Isles*, Oliver and Boyd, Edinburgh, 1953, vol. 2, pp. 253–263.

CEDAR WAXWING (*Bombycilla cedrorum*)

Appearance: Slightly smaller (6½–8 in.) than the Bohemian Waxwing. Generally a light buffy brown fading into medium gray on the rump, blackish near the yellow band at the tip of the tail, pale yellow on the lower abdomen, and whitish on the undertail feathers. The larger flight feathers of the wing are blackish gray, and the male bears the waxy scarlet tips on the smaller feathers of the wing. The bill, legs, feet, throat, and a streak from the base of the upper bill through the eye almost to the back of the crest are black. The crestless young lack the scarlet wax spots on the wing. They are streaked with whitish on the upper back and with buffy yellow on the breast and abdomen, and the throat is light buffy brown.

Voice: High-pitched hissing notes and interspersed trills and warbles; many human ears are unable to hear such high notes, and to some the bird is almost silent.

Range and status: Breeds from se. Alaska, n.-c. B.C., n. Alta., nw. Sask., c. Man., n. Ont., c. and se. Que., and Nfld. south to n. Calif., n. Utah, Colo., Okla., c. Mo., s. Ill., s. Ind., c. Ky., e. Tenn., n. Ala., and n. Ga. Winters from s. B.C., n. Idaho, c. Ariz., n.-c. N.Mex., ne. Colo., s. Nebr., c. Mo., s. Mich., s. Ont., and Mass. south to Panama, the Gulf Coast, and c. Fla. It has straggled to Bermuda, the Bahamas, the Greater Antilles, and nw. S. America. It is irregular in schedule and breeding area and may be locally common to abundant in some areas a few years and missing completely other years.

Seasonal movements: Irregular; generally moves north Mar.–May and returns Sept.–Nov.

Biology: Courtship seems to be restricted to feeding rituals between the sexes. Nest: Made of grasses, twigs, and weed stems, with a lining of rootlets or finer grasses in the neat cup; built 6–50 ft. high on tree branches. Eggs: 3–6, usually 3–5; pale grays or pale bluish grays, lightly and irregularly spotted with dark brown and black and blotched with pale brownish gray. Incubation: 12–16 days, by hen alone. Age at 1st flight: 14–18 days. Food: Almost 80% berries, fruit, and flowers; insects fill in the rest of its diet. Occasionally gets drunk from eating overripe cherries.

Suggested reading: L. S. Putnam, "The Life History of the Cedar Waxwing," *Wils. Bull.*, vol. 61, pp. 141–182, 1949.

THE SILKY FLYCATCHERS (PTILOGONATIDAE)

Arboreal birds smaller (7¼–10 in.) than Robins, silky flycatchers are related to the palmchats and waxwings. They are restricted to C. America and the sw. U.S. There are 4 species, but only 1 species, the Phainopepla, reaches America. They prefer arid and semiarid brushy country and are partially migratory. The plumage is rather long and silky. The colors are generally black, grays, or browns with yellowish and white markings, but not in spots or streaks; all species are crested. The wings are short and broad, and the tail is comparatively long; the bill is rather broad and short, the legs short, and the feet fairly strong. The female is much duller than the male and sometimes differently colored. The song is a weak warble. These birds are gregarious but not colonial. The nest is a shallow structure of twigs, grasses, etc., built in trees by the male. Both sexes incubate the 2–4 black-and-brown-marked, grayish white eggs. The hatchlings have a very meager covering of down. Food is mainly berries and fruits; many insects, captured on the wing, are consumed.

PHAINOPEPLA (*Phainopepla nitens*)

Appearance: Smaller (7–7¾ in.) than the Robin. Glossy black, with a laterally flattened, shaggy crest and a large white patch near the end of the wing that is prominent only while the bird is in flight. The female is like the male, but dark gray with light gray patches on the wings. The bill, legs, and feet are black, and the eye is dark brown. The young resemble the female, but are a browner gray.

Voice: A liquid *quert* repeated every 1–2 seconds, a loud, warning *ca-rack* by the male, and a weak, squeaky song, sometimes including bubbling, flutelike phrases, but somewhat disconnected.

Range and status: Resident from c. Calif., s. Nev., s. Utah, sw. N.Mex., and w. Tex. south to s. Baja Calif. and c. Mexico. Fairly common to locally common.

Habitat: Scrubby growths, usually in arid or semiarid areas but also in sparsely vegetated parklands, and oak forests of foothills.

Seasonal movements: Extent and schedule of movements uncertain; at least moves out of higher elevations in winter.

Biology: Nest: Made of leaves, plant stems, flower petals, plant down, and insect webbing, lined with wool, hair, and down; built, exclusively by the male, 4–50 ft. high on the branches of various trees. Eggs: 2–4, usually 2–3; grayish white, profusely spotted with browns and scrawled with black. Incubation: 14–16 days. Age at 1st flight: 19 days. Food: Many kinds of berries and a considerable number of flying insects.

Suggested reading: J. E. Crouch, "Distribution and Habitat Relationships of the Phainopepla," *Auk*, vol. 60, pp. 319–332, 1943. A. L. and R. M. Rand, "Breeding Notes on the Phainopepla," *Auk*, vol. 60, pp. 333–340, 1943.

An immature Northern Shrike has impaled a meadow mouse on a stout thorn.

THE SHRIKES (LANIIDAE)

Shrikes are small- to medium-sized (6¼–15 in.) predacious songbirds of rather uncertain affinities, but grouped with the helmet shrikes and vangas. There are 74 species found throughout N. America, Eurasia, Africa, Indonesia, and New Guinea; only 2 occur in America. The n. species are cyclically migratory. Most species prefer the more open country, rarely the forest edges. Many species are patterned in grays, browns, black, and white; a few African species are brightly colored with greens, yellows, and reds. The wing is moderately short and rounded, the tail is rather long and slender, the strong bill is well hooked and notched in some species, and the sturdy legs and feet have sharp claws. In the American species the females and younger birds are duller and more brownish than the males. Some species have well-developed and elaborate songs. Shrikes usually perch on a moderately high tree or bush overlooking more or less open terrain. When moving from 1 vantage point to another, they drop to within a few feet of the ground and proceed in undulating flight at this height to near the base of the new perch before swerving up. Courtship consists of rather simple display patterns and aerial pursuit of female by male. Nests are bulky affairs placed in trees or bushes, built by male or female alone or by both together. Incubation of the 2–8 spotted eggs is mainly by the female. The hatchlings have some down above and are tended by both sexes. Food consists of insects and small land vertebrates; rodents, birds, lizards, and large insects are usually impaled on the bigger thorns of trees or bushes as an aid in tearing the prey to eatable sizes. The talons are not well adapted to holding and tearing as are those of hawks and owls.

NORTHERN SHRIKE (Gray Shrike) (*Lanius excubitor*)

Appearance: Robin-sized (9–10¾ in.). Forehead, cap, nape, back, and rump are pale gray; wing, tail, and a rather broad mask starting just below the forepart of the eye are black; a small rectangle near the tip of the wing, the trailing edge of the inner flight feathers, and the outer edge and corners of the tail are white. It is very pale gray below, with fine, faint, wavy barring of a little darker gray especially on the breast and flank. Except for the basal 3rd of the lower mandible, which is flesh-

Loggerhead Shrike

colored, the bill, legs, and feet are black. The immature birds are cinnamon where the adults are pale gray, the light underparts have fine, wavy barring of light cinnamon, and the dark-tipped bill is smoke-gray. The female is slightly duller and browner than the adult male.

Voice: A rather long, disjointed song sounding like a harsh, squeaky Mockingbird or thrasher song, with soft warbles, caws, scraping notes, short, liquid trills, and occasionally 2–4 clear whistles. Also a rapid, high-pitched, rattling *pip-pip-pip-pip-pip.* Apparently able to mimic the notes of other birds.

Range and status: Breeds from n. Scandinavia, n. Russia, across n.-c. Siberia to the Bering Sea, n. Alaska, c. Yukon, nw. and c. Mack., n. Man., n. Ont., n. Que., and c. Lab. south to n.-c. Africa, s. Arabia, n. India, n. China, Sakhalin I., s. Alaska, nw. B.C., sw. Yuk., sw. Mack., n. Alta., Sask., n.-c. Ont., and c. and se. Que. It does not breed in Britain, n. France, Italy, the Balkans, Turkey, or the Caucasus. In the Old World it is mainly sedentary, seldom found south of the s. breeding limits described above. In America it ranges south in winter to n. Calif., c. Nev., c. Ariz., N.Mex., s. Kans., c. Mo., Ill., Ind., Ohio, Pa., n. Va., and Md. Where present it is conspicuous; may be locally common.

Habitat: All types of open areas, from humid to arid terrain, especially where scattered taller growths furnish vantage points for hunting.

Seasonal movements: Commonly erratic; moves north late Feb.–Apr. and returns Sept.–Nov.

Biology: Nest: Bulky structures woven of sticks, twigs, mosses, lichens, fur, and feathers, with a fairly neat cup; well hidden in dense-foliaged shrubs and trees. Eggs: 2–9, usually 4–6; grayish or greenish white, heavily spotted and blotched with browns, lavenders, and grays. Incubation and age at 1st flight apparently unknown. Food: Larger insects, small mammals, and small birds.

Suggested reading: T. J. Cade, "Ecological and Behavioral Aspects of Predation by the Northern Shrike," *The Living Bird,* pp. 43–86, 1967.

LOGGERHEAD SHRIKE (*Lanius ludovicianus*)

Appearance: Somewhat smaller (8–10 in.) than the Northern Shrike, from which it otherwise differs in being a darker light gray above, in having the black mask extend to the base of the bill (sometimes to the forehead), in lacking any wavy barring on the breast and flank, and in having a bill that is less heavy and is black above and medium gray below.

Voice: A harsh, unmusical song of shrill squeaks, piping whistles, and throaty gurgles mixed with a few pleasant notes. Also a few *chack-chack* calls.

Range and status: Breeds from s.-c. B.C., e. Wash., sw. Mont., c. Alta., c. Sask., s. Man., s. Ont., s. Que., s.-c. Maine, and sw. N.B. south to s. Baja Calif., s. Mexico, the Gulf Coast, and s. Fla. Winters mainly from 45° N. southward. May be locally common, usually conspicuous.

Habitat: Open terrain of all sorts with scattered or scrub growth furnishing vantage perches.

Seasonal movements: Only the more northerly subspecies migrate. Moves north Mar.–mid-Apr. and returns Oct.–Nov.

Biology: Nest: A bulky structure of sticks, twigs, weed stems, grasses, fibers, and feathers; built in dense-leaved trees or brush 5–20 ft. above the ground. Eggs: 4–6, usually 4–5; dull white, grayish, or buffy, spotted and blotched with browns and grays. Incubation: 11–16 days (apparently some geographic variation), by female alone; 2 broods commonly raised each year. Age at 1st flight: About 20 days. Food: Larger insects, small mammals, and birds.

Suggested reading: A. C. Bent, *Life Histories of North American Wagtails, Shrikes, Vireos, and Their Allies,* Dover, N.Y. (reprint of U.S. Nat. Mus. Bull. 197, 1950), 1965, pp. 131–182.

In winter the Starling's glossy feathers are tipped with white and buff.

THE STARLINGS (STURNIDAE)

Starlings are small- to medium-sized (7–17 in.) arboreal or terrestrial songbirds. They are probably most closely related to the weaverbirds, and possibly to the Old World orioles and the drongos. There are 112 species ranging through Africa and Eurasia down to ne. Australia and through some oceanic islands; 3 species have been introduced into America. Usually they are common and prominent parts of the avifauna. Most species are at least partially migratory. The feathers are commonly glossy, metallic-sheened blues, greens, purples, browns, and black with markings in white, grays, yellows, and browns, usually spotted, rarely streaked. Wings vary from short and rounded to long and pointed; a few species have heavy and some have hooked beaks. Legs and feet are robust. Wattles, patches of bare skin, or crests adorn the heads of some species. In most of the species it is impossible to separate the sexes by appearance alone. Most starlings are noisy, producing a great variety of calls and songs, and some are good mimics. Large flocks, mass migrations, and communal activities are common phenomena in the family; some starlings are colonial nesters. Nests are diverse: piles of plant debris in a variety of cavities, domed structures, cups in trees, and pensile baskets. The 2–9 unspotted or immaculate pale blue or white eggs are incubated by both male and female or by the female alone. The downy hatchlings are tended by both parents. Apparently all species are omnivorous, consuming invertebrates, small vertebrates, plant matter, and even offal.

STARLING (*Sturnus vulgaris*)

Appearance: Smaller (7½–8½ in.) than the Robin and black-plumaged, including the short, slightly notched, square-tipped tail. There is a purplish gloss on the cap, nape, and back and a greenish gloss on the face, underparts, and wing, with 2 rather indistinct dull buff wing bars and brownish spots on the back. The bill is yellow, and the legs and feet are buffy brown. In winter the adults are somewhat more brownish above and, except for the wing and tail, "spangled" with white and buff, leading to the common name; in this plumage the bill is blackish. Before molting into the first winter plumage, the young are a medium brownish olive above and somewhat lighter below, with smoke-gray streaking and a blackish bill.

Voice: Cacophonic; some pleasing measures are usually imitations of other birds. The bird performs like an untutored, untalented youngster of five, in love with harsh and squeaky notes, turned loose in a room full of brass and woodwind musical instruments. Starlings apparently imitate almost any sound from 1,200–8,250 vibrations per minute, including all manner of birds and the irate dog owner whistling home the errant canine.

Range and status: Resident, except in the highest and most northerly areas, from se. Iceland, n. Europe, and sw. and s.-c. Siberia south to France, Italy, the Balkans, n. Iran, W. Pakistan, and nw. India. Introduced in America in N.Y. in 1890 and now resident from se. Alaska, c. B.C., s. Alta, c. Sask., s. Man., c. Ont., s. Que., and s. Nfld. south to the s. borders of the U.S., possibly into Mexico. Also introduced in Jamaica and now common there, as it is throughout its natural and adopted range.

Habitat: Open fields, agricultural lands, suburbs, cities, and more open forest and scrub.

Seasonal movements: In Eurasia it makes pronounced mass migrations from 1 part of its range to another; in America it congregates in large roosting flocks in towns and cities as well as about farmlands where food is plentiful during winter. On bitterly cold days it takes advantage of the numerous protected niches about man's structures and uses the heat seeping through rooftops and around chimneys. Its ways are fascinating if not fastidious.

Biology: Courtship is merely intensified singing and display at the nesting site by the male. Nest: Packed with a mass of grasses, twigs, straw, debris, and waste material in any tree cavity, nesting box, or deserted or preempted woodpecker hole of suitable size. Nests used repeatedly season after season become quite foul-smelling as no sanitation is practiced. Eggs: 2–8, usually 4–6; white or pale bluish or greenish white. Incubation: 11–13 days, most commonly 12, by both sexes. Age at 1st flight: 19–22 days. Food: Almost 60% animal matter, mainly insects and other small invertebrates; vegetable matter is largely berries and other fruit with some seeds.

Suggested reading: B. Kessel, "A Study of the Breeding Biology of the European Starling (*Sturnus vulgaris*) in North America," *Amer. Midland Naturalist*, vol. 58, pp. 257–331, 1957.

COMMON MYNA (*Acridotheres tristis*)

Appearance: Size (ca. 9 in.) of a small Robin; forehead, nape, and white-tipped tail are sooty black; face, throat, back, rump, breast, flank, and wing are fuscous (darker at throat and face). The abdomen, undertail feathers, and small patch at the bend of the wing are white. The eye, bill, legs, feet, and a small patch of bare skin behind the eye are yellow.

Voice: A wide assortment of whistles and calls. A loud, much repeated *radio-radio-radio*, also series of *keek*'s, *kok*'s, and *chur*'s.

The Common Myna, introduced in Hawaii, is even bolder than the Starling.

Range and status: Resident from Afghanistan, s. Turkestan, and India south to Ceylon and Malaysia. Introduced and well established in Australia, New Zealand, S. Africa, and many oceanic islands, including Hawaii. Common and prominent.

Habitat: Open countryside, villages, towns, cities.

Seasonal movements: None.

Biology: Gregarious and communal, often in the extreme. Nest: Built of twigs, roots, paper, and rubbish in holes in trees, walls, or houses. Eggs: 4–5, glossy blue. Incubation: 15–17 days, by both sexes; usually 2–3 broods each season. Age at 1st flight: About 23–24 days. Food: Insects and other small invertebrates, berries and other fruit, and some seeds.

Suggested reading: R. S. P. Bates and E. H. N. Lowther, *Breeding Birds of Kashmir,* Oxford Univ. Press, London, 1952, pp. 149–151.

CRESTED MYNA (*Acridotheres cristatellus*)

Appearance: About the size (10½ in.) of the Robin. Almost entirely black, except for a patch of white on the wing and white on the tips of the outer tail feathers. The black is glossed with purplish on the ragged crest, which takes up the fore half of the cap, and on the wing; the rest of the plumage has a bluish sheen. The eye, bill, legs, and feet are yellow.

Voice: Much like the Starling, but perhaps less extensive.

Range and status: Resident from e. E. Pakistan, n. Burma, and s. China south to s. Burma, Thailand, S. Vietnam, Hainan I., and Formosa. Introduced successfully in Japan, the Philippines, and B.C.; in B.C. has spread from Vancouver I. to the nearby mainland and has straggled to w. Wash. and w. Ore. Fairly common on Vancouver I.

Habitat: Agricultural lands and open areas.

Seasonal movements: None.

Biology: Nest: A typical starling nest of rubbish in a hollow or hole in a tree, wall, or building. Eggs: 4–7, usually 4–5; glossy, greenish blue. Incubation: More than 15 days. Age at 1st flight: 27 days. Food: Fruits, insects, and garbage.

Suggested reading: V. M. Mackay and W. H. Hughes, "The Crested Mynah in British Columbia," *Canadian Field Naturalist,* vol. 77, pp. 154–161, 1963.

THE HONEY-EATERS (MELIPHAGIDAE)

Honey-eaters are small- to medium-sized (4–15 in.), mainly arboreal birds possibly distantly related to the flowerpeckers. There are 160 species distributed through Australia, Bali, New Guinea, New Zealand, and much of Oceania including Hawaii. A small group of species occupies S. Africa, but there is some reason to believe that these could be a case of parallel evolution and not members of the family at all. There have been 5 species recorded as natives of Hawaii, but 4 of these are extinct and the 5th is very rare. Most species are sedentary. Plumage colors are reds, greens, black, grays, and browns, usually solid or in large patch combinations. The wings are long and pointed, and the tail varies from moderately long to long. The bill is fairly long to long, slender, and decurved. The legs are sturdy and short or moderately long. In some species the sexes are alike. These birds are gregarious, a few being colonial nesters. The nests are cups or domed structures or are semi-pensile; found in trees or bushes, they are generally made of twigs. The 1–4 white or pinkish, red- or black-marked eggs are, except in a few species, incubated by both sexes. The hatchlings are sparsely downed and are tended by both parents. Food is primarily nectar, their tongues being of peculiar tubular design for this purpose, and many insects and fruits are also consumed.

OOAA (*Moho braccatus*)

Appearance: Small (7½–8 in.) and slender; blackish brown above, somewhat lighter below, with white edging on the feathers of the throat (more extensive on female). There is a small white patch in the wing, and the thighs are yellow. The long, slender, decurved bill and the legs and feet are black.

Voice: A mournful, whistled rendition of its name, *o-o* ("a'a" is the Hawaiian word for "small"), and a rapid *wip-poor-will-will.*

Range and status: The island of Kauai, Hawaii, where it was last reported in 1960; certainly very rare.

Habitat: Formerly common in forests throughout the island.

Seasonal movements: None.

Biology: Nest: Of small twigs and grass in dense-foliaged tree or shrub. Nothing known about eggs, incubation period, and age at 1st flight. Food: Insects and other small invertebrates, flower petals, nectar, and fruit.

BISHOP'S OO (*Moho bishopi*)

Appearance: Larger (10½–12 in.) than the Ooaa. Blackish brown (black on head), with a small patch of yellow slightly below and behind the eye. The undertail feathers and a fluff at the shoulder are also yellow. The long, slender, decurved bill and the legs and feet are black. The central feathers of the long, fan-shaped tail are sharply pointed.

Voice: A loud *ow-ow* or *ow-ow—ow.*

Range and status: Molokai I., Hawaii. Formerly rather rare and now apparently extinct.

Habitat: Higher woodlands.

Seasonal movements: None.

Biology: Very little known. It was hunted by the natives for its yellow feathers. Its food was primarily nectar and flower parts as well as some insects and smaller invertebrates.

Hawaii Oo

HAWAII OO (*Moho nobilis*)

Appearance: Larger (9½–12½ in.) than the Robin; black (somewhat browner below), with a yellow patch at the shoulder. The 2 outer tail feathers are white, and the central feathers of the fan-shaped tail are much elongated, sharply pointed, and spirally twisted. The long, decurved bill and the legs and feet are black, and the eye is dark brown.

Voice: A continuous, deep *took-took* conversational gambit from flocks.

Range and status: The island of Hawaii, introduced on the island of Kauai, but now probably extinct in both places.

Habitat: A forest species.

Seasonal movements: None.

Biology: Apparently nothing known about nest and eggs. Food: Flowers, nectar, and probably insects and other small invertebrates.

OAHU OO (*Moho apicalis*)

Appearance: About the same size (9–12 in.) as the Hawaiian Oo. Sooty black, with a dusky brown tail of which all but the 2 long, sharp-pointed, twisted central feathers are tipped with white. The undertail feathers and long-tufted feathers of the flank are yellow. The long, slender, decurved bill and the legs and feet are black.

Voice: Unknown.

Range and status: Oahu I., Hawaii; almost certainly extinct.

Habitat: Probably a forest species.

Seasonal movements: None.

Biology: Not certainly known, but reasonably assumed to be like that of other Oos.

KIOEA (*Chaetoptila angustipluma*)

Appearance: Larger (ca. 13 in.) than the Robin. Buffy brown above (somewhat more reddish on the tail) and dull white below, with a black mask through the eye. The fairly long, decurved bill, the feet, and the long legs are black.

Voice: Said to have been a good singer and to make a loud *chuck*.

Range and status: Extinct; formerly endemic to Hawaii I., Hawaii.

Habitat: Among large flowering trees.

Seasonal movements: None.

Biology: Unknown; probably ate flowers, nectar, and insects.

THE WHITE-EYES (ZOSTEROPIDAE)

The white-eyes are very small (4–6 in.) arboreal songbirds of unknown relationships, but are generally placed near the honey-eaters and flowerpeckers. There are 80 species distributed through Africa, Madagascar, and s. Asia and from China and Japan south to Australia, New Zealand, and the Fiji Is. The Japanese White-eye has been successfully introduced in Hawaii. These birds are usually sedentary, but many species are prone to fly off suddenly in large flocks in almost any direction. Most species are a dark yellowish green above and yellow or whitish below, with a distinct ring of white about the eye. There are some species with grays, browns, and black in the plumage. The wings are somewhat pointed, and the tail is rather short and square-tipped. The slender, sharp-pointed bill is slightly decurved; the legs are short but sturdy. Voice consists of rather musical warbles, trills, and twitters. The sexes are alike. The white-eyes commonly travel in small flocks, often mixed with other species, and are constantly on the move. The nest is commonly a basket, like those of the vireos, suspended between the forks of a tree branch. The 2–4 eggs are unspotted blues or blue-greens and are incubated by both male and female. The young, on hatching, have some down only on the head, and both parents share the tasks of rearing them. Food is primarily insects and some fruit.

JAPANESE WHITE-EYE (*Zosterops japonica*)

Appearance: Small (4–4½ in.); dusky green above, including face, wing, and tail, and dull white below, with a yellow throat. The flank and a band under the throat are a smoke-gray. It has the prominent ring of white around the eye; the bill, legs, and feet are black.

Voice: Calls are a thin, whining *tyee* or *tee-yee* and a sibilant *tssee*. The song is a rather long, drawn-out, whispery warble. This is a favorite caged singing bird of the Japanese.

Range and status: Resident from China and Japan south to Hainan I., Formosa, and the Philippines. Introduced and established in Hawaii on Oahu I. and from there has spread to all major islands of the archipelago; common.

Habitat: Trees and brushy areas in natural areas and in cities, suburbs, and agricultural areas.

Seasonal movements: None.

Biology: Nest: A neat cup of grasses, thin bark shreds, and plant down suspended between the forked branches of a tree or shrub. Eggs: 3–4, white or pale blue. Incubation: Not recorded (11–13 days known for other white-eye). Age at 1st flight: Unrecorded. Food: Insects in all stages and some berries and other fruits.

THE VIREOS (VIREONIDAE)

These small (4–7 in.) arboreal songbirds are possibly related to the tanagers and Hawaiian honeycreepers. There are 37 species distributed throughout the Americas except for the extreme north and the s. third of S. America but including the W. Indies; 12 of these occur in America. They are fairly common parts of the avifauna; many species are migratory. Vireos are commonly greenish, grayish, or brownish above and white, yellowish, or pale grayish below; a few species have black in the plumage. Except for wing bars in some species, there is no barred, streaked, or spotted plumage in young or old. The wings vary from long and pointed to short and rounded; the tail is moderately long. The bill is generally shorter than the head and is comparatively thick and slightly hooked. The legs are rather short. When differences exist between the sexes, they are minor. Most species have a courtship song sung by the male while in quivering display before the female. Vireos are usually solitary in habit. The nest is a very neat basket hung between the horizontal forked branches of trees or shrubs. The 2–5 white eggs, sometimes lightly peppered with browns, are incubated by both parents or by the female alone. The hatchlings may be naked or partially and sparsely covered with down; both parents share the care and feeding duties. Food is mainly insects and other small invertebrates and some fruit.

BLACK-CAPPED VIREO (*Vireo atricapilla*)

Appearance: Small (4¼–4¾ in.). Cap, face, and nape are black; the back, shoulder, and rump are light greenish gray; the wing, with 2 yellowish wing bars, and the tail are light gray tinged with green. A ring around the eye, a short streak from this toward the forehead, and the underparts are white, with pale yellow flanks grading into smoke-gray at the shoulder. The female is blackish gray where the male is black. The eye is brownish red, the dark-tipped bill is dusky straw-yellow, and the legs and feet are light gray.

Voice: A great variety of harsh, emphatic, and unmusical phrases in rapid succession and a harsh *chit-arr* of alarm.

Range and status: Breeds from s.-c. Kans. south through c. Okla. to w. Tex., the Mexican state of Coahuila, and c. Tex. Winters in c. Mexico; has straggled to Nebr. May be locally common.

Habitat: Brushy foothills, scrub oak; mountains in Mexico.

Seasonal movements: Moves north in Mar. and south in Sept., but the relative scarcity of records precludes any more accurate description of its migration schedule.

Biology: Nest: Constructed of strips of fine cedar bark, bleached dry leaves, various kinds of grasses, insect webbing, and plant down, and lined with fine conifer needles; characteristically suspended in the fork of slender tree branches. Eggs: 3–5, usually 4; white. Incubation: 14–17 days; by both sexes. Age at 1st flight: 10–12 days. Food: Insects; not much more known about diet or feeding habits.

Suggested reading: J. W. Graber, "Distribution, Habitat Requirements and Life History of the Black-capped Vireo (*Vireo atricapilla*)," *Ecol. Monogr.*, vol. 31, pp. 313–336, 1961.

WHITE-EYED VIREO (*Vireo griseus*)

Appearance: Small (4½–5½ in); greenish medium gray above, almost blackish gray on the wing and tail, and white below. A ring around the eye, a short streak joining it to the forehead, 2 wing bars, and the flank are light yellow. The bird is well named, as the iris of the eye is actually white. The bill is blackish, and the legs and feet are bluish gray.

Voice: The call is a simple *click;* the song is variable, but consists of many short, quick notes interspersed with long, clear, down-slurred whistles, as *wheeeoo*. Each individual may have 2–3 different songs.

Range and status: Breeds from e. Nebr., Iowa, s. Wis., s. Ind., and N.Y. south to ne. Mexico, the Gulf Coast, s. Fla., and Bermuda. Winters from s. Tex., the Gulf Coast, and s. Ga. south to Guatemala, Honduras, and Cuba. Casually farther north in both winter and summer. Locally fairly common.

Habitat: Swampy areas, wet meadows, 2nd-growth forests, shrubby regions, and forest undergrowth.

Seasonal movements: Moves north Mar.–early May and south Sept.–mid-Nov.

Biology: Nest: Neatly woven of strips of inner bark,

The White-eyed Vireo's white iris usually is conspicuous even at a distance.

grasses, and plant fibers bound together with spider webbing, lined with fine grasses, and decorated outside with mosses, lichens, and paper; hung in the fork of a slender branch. Eggs: 3–5, usually 4; white, sparsely peppered with black and dark browns. Incubation: About 15 days, by both sexes. Age at 1st flight unknown. Food: Insects in all stages, spiders, and other small invertebrates.

Suggested reading: A. A. Saunders, "The Fearless White-eyed Vireo," *Wils. Bull.*, vol. 27, pp. 316–321, 1915.

HUTTON'S VIREO (*Vireo huttoni*)

Appearance: Small (4½–4¾ in.). Light brownish olive above with darker, grayer wing and tail; dusky straw-yellow below. It has 2 whitish wing bars, and the whitish eye-ring is incomplete above the eye. The rather short bill is dark buffy brown, the legs and feet are bluish gray, and the eye is sepia.

Voice: Simple, light *kip-kip-kip* calls; the song is an almost endless repetition of paired notes, the first higher than the second, as *ser-ree, chee-wee,* or *chu-ween.*

Range and status: Resident from sw. B.C. and w. Wash. south to nw. Baja Calif.; and from c. Ariz., sw. N.Mex., n.-c. Mexico, and w. Tex. south through the highlands to s.-c. Guatemala. In winter it retreats to s. Ariz. from c. Ariz. May be locally common, but inconspicuous.

Habitat: Oak woodlands, other forests, and adjacent brush.

Seasonal movements: Some altitudinal shifts and short southward movements in Ariz. in fall, returning in spring.

Biology: Nest: Like those of other vireos, but made mainly of mosses and plant down; some entirely of Spanish moss. Eggs: 3–5, usually 4; white with scattered spots and dots of browns. Incubation: 14 days, by female alone. Age at 1st flight: About 14 days. Food: About 98% insects and spiders; a few seeds and berries.

Suggested reading: C. C. Van Fleet, "A Short Paper on the Hutton Vireo," *Condor*, vol. 21, pp. 162–165, 1919.

BELL'S VIREO (*Vireo bellii*)

Appearance: Small (4¼–5 in.). Green-tinged light gray above, darker on wing and tail. Whitish below, with a yellow-tinged flank, and grayish at the throat. There are 2 wing bars (1 may be indistinct) and a grayish eye-ring that is just discernible. The dark-tipped bill is buffy brown, and the legs and feet are bluish gray; the eye is dark brown.

Voice: A scolding *zip-zip-zip-zip-zip-zee* or *chee-chee-chee-chee;* the song has been paraphrased as *jiggledy-jiggledy-jiggledy-jee,* voiced with rapid if somewhat unmusical enthusiasm.

Range and status: Breeds from the Central Valley of

Hutton's Vireo

Calif., s. Nev., c. Ariz., sw. N.Mex., w. Tex., e. Colo., c. Nebr., se. S.Dak., Iowa, sw. Wis., and ne. Ill. south to n. Baja Calif., c. Mexico, s. Tex., and nw. La. Winters from s. Baja Calif., n. Mexico, and s. Tex. south to El Salvador and n. Nicaragua. May be locally fairly common.

Habitat: Lowland thickets, mesquite, and brushy bottomlands.

Seasonal movements: Arrives from South Mar.–Apr. and departs Sept.–Oct.

Biology: Nest: Composed of plant fibers, bark, and leaves, lined with fine grasses or down and hair; hung 2–3 ft. above the ground in fork of slender branch of tree or shrub. Eggs: 3–5, commonly 4; white with a few scattered dots of brown or black, sometimes immaculate. Incubation: 14 days, by female. Age at 1st flight: 10½–12 days. Food: Almost entirely insects, spiders, and other tiny invertebrates; very few berries and seeds.

Suggested reading: J. C. Barlow, *The Natural History of the Bell Vireo, Vireo bellii, Audubon*, Univ. Kans. Mus. Nat. Hist. Publ. 12, pp. 241–296, 1962. M. M. Nice, "Misadventures of a Pair of Bell's Vireos," *The Watcher at the Nest*, Macmillan, N.Y., 1939, chap. 15, pp. 112–118.

GRAY VIREO (*Vireo vicinior*)

Appearance: Small (5–5¾ in.). Medium gray above (darker on wing and tail) and white below, with a narrow white eye-ring, 1 obscure whitish wing bar, and pale smoke-gray flank. The bill, legs, and feet are medium bluish gray; the eye is brown.

Voice: No scrannel notes here; described as the most musical and pleasing of all the vireo songs. A series of single whistled notes of differing inflection, sometimes

with pauses between successive notes and at other times delivered smoothly and precisely, as *chee-wi, chee-wi, che-weet, chee, che-churr-weet.* Also wrenlike scolding and a low, harsh *churr* or *shray* by the female.

Range and status: Breeds from s.-c. Calif., s. Nev., sw. Utah, n.-c. Ariz., and sw. N.Mex. south to nw. Baja Calif. and c. Ariz. and locally to c. N.Mex., w. Okla, and w. Tex. Winters in s. Baja Calif. and nw. Mexico. Rather rare and inconspicuous.

Habitat: Arid and semiarid foothills of mountains and mesas covered with brush, scrub, junipers, chaparral, or scrub oak.

Seasonal movements: Moves north Mar.–Apr. and south Aug.–Sept.

Biology: Nest: Made of grasses and strips of inner bark, lined with fine grasses but unadorned; as with other vireos, suspended between the forks of a slender branch of a tree or bush. Eggs: 3–5, commonly 4; white or pinkish, spotted with browns and black. Incubation

*Like its relatives, Bell's Vireo hangs its cuplike nest in the fork of a tree **branch**.*

period and age at 1st flight unknown. Food: Insects; probably other small invertebrates.

YELLOW-THROATED VIREO (*Vireo flavifrons*)

Appearance: About the size (5–6 in.) of the House Sparrow. Crown, face, nape, and back light brownish olive; rump dark gray; tail and wing (except for 2 white bars) blackish gray to sooty black. The eye-ring, a streak from it to the forehead, and the throat and breast are yellow; the side of the breast is mottled with very light brownish olive; the rest of the underparts are white to pale gray. The dark-tipped bill, legs, and feet are bluish gray, and the eye is dark brown.

Voice: The call note is a soft, rather musical *whree-whree-orrrrr,* somewhat like the final running-down and stopping of an old fishing reel; the alarm notes are a more emphatic but down-slurred *chi-chi-cha-cha-chu-chu.* The lengthy, reedy song is of many slurred notes and phrases separated by measured pauses.

Range and status: Breeds from s. Man., n.-c. Minn., c. Wis., c. Mich., s. Ont., s. Que., n. N.H., and sw. Maine south to c. and e. Tex., the Gulf Coast, and c. Fla. Winters from s. Mexico (including Yucatan) south to Panama, casually to nw. S. America, s. Tex., Cuba, and the Bahamas. It has straggled to Nev., n. Maine, and Bermuda. Rather rare; may be locally common.

Habitat: Orchards and groves and more open, tall forests of deciduous trees.

Seasonal movements: Moves north mid-Mar.–mid-May and south mid-Aug.–mid-Nov.

Biology: Nest: A deep cup made of grasses and strips of fine inner bark bound together with spider webbing and plant down, decorated on the outside with mosses and lichens, and lined with fine grasses; a neat structure suspended between the forks of a slender branch of a tree or shrub 3–60 ft. above the ground. Eggs: 3–5, usually 4; white, yellowish or pinkish, well spotted and blotched with browns, most heavily at the large end. Incubation: 14(?) days, by both sexes. Age at 1st flight: About 15 days. Food: Over 95% insects; also a few spiders and other small invertebrates and less than 2% seeds and berries.

Suggested reading: D. Stoner, "Ornithology of the Oneida Lake Region," *Roosevelt Wildlife Annals,* vol. 2, nos. 3 and 4, pp. 619–620, 1932.

SOLITARY VIREO (Blue-headed Vireo) (*Vireo solitarius*)

Appearance: Smaller (5–6 in.) than the House Sparrow. The blue-gray of the crown, face, and nape grade into a medium brownish olive on the back and rump. The wing, with 2 white wing bars, and the tail are dark brownish olive to blackish. The prominent eye-ring, a streak from this to the forehead, and the underparts are

White eye-rings contrast sharply with the Solitary Vireo's blue-gray crown.

white, with side of breast and flank yellow, faintly streaked with light grayish green. The dark-tipped bill, legs, and feet are bluish gray, and the eye is brown. The w. forms generally lack any yellow in the plumage and, except for the white eye-ring, wing bars, and undersides, are a more uniform gray.

Voice: The song is a series of clear, sweet, high-pitched phrases separated by short pauses and delivered at a slow pace; the notes are a harsh *see-a* or *see-eep* and a sibilant, almost chattering *she-she-she-she-she* series.

Range and status: Breeds from c. B.C., sw. Mack., c. Sask., c. Man., n. Ont., s. Que., Nfld., and N.S. south to s. Baja Calif., Guatemala, and El Salvador. Winters from s. U.S. to n. Nicaragua and Cuba. Fairly common.

Habitat: Mixed woodlands.

Seasonal movements: Arrives in spring Mar.–May and departs in fall mid-Aug.–early Nov.

Biology: Courtship is a bobbing, bowing, feather-fluffing display by male before female. Nest: A neat, deep cup made of bark, mosses, grasses, and leaves, lined with fine grasses, and decorated outside with insect and spider webbing, plant down, and lichens; suspended 4–25 ft. up in fork of slender tree branch. Eggs: 3–5, usually 4; white or yellowish white, sparingly spotted with browns or blackish, especially about larger end.

Incubation: More than 11 days, by both sexes. Age at 1st flight unknown. Food: Over 95% insects and a few spiders; berries, other fruits, and a few seeds comprise less than 4% of the total diet through the year.

Suggested reading: A. A. Saunders, *Studies of Breeding Birds in the Allegany State Park*, N.Y.S. Mus. Bull. 318, pp. 102–105, 1938.

BLACK-WHISKERED VIREO (*Vireo altiloquus*)

Appearance: Small (about 6½ in.); light brownish olive above (including the face) and whitish below. There is a white streak just above the eye, a black streak through the eye, and a black whisker between the cheek and the throat. The flank is a very pale greenish brown. The bill, legs, and feet are bluish gray, and the eye is brownish red.

Voice: Many short, abrupt phrases separated by distinct pauses, as *whip-Tom-Kelly, cheap-John-Stirrup,* or *Juan-Chivi,* all of which serve as local-common names of the species.

Range and status: Breeds in s. Fla. and through the W. Indies. Winters in n. S. America and casually in the Greater Antilles. Rare to locally common in Fla.

Habitat: Mangrove tangles in Fla.

Seasonal movements: Mar.–Apr. and Sept.–early Dec.

Biology: Nest: Made of grasses, sedges, mosses, leaves, and plant down, bound with spider or insect webbing and lined with fine grasses; suspended 5–15 ft. high in fork of slender tree or shrub branch. Eggs: 2–3, usually 3; whitish, sparingly spotted and peppered with browns. Incubation and age at 1st flight unknown. Food: Almost 90% spiders and insects; some berries and seeds.

YELLOW-GREEN VIREO (*Vireo flavoviridis*)

A large (6¼–6¾ in.) vireo with a medium gray cap and face and a pale gray streak through the eye. It is light olive above and whitish below, with a greenish yellow lower abdomen and yellow undertail feathers. It has no wing bars. The bill is buffy brown, the legs and feet are bluish gray, and the eye is red. It ranges from n. Mexico to c. and nw. S. America and is migratory in the n. part of its range. It has straggled to Calif. and Que.

RED-EYED VIREO (*Vireo olivaceus*)

Appearance: About House Sparrow size (5½–6½ in.). Cap and nape are medium gray; face, back, rump, tail, and wing are light olive; white below. A white streak just above the eye is separated from the cap by a narrow black streak, and there is a blackish streak through the eye. The bill, legs, and feet are bluish gray, and the eye is a bright brownish red.

Voice: A complaining *queee* call; the song is a series of short, monotonously repeated phrases from a repertoire of 20–40 Robinlike notes, separated by distinct pauses. One series has been transliterated as *cherry-owit, cheree, sissy-a-wit, tee-oo.*

Range and status: Breeds from sw. and ne. B.C., sw. Mack., ne. Alta., c. Sask., c. Man., n. Ont., c. Que., P.E.I., and N.S. south, east of the Coast Ranges, to n. Ore., n. Idaho, c. Mont., c. Tex., the Gulf Coast, and c. Fla. Winters in the Amazon Basin of S. America, migrating through the W. Indies and C. America. It has straggled to Calif., Ariz., Utah, Nfld., Bermuda, Greenland, and Ireland. Common.

Habitat: 2nd-growth forests, woodlands with thick undergrowth, groves, wooded parklands, and suburbs in forest areas.

Seasonal movements: Arrives at breeding grounds mid-Mar.–May and departs mid-Aug.–Oct.

Biology: In courtship male sings softly while posing with quivering wings before female. Nest: A common sight in the e. U.S. when fall has brushed aside the screening leaves from the neat, deep cup suspended between the horizontal forks of a slender tree branch 2–60 ft. above the ground. Made of grasses, birch bark,

A Red-eyed Vireo unwittingly cares for nestlings hatched from eggs laid by a cowbird.

rootlets, and flexible strands of grapevine bark and lined with the finer grasses; bound to supports and coated on the outside with spider and insect webbing and decorated with lichens. Eggs: 3–5, commonly 4; white, with a few scattered fine spots of browns and black, most concentrated at larger end. Incubation: 11–14 days, by both sexes. Age at 1st flight: About 12 days. Food: Over 85% insects, spiders, and other small invertebrates; the 10–15% vegetable matter is mainly berries and other fruits.

Suggested reading: W. E. Southern, "Nesting of the Red-eyed Vireo in the Douglas Lake Region, Michigan," *Jack-pine Warbler*, vol. 36, pp. 105–130, 185–207, 1958.

PHILADELPHIA VIREO (*Vireo philadelphicus*)

Appearance: Smaller (4½–5 in.) than the House Sparrow. Light grayish olive-green above (lighter on face) and yellow below (paler toward throat and undertail feathers). There are no wing bars. The bill, legs, and feet are bluish gray, and the eye is dark brown.

Voice: Very similar to that of the Red-eyed Vireo, but higher and slower; this is of no help unless one is familiar with 1 song or the other.

Range and status: Breeds from ne. B.C., c. Alta., s. Sask., s. Man., n. Ont., c. Que., and sw. Nfld. south to n.-c. N.Dak., s. Ont., s. Que., n. N.H., c. Maine, and n. N.B.; possibly in mountains of ne. N.Y. Winters from c. Guatemala south to Panama and nw. Colombia. Migration is mainly through the Mississippi Basin.

Habitat: 2nd-growth forests and brushy areas of poplar, willow, and alder; rarely near villages or towns.

Seasonal movements: Moves north Apr.–May and south mid-Aug.–Oct. Very rare as a transient in e. Mexico.

Biology: Nest: Made of fine birch bark, grasses, lichens, and plant downs, lined with fine grasses, and bound to the supports and strengthened outside with spider and insect webbing; as with the other vireos, a deep, neat cup cradled in the arms of a horizontally forked slender tree branch 10–40 ft. above the ground. Eggs: 3–5, usually 4; white, with scattered fine spots of browns and black. Incubation: 14 days, by both sexes. Age at 1st flight unknown. Food: Insects, a few spiders,

The Warbling Vireo sings its pleasant song almost constantly.

and other small invertebrates; less than 10% berries, other fruit, and seeds.

Suggested reading: H. F. Lewis, "A Nesting of the Philadelphia Vireo," *Auk,* vol. 38, pp. 26–44, 185–202, 1921.

WARBLING VIREO (*Vireo gilvus*)

Appearance: About the same size (4½–5½ in.) as the Philadelphia Vireo, which it resembles closely except that it is white below, with pale smoke-gray at the side of the breast and down the flank, and has an indistinct pale brownish streak just above the eye.

Voice: Calls are a sharp *shirr* and a hard, snarling *quee* of complaint; the song is a series of 8–20 clear, musical, whistling notes arranged in a pleasant, somewhat slow warble, which is generally repeated again and again after a short, distinct pause.

Range and status: Breeds from n. B.C., s. Mack., c. Sask., s. Man., w. Ont., n. Minn., n. Mich., s. Ont., s. Que., s. Maine, s. N.B., and c. N.S. south to Baja Calif., n. Mexico, c. Tex., s. La., n. Ala., w. N.C., and se. Va. Winters from c. Mexico to Guatemala and El Salvador. Rare to locally common.

Habitat: Mixed and deciduous forests of more open type, groves, orchards, and shade trees along village streets and in suburbs.

Seasonal movements: Moves north Mar.–late May and returns Aug.–mid-Oct.

Biology: Courtship involves the male in a strut, with spread wing and tail, around the female while singing a very low, sweet warble. Nest: Made of strips of inner bark, leaves, grasses, feathers, cobwebs, and plant down, with edges overhanging the deep bowl; cradled in the horizontal fork of a slender tree branch 10–90 ft. above the ground. Eggs: 3–5, usually 4; white, very sparsely dotted with dark browns and blackish. Incubation: 12(?) days. Age at 1st flight: 16(?) days. Food: Insects, a few spiders, etc.; very little plant food.

THE HONEYCREEPERS (COEREBIDAE)

Honeycreepers are small (4–6 in.) songbirds most likely related to the wood warblers, Hawaiian honeycreepers, and vireos. Some authorities consider them but a subfamily of the wood warblers. There are 39 species spread from s. Mexico and the W. Indies south to ne. Peru, n. Argentina, and s. Brazil; 1 species, the Bahama Honeycreeper, has straggled into s. Fla. several times. Most species are found in the neotropical rain forests; no species are truly migratory. Plumage colors are often in bright blues and greens, occasionally in yellow or black; where the sexes differ, the females generally have some brownish colors. Brown and white appear in several species. The wings are usually pointed, the tail generally square-tipped and of moderate length. The shape of the bill is highly variable, from long, slender, and decurved to short, straight, and wedge-shaped. The voice is variable. Nests vary from thin cups to thick globular masses; they are usually made of twigs, grasses, mosses, leaves, and/or plant down. The 2–5 eggs are commonly white or pale-colored and spotted; incubation is by the female. The hatchlings may be naked or covered above by scanty down. The male joins the female in feeding and taking care of the family. Food varies from mainly insects to nectar, flowers, fruit, and some seeds or mixtures of these.

BAHAMA HONEYCREEPER (*Coereba bahamensis*)

Small (4½–5 in.); blackish brown to sooty black above, and white below, with a broad band of yellow across the breast. There is a white streak just above the eye, and the outer tail feathers and a patch on the wing are white. The blackish bill is moderately long, slender, and decurved. The legs and feet are dark brown, and the eye is brown. The voice is a series of long crackling notes or a harsh chatter. It is resident on Cozumel I. off the Yucatan Peninsula, Old Providence I. in the w. Caribbean, Grand Cayman and Cayman Brac Is., and the Bahamas. It has straggled several times to s. Fla.

Bahama Honeycreeper

The Golden-crowned Kinglet usually builds its nest in the branches of conifers. The cuplike structure of mosses and lichens is lined with rootlets and fine bark.

In North America the Bohemian Waxwing is most common in southwestern Canada and the northwestern United States. It is very rarely seen in the East.

Like all the vireos, the Yellow-throated Vireo typically suspends its neatly constructed, cuplike nest from the fork of a horizontal branch.

THE HAWAIIAN HONEYCREEPERS (DREPANIDIDAE)

These small (4¼–9½ in.) arboreal songbirds are probably most closely related to the honeycreepers and wood warblers. There are 22 species, but 8 of these are believed to be extinct; they are found only in the Hawaiian Is. Most species occur in forest or shrubby areas, but some are finchlike and adapted to grassy regions. They are nonmigratory. The plumage color is generally in large patches of greens, brownish greens, yellows, oranges, reds, browns, grays, and black, with only 1 spotted, streaked, and crested species. The group apparently evolved over many years from 1 flock of birds that found its way to the islands before any other land birds and was able to adapt, unhindered, to many of the feeding and living niches available on the islands. Hence the bill, for instance, is very variable, but of 2 main adaptations: long, slender, pointed, and decurved; straight or short, stout, and parrot-hooked or finchlike. The tongue is usually tubular, with a brushy tip. The wing is pointed, and the tail is moderately long and square-tipped or slightly forked. The legs are moderately long or short, the feet sturdy. Methods of flying and feeding vary. Calls are trills and rather loud, clear notes; the songs are musical, but usually simple. Although the male is at least slightly larger in all species, the plumages of the sexes are dissimilar in only a few species. Most species nest in the n. spring season, Mar.–May. Nests are loosely woven cups of twigs and grasses, on the ground in grass or in trees or bushes. The 2–4 eggs are white with brown spotting, and are incubated solely by the female. The hatchlings have a scattering of down above. Both sexes feed and otherwise care for the young. Food is fruit, nectar, flowers, insects, and seeds.

Suggested reading: D. Amadon, *The Hawaiian Honeycreepers*, Amer. Mus. Nat. Hist. Bull., vol. 95, pp. 155–262, 1950. P. H. Baldwin, *Annual Cycle, Environment and Evolution in the Hawaiian Honeycreepers*, Univ. Calif. Publ. Zool., vol. 52, pp. 285–398, 1953.

AMAKIHI (*Loxops virens*)

Appearance: Small (ca. 4½ in.); light olive above (darker on wing and tail) and yellow below. The well-decurved brownish-tipped greenish yellow bill is about as long as the head. The legs and feet are greenish yellow.

Voice: The call is a loud, whistled *tseet* or a *meuu;* the song is a monotonous chipping *ti-ti-ti-ti-ti-ti*.

Range and status: Through the main Hawaiian Is.; common on Oahu, Hawaii, Kauai, and Maui; locally common on Molokai.

Habitat: Dense forests and brush.

Seasonal movements: None.

Biology: Nest: A loosely woven cup of grasses, rootlets, and twigs, in a tree fern or tree. Eggs: 2–4; white, dotted with browns. Incubation period and age at 1st flight unknown. Food: Insects, nectar, berries, and other fruit.

ANIANIAU (*Loxops parva*)

Appearance: Slightly smaller (4–4½ in.) than the Amakihi (sometimes called the Lesser Amakihi) and yellower above, especially about the head, with a shorter, less decurved bill.

Voice: Call is an explosive, sibilant *ps-seet*.

Range and status: Kauai I., Hawaii; locally common.

Habitat: Forests, especially those at higher altitudes.

Seasonal movements: None.

Biology: Little is known except that its food is primarily insects, nectar, berries, and other fruit.

GREEN SOLITAIRE (Greater Amakihi) (*Loxops sagittirostris*)

Appearance: Larger (ca. 6½ in.) than the Amakihi. Bright olive-green above and greenish yellow below, with a heavier and straighter bill than that of the Amakihi.

Voice: The call, a low plaintive 2-part *ma-mow;* the song, a trilling *ti-ti-ti-ti*, ending in 2 louder, higher notes.

Range and status: Only on the island of Hawaii; almost certainly extinct.

Habitat: Dense forests between 2,000 and 4,000 ft. in altitude, now replaced by sugar plantations.

Seasonal movements: None.

Biology: Little is known; in fact, the native Hawaiians had no name for this bird. Its food was mainly insects, but it probably ate nectar and fruit too.

CREEPER (*Loxops maculata*)

Appearance: Small (4½–5 in.). On the island of Hawaii, olive above and pale yellow below, almost white at the throat, with dusky yellow-green on the flank. On Oahu I., olive above and yellow below, with a yellow-green streak above the eye. On Kauai I., brownish olive above and white to pale gray below, with a pale gray streak above the eye. On Molokai I., the male is bright scarlet, with brownish wing and tail and pinkish bill, legs, and feet, while the female is dull brownish gray above, with some scarlet spots, and whitish below. The bill is moderately long, with a longer down-curved upper mandible and straight lower mandible. The legs and feet are buffy brown.
Voice: Call is a rather sharp *tscheep,* and the song is a twittering, chipping series of soft notes ending in a rapid downward-scaling trill.
Range and status: All the larger islands of Hawaii. The scarlet form on Molokai I. is believed extinct; otherwise it is locally common on Kauai I. and rare on the other large islands.
Habitat: Mountain forests.
Seasonal movements: None.
Biology: Nest: A rather neatly woven cup of mosses, lined with rootlets and leaf fibers, in tree branches. Eggs: Apparently not known or described. Incubation period and age at 1st flight unknown. Food: Primarily insects, some nectar.

AKEPA (*Loxops coccinea*)

Appearance: Small (4½–5 in.); varies from island to island. The male ranges from bright scarlet-orange through shades of orange and yellow to a femalelike medium olive-green above and dusky yellow-green below. All these color varieties have a dusky wing and black tail. There is a black spot between the eye and bill. The female lacks this black on the face and is somewhat duller. The yellowish or brownish bill is short, stout, and tanagerlike, with slightly crossed tips; the legs and feet are black in the red variations and brown in the yellow-green variations. The tail is noticeably forked or notched.
Voice: A short trill and a low *kee-whit;* the song is a soft, uneven twittering.
Range and status: Resident on the 4 largest Hawaiian Is.: Hawaii, Maui, Oahu, and Kauai. Extinct on Oahu, near extinction on Maui, and rare to locally common on the other islands.
Habitat: Koa forests.
Seasonal movements: None.
Biology: Rather sprightly; during what may be courtship performances in spring, a pair or more will

chandelle higher and higher into the air above the forest. Apparently nothing is known of the nest or eggs. Food: Insects, spiders, etc.; very little nectar if any at all.

AKIALOA (*Hemignathus obscurus*)

Appearance: Larger (ca. 6½ in.) than the House Sparrow; medium olive-green above and yellow below. The bill is at least half again as long as the head and very pronouncedly decurved.
Voice: Not described well enough to exclude confusion with that of other birds.
Range and status: Oahu, Hawaii, and Lanai Is., Hawaii; extinct on Oahu and Lanai and probably on Hawaii.
Habitat: Forests.
Seasonal movements: None.
Biology: Nest: In a fork near the end of a large spreading branch of a koa tree; made of mosses and leaves and decorated with lichens. Nothing seems to be known about eggs, incubation, and age at 1st flight. Food: Insects and spiders probed from bark of trees, mosses, rotting logs, etc.

KAUAI AKIALOA (*Hemignathus procerus*)

Appearance: Larger (ca. 7½ in.) than the Akialoa, which it resembles very closely, though its bill is much longer (more than twice as long as the head) and heavier.
Voice: Calls are sparrowlike chirps, and both sexes have been described as singing a light, sweet song, without further details.
Range and status: Kauai I., Hawaii; very rare and in danger of extinction.
Habitat: Forests and forest edges; now survives only in rain forests at higher altitudes.
Seasonal movements: None.
Biology: Very little known. Food: Insects, spiders, etc., dug from crevices and holes in bark and rotting wood and from litter on forest floor.

NUKUPUU (*Hemignathus lucidus*)

Appearance: Small (ca. 5⅔ in.). Back, rump, tail, and wing are medium olive-green, and rest of plumage is bright yellow. The lower mandible of the long, well-decurved bill is very noticeably shorter than the upper bill. The female and immature birds are duller-colored, and the top of the head and nape are medium olive-green.
Voice: A clear, distinct *kee-whit* and a short trill; sometimes a longer trilling song.
Range and status: Extinct on Oahu and Hawaii Is. and very rare on Kauai I., Hawaii.
Habitat: Woodlands.
Seasonal movements: None.

Biology: Very little is known. Food: Insects, spiders, etc., pried from holes and crevices in trees, bark, and rotting wood.

AKIAPOLAAU (*Hemignathus wilsoni*)

Appearance: Small (5½ in.). Medium olive-green above (lighter and yellower on head and nape) and yellow below; somewhat duskier along flank. The lower bill is straight and stout, rather like a woodpecker's, and the longer upper mandible is well decurved. The bill is black, and the legs and feet are brownish.

Voice: A resonant whistle; the song is a pleasant warble and rich trill.

Range and status: Hawaii I.; rare and local.

Habitat: Forests on higher slopes of mountains.

Seasonal movements: None.

Biology: Information on nest, eggs, incubation, and age at 1st flight lacking. Food: The bird uses its lower bill as a chisel, even hammering like a woodpecker, and after digging into the wood uses the upper bill to probe for the insects, their larvae, and the spiders that form its diet.

PSEUDONESTOR (*Pseudonestor xanthophrys*)

Appearance: Small (ca. 5½ in.). The brownish bill is like that of a parrot; the upper mandible, much longer than the almost straight lower beak, is high, laterally compressed, and arched. The bird is olive-green above and yellow below, with a yellow streak above the eye and light olive along the flank. The eye is brown, and the legs and feet are dusky. The female is distinctly smaller than the male.

Voice: The call is a loud *kee-wit;* the song is a rather short, vigorous trill, sometimes given during flight.

Range and status: Mt. Haleakala, Maui I., Hawaii. Very rare.

Habitat: Koa forests above 5,000 ft. on the slopes of the mountain.

Seasonal movements: None.

Biology: Nest: A cup made of lichens and other plant material; built in a tree. No information on eggs, incubation period, etc. Food: Described as almost entirely insects, especially the immature forms, gleaned from the bark crevices of the koa and occasionally other trees.

OU (*Psittirostra psittacea*)

Appearance: The size (6–6½ in.) of a House Sparrow. The entire head is a bright yellow, and the rest of the plumage is olive-green above and a dusky lime-green below. The moderately long, rather stout bill, somewhat like that of a parrot, is straw-yellow; the legs and feet are buffy yellow. The female is olive-green above, grading into a pale gray below. Young resemble the female.

Voice: The song starts with several clear whistled notes and ends in a trill; the call is described as plaintive.

Range and status: Resident on Hawaii and Kauai Is., Hawaii, where it is local and very scarce; extirpated from Maui, Molokai, Lanai, and Oahu Is.

Habitat: Dense rain forests with heavy undergrowth of ferns.

Seasonal movements: None.

Biology: No information on nest, eggs, incubation period, or age at 1st flight. Food: Apparently almost exclusively fruits, especially soft-bodied fruits and berries.

LAYSAN FINCH (*Psittirostra cantans*)

Appearance: Larger (6–7 in.) than the House Sparrow. The head and breast are yellow, fading to dull white on the abdomen, and the back, rump, wing, and tail are yellowish brown. The female has a brown-streaked pale yellow throat and breast, fading to pale gray on the abdomen. Above, including the face, she is

The Laysan Finch's stout bill is especially well suited to eating seeds.

buffy brown, streaked on the cap, face, back, and non-flight feathers of the wing with dark brown or blackish, and there is some yellowish on the wing. The large, stout, dark-tipped straw-yellow bill resembles that of an Evening Grosbeak in shape. The legs, feet, and eyes are dark brown. The young are like the female.

Voice: Its song has been described as "fine" (Peterson). It is known to mimic the cries of its seabird neighbors.

Range and status: Resident on Laysan and Nihoa Is., Hawaii; introduced and then extirpated on Midway I. Destruction of much of the natural vegetation on the islands has seriously reduced the population, but it has a good chance of surviving if given proper protection and consideration.

Habitat: Grassy and shrubby areas.

Seasonal movements: None.

Biology: Nest: A low cup woven of grasses, on ground among grasses, on rocks, or in bushes. Eggs: 2–3; white, spotted with dark browns. Incubation period and age at 1st flight apparently unknown. Food: Practically omnivorous. Insects, birds' eggs, roots, dead animals, seeds, and fruits have been listed.

PALILA (*Psittirostra bailleui*)

Appearance: Of House Sparrow size (6–6½ in.). The head, nape, throat, and breast are bright orangish yellow; the medium gray of the back grades into a light gray on the rump; the wing and tail are medium olive-green. The abdomen and undertail feathers are pale gray to white. The brown bill resembles a grosbeak's, with a much rounded upper mandible; the eye is brown, and the legs and feet are buffy brown. The females are duller-colored.

Voice: The calls are a complaining *whee-whee-o* and a vigorous *wheet-feeu* "wolf-whistle."

Range and status: At altitudes between 4,000 and 7,000 ft. on Hawaii I., Hawaii. Locally common, but generally rare and much reduced in numbers from former years.

Habitat: The more open mamani-naio forests on mountain slopes, particularly on Mauna Loa.

Seasonal movements: None.

Biology: No information on nest, eggs, incubation period, or age at 1st flight. Food: Seeds of the mamani and naio trees, poha fruit, and insects; apparently the young are fed mainly on insects.

GREATER KOA FINCH (*Psittirostra palmeri*)

Appearance: Largest (8¼–8¾ in.) of the family. Head and breast are bright scarlet-orange fading to dull yellow on the abdomen; the back, rump, tail, and wing are olive-green, with some orange on the rump. The female is olive-green above, fading to whitish below,

with yellowish crown, throat, and breast. The young resemble the female, but are blotched with smoke-gray on the breast. The large bill, like that of a grosbeak, and the legs and feet are brown.

Voice: Flutelike notes, with the final ones of each series prolonged; quite distinctive, but now heard no more.

Range and status: Hawaii I., Hawaii. Believed to be extinct.

Habitat: Koa forests at about 4,000-ft. elevation.

Seasonal movements: None.

Biology: Little is known, except that it fed mainly on seeds as well as occasionally on insects, which it also fed to the young.

LESSER KOA FINCH (*Psittirostra flaviceps*)

Appearance: Smaller (ca. 7½ in.) than the Greater Koa Finch and otherwise differing from it only in that the male has a yellow rather than a scarlet-orange head.

Voice: Not known certainly.

Range and status: Hawaii I., Hawaii. Believed to be extinct.

Habitat: Koa forests at medium altitudes.

Seasonal movements: None.

Biology: Fed on seeds of the koa and other trees, as well as a few insects. Nothing else seems to be known of its biology.

GROSBEAK FINCH (Kona Finch) (*Psittirostra kona*)

Appearance: Of House Sparrow size (ca. 6 in.). The bill is proportionately much larger than that of the Koa Finch, and very similar to a grosbeak's. The plumage is a fairly even greenish yellow, perhaps somewhat lighter below; the young and female birds are a bit duller.

Voice: A small squeak, a light cheep, and a low, sweet song.

Range and status: Kona District of the island of Hawaii. Probably extinct.

Habitat: Naio and koa forests near lava fields, at about 4,000-ft. elevation.

Seasonal movements: None.

Biology: Except for the food (naio seeds, some green leaves, caterpillars, and perhaps other seeds), nothing is known of its biology.

APAPANE (*Himatione sanguinea*)

Appearance: Small (5¼ in.). The wing and tail are black, the lower abdomen and undertail feathers are white, and the rest of the plumage is dusky scarlet. The sharp-pointed, slightly decurved brown bill is almost as long as the head. The legs, feet, and eye are brown. The immature birds have black wing and tail, but the crown, nape, and back are blackish brown; the rump is smoke-gray, the forehead and most of the undersides are light smoke-gray, and the lower abdomen and undertail feathers are whitish.

Voice: Short, reedy whistled *eep*'s and *erp*'s; song is composed of series of these notes, much repeated, and *tchee-tchee* or *tikka-tikka-tikka* notes.

Range and status: Resident on all the larger islands of Hawaii. Abundant on Hawaii I., common on Kauai, Oahu, and Maui; locally common on Molokai; extirpated from Laysan I.

Habitat: Montane forests up and into the higher scrubby growth and areas where large-flowering trees are found.

Seasonal movements: None.

Biology: Nest: Made of grasses, mosses, twigs, and plant down, lined with fine grasses; built 7–10 ft. above the ground in scrubby trees. Eggs: 3; white, with small, short streaks of reddish brown mostly concentrated in a ring about the larger end. Incubation period and age at 1st flight unknown. Food: Nectar and insects.

Suggested reading: W. V. Ward, "The Songs of the Apapane," *The Living Bird*, vol. 3, pp. 97–118, 1964.

The colorful Iiwi probes for nectar and insects with its long, slender bill.

CRESTED HONEYCREEPER (*Palmeria dolei*)

Appearance: Larger (ca. 7 in.) than the House Sparrow. The moderately long, pointed bill, the legs, the feet, and most of the plumage are black. A ring around the eye, a streak joining this to the nape, and the nape and a line from this to the shoulder are scarlet-orange. The crest, which consists of rather long white feathers curling forward, covers the head from the forehead to the center of the crown. Except for the wing and tail, the feathers are streaked with gray on the throat and breast and with light scarlet-orange elsewhere. The immature birds are a dull, dusky brown and have only a partial crest.

Voice: A single loud, clear whistle, a rasping *churr*, and a forced, unmusical song.

Range and status: Maui I., Hawaii, where it persists only on the ne. slope of Mt. Haleakala and is very rare there. Extinct on Molokai I.

Habitat: Dense montane rain forests where there are large-flowering trees.

Seasonal movements: None.

Biology: Nothing is known of the nest or eggs or of the young. Food is largely nectar and insects.

ULA-AI-HAWANE (*Ciridops anna*)

Appearance: Small (ca. 4¼ in.). The flight feathers of the wing and the tail, breast, forehead, chin, and crown are black; the crown feathers are tipped with whitish or very pale gray. The nape, upper back, neck, and throat are light gray. The lower abdomen and undertail feathers are light buffy brown, and the rest of the plumage is scarlet. The rather short, conical bill is yellowish brown, and the legs and feet dark brown. The immature bird is grayish brown above and on the throat, with a dingy gray breast and a pale yellowish olive abdomen.

Voice: Not known.

Range and status: Hawaii I., Hawaii; believed extinct, apparently never common.

Habitat: Forests of hawane, the native Hawaiian palm tree.

Seasonal movements: None.

Biology: Very little known. Its name means "red bird that feeds on the hawane," so it is reputed to eat the fruit of that tree, but this is not certain.

IIWI (*Vestiaria coccinea*)

Appearance: Small (5¾ in.); plumage is bright ruby except for the black tail and the black wing with its white patch. The pinkish red bill is about as long as the head, sharp-pointed, rather sturdy, and decidedly de-curved; the legs and feet are also pinkish red. Immature birds have the same black wing and tail but are mottled black and tawny above and yellow below, with dark streaking on the throat and breast.

Voice: A high-pitched *ee-wee* or *ee-ee-vee,* noises like those produced by the squeaky wheel of a small wooden wagon, and a series of harsh, metallic notes.

Range and status: Common on Kauai and Hawaii Is., Hawaii, and rare on Oahu and Maui Is.; almost extinct on Molokai I. and extirpated from Lanai I.

Habitat: Forests with large-flowering trees such as ohia and mamani trees.

Seasonal movements: None.

Biology: Strong fliers; they were evidently able to fly from island to island, as there are no measurable color or size differences among the populations of the several islands. Nest: A shallow cup built of dry weed stems, leaves, and rootlets, in the branches of ohia or koa trees. There is apparently no information on eggs, incubation period, or age at 1st flight. Food: Nectar and insects.

MAMO (*Drepanis pacifica*)

Appearance: About the size (9½ in.) of a small Robin. The lower back, rump, flank, undertail feathers, a patch at the bend of the wing, and the thighs are orange-yellow. The rest of the plumage is black except for a patch of white at the bases of the larger flight feathers of the wing. The legs and feet and the long, slender, well-decurved bill are black.

Voice: Not described.

Range and status: Hawaii I., Hawaii; believed extinct.

Habitat: Formerly throughout forests of Hawaii I.

Seasonal movements: None.

Biology: Very little is known except that it ate nectar and probably insects. It was tame and easily lured by imitations of its call or by flowers offered in the hand; the natives captured the bird alive by holding a tubular flower and pressing it together to seize the bird when it inserted its bill for the nectar.

BLACK MAMO (Perkin's Mamo) (*Drepanis funerea*)

Appearance: Smaller (ca. 8 in.) than the Mamo. It is very much like the Mamo, but the plumage is entirely black except for some white on the larger flight feathers of the wing, and the bill is longer and more decurved.

Voice: A loud, rather piercing cry and a gentler call note described as *hoa.*

Range and status: Molokai I., Hawaii; extinct, not seen since 1907.

Habitat: Underbrush and low forest trees.

Seasonal movements: None.

Biology: Apparently nothing is known except that it ate nectar; there are no authentic reports of its eating insects, but it may have fed these to the young.

The Black-and-white Warbler often creeps headfirst down tree trunks.

THE AMERICAN WOOD WARBLERS (PARULIDAE)

These small (4–7½ in.) songbirds are related to the typical honeycreepers and the tanagers, and probably to the finches, vireos, and Hawaiian honeycreepers. There are 109 species (some authorities include the Coerebidae here); 54 of these occur in America. The family regularly ranges from n. N. America south, including the W. Indies, to n. Argentina and Uruguay; most of the N. American species are migratory. The great majority are habitants of the forests, but some are terrestrial, and even these prefer woodland floors. American wood warblers are commonly plumaged in grays and grayish greens, but many are marked or patterned in bright yellows, oranges, reds, blues, and black and white; streaks, bars, and other markings are common. The wings are rather short to moderately long and are somewhat square-tipped in most species. The tail varies in length from moderately short to somewhat long; it may be rounded or, in some species, graduated or even slightly forked. The short bill is usually slender and sharp-pointed, but some species have broad, rather flattened bills, and the bills of others resemble those of tanagers. The legs are commonly slender and may be comparatively short or fairly long; the toes are usually long and slender. Most species seem to be constantly active, flitting or scurrying among the forest leaves and twigs or creeping about the boles of trees. In quite a few species the plumage of the sexes is alike, in many the female is simply duller-colored, and in others there is a sharp difference; in many the fall and winter aspect differs from that of spring and summer. The song is well developed in only a few species. Nests may be on the ground, in holes in trees or banks, among grasses or sedges, in low bushes, or in trees. They are usually cup-shaped or domed structures of grasses, root-lets, plant fibers, plant down, and other vegetable material. Very rarely does the male help his mate build the nest, and almost never does he take part in the incubation of the 2–8 brown-spotted white eggs. The hatchlings are naked or, in a few species, sparsely covered with down above. Insects form the largest part of the diet by far, although nearly all species will eat berries or other fruit on occasion.

Suggested reading: R. M. Mengel, "The Probable History of Species Formation in Some Northern Wood Warblers (Parulidae)," *The Living Bird*, pp. 8–43, 1964. R. H. MacArthur, "Population Ecology of Some Warblers of Northeastern Coniferous Forests," *Ecology*, vol. 39, pp. 599–619, 1958.

The Prothonotary Warbler commonly nests in abandoned woodpecker holes.

BLACK-AND-WHITE WARBLER (*Mniotilta varia*)

Appearance: Smaller (4½–5½ in.) than the House Sparrow and aptly named. Above it is predominantly streaked longitudinally beginning with white at the center of the cap, which is broadly edged with black, then a white line above the eye, and finally a black streak through the eye flaring out into a white-edged black cheek. It is white below, with a black chin, from which stuttering black stripes radiate to the breast and flank. The black wing has 2 white wing bars and white edging to some of the larger flight feathers. The slightly forked black tail has some white, especially on the outer edges of the feathers. The female resembles the male above but is white below, with light gray cheek and streaking at side of breast and flank. The eye is dark brown, the bill is black, and the legs and feet are straw-yellow. The young resemble the female; the immature male is like the adult male, but has a white throat.

Voice: Song is a rather high-pitched, reedy *weesee* repeated rapidly at least 7 times; sometimes this is elaborated by a drop in pitch near the middle of the series. The call is an abrupt *chi,* sounding like 2 fair-sized quartz pebbles rapped together.

Range and status: Breeds from sw. Mack., c. Sask., c. Man., s. Ont., s. Que., and n. Nfld. south to ne. B.C., c. Alta., e. Mont., sw. S.Dak., c. Tex., se. La., n. Miss., c. Ala., c. Ga., c. S.C., and se. N.C. Winters from s. Baja Calif., n.-c. Mexico, s. Tex., c. Fla., and the Bahamas south through C. America and the W. Indies to nw. S. America; casually farther north. It has straggled to Scotland. Fairly common and generally a common migrant.

Habitat: Many types of deciduous forests, particularly those with some openings in the canopy.

Seasonal movements: Arrives within breeding range late Mar.–late May and departs Aug.–mid-Nov.

Biology: Nest: Made of dead leaves and usually arched over with the same material; the cup is woven of grasses, strips of bark, plant fibers, rootlets, etc., and lined with finer grasses, rootlets, and hair. Usually built on the ground at the base of a tree, shrub, stump, etc. Eggs: 4–5, usually 5; white or creamy white, finely peppered or boldly spotted and splotched with browns. Incubation: More than 10 days. Age at 1st flight: 8–12 days. Food: Almost entirely insects in all stages, gleaned from bark of trees or caught in flight; no vegetable food is mentioned.

Suggested reading: W. P. Smith, "Observations of the Nesting Habits of the Black-and-white Warbler," *Bird-banding,* vol. 5, pp. 31–36, 1934.

PROTHONOTARY WARBLER (*Protonotaria citrea*)

Appearance: Slightly smaller (5¼–5¾ in.) than the House Sparrow. Entire head, neck, and underparts are orange-yellow or orange becoming paler toward tail; the back is a light olive; and the wing, tail, and rump are bluish gray. The female is duller, and her crown, cheek, and nape are a grayed orange-yellow or orange. In winter both sexes are duller and somewhat browner. The bill is black, the eye is brown, and the legs and feet are bluish gray.

Voice: The call note is a musical, somewhat sibilant, whistled *tseet;* the song is a series of loud, clear whistles, as *tweet-weet-weet-weet-weet-weet.*

Range and status: Breeds from e.-c. Minn., s.-c. Wis., s. Mich., s. Ont., c. N.Y., and N.J. south to the Gulf Coast and c. Fla.; rare and local on n. edge.

Winters from s. Mexico, including the Yucatan Peninsula, through C. America to nw. S. America. It has been recorded during the breeding season in N.H. and Maine; it has straggled west to Ariz., Calif., and Wyo.; in migration it has reached Bermuda, the Bahamas, and some of the W. Indies. Abundant in favored habitats to rare in fringe parts of range.

Habitat: Lowland, wooded river swamps, other forested swamps, and moist, periodically flooded woodlands.

Seasonal movements: Arrives within breeding range mid-Mar.–mid-May and departs Aug.–Oct.

Biology: Nest: Made of mosses and lined with grape bark, rootlets, and fine grasses; built in cavities or holes in trees or stumps 3–30 ft. above the ground, but generally below 10 ft. Unlike most other warblers, the male of this species will build 1–2 dummy nests by himself and will occasionally assist the female in constructing the real nest at least by bringing materials. Eggs: 3–8, usually 4–6; cream or pinkish, boldly and well sprinkled and blotched with dark browns and light grays; some are very sparingly marked, and a few are immaculate. Incubation: 13½–14 days. Age at 1st flight: About 11 days. Food: Probably almost entirely insects, spiders, and other small invertebrates.

Suggested reading: L. H. Walkinshaw, "Life History of the Prothonotary Warbler," *Wils. Bull.*, vol. 65, pp. 152–168, 1953.

SWAINSON'S WARBLER (*Limnothlypis swainsonii*)

Appearance: Small (5 in.). Brownish olive above, with tawny cap and nape, a pale buff streak above the eye, and a dusky smoke-gray face. Below it is pale smoke-gray to whitish. The bill is light buffy brown, the legs and feet are flesh-colored, and the eye is brown. The sexes are alike.

Voice: The call is a soft *tschip* note; song starts with a few notes sung at rather slow cadence, moving abruptly into a faster-paced, descending series, as *whee-whee-whee-whip-poor-will*.

Range and status: Breeds locally from ne. Okla., se. Mo., s. Ill., sw. Ind., s. Ohio, w. W.Va., s. Va., and se. Md. south to se. La., Miss., Ala., and n. Fla. Winters in the Yucatan Peninsula, British Honduras, Cuba, and Jamaica. Has straggled to Vera Cruz and the Bahamas. Rather rare; inconspicuous and hard to find.

Habitat: Patches of cane growth in wooded swamps; in Appalachians, thickets of rhododendron and hemlock.

Seasonal movements: Arrives late Mar.–Apr. and departs mid-Aug.–early Nov.

Biology: Nest: A bulky structure made of leaves and lined with pine needles, moss fibers, rootlets, fine leaves, and grasses; built 2–10 ft. from ground in bushes, canebrake, and snarls of vine. Eggs: 3–5, most often 3; white, very rarely spotted with browns; almost spherical. Incubation period and age at 1st flight unknown. Food: Mainly insects and spiders.

Suggested reading: B. Meanley, "Notes on Swainson's Warbler in Central Georgia," *Auk*, vol. 62, pp. 395–400, 1945.

WORM-EATING WARBLER (*Helmitheros vermivorus*)

Appearance: Smaller (5–5½ in.) than the House Sparrow. Back, rump, wing, and tail brownish olive; head, neck, and underparts are buff, and there is a black streak through the eye and another at the edge of the crown. The iris is brown, and the bill, legs, and feet are a pale yellowish flesh color. The sexes are alike.

Voice: The song is a simple trill, 1½–2 seconds long, similar to the song of the Chipping Sparrow.

Range and status: Breeds from ne. Kans., se. Iowa, n. Ill., s. Ind., s. and e.-c. Ohio, sw. and c. Pa., c. and se.

The rare Swainson's Warbler inhabits both lowland swamps and mountain thickets.

Despite its name, the Worm-eating Warbler eats more insects than worms.

N.Y., w. Mass., and s. Conn. south to ne. Tex., c. Ark., c. La., w. Tenn., n. Ala., n. Ga., nw. S.C., and ne. N.C. Winters from e.-c. Mexico, Cuba, and the Bahamas south to Panama and Jamaica; rarely to ne. Mexico and c. Fla. Has straggled to Wis., s. Ont., Vt., and Bermuda. Inconspicuous although sometimes locally common.

Habitat: Deciduous forests, especially mountain slopes and plateaus.

Seasonal movements: Arrives at breeding sites late Mar.–early May and departs mid-Aug.–mid-Oct.

Biology: Nest: Constructed of dead and skeletonized leaves and lined with flower stems of hair moss and occasionally hairs; well hidden among dead leaves on the ground of sloping hillsides. Eggs: 3–6, usually 4–5; white, peppered and spotted with browns. Incubation: 13 days, by female alone. Age at 1st flight: 10 days. Food: The scientific name means "worm-hunting wormeater" and is just as erroneous as the common name. It may consume a worm or two, but insects in various stages make up the bulk of its diet.

Suggested reading: A. C. Bent, *Life Histories of North American Wood Warblers*, Dover, N.Y. (reprint of U.S. Nat. Mus. Bull. 203, 1953), 1963, pp. 38–47.

GOLDEN-WINGED WARBLER (*Vermivora chrysoptera*)

Appearance: Small (5–5¼ in.); medium gray above and white below. The front half of the crown and a large patch on the wing are bright yellow, the sides of the breast are medium gray, the flank is pale gray, the face is white with a black streak through the eye flaring out behind the eye, and the throat and upper edge of the breast are black. The eye streak and throat of the female are medium gray. The bill is black, and the legs and feet are bluish gray.

Voice: 1 song is a sequence of 4 buzzes, as *zeee-zer-zer-zer*, and another is a higher-pitched, almost buzzless *th-th-th-th-th-thee*. The common call is a short *dzz* and an excited *tchu-tchu-tchu* series.

Range and status: Breeds from se. Man., e.-c. Minn., n.-c. Wis., n. Mich., s. Ont., c. N.Y., s. Conn., and e. Mass. south to se. Iowa, n. Ill., n. Ind., s. Ohio, e. Tenn., n. Ga., nw. S.C., w. Va., n.-c. Md., and se. Pa. Winters from Guatemala to nw. S. America. Has straggled to Vt., N.H., and Maine. Locally fairly common.

Habitat: Brushy openings in deciduous forests and brushy edges of such forests.

Seasonal movements: Arrives in breeding areas Apr.–mid-May and departs mid-Aug.–early Oct.

Biology: Nest: Made of grasses and vegetable fibers, lined with dried grasses, grapevine bark, and hairs; on the ground among dead leaves supported by weed stalks or hidden in clump of grass or ferns. Eggs: 4–7, usually 4–5; white or creamy white, peppered, spotted, and scrawled with browns. Incubation: 10(?) days. Age at 1st flight: 10(?) days. Food: Insects.

Suggested reading: L. L. Short, Jr., "The Blue-winged and Golden-winged Warbler in New York," *Kingbird*, vol. 12, pp. 59–67, 1962.

BLUE-WINGED WARBLER (*Vermivora pinus*)

Appearance: Somewhat smaller (4½–5 in.) than the Golden-winged Warbler. Back of head and the nape, back, and rump are brownish olive, the rump often much more yellowish. The wing and tail are bluish gray, with 2 white wing bars. The rest of the plumage is yellow, with a small black streak running from the bill to just behind the eye. The female is duller, and the brownish olive often covers the top of the head. The bill is black; the eye, legs, and feet are brown.

The Golden-winged Warbler often hybridizes with its near relative, the Blue-winged Warbler.

Voice: Territorial song is composed of 2 rather long buzzy notes, the second coarser and lower-pitched than the first, as *bzzzzzzzzz-brrrrrrrr;* its flight song has been transliterated as *tzip-tsee-zee-zee-zee-zee-zee-zee, swee-tzip-zee-zee-zee-zee-zee-zee-zee.* The call and alarm note is a low *chip.*

Range and status: Breeds from w.-c. Nebr., c. Iowa, se. Minn., s. Wis., s. Mich., n. Ohio, nw. Pa., w. and se. N.Y., and se. Mass. south to nw. Ark., e.-c. Mo., s. Ill., c. Tenn., n. Ala., n. Ga., N.C., n. Va., c. and ne. Md., and Del. Winters from e.-c. Mexico (including Yucatan) south to Nicaragua, rarely to Panama and casually to Colombia. It has straggled to Calif., s. Ont., N.H., Cuba, and the Bahamas. Fairly common, at least locally. This species commonly interbreeds with the Golden-winged Warbler where their ranges overlap, and the hybrid progeny were given separate names until their origin was understood. The most common of the named hybrids are the Brewster's Warbler, most easily described as a Golden-winged Warbler without the black bib and eye streak and with 2 pale yellow wing bars and a yellow breast fading into a very pale yellow throat; and the Lawrence's Warbler, which looks like a Blue-winged Warbler with the black throat and eye streak of the Golden-winged Warbler. There are other combinations arising from crosses between the hybrids and between the hybrids and either of the parent species, not all of which have been or could be pictured in the field guides.

Habitat: Overgrown pasturelands, woodland edges, weedy and grassy borders of swamps and streams, and into more open forests.

Seasonal movements: Arrives at breeding sites Apr.–May and departs mid-Aug.–early Oct.

Biology: Nest: Made of grasses and dead tree leaves formed into a cup and lined with fine grapevine bark and fine grasses; built close to the ground in tangles of brush, vines, or grasses. Eggs: 4–7, usually 5–6; white, peppered or sparingly spotted with browns. Incubation: 10–12(?) days. Age at 1st flight: 8–10 days. Food: Insects and spiders; probably a few other small invertebrates.

Suggested reading: K. C. Parkes, "The Genetics of the Golden-winged X Blue-winged Warbler Complex," *Wils. Bull.*, vol. 63, pp. 5–15, 1951.

BACHMAN'S WARBLER (*Vermivora bachmanii*)

Appearance: Small (4¼ in.). Brownish olive above and yellow below, with yellow forehead and face. The throat and the edge of the crown near the forehead are black. The female has a blue-gray cap and nape, a narrow yellow forehead, and a distinct yellow eye-ring; she has no black bib, and the yellow fades to whitish on the undertail feathers. The bill is black above and straw-yellow below, and the legs and feet are flesh-colored.

Voice: The call is a low, hissing *zee-ee-eep;* song is

Bachman's Warbler

TENNESSEE WARBLER (*Vermivora peregrina*)

Appearance: Small (4½–5 in.). Crown and nape are medium gray, and face is streaked with grayish. The back, rump, wing, and tail are olive; the underparts and a streak just above the eye are white. The hen has a somewhat greenish gray cap and nape and is slightly yellowish below. The immature birds and the adults in fall are brownish olive above, more brownish on the cap and nape, and buffy yellow below, mottled with grayish on the throat, breast, and flank, with a dingy yellow streak above the eye. The bill, legs, and feet are blackish; the eye is brown.

Tennessee Warbler

a scratchy, tittering or rattling, monotonous series of 6–8 notes.

Range and status: Breeds in se. Mo., ne. Ark., s.-c. Ky., c. Ala., and se. S.C.; may breed in larger area from w. Ark., s.-c. Mo., n.-c. Ky., and Va. south to La., Miss., s. Ala., and S.C. Winters in Cuba and the Isle of Pines, casually in s. Miss. and s. Ga. Has occurred in the Fla. Keys and the Bahamas. Very rare and local.

Habitat: Rich, humid, wooded, dense-foliaged river-bottom or lowland swamps.

Seasonal movements: Arrives in breeding areas late Feb.–Mar. and has generally departed before the end of Sept.

Biology: Nest: Made of dried weed and grass stalks and dead leaves, lined with black rootlets and plant fibers; built near the ground in tangled undergrowth. Eggs: 3–5, usually 3–4; white, very rarely spotted with browns. Incubation and age at 1st flight unknown. Food: Probably almost entirely insects.

Suggested reading: H. M. Stevenson, Jr., "Bachman's Warbler in Alabama," *Wils. Bull.,* vol. 50, pp. 36–41, 1938.

Voice: The song is a high-pitched, loud, unmusical series of 9–25 chipping notes seldom given at the speed of a true trill; some songs rise and some drop in pitch near the end.

Range and status: Breeds from s. Yuk., c. Mack., n. Man., n. Ont., n. Que., s. Lab., and w. Nfld. south to s.-c. B.C., nw. Mont., c. Alta., c. Sask., s. Man., n. Minn., n. Wis., n. Mich., s.-c. Ont., ne. N.Y., s. Vt., c. N.H., s. Maine, s. N.B., and c. N.S. Winters from s. Mexico to nw. S. America. Migrates mainly east of the Mississippi River, but has straggled to Calif. and Baja Calif. and has reached Greenland and Bermuda. Fairly common.

Habitat: More open types of deciduous and mixed woodlands, forest clearings, groves, brushy areas, and edges of forests.

Seasonal movements: Arrives at breeding areas mid-Apr.–May and departs mid-Aug.–Oct.

Biology: Nest: Made of mosses and lined with fine grasses, hairs, and rootlets; built in a fairly wet situation on the ground, at the base of a shrub. These warblers seemingly nest in loose colonies, with several pairs occupying 1 small overgrown clearing. Eggs: 4–7, usually 5–6; white or creamy white, specked and spotted with browns, with these markings sometimes wreathed about larger end of egg. Incubation period and age at 1st flight unknown. Food: Insects and a few other small invertebrates as well as some fruit and seeds.

Suggested reading: B. S. Bowdish and P. B. Philipp, "The Tennessee Warbler in New Brunswick," *Auk*, vol. 33, pp. 1–8, 1916.

ORANGE-CROWNED WARBLER (*Vermivora celata*)

Appearance: Small (4½–5½ in.). Olive above and buffy yellow below, with a brownish orange crown, which is usually hidden by the olive tips of the feathers. The breast, face, and flank are streaked and mottled with brownish olive, which may be almost solid on the breast. The variety on the Pacific Coast is an almost even brownish olive, but slightly lighter below. The sexes are alike, but the immature birds lack the brownish orange crown. The bill is black, and the eye, legs, and feet are brown.

Voice: Song is a rather monotonous trill or a series of variably pitched *chip-ee, chip-ee, chip-ee* notes.

Range and status: Breeds from c. Alaska, nw. and c. Mack., n. Man., n. Ont., and nw. Que. south to nw. Baja Calif., se. Ariz., w. Tex., se. Sask., s. Man., and w. and c. Ont. Winters from n. Calif., s. Nev., c. Ariz., s. Tex., the Gulf Coast, and S.C. south to s. Baja Calif., Guatemala, and s. Fla. Rare; because of nondescript appearance, not noted very often.

Habitat: Brushy clearings in and along edges of forests, wooded hillsides, undergrowth, chaparral, and groves of aspen, etc.

Seasonal movements: Reaches breeding areas late Mar.–mid-May and departs mid-Aug.–early Oct.

The Orange-crowned Warbler's rust-red crown usually is hidden by surrounding feathers.

Biology: Nest: Made of coarse grasses laced together with strips of bark and plant down; built on the ground or close to it in bushes or low trees. Eggs: 4–6, commonly 5; whites heavily peppered and spotted with dark reds and brown. Incubation period and age at 1st flight unknown. Food: Mainly insects.

NASHVILLE WARBLER (*Vermivora ruficapilla*)

Appearance: Small (4–5 in.). Forehead, face, and nape are medium gray; back, rump, wing, and tail are olive; crown is chestnut. The bird is yellow below. It has a distinct white eye-ring. The female is duller, with little

Here a male Nashville Warbler presents food to the incubating female.

or no chestnut on crown. The immature bird is a duller olive above and a light yellowish flesh color below. The bill is blackish brown above and a medium dusky brown below; the eye is brown, and the legs and feet are straw-yellow.

Voice: The call is a terse *chip.* The song starts with 6–8 distinct but rapid lively notes, then many notes run together in a musical, rolling twitter; another variety slows up the delivery of the twitter until the notes are almost separable to the ear.

Range and status: Breeds from s. Canada to c. Calif., n. Utah, s. Minn., n. Ill., s. Mich., n. Ohio, ne. W.Va., w. Md., and Pa. Winters from n. Mexico, s. Tex., and s. Fla. south to Guatemala. It has straggled to Greenland and Bermuda. Irregular in appearance, and numbers fluctuate; may be locally common.

Habitat: Undergrowth of more open forests and forest edges.

Seasonal movements: Moves north Mar.–mid-May and returns mid-Aug.–mid-Oct.

Biology: Nest: Constructed of mosses and lined with fine grasses, vegetable fiber, and fur; well hidden among vegetation on ground. Eggs: 4–5; white or creamy white, speckled with browns. Incubation: 11–12 days. Age at 1st flight: About 11 days. Food: Insects and their larvae and eggs; probably other small invertebrates.

Suggested reading: L. deK. Lawrence, "Comparative Study of the Nesting Behavior of Chestnut-sided and Nashville Warblers," *Auk,* vol. 65, pp. 204–219, 1948.

VIRGINIA'S WARBLER (*Vermivora virginiae*)

Appearance: Small (4–4½ in.). Dark smoke-gray above, with fairly large spot of brownish red on the crown and a pale greenish yellow rump. White below, with the breast and undertail feathers a light greenish yellow. The female is duller-colored; the immature birds resemble the female but are somewhat browner above. The bill, legs, and feet are black, and the eye is brown.

Voice: The common call is a sharp *chip.* Song is rather variable but is generally a couplet of notes repeated 7–10 times with more rapid cadence at the end, as *che-wee-che-wee-che-wee.*

Range and status: Breeds from c. Nev., se. Idaho, ne. Utah, and n.-c. Colo. south to se. Calif., s. Nev., c. and se. Ariz., and n.-c. N.Mex. Winters in s. Mexico. Rather rare and inconspicuous.

Habitat: Brushy foothills and mountain slopes, canyons, oak forests, and piñon groves.

Seasonal movements: Migrates north Apr.–early May and south late July–Sept.

Biology: Nest: Made of fine strips of inner bark, grasses roots, and mosses and lined with finer grades of the same materials and hair; built on ground, embedded in dead leaves of forest floor. Eggs: 3–5, usually 4; white, peppered and spotted with browns, which may sometimes be wreathed about the larger end. Incubation period and age at 1st flight unknown. Food: Insects; very little known.

Suggested reading: A. M. Bailey and R. J. Neidrach, "Nesting of Virginia's Warbler," *Auk,* vol. 55, pp. 176–178, 1938.

COLIMA WARBLER (*Vermivora crissalis*)

Appearance: A larger (5¼ in.) edition of the Virginia's Warbler, but the breast is mottled with pale smoke-gray instead of yellow.

Voice: The call is a sharp, abrupt *psit.* Songs are a rather short trill ending in 2 distinct notes and a rather soft trilling warble.

Range and status: Breeds in Chisos Mountains of sw. Tex. and the Sierra Madre Oriental of ne. Mexico. Winters in s. Mexico. Common, but inconspicuous and seldom seen because of the rough terrain it inhabits.

Habitat: Stunted forests of oaks, maples, and pines in canyons and mountain slopes.

Seasonal movements: Not enough data.

Biology: Nest: Made of grasses, mosses, and inner bark, and lined with finer grasses and fur or hair; built on the ground among dead leaves or under tangle of vines and herbs. Eggs: 4; creamy white, speckled and blotched with browns often gathered in a wreath about the larger end. Incubation period and age at 1st flight unknown. Food: Insects; not much else known.

Suggested reading: E. R. Blake, "The Nest of the Colima Warbler in Texas," *Wils. Bull.,* vol. 61, pp. 65–67, 1949.

LUCY'S WARBLER (*Vermivora luciae*)

Appearance: Small (4 in.). Medium gray above (darker wing and tail), with a chestnut patch in the crown and on the rump, and whitish below. In winter both sexes are brownish gray above.

Voice: The call is a faint *chip.* Song is rather sprightly and like that of the Yellow Warbler, *whee-tee, whee-tee, whee-tee, whee-tee, whee-tee, whee-tee, whee-tee, whee-tee, whee-tee, whee-tee, whee-tee, wheet* (F. M. Bailey).

Range and status: Breeds from s. Nev., Utah, and sw. Colo. south to nw. Mexico and sw. N.Mex. Winters in s. Mexico. Has straggled to w. Tex. May be locally common, but is inconspicuous.

Habitat: Mesquite and wooded desert streams.

Lucy's Warbler is common in semiarid wooded areas of the Southwest.

Seasonal movements: Not enough data.

Biology: Nest: Made of bark, hairs, feathers, and fur; built in natural cavities, under loose bark, in woodpecker holes, and in deserted Verdin nests 1½–15 ft. above the ground. Eggs: 3–7, commonly 4–5; white or creamy white, speckled with browns. Incubation period and age at 1st flight unknown. Food: Insects are the only item certainly known.

PARULA WARBLER (*Parula americana*)

Appearance: Small (4¼–4¾ in.). Bluish gray above, including face, with a yellowish olive triangle, apex down, on the upper back. The throat, breast, and flank are yellow, with a mottling of bluish gray forming a line between the throat and breast. Below this is a diffusion of tawny on the upper breast and down the flank. An incomplete eye-ring, 2 wing bars, and the rest of the

The Parula Warbler frequently builds its nest in tangled masses of Spanish moss.

underparts are white. The female is somewhat duller and has little if any of the blue-gray or tawny mottling on the breast. The immature birds are more grayish above, with a spot of olive on the upper back; they have a clear yellow throat, breast, and flank. The upper bill is black, the lower yellow; the eye is brown, and the legs and feet are dusky yellow.

Voice: The call note is a faint *chip*, barely distinguishable from that of many other warblers. The song is a simple husky trill rising in pitch and ending on a sharp, lower-pitched note.

Range and status: Breeds from se. Man., w. and c. Ont., s. Que., n. Maine, n. N.B., P.E.I., and n. N.S. south to e. Tex., the Gulf Coast, and c. Fla. Winters from ne. Mexico, the Yucatan Peninsula, Fla., and the Bahamas south to Nicaragua (casually to Costa Rica), the Greater Antilles, and the Lesser Antilles to Barbados. Rather rare to common.

Habitat: Most common in humid woodlands where hanging mosses grow on tree branches; also near openings in forests, generally near still water.

Seasonal movements: Arrives within breeding range Mar.–mid-May and departs mid-Aug.–mid-Nov.

Biology: Nest: Where old-man's-beard and hanging mosses (these are both lichens, not mosses) abound and where Spanish moss (a higher type of plant than a moss, related to the pineapple) drapes the trees, the Parula is a common breeder, burrowing its nest into a mass of these plants or using the long "moss" strands to weave a pendant basket, like that of the Baltimore Oriole, from the slender drooping branches of a tree. Such nests are usually open at or near the top and may be lined with grasses or rootlets. If it can find no mosses, the bird may construct its free-swinging basket of fine grasses, bark shreds, and plant down. The hen does all the work. Eggs: 3–7, commonly 4–5; white or creamy white, peppered and spotted with browns. Incubation: 12–14 days; some authorities claim the male helps with this task. Age at 1st flight unknown. Food: Insects and their larvae and eggs; also some spiders and other small invertebrates and a few small seeds.

Suggested reading: R. Graber and J. Graber, "Nesting of the Parula Warbler in Michigan," *Wils. Bull.*, vol. 63, pp. 75–83, 1951.

OLIVE-BACKED WARBLER (*Parula pitiayumi*)

Appearance: Small (4–4¾ in.). Bluish gray above, with 2 white wing bars and a triangular patch of olive on the upper back. A streak through and a patch under the eye are black. The throat, breast, and flank are yellow (in the male the breast may be largely orange), and the rest of the underparts are white. The female is duller and lacks the black at the eye. The bill, legs, and feet are straw-yellow, and the eye is brown.

Voice: A buzzy trill very much like that of the Parula Warbler.

Range and status: Resident from n. Mexico and s. Tex. south to Peru, n. Argentina, and Uruguay. Fairly common in southernmost Texas.

Habitat: Woodlands with long-fibered plants such as Spanish moss.

Seasonal movements: None.

Biology: Nest: Dug into soft epiphytic orchids or built in hanging mosses, lichens, or Spanish moss; usually lined with plant down. Eggs: 3–4; white or yellowish white spotted with brown. Incubation period and age at 1st flight unknown. Food: Insects; probably some other small invertebrates and small seeds.

OLIVE WARBLER (*Peucedramus taeniatus*)

Appearance: Small (4½–5 in.); poorly named, as the only olive in the plumage is a small spot in the center of the nape and along the upper edge of the back. The head, throat, and upper breast are light tawny or a dusky flesh color, with a black mask extending from the bill and flaring out beyond the eye. The back, rump, and side of the breast are medium gray, and the wing and tail are dark gray. The 2 wing bars, some of the webbing of the outer tail feathers, and the rest of the underparts are white. The female is greenish gray above, with medium gray wing and tail, and pale buffy brown to whitish below. The bill is blackish, the eye is brown, and the legs and feet are dusky brown. Both sexes are duller-colored in the winter, and the immature birds resemble the female.

Voice: 1 call is a loud whistled *peto;* the song has been described as like a vireo's: detached, melodious whistling notes.

Range and status: Breeds from c. and se. Ariz., sw. N.Mex., and n.-c. Mexico south through the mountains to El Salvador and Nicaragua. Retreats from c. to se. Ariz. in winter. Rare to locally common.

Habitat: Higher mountains with evergreen forests.

Seasonal movements: Schedule not known.

Biology: Nest: A compact structure made of rootlets and flower stalks and lined with finer rootlets and vegetable down; built in the fork of a tree limb 30–60 ft. high. Eggs: 3–4; grayish or bluish white, liberally spotted and blotched with grays and browns. Incubation period and age at 1st flight unknown. Food: Insects.

Suggested reading: J. D. Webster, "Systematic and Ecological Notes on the Olive Warbler," *Wils. Bull.*, vol. 74, pp. 417–425, 1962.

YELLOW WARBLER (*Dendroica petechia*)

Appearance: Small (4½–5¼ in.); considerable variation in intensity and extent of yellow coloring from 1 part of its vast range to another. It varies from an almost solid orange-yellow with a brownish green cast on the back, rump, wing, and tail and brownish red streaks on the breast and flank to a subspecies that is a yellowish olive-green above and a pale unstreaked greenish yellow below. The female is usually olive-green above, including the cap, and pale yellow below. The bill is blackish, the eye is brown, and the legs and feet are dusky smoke-gray.

Voice: The song is variable, but in general is a pleasant if sibilant refrain of 5–15 notes, as *see-see-see-see-tititi-see;* sometimes 4–6 monotonous notes, as *weet-weet-weet-weet-weet.*

Range and status: Breeds from n.-c. Alaska, n. Yuk., nw. and c. Mack., n. Man., n. Ont., n.-c. Que., c. Lab., and Nfld. south to the Galápagos Is., c. Peru, the coast of Venezuela, and Trinidad. Winters from s. Baja Calif., c. Mexico, Yucatan, and the Bahamas south to Peru and

Because of its coloration, the Yellow Warbler is sometimes called the Wild Canary.

Brazil. Reaches Bermuda in migration and has straggled to England. Common.

Habitat: Riparian woodlands, willow and poplar groves, shade trees and shrubs of parks, villages, and suburbs.

Seasonal movements: Moves northward Mar.–mid-May and returns mid-July–Oct.

Biology: Nest: A neat, deep cup of felted grasses and plant down, in crotch of tree or shrub 2–15 ft. above the ground. Eggs: 3–6, usually 4–5; white or greenish or bluish white, spotted and blotched with browns and grays. Incubation: About 11 days; there is probably some variation in this period throughout such an extensive range. Age at 1st flight: 9–12 days. Food: Insects, other small invertebrates, and a few berries.

Suggested reading: F. G. Schrantz, "Nest Life of the Eastern Yellow Warbler," *Auk*, vol. 60, pp. 367–387, 1943.

MAGNOLIA WARBLER (*Dendroica magnolia*)

Appearance: Small (4½–5 in.). Cap and nape are light gray, and back, wing, and tail are blackish gray, with a large white patch on the wing. The central part of the outer tail feathers is white. The rump and underparts are orange-yellow, the breast and flank are streaked with black, and there is a streak of white just above and a broad mask of black through the eye. The bill, legs, and feet are blackish. In the female the grays are paler, the blacks are dark grays, the back is a light brownish olive, and the yellow is lighter. Immature birds are light brownish olive above, with a yellow rump, dark gray tail, and 2 white wing bars on the dark gray wing; they are yellow below, with a few dark gray spots along the flank.

Voice: A *tit* of alarm, a sharp *kree*, and a squeaky *eep*; the song is rather variable, consisting usually of 4–9 notes, with 1 version being rendered as *pretty, pretty Rachel.*

Range and status: Breeds from sw. and s.-c. Mack., n. Sask., c. Man., n. Ont., c. and e. Que., and sw. Nfld. south to c. B.C., s.-c. Alta., s.-c. Sask., s. Man., ne. Minn., c. Wis., c. Mich., and s. Ont. Rarely to ne. Ohio, c. W.Va., w. Va., c. Pa., nw. N.J., and Mass. Winters from s.-c. Mexico and Yucatan south to Panama and in the Bahamas and Greater Antilles. Rare to casual as a migrant west of the Rockies in U.S.; has straggled to Alaska, Greenland, and Barbados. A common to abundant migrant east of the Rockies.

Habitat: Woodlands; breeds in coniferous forests.

Seasonal movements: Moves north Mar.–May and returns mid-Aug.–early Nov.

Biology: Nest: Loosely made of fine twigs, weed stalks, and rootlets, 1–10 ft. above the ground in small conifers. Eggs: 4–5, usually 4; white or yellowish,

Despite its name, the Magnolia Warbler is most often seen in coniferous forests.

Cape May Warbler

on the wing are white. A patch around the eye, nearly covering the face, is brownish red. The cap (most heavily toward the forehead) and back are spotted with black, and the lower throat, the entire breast, and the flank are stutteringly streaked with black. The female and the immature birds in fall are much duller-colored; they lack the black spotting above, the yellow is much paler, the patch of white on the wing has faded to 2 yellowish wing bars, the streaking on the underparts is a dull, light brownish olive or is a series of small, distinct dark spots, and instead of brownish red on the face they have a patch of light brownish olive. The eye is dark brown, and the bill, legs, and feet are blackish.

Voice: A weak, squeaky, sibilant series of 4–11 repetitions of *seet;* there is some variation, and the song may be mistaken for those of the Prothonotary, Tennessee, or Black-and-White Warbler.

Range and status: Breeds from sw. and s.-c. Mack., ne. B.C., n. Alta., c. Sask., Man., n. Ont., and s. Que. south to ne. N.Dak., nw. and e.-c. Minn., n. Wis., n. Mich., s. Ont., ne. N.Y., Vt., s. Maine, s. N.B., and c. N.S. Winters in Yucatan, the Bahamas, the Greater Antilles, and casually in the Lesser Antilles and other Caribbean islands. Accidental in Calif. and Ariz. Fairly common.

Habitat: Woodlands; breeds in spruce forests.

Seasonal movements: Migrates Apr.–mid-May and Aug.–Dec.

Biology: Nest: Made of mosses, vine stems, a few twigs, and plant down felted and woven together with grasses, and lined with rootlets, hair, fur, and a few feathers; generally built near the top of a tall spruce 30–60 ft. above the ground. **Eggs:** 4–9, usually 6–7; white or pale yellow, spotted and blotched with browns and grays. Incubation period and age at 1st flight unknown. **Food:** Largely insects and some fruit, especially during fall migration.

Suggested reading: A. C. Bent, *Life Histories of North American Wood Warblers*, Dover, N.Y. (reprint of U.S. Nat. Mus. Bull. 203, 1953), 1963, pp. 212–224.

spotted, blotched, and clouded with browns. Incubation: 11–13 days. Age at 1st flight: About 10 days. Food: All forms of insects, mainly gleaned from bark crevices in woodlands, and some spiders and other small invertebrates; eats very little fruit.

Suggested reading: M. M. Nice, "The Nest in the Juniper," *The Watcher at the Nest*, Macmillan, N.Y., 1939, chap. 12, pp. 86–93.

CAPE MAY WARBLER (*Dendroica tigrina*)

Appearance: Small (5–5½ in.). Cap, center of nape, back, wing, and tail are a light brownish olive; the rump, breast, throat, face, and side of the neck are yellow; and the abdomen, undertail feathers, and a patch

BLACK-THROATED BLUE WARBLER (*Dendroica caerulescens*)

Appearance: Small (5–5½ in.). Light blue-gray above, with prominent white spot on wing and white inner webbing on outer tail feathers. Throat, face, upper breast, flank, bill, legs, and feet are black, and the rest of the underparts are white. The female and immature birds are dark smoke-gray above, including the face, wing, and tail; pale, somewhat yellowish gray below; the immature birds are somewhat more brownish about the head, and both have a distinct white spot on the wing.

Voice: The song is 3–5 husky, drawling notes, the last usually slurred upward, as *zee-zee-zee-ee;* the call is an abrupt *chut* or *chet.*

The Black-throated Blue Warbler's white wing spots are a good field mark in all plumages.

Range and status: Breeds from c. Sask., s. Man., c. Ont., s. Que., and N.S. south to c. Minn., n. Mich., s. Ont., through the Appalachians to ne. Ga., and n. Conn. Winters from the Gulf Coast to islands off Yucatan, the Greater Antilles, the Virgin Is., the Bahamas, and Bermuda. Has straggled to Calif. and C. and S. America. Common; sometimes an abundant migrant.

Habitat: Deciduous and mixed forests with heavy undergrowth.

Seasonal movements: Moves northward Mar.–May and returns mid-Aug.–mid-Nov.

Biology: Nest: Made of fine twigs, papery bark, and leaves, anchored and bound together with spider and insect webbing and lined with rootlets and hair; built close to the ground to 3–4 ft. above in a low tree or shrub. Eggs: 3–5, usually 4; white or pale yellowish, spotted and blotched with browns and grays. Incubation: About 12 days. Age at 1st flight: About 10 days; the male helps feed the young. Food: Insects and a few spiders and other small invertebrates. During fall migration and winter as much as 25% of the food may consist of seeds and fruit.

Suggested reading: M. M. Nice, "A Study of a Nesting of Black-throated Blue Warblers," *Auk*, vol. 47, pp. 338–345, 1930.

MYRTLE WARBLER (*Dendroica coronata*)

Appearance: About the size (5–6 in.) of the House Sparrow. Medium gray above, with rump, center of crown, and a patch at the bend of the wing yellow. White below, with heavy black streaking on the breast and flank. It has 2 white wing bars, black streaking on the back and at the side of the crown, a white streak just above the eye, and a black band through the eye. The female and immature birds in fall are dark smoke-gray where the male is medium gray and black above; also, the black streaking on the white below occurs in more scattered spotting.

Voice: Call notes are a loud *tschick* and a softer *tseet-tseet*. The song is a short, rapid series of 7–21 simple notes on rising and falling pitch.

Range and status: Breeds from n. Alaska, n. Yukon, w. and c. Mack., n. Man., n. Ont., c. Que., n.-c. Lab., and Nfld. south to n. B.C., s. Alta., n. Minn., n. Mich., c. Ont., ne. N.Y., Mass., and Maine. Winters from Kans., the s. Great Lakes region, and s. New England south to c. Panama, the Greater Antilles, the Virgin Is., the Bahamas, and Bermuda and coastally from nw. Ore. to n. Baja Calif. Has straggled to Siberia, Greenland, England, and nw. S. America. Common to abundant.

Habitat: Mixed and coniferous forests; in migration and winter any woodlands, thickets, gardens, or brush.

Seasonal movements: Moves north Mar.–early June and returns late Aug.–Nov.

Biology: Nest: Made of fine, rough coniferous twigs woven with a few grasses, hair, and rootlets, with fine hair and feathers lining the neat, deep cup; commonly built about 15 ft. up in conifer, but may be 5–50 ft. high. Eggs: 3–5, commonly 4–5; white or pale yellowish, peppered, spotted, and blotched with browns, with these patterns sometimes wreathed most heavily about larger end. Incubation: 12–13 days. Age at 1st flight: 12–14 days. Food: Mostly insects, particularly in summer, but large amounts of seeds and berries and other fruit.

Suggested reading: A. C. Bent, *Life Histories of North American Wood Warblers*, Dover, N.Y. (reprint of U.S. Nat. Mus. Bull. 203, 1953), 1963, pp. 239–260.

AUDUBON'S WARBLER (*Dendroica auduboni*)

Appearance: About the same size (5–5½ in.) and general appearance as the Myrtle Warbler, but the throat is yellow, the breast and flank are solid black, and there is no streak of white above the eye. The female is much duller and browner, sometimes gray where the male is black. Immature birds and the adults in winter are brownish olive above, with yellow on the rump, and whitish below, with some pale yellow on the throat and smoke-gray streaking on the breast and flank.

Voice: A lisping *tslip* call note; the song is a rather plain, almost monotonous series of 6–8 notes, as *tsil-tsil-tsil-tsi-tsi-tsi-tsi-tsi*.

Range and status: Breeds from c. B.C., s. Alta., sw. Sask., c. and se. Mont., and w. S.Dak. south, mainly through the mountains, to n. Baja Calif., s. Ariz., w.-c. Mexico, and s. N.Mex. Winters along coast from sw. B.C. and from c. Nev., sw. Utah, c. N.Mex., and s. Tex. south to Costa Rica. Common to abundant.

Habitat: Breeds in coniferous woodlands; during migration and in winter, ranges from beaches through gardens and brushlands to all types of forests.

Seasonal movements: Arrives at breeding areas Mar.–May and departs Sept.–mid-Nov.

Biology: Nest: Made of twigs, weed stems, bark strips, and weed tops and lined with rootlets, hair, and feathers; built 3–50 ft. above the ground, near the ends of tree branches, most commonly conifers. Eggs: 3–5, usually 4; pale gray or very pale yellow, spotted and blotched with browns and grays. Incubation: 12–13(?) days. Age at 1st flight is unknown. Food: About 85% insects and a few spiders; the 15% vegetable food is fruit and seeds.

BLACK-THROATED GRAY WARBLER (*Dendroica nigrescens*)

Appearance: Small (4½–5 in.). Back, rump, wing, and tail are medium bluish gray; head, throat, upper edge of breast, jagged streaks on the flank, and spots on the back are black. The rest of the underparts, a broad streak through the eye extending to the back, a V extending to the shoulder from the apex at the base of the lower bill, 2 wing bars, and the inner webbing of the outer tail feathers are all white. The gray and black above are replaced in the female and immature birds with brownish

The Myrtle Warbler is a relatively common migrant across most of the United States.

The Audubon's Warbler breeds in coniferous forests on the western mountains.

olive streaks at the sides of the breast and on the flank. The eye is dark brown, the legs and feet are dusky brown, and the bill is black.

Voice: The call is a low *chit;* the song is a rapid, wheezing, lisping series of 4–8 notes, with the last slurred up or down.

Range and status: Breeds from sw. B.C., c. Ore., sw. Idaho, n. Utah, sw. Wyo., and nw. and c. Colo. south, mainly through the mountains, to n. Baja Calif., nw., c., and se. Ariz., and s. N.Mex. Winters from w. and s. Calif. and s. Ariz. south to s. Baja Calif. and s.-c. Mexico; casually to Guatemala. It has straggled to Tex., La., Ohio, Ont., N.Y., and Mass. Common; sometimes locally abundant.

Habitat: More open forests of oak, piñon, and juniper or mixed forests with dense undergrowth.

Seasonal movements: Moves north mid-Mar.–Apr. and returns Sept.–mid-Nov.

Biology: Nest: Made of plant fibers, grasses, and weed stems woven into a neat cup lined with finer fibers, hair, and feathers; built 3–50 ft. up in the branches of a tree or shrub. Eggs: 3–5, commonly 4; white or very pale yellow, peppered, spotted, and sometimes blotched with browns. Incubation period and age at 1st flight unknown. Food: Insects and other small invertebrates; possibly some fruit and seeds.

TOWNSEND'S WARBLER (*Dendroica townsendi*)

Appearance: Small (4¼–5 in.). Very much like the Black-throated Gray Warbler, but the white on the head and breast is replaced with yellow, and the back, rump, wing, and tail are a yellowish rather than a bluish gray. The female and immature birds are also similar to those of the Black-throated Gray, but with pale yellow about the face, throat, and upper breast.

Voice: The call note is a soft *chip;* the song is a spiraling, rising series of about 5 notes, as *weazy-weazy-weazy-weazy-tweea.*

Range and status: Breeds from s. Alaska and s. Yuk. south to nw. and c. Wash., c. and ne. Ore., n. Idaho, nw. Wyo., and s.-c. Mont. Winters from w.-c. and s. Calif. and w. and c. Mexico south to El Salvador and n.-c. Nicaragua; casually farther north. It has straggled to Kans., Tex., ne. Mexico, Miss., and Pa. Fairly common; often an abundant migrant.

Habitat: Taller coniferous forests; in winter and migration, oak and other types of woodlands and shrubby areas.

Seasonal movements: Arrives within breeding areas mid-Apr.–mid-May and departs in Sept.

Biology: Nest: Made of plant down, grasses, mosses, lichens, strips of bark, and insect webbing woven and felted together into a rather shallow cup that is lined with hair and feathers; built 8–15 ft. up in tree. Eggs: 3–5, usually 4; white, peppered and spotted with browns. Incubation period and age at 1st flight unknown. Food: Over 95% insects, with a few spiders, etc.; less than 5% seeds.

BLACK-THROATED GREEN WARBLER (*Dendroica virens*)

Appearance: Small (4½–5¼ in.). Medium greenish olive above, with dark gray wing and tail, 2 white wing bars, and a yellow face. White below, with black throat, breast, and jagged lines on the flank. The female and the immature birds are somewhat duller above, with pale yellow face, throat, and breast; the sides of the breast and the flank are spotted with dark gray. The eye is dark brown, the bill is black, and the legs and feet are dusky brown.

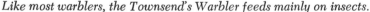

Like most warblers, the Townsend's Warbler feeds mainly on insects.

Voice: The call note is a simple *tsick;* the food-begging cry of the young is a high-pitched *tseet-tseet-tseetut-tseetut-tseeti-tseeti-tut.* There are 2 songs: in the 1st song all the notes are the same length, 3–9 notes at a high pitch, then a low note, and finally a medium-high note, as *see-see-see-see-see-sah-say;* in the 2nd song the 1st note is about 3 times as long as the last, and the 2nd note twice as long as the last, as *sa-a-a-ah, say, tse-tsee.* Many consider it the prettiest and most musical of the warbler songs.

Range and status: Breeds from s.-c. Mack., c. Sask., c. Man., c. Ont., s. Que., s. Lab., s. Nfld., and s. N.S. south to c. Alta., s. Man., e.-c. Minn., c. Wis., c. Mich., s.-c. Ohio, through the Appalachians to n. Ala. and n. Ga., and to n. N.J. Winters from s. Tex. and s. Fla. through e. Mexico and C. America to Panama and to the Greater Antilles. It has straggled to Calif., Ariz., Greenland, and Germany. Common; sometimes an abundant migrant.

Habitat: Coniferous woodlands; other forests in migration and winter.

Seasonal movements: Moves north Mar.–May and returns late Aug.–mid-Nov.

Biology: Nest: Made of spider webbing, fine bark, grasses, mosses, lichens, and twigs and lined with a thick felting of fur and hair; saddled on a branch or in the fork of a tree limb, 3–80 ft. above the ground. Eggs: 4–5, usually 4; white or very pale yellow, specked, spotted, blotched, and sometimes scrawled with browns. Incubation: 12 days. Age at 1st flight: 8–10 days; the male helps very little with feeding chores. Food: Almost entirely insects, with a few spiders and, in fall, some berries and other fruit.

Suggested reading: M. M. Nice, "The Warblers in the Hemlocks," *The Watcher at the Nest,* Macmillan, N.Y., 1939, chap. 13, pp. 94–102.

GOLDEN-CHEEKED WARBLER (*Dendroica chrysoparia*)

Appearance: Small (4½–5 in.). Cap, nape, back, throat, breast, and streaks along the flank are black, and rump, tail, and wing are dark gray. The rest of the underparts and 2 wing bars are white. The face, except for a black streak through the eye, is yellow. The female and immature birds in fall resemble those of the Black-throated Green Warbler, but the back is flecked with black and there is no yellowish tinge below. The eye is dark brown, the bill is black, and the legs and feet are blackish gray.

Voice: The call is a low chirping during migration, and the females make a slow, scolding *check—check—check.* The song is variable in cadence, usually a soft *tweah, tweak, twee-see.*

Range and status: Breeds in the Edwards Plateau of s.-c. Tex. and winters from s. Mexico to Honduras and Nicaragua. Increasingly local.

Habitat: Oak and juniper woodlands and riparian groves.

Seasonal movements: Arrives in Tex. in Mar. and leaves mid-July–mid-Aug.

Biology: Nest: Compactly woven and felted of plant fibers, fine bark, grasses, rootlets, twigs, and spider webbing and lined with hair and feathers; built in forks of juniper branches 10–20 ft. above the ground. Eggs: 3–5, commonly 4; white or very pale yellow, peppered and spotted with browns and grays. Incubation period and age at 1st flight unknown. Food: Little known; probably mainly insects.

Suggested reading: A. Sprunt, Jr., "Golden-cheek of the Cedar Brakes," *Aud. Mag.,* vol. 53, pp. 12–16, 1951.

HERMIT WARBLER (*Dendroica occidentalis*)

Appearance: Small (4½–4¾ in.). Throat, upper edge of breast, streaking on flank, and lines on back are black; back, rump, wing, and tail are medium gray; rest of underparts and 2 wing bars are white. The head is yellow, with some dark gray mottling on nape. The female and immature birds in fall are similar, but throat is yellow and there is no black except for some short streaking on the cap, back, and flank. The eye is dark brown, and the bill, legs, and feet are black.

Voice: The song is an undulating series of 4–7 rapid, penetrating notes, as *tsit-tsit-tsit-tsit-chee-chee-chee,* the last 3 notes quite emphatic.

Range and status: Breeds from sw. Wash. through the Coast Ranges and the Sierra Nevadas to nw. and c. Calif., with a few isolated colonies in w.-c. Calif. Winters from s.-c. Mexico to El Salvador and Nicaragua. Has straggled to Minn. Rather rare and local.

Habitat: Coniferous woodlands and, during migration, other types of forests.

Seasonal movements: Arrives in breeding range late Mar.–Apr. and departs mid-July–Oct.

Biology: Nest: Made of plant fiber, fine twigs, lichens, and mosses and lined with fine bark strips and hair; built 25–120 ft. high in conifer. Eggs: 3–5, commonly 4; white, peppered and spotted with browns. Incubation period and age at 1st flight unknown. Food: Insects, so far as diet is known.

CERULEAN WARBLER (*Dendroica cerulea*)

Appearance: Small (4–5 in.). Light bluish gray above, with several blackish gray streaks on the back and a streak near the edge of the cap. There are 2 white wing bars and a short streak of white just behind the eye. White below, with a narrow band of dark bluish gray separating the throat from the breast and continuing as dashed streaks on the flank. The female and the immature birds in fall are a duller, more brownish gray above, with a yellow streak below. There is another yellow streak

Nearly full-grown Blackburnian Warblers here beg the adult male for food.

above the eye. They also have 2 white wing bars. The eye is dark brown, the bill is black, and the legs and feet are dusky brown.

Voice: The song is usually 4–8 notes of regular cadence and on 1 pitch, followed by a short, higher-pitched, buzzy trill, as *wee-wee-wee-wee-bz-z-z.*

Range and status: Breeds from se. Nebr., n. Iowa, se. Minn., s. Wis., s. Mich., s. Ont., w. N.Y., e. Pa., se. N.Y., and n. N.J. south to ne. Tex., se. La., c. Ala., c. N.C., c. Va., ne. Md., and Del. Winters from Colombia and Venezuela to Peru and Bolivia. It has straggled to Calif., Baja Calif., Man., Colo., and in summer has appeared rather regularly as far north as Mass. and N.Y. Rather rare and local.

Habitat: Upper stories of dense deciduous forests with little undergrowth.

Seasonal movements: Arrives within breeding areas mid-Mar.–mid-May and departs late July–Sept.

Biology: Nest: Made of plant fibers, strips of bark, weed stems, and mosses, neatly interlaced and lined with finer fibers and mosses, and bound on the outside with spider webbing; built on the branch of a tree 20–60 ft. above the ground and 10–15 ft. from the bole. Eggs: 3–5, usually 4; white, very pale green, or very pale yellow, peppered, spotted, and blotched with browns. Incubation period and age at 1st flight unknown. Food: Mainly insects, many caught in midair; very little data available.

BLACKBURNIAN WARBLER (*Dendroica fusca*)

Appearance: Small (4½–5½ in.). Black above, including most of the face, wing, and tail, with a small orange patch on the forepart of the crown. An orange streak just above the eye turns abruptly at the side of the neck toward the breast and widens, and a tiny patch just below the eye is also orange. There are 2 buffy yellow streaks down the sides of the back, some white on the inner webbing of the outer tail feathers, and 2 white wing bars that merge toward the back. The throat and upperpart of the breast are scarlet-orange, fading to orange at the lower part of the breast and then to a pale buff over the rest of the underparts; the flank is streaked with black. In fall and winter the male becomes duller. The female and immature birds are much duller in fall; the black of the male becomes a somewhat brownish light gray, and the orange becomes a washed-out yellow. The bill, legs, and feet are black, the eye dark brown.

Voice: The song is variable; a common song consists of a series of unmusical, wiry 2-note phrases all on 1 pitch, then a rapid series or trill on a different pitch. Some of the notes are too high for most human ears to catch.

Range and status: Breeds across s. Canada from s.-c. Sask. to n. N.S. south to c. Minn., c. Wis., c. Mich., s. Ont., ne. Ohio, through the Appalachians to c. W.Va., e. Tenn., n.-c. Ga., and nw. S.C., and to se. N.Y. and

Mass. Winters from Guatemala to c. Peru; migrates through e. Mexico. Has straggled to Mont., N.Mex., and Bermuda. Fairly common; sometimes abundant in migration.

Habitat: Breeds in coniferous woodlands; in winter and migration through other types of forests.

Seasonal movements: Moves north Mar.–May and returns Aug.–Oct. Probably most of the migrants fly across the Gulf of Mexico.

Biology: Nest: Made of small twigs and rootlets and dense woven mats of plant down, lined with lichens, mosses, and hair; saddled on a horizontal branch in conifers, 5–80 ft. above the ground. Eggs: 4–5, usually 4; white or very pale green, spotted and blotched with brown. Incubation period and age at 1st flight unknown. Food: Almost entirely insects and a few spiders and some berries.

Suggested reading: L. deK. Lawrence, "Notes on the Nesting Behavior of the Blackburnian Warbler," *Wils. Bull.*, vol. 65, pp. 135–144, 1953.

YELLOW-THROATED WARBLER (*Dendroica dominica*)

Appearance: Small (5–5½ in.). Medium gray above (darker at forehead and on wing), with 2 distinct white wing bars. The white face has a T of black, with the crossbar just under the eye and the upright bar down the side of the throat to the side of the breast. White below, with yellow throat and breast and with black streaks on the flank. The female is usually only slightly duller; the immature birds in fall are somewhat brownish above. The bill, legs, and feet are black; the eye is dark brown.

Voice: The song consists of 5–8 distinct but slurred notes, followed by several run into a trill.

Range and status: Breeds from c. Mo., s. Ill., c. Ind., s. Ohio, sw. W.Va., w.-c. N.C., c. Va., e. Md., and c. N.J. south to e. Tex., the Gulf Coast, and s.-c. Fla. Recorded casually farther north. Winters from s. Tex. to c. Costa Rica and from s. S.C. to the Greater Antilles and the Bahamas. Rare to locally common.

Habitat: Pine forests, cypress swamps, oak forests festooned with Spanish moss, etc.

Seasonal movements: Moves north Mar.–Apr. and south mid-July–mid-Oct.

Biology: Nest: Made of fine grasses, insect webbing, plant down, fine bark strips, and weed stems and lined with plant down and feathers; built 10–120 ft. above the ground in the crotch of a tree limb, shrub, or clump of Spanish moss. Eggs: 4–5, most commonly 4; very pale green or gray, speckled and blotched with browns and dark grays, usually wreathed about larger end. Incubation period and age at 1st flight unknown. Apparently 2 broods are raised each year, at least in the South. Food: Little known; probably mainly insects.

GRACE'S WARBLER (*Dendroica graciae*)

Appearance: Small (4½–5 in.). Light gray above, including face, wing, and tail, with a streak of yellow above the eye. The 2 wing bars are white, there is some white inner webbing near the tip of the outer tail feathers, and the bird is white below. Throat and upper breast are yellow, and there is dark gray streaking along the flank. The female is somewhat duller; the males in fall and winter are tinged with brown above. The bill, legs, and feet are black; the eye is dark brown.

Voice: The song is a series of evenly spaced *chip* notes speeding up at the end into a trill.

Range and status: Breeds from s. Utah, sw. Colo., and n.-c. N.Mex. south to n. Nicaragua. Winters from n. Mexico to n. Nicaragua. Locally and irregularly common.

Habitat: Montane pine-oak woodlands.

Seasonal movements: Arrives in U.S. mid-Mar.–Apr. and has departed by mid-Sept.

Biology: Nest: Made of hair, vegetable fibers, and insect webbing and lined with hair and feathers; built on tree limb 20–60 ft. above the ground. Eggs: 3–4, usually

Yellow-throated Warbler

The Chestnut-sided Warbler often nests in hedgerows beside country roads.

3; white, peppered and spotted about the larger end with browns. Incubation period and age at 1st flight unknown. Food: Little known; probably mainly insects.

Suggested reading: J. D. Webster, "Revision of Grace's Warbler," *Auk*, vol. 78, pp. 554–566, 1961.

CHESTNUT-SIDED WARBLER (*Dendroica pensylvanica*)

Appearance: Small (4½–5¼ in.). Cap yellow; nape, back, and rump light olive, with blackish streaking; wing and tail gray, with 2 whitish wing bars and some white on the inner webbing on the outer tail feathers. White below, including face, with a black streak through the eye and a black line from the eye to the side of the breast where it meets the brownish red flank. The female is duller, her cap is more buffy yellow, and the black and brownish red marking is less distinct. The immature birds in fall are light olive above and pale gray below, with a light gray face and 2 pale buff wing bars. The bill, legs, and feet are black, and the eye is dark brown.

Voice: 1 song has been transliterated as *see-see-see-see-see-Miss-Beech-er;* the nesting song is very variable, consisting of long series of slurred notes, chatters, and trills. The call note is a rather loud *tsick*.

Range and status: Breeds from e.-c. Sask., c. Man., c. Ont., s. Que., c. N.B., and n. N.S. south to e. Nebr., nw. and se. Minn., s. Wis., s. Mich., n. Ohio, se. Tenn., n.-c. Ga., nw. S.C., c. Md., se. Pa., c. N.J., and Mass. Winters from s. Nicaragua to Panama; during migration has been recorded from Cuba, Jamaica, and the Bahamas. Has straggled to Calif., Alta., Wyo., Colo., Okla., Bermuda, and Greenland. Common.

Habitat: Shrubby, brushy areas; hedgerows, etc., in farm areas.

Seasonal movements: Migrates through U.S. Apr.– May and mid-Aug.–Oct.

Biology: Nest: Usually rather bulky and loosely woven of grasses, straw, and plant fiber, bound together with insect webbing, and lined with soft grasses, rootlets, and fine plant fibers; built in bush or low tree 1–4 ft. above the ground. Eggs: 3–5, usually 4; white, very pale yellow, or green and speckled, spotted, and blotched to varying degrees with browns. Incubation: 12–13 days. Age at 1st flight: 10–12 days. Food: It is said that the hatchlings are first fed by regurgitation. The adults are almost wholly insectivorous, eating very few seeds and berries.

Suggested reading: L. deK. Lawrence, "Comparative Study of the Nesting Behavior of Chestnut-sided and Nashville Warblers," *Auk*, vol. 65, pp. 204–219, 1948.

BAY-BREASTED WARBLER (*Dendroica castanea*)

Appearance: Small (5–6 in.). Back, rump, wing, and tail are medium gray, with 2 white wing bars and darker streaks on back. The cap, nape, throat, breast, and flank are dark brownish red; the forehead and a broad mask through the eye are black. The side of the neck between this mask and the back is white, as are the rest of the underparts. The female is vaguely similar since the brownish red below is so pale as to be almost white, the black forehead and mask are mottled medium gray, and the brownish red cap is duller and somewhat streaked with black. The immature birds in fall and winter are dingy straw-yellow below and light olive above, with darker wing and tail and very faint streaking on the flank. The bill, legs, and feet are black, and the eye is dark brown.

Voice: The song is an irregular mixture of short and long notes all on 1 high pitch; *tee-teelelee-te-te-teee-teee-teelelee-teelelee-teelelee-tee* is one common variation.

Range and status: Breeds from c. Man., n. Ont., c. Que., and c. N.S. south to s. Man., ne. Minn., n. Wis., s. Ont., s. Que., ne. N.Y., c. Vt., N.H., s. Maine, and s. N.S. Winters from c. Panama to n. Colombia and w. Venezuela. It has been recorded in summer in B.C., Mack., Alta., Sask., and n. Mich. and has straggled to Greenland and Bermuda. Rather rare, but sometimes common in migration.

Habitat: Coniferous woodlands; during migration in other types of forests.

Seasonal movements: Migrates mainly through e. Mexico and e. C. America. Moves north Apr.–early June and returns Aug.–Oct.

Biology: Nest: Rather loosely woven of coarse grasses, twigs, and spider or insect webbing and lined with rootlets and hair; saddled on a horizontal limb of a conifer 4–40 ft. above the ground. Eggs: 4–7, commonly 5–6; white, pale yellow, pale green or pale blue, peppered, spotted, and blotched with browns and grays. Incubation: 12–13 days. Age at 1st flight: 11–12 days. Food: Insects; possibly some spiders and other small invertebrates.

Suggested reading: H. L. Mendall, "Nesting of the Bay-breasted Warbler," *Auk*, vol. 54, pp. 429–439, 1937.

BLACKPOLL WARBLER (*Dendroica striata*)

Appearance: Small (5–5¾ in.). Nape, back, tail, and wing are smoke-gray, with 2 white wing bars and black streaks on the back and rump. White below, including the face; the streaks along the flank, a line separating the face and throat, and the entire cap are black. In fall and winter the male is dull light olive above and dingy straw-yellow below, with some dark streaking on the back and rump and 2 very pale yellow wing bars. The female resembles the winter-plumaged male, but is finely and distinctly streaked with blackish on the cap, nape, back, rump, and flank. Both sexes, at all seasons, have white undertail feathers. The eye is dark brown, the upper bill sepia, the lower bill buffy brown to buffy yellow at the base; the legs and feet are yellowish.

As with most warblers, the female Bay-breasted Warbler is less colorful than the male.

The Blackpoll Warbler breeds in northern forests but winters in South America.

True to its name, the Pine Warbler usually nests in pine trees.

Voice: The call is a simple high-pitched *tsit;* the song a long, wiry, high-pitched crescendo-diminuendo series of *tsit's*, with the cadence speeding into a sputter at the end.

Range and status: Breeds from n.-c. Alaska, n. Yuk., nw. and c. Mack., n. Man., n. Ont., n. Que., n. Lab., and Nfld. south to c. B.C., c. Alta., c. Man., n.-c. Ont., s. Que., e. N.Y., nw. Mass., c. N.H., s. Maine, s. N.B., and s. N.S. Winters from c. Colombia and Venezuela south to ne. Peru, c. Chile, and w.-c. Brazil. Migrates through the W. Indies. Has straggled to N.Mex., Mexico, and Greenland. One of the most common warblers.

Habitat: Breeds in low coniferous forests; during migration ranges into other types of woodland.

Seasonal movements: Moves north Apr.–mid-June and returns mid-Aug.–mid-Nov.

Biology: Nest: Made of small twigs, grasses, weeds, mosses, lichens, and hair and lined with plant fibers, rootlets, hair, and feathers; built in a small conifer 2–12 ft. above the ground. Eggs: 3–5, usually 4–5; white, very pale green, or very pale yellow, evenly speckled all over and spotted and blotched with browns in a wreath about the larger end. The male brings food to the incubating female. Incubation: More than 11 days. Age at 1st flight: 11–12 days. Food: All stages of insects and a few spiders; in fall a few seeds and berries.

Suggested reading: A. C. Bent, *Life Histories of North American Wood Warblers*, Dover, N.Y. (reprint of U.S. Nat. Mus. Bull. 203, 1953), 1963, pp. 389–408.

PINE WARBLER (*Dendroica pinus*)

Appearance: Small (5–5½ in.). Light olive-green above, with 2 white wing bars and some white on the outer webbing near the tip of the outer tail feathers. Below, it is a rather dusky yellow, with light gray streaking on the side of the breast and flank. The yellow below is a more dingy, buffy yellow on the duller-colored female. The immature bird in fall is almost white below, becoming lighter toward the center of the breast and dusky at the side. The bill is blackish, the legs and feet are dusky brown, and the eye is dark brown.

Voice: The song is a series of rather rapid, pleasing, musical notes ending in a trill, or is sometimes just a simple trill. The call notes are a *tsip* and a loud, high *chip* or *tip*.

Range and status: Breeds from s. Man., w. Ont., ne. Minn., n. Wis., n. Mich., c. Ont., s. Que., and c. Maine south to se. Tex., the Gulf Coast, Fla., the Bahamas, and Hispaniola. Has straggled to Alta., Sask., N.B., P.E.I., N.S., Bermuda, and Greenland. Winters in s. half of breeding range. Fairly common; local to rare except as a migrant south of the Great Lakes area.

Habitat: Open pine forests; other types of woodland in migration.

Seasonal movements: Moves north late Feb.–Apr. and returns Sept.–Oct.

Biology: Nest: Made of weed stalks, bark strips, pine needles, twigs, and insect or spider webbing and lined with plant down, hair, and feathers; usually saddled on horizontal limbs in pines, from 10 ft. above the ground to top of tallest trees. Eggs: 3–5, usually 4; white or very pale green; peppered, spotted, and blotched with browns, with these markings usually concentrated at larger end. Incubation period unknown; by both parents. Age at 1st flight unknown. Food: insects and spiders and, especially in winter, some pine and other seeds, berries, and other fruits.

KIRTLAND'S WARBLER (*Dendroica kirtlandii*)

Appearance: Small (5¾ in.). Medium bluish gray above, with black streaks on back. Upper wing, a broad eye mask, and some markings on the wing and tail are also black. Yellow below, with black dashes at side of breast and along flank. Undertail feathers are white. The female is somewhat duller. The bill is black to dusky brown, the legs and feet are dusky brown, and the eyes are dark brown. The tail is constantly being flicked up and then slowly lowered.

Voice: The song is a low-pitched, much repeated series of 6–8 rapid, loud notes of a bubbling, liquid character, like those of the wrens. The calls are a scold-ing *tsyip* or *tshyook,* a low *churk* at the nest, and a harsh *chirp.*

Range and status: Breeds only in c. Mich. and winters in the Bahamas. It has been recorded in summer from Minn., n. Mich., Ont., Ill., Mo., and Va. A rare species, but locally common.

Habitat: Breeds in groves of young jack pines that spring up after forest fires, usually where there is a ground cover of berry bushes and ferns. Found in other types of forests during migration.

Seasonal movements: Moves north Apr.–mid-May and returns in Oct. Migrates through se. U.S., but route is not well defined.

Biology: Nest: Made of grasses and lined with finer grasses and sometimes hair; built on the ground near the base of a jack pine and well arched-over with vegetation. Eggs: 4–5; very pale yellow or pale pink, peppered and blotched with browns. Incubation: 14–15 days; the male feeds the incubating female. Age at 1st flight: 12–13 days. Food: Insects and other small invertebrates; eats or drinks the pitch from the jack pine. Not known to drink water.

Suggested reading: H. F. Mayfield, *The Kirtland's Warbler,* Cranbrook Inst. Sci. Bull. 40, 242 pp., 1960.

The Kirtland's Warbler is one of the rarest warblers in the United States.

PRAIRIE WARBLER (*Dendroica discolor*)

Appearance: Small (4½–5 in.). Light olive-green above, with brownish red slashes down the upper back. There is a pale yellow wing bar, a yellow streak from the forehead just above the eye, a black streak through the eye, a yellow streak below this, and finally a black whisker streak. The bird is orange-yellow below, with a black spot at the side of the throat and black streaks at the side of the breast and on the flank. The female is similar, but the yellow is paler, the brownish red streaks on the back are obscure or lacking, and the black on the side of the head is replaced with dull gray. The bill, legs, and feet are dusky brown, and the eye is brown.

Voice: The call note is a fairly low *tseet;* the song is a series of 5–13 distinct, rather sibilant notes, the 1st 1–4 low, then each succeeding note pitched higher.

Range and status: Breeds from se. S.Dak., e. Nebr., e. Kans., c. Mo., Ill., s. Wis., n. Mich., s. Ont., s.-c. Pa., e.-c. N.Y., Mass., and s. N.H. south to e. Okla., s. La., n. Miss., s. Ala., and s. Fla. Winters on islands off se. Mexico and e. C. America and from c. Fla. through the W. Indies. Population fluctuates; now rather rare to locally common.

Habitat: Scrub oak and pine, brushy openings in woodlands, and dry bushy areas.

Seasonal movements: Moves north mid-Mar.–May and returns late July–Oct.

Biology: Nest: Made of felted plant down inter-woven with a few grasses, decorated on the outside with shreds and pieces of bark, and lined with hair and feathers; built 1–25 ft. above the ground in bushes or brambles or on the horizontal limbs of trees. Eggs: 3–5, usually 4; white, very pale yellow, or very pale green, peppered and spotted with browns and some gray; the eggs usually bear a distinct wreath about the larger end. Incubation: 12 days. Age at 1st flight: 8–10 days. Food: The few accurate data available indicate a diet almost entirely of insects, with a few spiders and other small invertebrates.

PALM WARBLER (*Dendroica palmarum*)

Appearance: Small (4½–5½ in.). In the e. part of the breeding range, the cap is a brownish red, with a streak of buffy yellow between this and the eye. The rest of the upperparts, including the face, are a dark smoke-gray, somewhat darker on the wing and tail. The bird is entirely a bright orange-yellow below, with brownish red streaks at the side of the throat, on the upper breast, and along the flank. In w. area, the underparts are straw-yellow, and the side of the throat, the upper breast, and the flank are streaked with thin lines and dashes of dark smoke-gray or blackish. There are 2 rather indistinct whitish wing bars. The bill, legs, and feet are blackish brown, and the eye is brown. In winter the cap is grayer and streaked with dark brown. The tail is constantly bobbing up and down.

Prairie Warbler

Voice: The call is a faint *tsip;* the song is a trill somewhat like the song of the Chipping Sparrow, but composed of *tsee* notes or double *hee-u* notes rising and falling in volume.

Range and status: Breeds from sw. Mack., n. Alta., n. Sask., n. Man., n. Ont., s. Que., and s. Nfld. south to ne. B.C., c. Alta., c. Sask., se. Man., ne. Minn., c. Mich., s. Ont., s. Que., Maine, and N.S. Winters from La., Miss., Tenn., and N.C. through the Yucatan Peninsula to n. Honduras and to the Greater Antilles, the Bahamas, the Virgin Is., and Bermuda. Rather rare to common and locally common.

Habitat: Both scientific and common names are misnomers. It nests along the wooded edge of n. swampy areas or muskegs, and in migration and winter is found in brushy and scrubby areas and even on the ground in more open places.

Seasonal movements: Moves north Mar.–May and returns Aug.–mid-Nov.

Biology: Nest: Made of plant fibers, grasses, and bark shreds and lined with hair, fine grasses, rootlets, and feathers; built on or close to the ground among tussocks of grass or sedges and in or hidden by low shrubs and other vegetation. Eggs: 4–5; white or very pale yellow, speckled, spotted, and blotched with browns, chiefly in a wreath about the larger end. Some have a few scrawling black markings. Incubation: About 12 days. Age at 1st flight: 12 days. Food: Mainly insects, but some berries are also consumed.

Suggested reading: L. H. Walkinshaw and A. M. Wolf, "Distribution of the Palm Warbler and Its Status in Michigan," *Wils. Bull.,* vol. 69, pp. 338–351, 1957.

OVENBIRD (*Seiurus aurocapillus*)

Appearance: A medium-sized (5½–6½ in.) warbler. It is brownish olive above, somewhat lighter on the upper back and head, and there is a wide stripe of tawny, edged with blackish brown, down the center of the top of the head. It is white below, with streaks of black and dusky brown at the side of the throat, on the upper breast, and along the flank. The eye is ringed with white. The upper bill is dusky brown, the lower bill buffy brown; the legs and feet are pale flesh, and the eye is brown. The sexes are alike.

Voice: A loud *tzick* of alarm, softer *tseet* notes, and a *chip-ip-ip-ip* of surprise. The common song sounds like a series of *teacher* calls repeated rapidly and with increasing vigor 6–12 times, but it is shown by recording devices to be 1 continuous call that varies sharply in pitch at frequent intervals. In addition, the Ovenbird sings a variable pleasing flight song identified by the inclusion of several *teach* notes.

Range and status: Breeds from ne. B.C., s.-c. Mack., c. Sask., c. Man., n. Ont., s. Que., and Nfld. south to Alta., e. Colo., se. Okla., n. Ark., n. Ala., and n. Ga.

Frequently hidden by arching vegetation, the Ovenbird's nest is difficult to find.

Winters from ne. Mexico, the Gulf Coast, s. Ga., and s. S.C. south to nw. S. America and the Lesser Antilles. Common.

Habitat: Deciduous forest floors, especially those with some undergrowth, herbs, and ferns.

Seasonal movements: In spring late Mar.–May and in fall July–Nov.

Biology: Nest: Made of grasses, vegetable fibers, weed stems, leaves, rootlets, mosses, and bark and lined with finer rootlets, fibers, and hair; usually built in a slight depression among the leaves on the forest floor, sometimes at the base of a tree or log or canopied by ferns. Eggs: 3–6, usually 4–5; white, speckled and spotted with browns and grays commonly concentrated in a wreath about the larger end. Incubation: 11½–14 days. Age at 1st flight: 7–10 days. Food: Snails, slugs, earthworms, insects, and other small invertebrates primarily gleaned from beneath leaves and debris of the woodland carpet; also a few seeds, berries, and other wild fruit.

Suggested reading: H. W. Hann, "Life History of the Ovenbird in Southern Michigan," *Wils. Bull.,* vol. 49, pp. 145–237, 1937.

Not a thrush at all, the Northern Waterthrush is an American wood warbler.

NORTHERN WATERTHRUSH (*Seiurus noveboracensis*)

Appearance: A medium-sized (5½–6½ in.) thrush-like warbler. Plain olive or medium fuscous above, with a pale smoke-gray streak above the eye. Very pale smoke-gray below, with black streaking on the throat, breast, upper abdomen, and flank. The bill is dusky brown, the eye is dark brown, and the legs and feet are pale flesh. The sexes are alike.

Voice: The song is a series of short, staccato, liquid notes accelerating near the end; they have been transliterated by Dr. G. M. Sutton as *hurry, hurry, hurry, pretty, pretty, pretty.* The call note is a sharp, somewhat metallic *chip.*

Range and status: Breeds from the tree limit of N. America south to c. B.C., n. Idaho, w. Mont., c. Sask., n. N.Dak., n. Minn., n. Wis., n. Mich., ne. Ohio, n. Pa., and Mass. Winters from s. Baja Calif., c. Mexico, the Greater Antilles, the Bahamas, and Bermuda south to nw. and n.-c. S. America. Has been recorded from France. Fairly common.

Habitat: Wet or swampy woodlands, near streams and lake shores, and brushy areas in migration.

Seasonal movements: Spring movements mid-Mar.–May and fall return mid-July–Oct.

Biology: Nest: Made of sphagnum moss and skeletonized leaves and lined with mosses; built on the ground in the mossy hollow of a decaying stump or under an overhanging bank that is usually partially protected by surrounding vegetation. Eggs: 3–6, usually 4–5; white or very pale yellow, peppered, spotted, blotched, and sometimes scrawled with browns. Incubation period and age at 1st flight unknown. Food: Insects, primarily aquatic forms, small worms and other small invertebrates, and some seeds.

LOUISIANA WATERTHRUSH (*Seiurus motacilla*)

Appearance: Medium-sized (6¼ in.). Very much like the Northern Waterthrush, but darker above, especially on cap, and the underparts and the stripe above eye are much whiter.

Voice: The song is a loud, rather high-pitched 2-part series of 6–19 notes; the 1st part consists of 2–4 slow, slurry notes, and the 2nd part of rapid, descending, twittering notes. The call is a loud, musical *chink.*

Range and status: Breeds from e. Nebr., n. Iowa, e.-c. Minn., c. Wis., s. Mich., s. Ont., c. N.Y., c. Vt., sw. N.H., and R.I. south to e. Tex., c. La., s. Miss., s. Ala., c. and sw. Ga., c. S.C., and c. and ne. N.C. Winters from n.-c. Mexico, the Greater Antilles, the Bahamas, and Bermuda south to nw. S. America and Trinidad. It has straggled to Calif. and Maine. Fairly common.

Habitat: Low wet areas, borders of flowing streams, and bottomlands of rivers, usually forested.

Seasonal movements: Moves north Mar.–early May and returns Aug.–Oct.

Biology: Nest: Made of twigs and mosses and lined with dry grasses and hair; built on a mass of soggy dead

The Yellowthroat, the most widespread and geographically variable of the American wood warblers, breeds across almost all of North America.

The rather rare and very secretive Yellow-breasted Chat is our largest warbler. It lives in dense thickets and tangled, overgrown bramble patches.

leaves in cavities among the roots of overturned trees or banks of streams. Eggs: 4–6, commonly 5; white or very pale yellow, peppered, spotted, and blotched with browns and grays, with these colors usually most heavily concentrated at the larger end. Incubation: 12–14 days. Age at 1st flight: 9–10 days. Food: Insects, spiders, small invertebrates, and very few seeds.

Suggested reading: S. W. Eaton, "A Life History of the Louisiana Waterthrush," *Wils. Bull.*, vol. 70, pp. 211–236, 1958.

KENTUCKY WARBLER (*Oporornis formosus*)

Appearance: Small (5½ in.). Medium olive-green above, with black on forehead extending in a scattering of spots over fore half of cap. Below this, a streak of yellow goes from the forehead to the top and around the rear half of the eye, and a small black mask curves partway down the side of the neck. The bird is completely yellow below, somewhat duskier at the side of the breast and on the flank. The bill is blackish, the eye is brown, and the legs and feet are light buffy brown. The female is often somewhat duller, with less pronounced black markings. The Kentucky Warbler walks along the branches and ground instead of hopping or flitting.

Voice: The alarm call is a series of rapid metallic *chip*'s. The song is 5–7 loud, clearly whistled and rather liquid or rolling notes, as *turdle-turdle-turdle* or *churry-churry-churry;* there is also a complicated flight song that is not described.

Range and status: Breeds from se. Nebr., c. Iowa, sw. Wis., ne. Ill., c. Ind., c. and e. Ohio, s. Pa., n. N.J., se. N.Y., and sw. Conn. south to se. Tex., s. La., s. Miss., s. Ala., nw. Fla., c. Ga., and S.C. Winters from e.-c. Mexico (including the Yucatan Peninsula) to nw. S. America. It has straggled to s. Ont., n. N.Y., s. Que., Vt., and N.S. Fairly common to rare; it is not too poorly named, as Kentucky seems to be the center of abundance of the breeding population.

Habitat: Thickets bordering deciduous woodlands and glades with some water or moisture.

Seasonal movements: Arrives in breeding areas late Mar.–mid-May and departs mid-July–Oct.

Biology: Nest: Made of grasses, plant fibers, and rootlets, commonly on a base of dead leaves, and lined with rootlets; built on the ground or just above it in low shrubs or other vegetation, usually well concealed in surrounding plants. Eggs: 3–6, usually 4–5; white or very pale yellow, blotched (sometimes speckled and spotted) with browns and grays, often concentrated most heavily at larger end. Incubation: 12 days. Age at 1st flight: 10 days. Food: Insects, some berries, and probably some spiders and other small invertebrates.

Suggested reading: C. F. de Garis, "Notes on Six Nests of the Kentucky Warbler," *Auk*, vol. 53, pp. 418–428, 1936.

CONNECTICUT WARBLER (*Oporornis agilis*)

Appearance: Small (5¼–6 in.). Medium olive-green above and yellow below, with face, throat, and breast (sometimes the entire head) medium gray. The eye is completely circled with white. The grays of the somewhat duller-colored female are tinged with brown. In fall the face, throat, and breast of the immature birds are a greenish smoke-gray. The upper bill is dusky brown, the lower bill a dusky straw-yellow; the legs and feet are pale flesh.

Voice: The song is a *beecher-beecher-beecher-beecher,* all on 1 pitch, starting at almost a whisper and increasing in vigor toward the end. Another song is described as *fru-chapple, fru-chapple-fru-chapple, whoit,* sung in a loud, ringing voice. Call notes are sharp *peek*'s and *witch*'s and a metallic *plink.*

Range and status: Breeds from c. B.C., c. Alta., c. Man., n. Ont., and nw. Que. south to n. Minn., n. Wis.,

Duller facial markings distinguish the female Kentucky Warbler (above) from the male.

The rather rare Mourning Warbler nests in dense brushy thickets.

n. Mich., and c. Ont. Winters from e.-c. and se. Mexico to nw. S. America. Has straggled to N.S., Utah, Ariz., the Bahamas, and Curaçao I. Rather rare. It was first discovered by Alexander Wilson in the state of Connecticut and thus received its ill-fitting name; it is rare, even in fall migration, in that state.

Habitat: Wet, mixed woodlands, muskeg, brushy openings in coniferous forests, poplar and aspen groves near rivers, and brushy areas in migration.

Seasonal movements: Moves north late Apr.–May and returns Aug.–Oct. In fall there is considerable movement east of the Appalachians; in spring the majority move up the Mississippi Valley.

Biology: Nest: Made entirely of grasses or composed of leaves, bark strips, and vine stems and lined with fine plant fibers and hair; built on the ground or a few inches above it in brambles or bushes, well hidden and masked by surrounding vegetation. Eggs: 4–5; light cream or white, peppered, spotted, and blotched with browns. Incubation period and age at 1st flight unknown. Food: Little known, but mainly insects and spiders, with some seeds and berries.

Suggested reading: L. H. Walkinshaw and W. A. Dyer, "The Connecticut Warbler in Michigan," *Auk,* vol. 78, pp. 379–388, 1961.

MOURNING WARBLER (*Oporornis philadelphia*)

Appearance: Small (5–5¾ in.). The entire head is dark gray, and the black of the breast extends up onto the throat to a greater or lesser extent. The rest of the upperparts are medium olive-green, and the rest of the underparts are yellow. The entire head and breast of the female is a light, pale gray on the throat, but otherwise it resembles the male. The upper bill is blackish brown; the lower bill and the legs and feet are a pale flesh color.

Voice: The call or alarm note is a sharp, rough *chip.* The song consists of 2–5 slurred single or double notes, usually followed by a series of lower, more rapid notes, as *yeee, yeee, yeee, churr-churr-churr.*

Range and status: Breeds from c. Alta., c. Sask., c. Man., n. Ont., s. Que., and Nfld. south to ne. N.Dak., nw. and e.-c. Minn., c. Wis., ne. Ill., s. Mich., n. Ohio, ne. Pa., se. N.Y., nw. and c. Mass., c. N.H., s. Maine, and c. N.S. Winters from s. Nicaragua to nw. S. America. It has straggled to Puerto Rico and Greenland. Rather rare.

Habitat: Extensive, dense brush stands, woodland clearings, and thickets.

Seasonal movements: Moves north mid-Mar.–May and returns Aug.–mid-Oct.

Biology: Nest: Made of leaves and vine stalks, then coarse grasses and weed stems, and lined with fine grasses and hair; built on the ground or a few inches above it in brambles or other vegetation. Eggs: 3–5, usually 4; white or pale cream, peppered, spotted, and blotched with browns and sometimes a few black scrawls. Incubation: About 12 days. Age at 1st flight: 7–9 days. Food: Mainly insects, some vegetable matter.

Suggested reading: G. W. Cox, "A Life History of the Mourning Warbler," *Wils. Bull.,* vol. 72, pp. 5–28, 1960.

MacGILLIVRAY'S WARBLER (*Oporornis tolmiei*)

Appearance: Small (4¾–5½ in.); very much like the Mourning Warbler, but with an incomplete white eye-ring broken to the front and rear of the eye.

Voice: A rapid, harsh *chit* of alarm; the song is a swift-cadenced *te-te-te-te-cheweet-cheweet-cheweet* or *peachy-peachy-peachy-twit-twit-twit* and other variations.

Range and status: Breeds from s. Alaska, sw. Yuk., ne. B.C., c. Alta., and sw. Sask. south to c. Calif., c. Ariz., and c. N.Mex. Winters from s. Baja Calif. and n.-c. Mexico to Panama. Rare to rather common.

Habitat: Low, dense brushy areas and moist thickets.

Seasonal movements: Moves north Mar.–early June and returns Aug.–Oct.

Biology: Nest: Made of weed stems and coarse grasses, lined with finer grasses, rootlets, and hair; built from a few inches to 5 ft. above the ground. Eggs: 3–6, usually 4; white or pale cream, speckled, spotted, and blotched with browns, generally concentrated at larger end. Incubation: More than 11 days. Age at 1st flight: 8–9 days. Food: Insects; little other data available.

YELLOWTHROAT (*Geothlypis trichas*)

Appearance: Small (4½–5¾ in.); medium olive-green above. A black mask covering the forehead extends to the side of the neck and is separated from the cap by a narrow edging of white. The throat and breast are yellow, and the rest of the underparts are very pale gray. The female is similar but lacks the black mask, and only the throat and upper central part of the breast are yellow; the rest of her underparts are pale gray. The bill is black, the eye is brown, and the legs and feet are a dusky flesh color.

Voice: The call note is a sharp *tchch*; the song varies geographically and even individually, but is usually a loud, clear, strongly accented and much repeated phrase, as *witchity-witchity-witchity*. The Yellowthroat has been known to imitate other birdcalls and songs.

Range and status: It is the most widespread and variable of the American warblers, with 12 subspecies in the U.S. and Canada alone. Breeds from se. Alaska, s. Yuk., n. Alta., c. Sask., c. Man., c. and ne. Ont., c. Que., and sw. Nfld. south to n. Baja Calif., s.-c. Mexico, the Gulf Coast, and s. Fla. Winters from the s. U.S. to Panama, the Greater Antilles, the Virgin Is., and the Bahamas. It has straggled to the Lesser Antilles, Bermuda, and Greenland. Common.

Habitat: Freshwater and saltwater marshes and swamps, riparian thickets, and wet brushland.

Seasonal movements: Arrives at breeding grounds mid-Mar.–mid-May and departs mid-Aug.–Nov.

Biology: Nest: A rather bulky structure of reed shreds, coarse grasses, leaves, and mosses, lined with fine grasses, bark fiber, and hair; built on or close to the ground in weed stalks or bushes. Eggs: 3–6, usually 4; white or pale cream, peppered with browns, grays, and black, mainly at the larger end. Incubation: 11–13 days. Age at 1st flight: 9–10 days. Food: Almost entirely insects; only a few seeds.

Suggested reading: R. E. Stewart, "A Life History Study of the Yellow-throat," *Wils. Bull.*, vol. 65, pp. 99–115, 1953.

GROUND-CHAT (*Chamaethlypis poliocephala*)

Appearance: Small (5–5½ in.). Cap, nape, and eye region are medium gray; the eye is arched above and below by an incomplete white eye-ring and has a small black patch in front of it. The rest of the upperparts are brownish olive, and below the bird is completely yellow.

Broken white eye-rings are the best field marks of the MacGillivray's Warbler.

The tail is almost as long as the body. The female has a brownish olive cap and nape and no white near the eye. The upper bill is dusky brown, the lower bill buffy brown; the eye is brown, and the legs and feet are pale buffy brown.

Voice: A short, low-pitched, pleasant warble.

Range and status: Resident from w.-c. and ne. Mexico to w. Panama. Formerly resident in extreme s. Tex., but not recorded from there recently.

Habitat: Areas of tall, dense grass with scattered shrubs; also thickets and weedy fields.

Seasonal movements: None.

Biology: Nest: Made of grasses and lined with finer grasses and hair; built on or close to the ground in clumps of grasses or other vegetation. Eggs: 4; white, peppered, spotted, and blotched sparingly with browns. Incubation period and age at 1st flight unknown. Food: Little known; probably mainly insects.

YELLOW-BREASTED CHAT (*Icteria virens*)

Appearance: Largest (6½–7½ in.) of the warblers. Medium olive brownish above, including the face, with a streak of white from the forehead to just above the eye

Red-faced Warbler

and a tiny half-circle of white below the eye. The throat and breast are orange-yellow, and the rest of the underparts are white. The bill is black, the eye is brown, and the legs and feet are pale bluish gray. The sexes are alike.

Voice: Its song is 2–3 clear whistled notes interspersed with a great variety of squeals, cackles, squawks, and other odd noises that are difficult to describe. Its repertoire is so varied that it has a great reputation as a mimic, which may be due only to the fact that some of its notes resemble parts of the songs or calls of other birds. It often sings while fluttering in the air and, like the Mockingbird, frequently sings at night.

Range and status: Breeds from s. B.C., s. Alta., s. Sask., N.Dak., s. Minn., s. Wis., s. Mich., s. Ont., c. N.Y., s. Vt., and s. N.H. south to s.-c. Baja Calif., c. Mexico, the Gulf Coast, and n. Fla. Winters from s. Baja Calif., w.-c. Mexico, s. Tex., and Yucatan south to Panama. Rather rare to locally common.

Habitat: Dense thickets and bramble patches on low, wet ground near streams or at the edges of ponds or swamps; also patches of thick shrubbery in upland pastures and woodland edges.

Seasonal movements: Arrives in breeding range Apr.–May and departs mid-Aug.–Oct.

Biology: Nest: Made of vine and weed stems, then a thick layer of leaves, and lined with fine grasses and fine plant stems; built 2–8 ft. above the ground in a low tree, a bush, or a tangle of vines or briers. Eggs: 3–6, commonly 5; white or light cream, speckled and spotted with browns. Incubation: 11–15(?) days. Age at 1st flight: 8–11 days. Food: Insects and berries and other wild fruit.

Suggested reading: G. A. Petrides, "A Life-history Study of the Yellow-breasted Chat," *Wils. Bull.*, vol. 50, pp. 184–189, 1938.

RED-FACED WARBLER (*Cardellina rubrifrons*)

Appearance: Small (5–5¼ in.). Back, wing, and tail are medium gray; the forehead, throat, breast, feathers between the eye and the bill, and a collar extension to the side of the neck form a bright scarlet patch. The rump, the rest of the underparts, and the part of the collar at the back of the neck are white. The cap, the upper nape, and the portion of the face behind the eye is black. There are 2 rather indistinct white wing bars. The female is somewhat duller-colored; the immature bird in fall is considerably duller, with blackish gray instead of black on the head and pale flesh instead of scarlet on the face and head. The bill is black, the eye is brown, and the legs and feet are light buffy brown.

Voice: The calls are a simple *chip* and a *psst;* the song is a variable and rather bell-like whistled *a-tink-a-tink-a-tink-tsee-tsee-tsee-tswee-tsweep.*

Range and status: Breeds from c. Ariz. and sw.

A striking black hood identifies the male Hooded Warbler.

N.Mex. south through the mountains of nw. Mexico. Winters from c. Mexico to Guatemala. Rather rare.

Habitat: Open, montane forests.

Seasonal movements: Arrives in U.S. Apr.–early May and departs Aug.–Sept.

Biology: Nest: Made of grasses, bark fibers, and plant stems and lined with plant fibers and hair; built on the ground, well hidden by vegetation. Eggs: 3–4; white, peppered or sometimes spotted with browns, usually concentrated at the larger end. Incubation period and age at 1st flight unknown. Food: Unknown, but probably mainly insects.

HOODED WARBLER (*Wilsonia citrina*)

Appearance: Small- to medium-sized (5–6 in.). Medium olive above and bright yellow below, with a broad mask of bright yellow extending from the forehead and side of the chin to the rear of the cheek. A black hood envelops this mask from the cap to the throat. The female lacks the hood, except for rather sparse representation on the cap and side of the neck; the rest is replaced with yellow. The bill is black, the eye is brown, and the legs and feet are pale flesh. The immature birds are slightly paler duplicates of the adults.

Voice: The call notes are a soft *tsink* and a more emphatic *tchick;* the song is a high-pitched, loud, and emphatic but clearly musical series of 5–11 notes, usually paired low-high and high-low. A variation transliterates as *tawit-tawit-tawit-tee-too.*

Range and status: Breeds from se. Nebr., c. Iowa, n. Ill., s. Mich., s. Ont., nw. Pa., c. and se. N.Y., s. Conn., and R.I. south to se. Tex., the Gulf Coast, and n. Fla. Winters from e.-c. Mexico, including Yucatan, south to Costa Rica and occasionally Panama. Found casually farther north in summer; has straggled to Colo., Bermuda, the Bahamas, and the Virgin Is. Common to locally common and rare.

Habitat: Thickets and undergrowth of dense deciduous woodlands or wooded swamps; most commonly near rivers, streams, and ponds.

Seasonal movements: Arrives in breeding areas mid-Mar.–mid-May and departs mid-July–early Nov.

Biology: Nest: Neatly woven of dry plant fibers, grasses, and spider or insect webbing, usually on a rather bulky base of dry matted leaves, and lined with fine grasses, bits of plant fiber, and hair; built in thickets or in crotches of low saplings, 6 in.–5 ft. above the ground. Eggs: 3–4, usually 3; light cream, blotched, spotted, and peppered with browns, usually somewhat concentrated

In the West, the Wilson's Warbler breeds all the way from Alaska to southern California.

in a wreath at the larger end. Incubation: 12 days. Age at 1st flight: 8–9 days. Food: Insects, many caught on wing; possibly some berries, but little more is known.

Suggested reading: S. A. Grimes, "The Hooded Warbler in Florida," *Florida Naturalist*, vol. 8, pp. 16–22, 1935.

WILSON'S WARBLER (*Wilsonia pusilla*)

Appearance: Small (4¼–5 in.). Medium olive-green above and orange-yellow below, with the flank tinged with olive. The forehead, a streak above the eye, and most of the face are orange-yellow; the medium-sized cap is black. The female has no black cap and is yellow instead of orange-yellow. The black-tipped upper bill is dusky brown, and the lower bill buffy brown; the eye is brown, and the legs and feet are light buffy brown.

Voice: The call is a weak but reverberating *tschip;* the song is a bright, emphatic, staccato, chattering series of high, squeaky notes, as *wititititititititatoo.*

Range and status: Breeds from n. Alaska, n. Yuk., nw. and c. Mack., ne. Man., n. Ont., s. Lab., and Nfld. south to s. Calif., c. Nev., n. Utah, n. N.Mex., c. Sask., s. Man., n. Minn., s. Ont., n. Vt., c. Maine, and N.S. Winters from s. Baja Calif., w.-c. and ne. Mexico, and s. Tex. to w. Panama. It has straggled to Cuba. Winters very rarely in se. U.S. Common.

Habitat: Brush and thickets bordering woodland streams and marshes; in migration, park and garden shrubbery as well.

Seasonal movements: Moves through U.S. Apr.–mid-May and Aug.–Sept.

Biology: Nest: Made almost entirely of fine grasses or sedges; built on the ground, sunk in moss of bog at base of small tree or shrub. Eggs: 4–6, usually 5; white or light cream, speckled and spotted with browns. Incubation: 10–11(?) days. Age at 1st flight: 10–11 days. Food: Insects, many caught in the air, and, in winter, flower parts; very little more is known.

CANADA WARBLER (*Wilsonia canadensis*)

Appearance: Small (5–5¾ in.). Medium gray above and bright yellow below, with white undertail feathers and a streak of yellow from the base of the upper bill to the top of the yellow eye-ring. The forehead, some spotting on the forepart of the cap, a patch between the eye and the throat, and a broad necklace of jagged streaks over the upper breast are black. On the female, the black is replaced with dark gray, and the necklace is sometimes barely discernible. The bill is dusky brown, the eye is brown, and the legs and feet are light flesh.

Voice: The song is a series of irregularly alternating rapid notes on the same pitch, as *ker-chicharew-chichew-chicherew-chew;* the call note is a *tchip.*

Range and status: Breeds from n.-c. Alta., c. Sask., c. Man., n. Ont., and s. Que. south to s. Man., c. Minn., n. Wis., c. Mich., n. Ohio, through the Appalachians to e. Tenn., nw. Ga., w. N.C., w. Va., w. Md., e.-c. Pa., and n. N.J. Winters from n. Colombia and nw. Venezuela to c. Peru. It has straggled to Alaska, Greenland, and Guadalupe I. Common.

Habitat: Heavy undergrowth of mature forests, preferably near streams or swamps or moist brushlands and 2nd-growth forests.

Seasonal movements: Moves north through U.S. Mar.–May and returns mid-Aug.–Oct. Rare in Fla., as it apparently migrates over the Gulf of Mexico between the Mississippi Delta and Yucatan.

Biology: Nest: Made of bark fibers, grasses, weed stems, and skeletonized leaves on a base of large dead leaves and lined with rootlets, plant down, and hair; built on or near the ground, generally not far from water, in mossy hummocks, in cavities formed in banks or upturned tree roots, or near moss-covered logs. Eggs: 3–5, usually 4; white or light cream, speckled, spotted, and sometimes blotched with browns, frequently more or less concentrated in a wreath at the larger end. Incubation period and age at 1st flight unknown. Food: Almost entirely insects; mainly caught on the wing or searched out on the ground.

AMERICAN REDSTART (*Setophaga ruticilla*)

Appearance: Small (4½–5¾ in.). Black above, including face, throat, breast, and lower edge of flank. The wing bar, the upper ⅔ of the outer tail feathers, the side of the breast, and the flank are orange. The rest of the underparts are white. The female and the immature birds in fall are light gray above (browner on wing and tail) and white below, with yellow where the male has orange. The eye is brown, and the bill, legs, and feet are black.

Voice: The note is a distinct *tseet*. The song is a soft but high-pitched, sibilant, short, repetitive series, as *tseet-tseet-tseet-tseet*, varying somewhat from individual to individual.

Range and status: Breeds from se. Alaska, n. B.C., s.-c. Mack., c. Sask., c. Man., n. Ont., c. Que., and Nfld. south to e. Ore., n. Utah, n. Colo., se. Okla., s. La., c.

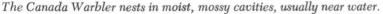

The Canada Warbler nests in moist, mossy cavities, usually near water.

The widespread American Redstart is common even in suburban gardens and city parks.

Ala., and c. Ga. Winters from s. Baja Calif., c. Mexico, and the Greater Antilles south to Ecuador, n. Brazil, and Guyana. It has straggled to Greenland and Bermuda. Believed to be one of the most common warblers nesting in N. America.

Habitat: Young deciduous woodlands, gardens and parks with many young trees, and alder thickets, etc.

Seasonal movements: Moves north through U.S. and into breeding areas mid-Mar.–May and returns mid-July–Nov.

Biology: Nest: Well constructed of plant down, bark fibers, rootlets, and grasses, felted and bound together with insect and spider webbing, and lined with fine grasses, weed and bark fibers, and hair; built in the crotch of a tree or shrub 4–25 ft. above the ground. Eggs: 2–5, usually 4; white, light cream, or very pale green, peppered, spotted, and frequently blotched with browns and grays, which are often largely concentrated in a wreath at the larger end. Incubation: 12 days. Age at 1st flight: 8–9 days. Food: All stages of insects, caught mainly on the wing in the manner of flycatchers; some berries and seeds, as well as a few spiders and other small invertebrates.

Suggested reading: William Brewster, "Notes on Setophaga Ruticilla (American Redstart)," *October Farm*, Harvard Univ. Press, Cambridge, Mass., 1936, pp. 144–148. M. Ficken, "Courtship of the American Redstart," *Auk*, vol. 80, pp. 307–317, 1963.

PAINTED REDSTART (*Setophaga picta*)

Appearance: Small (5–5¼ in.). Black above, including throat, upper breast, flank, wing, and tail, with a broad white wing bar and white outer tail feathers. The rest of the breast is scarlet, and the rest of the underparts white. The bill, legs, and feet are black, and the eye is brown. The sexes are alike.

Voice: The call is a high peep; the song is a rather low, monotonous *weecher-weecher-weecher*, with some variation.

Range and status: Breeds from nw. and n.-c. Ariz., sw. N.Mex., and w. Tex. south through the mountains to El Salvador and n. Nicaragua. Winters from n. Mexico southward. Straggles frequently to Calif; has reached Utah and Mass. Locally common.

Habitat: Montane oak and pine-oak woodlands, in canyons and on slopes.

Seasonal movements: Arrives in U.S. Mar. and Apr. and retires Aug.–mid-Oct.

Biology: Nest: Made of bark fibers, weed stalks, and grasses and lined with fine grasses and hair; built on the ground, generally hidden under grass or other vegetation. Eggs: 3–4, usually 4; pale cream, peppered with browns, often most concentrated at larger end. Incubation period and age at 1st flight unknown. Food: An expert flycatcher; probably almost entirely insectivorous.

THE WEAVERBIRDS (PLOCEIDAE)

Weaverbirds are small to medium-large (3–25½ in.) songbirds most closely related to the troupials, tanagers, and finches. There is considerable difference of opinion among the experts as to whether certain subfamilies belong here or with the finches or tanagers. As considered here, there are more than 260 species ranging from n.-c. Eurasia to s. Africa, Madagascar, Australia, Tasmania, New Caledonia, and the Fiji Is. Several species have been successfully introduced in America and Hawaii. Only a few species are migratory; those in America do not migrate. These are mainly birds of the open woodlands; some are terrestrial. The plumage is in a great variety of colors and patterns, and many of the more colorful species have appeared as cage birds in the U.S. and Canada. The wings are comparatively short and commonly square-tipped. The tail varies from short and square-tipped to very long and graduated, with the longest central feathers graduating to the shortest outer tail feathers. The majority of species have a rather short, stout, conical bill. The legs are short but strong. The sexes may be alike or dissimilar. Although many of the species have pleasant songs, those introduced here do not by any stretch of the imagination have melodious voices. Many species are colonial, most are gregarious, and only a few are solitary nesters. Quite a few are parasitic, laying their eggs in the nests of other species. Most weaverbirds build their own nests; the architecture varies from careless heaping of debris to beautiful, carefully woven flask-shaped structures and bulky but well-built apartment houses. The males of at least some species help to build the nests. The eggs, usually of some pastel shade or white, are spotted with browns or are immaculate, and may be incubated by the female alone or with some assistance from the male. The hatchlings, with or without down, are tended by both parents. Food is largely vegetable matter, but most species eat some animal matter or at least feed the nestlings on insects or similar food.

HOUSE SPARROW (English Sparrow) (*Passer domesticus*)

Appearance: Small (5½–6¼ in.). Crown, center of nape, rump, and tail are light to medium gray; back and wing are buffy brown, with 2 thin white wing bars, black streaking on upper back, and some black spotting on shoulder of wing. The throat and adjoining center of the upper breast are black. A small spot behind the eye, the cheeks, and the rest of the underparts are very pale gray, and there is a half-loop of tawny between the cheek and the cap and nape. The female is light buffy brown above and very pale gray below, with back and wing similar to those of the male; she has a dark streak through the eye. The bill is black (dusky brown in winter), the eye is brown, and the legs and feet are buffy brown.

Voice: Twittering and chirping and loud cheeps. Author Kenneth Roberts once referred to the House Sparrow's sounds as "squirplings."

Range and status: Native resident throughout Europe, c. Asia, nw. Africa, the Nile Valley, Arabia, sw. Asia, India, Ceylon, and Burma. Introduced successfully in N. America, Hawaii, Chile, Argentina, Paraguay, Brazil, the Falkland Is., Cuba, Jamaica, S. Africa, Australia, New Zealand, and elsewhere. In N. America it is now established from c. Canada to n. Mexico and is still spreading; the 1st success was in New York, N.Y., in

The House Sparrow, first introduced in the 1850s, has spread across most of North America.

1852–1853, and others followed quickly in such cities as Portland, Maine; New Haven, Conn.; Galveston, Tex.; Salt Lake City, Utah; Iowa City, Iowa, and others. It was, at the turn of the century, one of the most abundant birds in the U.S.; its decline in numbers coincided with the increased use of automobiles and the contemporaneous decline in the number of horses. Today it is locally common in cities and about farm buildings and scattered throughout open country, especially in the South.

Habitat: Cities, towns, villages, agricultural areas, and in its indigenous areas a great variety of open lands.

Seasonal movements: None in N. America.

Biology: Courtship is a series of violent acrobatic posturings before the female; this ardent activity commonly disintegrates into knockdown, drag-out fights between competing males and sometimes between females. Nest: Located almost anywhere: in birdhouses, on ledges, in abandoned woodpecker holes, etc., near houses or barns. Nests are sometimes almost close enough together to be called colonial; they are an unsightly collection of grass, straw, and debris. Both sexes participate in nestbuilding, which may begin as early as Feb. Eggs: 3–7, commonly 5; white, pale blue, or pale green with a few gray or brown spots. Incubation: 11–12 days, by the female alone; several broods are raised each year. Age at 1st flight: About 15 days. Food: Grain, other seeds, other vegetable matter, and some insects and other animal matter; the young are fed mainly insects and other small invertebrates.

Suggested reading: D. Summers-Smith, *The House Sparrow*, Collins, London, 1963, 269 pp.

EUROPEAN TREE SPARROW (*Passer montanus*)

Appearance: Small (6–6¾ in.), with brownish red cap and nape. The rest of the upperparts are dark smoke-gray (browner on wing and tail), with black streaks on back and wing and with 2 rather indistinct whitish wing bars. The throat, the area just around the eye, the center of the upper breast, and a patch in the cheek are black; the cheek, side of breast, and rest of underparts are white to pale gray. The bill is dusky brown, the eye is brown, and the legs and feet are light buffy brown. The sexes are alike.

Voice: The *chirp* call is not as shrill as that of the House Sparrow. The song is a somewhat melodic series of tinkling notes.

Range and status: Native resident of Eurasia (exclusive of parts of Scandinavia, Greece, most of the Near East and Middle East, and the tundra regions) south to Sumatra and Java and to Japan. Introduced and established in e.-c. Mo. in and around St. Louis and in w. Ill., where it is locally common.

Habitat: City parks and around farms.

Seasonal movements: None.

Biology: Nest: A rather sloppy structure of grasses, feathers, and rubbish, in holes in haystacks, on ledges of buildings, in abandoned woodpecker holes, and in deserted Bank Swallow burrows as well as birdhouses. Eggs: 4–8, usually 4–6; white or pale gray, peppered with browns. Incubation: 13–14 days, by both sexes; 2 or sometimes 3 broods each year. Age at 1st flight: 12–14 days. Food: Grain, weed seeds, other vegetable matter, and some insects; the young are fed insects exclusively.

Suggested reading: D. A. Bannerman, *Birds of the British Isles*, Oliver and Boyd, Edinburgh, vol. 1, 1953, pp. 345–353.

STRAWBERRY FINCH (*Estrilda amandava*)

Appearance: Small (ca. 4 in.). Scarlet, darkened almost to a brownish red on the cap, nape, and back and to a chestnut on the wing. The lower ⅓ of the tail is black, and there are white spots on wing, flank, and side of breast. The female is dark buffy brown above and straw-yellow below, with the rump and upper ⅔ of the black-tipped tail scarlet. The bill is an orange-yellow, the eye is brown, and the legs and feet are buffy yellow.

Voice: Song is short and feeble but melodious.

Range and status: Native to India, Burma, and s. China to Ceylon, Java, and Bali; established, but rare, on Oahu I., Hawaii, near Pearl Harbor.

Habitat: Cultivated areas and open fields.

Seasonal movements: None in Hawaii.

Biology: Nest: A small and neat but flimsy structure of grasses, found at almost any time of the year on ground among grasses. Eggs: 5–10, usually 5–7. Incubation period and age at 1st flight unknown or undescribed. Food: Grain, seed, fruit, and some insects.

RICEBIRD (*Lonchura punctulata*)

Appearance: Small (ca. 4 in.). Fuscous above, including wing, tail, throat, and entire head; white below. The tawny edges to the feathers of the breast and flank give them a scaled appearance. The immature bird is fuscous above and lighter fuscous below. The bill is blackish brown, the eye is brownish red, and the legs and feet are dark gray.

Voice: A querulous *chee* and *ba-hee*.

Range and status: Native resident from India and s. China to Sumatra, Java, and the Celebes. Introduced and now a fairly common resident on all the main islands of Hawaii.

Habitat: Grassy fields and rice paddies.

Seasonal movements: None in Hawaii.

Biology: Nest: Sometimes in loose colonies of up to 40 nests in a tree; each nest is a spherical structure of grasses with a side entrance. Eggs: 3–4, white. Incubation period and age at 1st flight unrecorded. Food: Grain, seeds, etc; the bird is a nuisance in Oriental rice fields. Young are fed insects, etc.

The male Bobolink often sings as it flies over its breeding territory.

BLACKBIRDS, MEADOWLARKS, ORIOLES, AND TROUPIALS (ICTERIDAE)

This family of small to medium-large (6½–22 in.) songbirds is related most closely to the weaverbirds, tanagers, and finches. There are 94 species ranging from n. N. America to s. S. America and the Falkland Is.; 22 species occur or have been recorded from the U.S. and 12 of these in Canada. They are numerous and prominent parts of the avifuana; 1 species, the Red-winged Blackbird, is considered by some to be the most numerous land bird in the world. Many of the species are migratory. They occupy a great variety of habitats, from grasslands to dense, humid jungles. The majority of species are black or have black in the plumage, with varying degrees and patterns of iridescence and bold designs in browns, oranges, yellows, and reds. Some have neck ruffs, and a few have meager crests. Most species have long, pointed wings, and the generally rounded tail may be short to long. The bill varies from short, stout, and conical in a few varieties to long and slender and even long and heavy with a prominent casque in others. The legs are fairly long and sturdy, and the feet large and strong; these birds walk rather than hop over the ground. They are strong fliers. The voice is usually strident, but some have flutelike calls and a few have well-developed, melodious songs. The sexes are alike in only a few species. Most species are highly gregarious, and a few are distinctly colonial; some are nest parasites, laying their eggs in the nests of other species. The colonial species are often polygamous. Nests may be simple cup shapes in trees or on the ground or complex woven pensile or semipensile structures in trees; or they may be built in holes or crevices. Most nests are made of grasses or other vegetable fiber. The eggs, commonly 2–7, are often heavily marked with browns and black on backgrounds of white, pale blue, pale green, pale gray, or buffy. Incubation is entirely by the female, and only in a very few species does the male assist in feeding or otherwise caring for the nestlings. The hatchlings have a sparse covering of down, except in 1 species where they are naked. The nestlings are fed primarily insects, but the food of the adults also includes other small invertebrates, small vertebrates, seeds, flowers, fruit, nectar, etc.

The Eastern Meadowlark is best distinguished from its western counterpart by song.

BOBOLINK (*Dolichonyx oryzivorus*)

Appearance: Small (6–8 in.); dull-glossed black, with a white rump and lower back and a broad white streak from the lower back extending to the shoulder of the wing. The nape is buffy yellow. The female is a light buffy brown, with a broad streak of dark brown above the eye and a very narrow streak through the eye; the tail, the streaks and spots on the back and rump, and dashes on the flank are dusky brown; the wing is dusky brown, with light buffy brown edging on most of the feathers. In fall and winter the male resembles the female, but is larger and somewhat darker. The rather short, sparrowlike bill is black, the legs and feet are dusky brown, and the eyes are brown.

Voice: The most common call notes are a rapidly and often repeated *quick* by the female, a lower and slower but repetitive *tchow* by the male when disturbed, and a *pink* heard during flight; a much repeated

tcheteeta is also common. The song is a succession of short, loud, clear notes rising irregularly in pitch, with no 2 successive notes on the same pitch. Most often the male sings in flight above the courtship territory and nesting fields, but he also sings from perches on trees, shrubs, or high weeds. The bubbling, harplike quality is familiarly expressed by W. S. Bryant in the poem "Robert of Lincoln" as "*Bob-o'-link, bob-o'-link/Spink, spank, spink.*"

Range and status: Breeds from s.-c. and se. B.C., s. Alta., s. Sask., s. Man., c. and s. Ont., sw. and s.-c. Que., P.E.I., and n. N.S. south, east of the Cascades, to ne. Calif., n. Nev., n. Utah, c. Colo., c. Nebr., n. Mo., c. Ill., Ind., Ohio, n. W.Va., w. Md., Pa., and c. N.J.; possibly casually and irregularly farther south, west of the Rockies. Winters in c. S. American tropics; migrates mainly through the Mississippi Valley and along the Atlantic Coast, across the Gulf of Mexico and the Caribbean and through the W. Indies; rarely through e. Mexico, C. America, and w. S. America. It has straggled to n. Ont., Lab., Greenland, the Galápagos, and Helgoland. Rare west of the Rockies; locally common elsewhere in breeding range.

Habitat: Open fields, especially hayfields and moist meadows; marshes during migration.

Seasonal movements: Moves north through the U.S. Apr.–mid-June and returns Aug.–Nov.

Biology: Courtship is largely pursuit of female, sometimes by several males at once, and strutting display in front of the female. Increased song activity and fighting among the males is a sign that the females have arrived and that the males are attempting to drive away the other males before starting real courtship. Nest: A simple hollow on the ground among the grasses, surrounded by coarse grass and weed stems and sparsely lined with finer grasses. Eggs: 4–7, usually 5–6; very pale gray or pale buff, varyingly and irregularly spotted and blotched with browns. Incubation: 13 days, by female alone. Age at 1st flight: 10–14 days; the male assists in care of the young. Food: In the summer and early fall, insects and other small invertebrates make up more than 50% of the diet, and weed seeds and grain compose the remainder. During migration the bird consumes large amounts of seedling rice and other grains in spring and maturing rice and other seed crops in fall, but where rice is of no commercial importance its diet of weed seeds is beneficial to man.

Suggested reading: A. C. Bent, *Life Histories of North American Blackbirds, Orioles, Tanagers, and Their Allies*, Dover, N.Y. (reprint of U.S. Nat. Mus. Bull. 211, 1958), 1965, pp. 28–52.

EASTERN MEADOWLARK (*Sturnella magna*)

Appearance: Small (8½–11 in.). Smoke-gray above, with the back, rump, tail, and wing feathers barred with blackish and with centers of tawny or fuscous. The nape is finely streaked with blackish brown, and the crown has a broad stripe of chestnut mottled with blackish on each side of the narrow central streak. There is a thin black streak through the eye, and the fore half of the smoke-gray streak above the eye is yellow. The cheek is pale gray. The amount of white on the outer 3 tail feathers on each side varies according to geographical location. The black-spotted flank is light gray, and the throat and breast, separated from each other by a broad black V, are bright yellow. The stout, sharp-pointed bill, which is almost as long as the head, is dark gray above and bluish gray below. The eye is brown, and the legs and feet are pale smoke-gray. The sexes are similar except that the female is slightly smaller and duller-colored; in winter both sexes are more brownish and less blackish.

Voice: The common call is a rapid, nasal *weet, weet, weet* and a *dzert-tet-tet-tet-t-t-t* when alarmed. The song has been described as plaintive and melancholy, but to me the rich, slurred notes seem to say, "Ah, spring is here"—a happy message usually at an appropriate time.

Range and status: Breeds from nw. and c. Ariz., s. N.Mex., sw. S.Dak., ne. Minn., n. Wis., n. Mich., se. Ont., sw. and s.-c. Que., and c. N.S. south through mainland Mexico and C. America to nw. and n.-c. S. America and Cuba. In winter it retreats a rather short distance from the n. edges of its breeding range and is then common only south of the Ohio River Valley and coastal Md.

Habitat: Open grasslands, prairies, and meadows.

Seasonal movements: The large numbers that winter in the more southerly states move northward in flocks mid-Feb.–Apr. and return in Sept.–Oct.

Biology: In courtship the arrival of the females at the nesting territories, chosen by the males earlier in the season, is signaled by knockdown, drag-out fights among the males and by more frenzied singing activity. Several males may pursue the female through the air over the fields, but usually only 1 male will perform the stretching, contorting postures and short hopping flights before the female, who may respond by stretching, fluffing her plumage, and flashing her wings. Nest: In a hollow in the ground in meadows, weedy orchards, or fields of corn or alfalfa; loosely woven of rather coarse grasses and arched over, with an opening on only 1 side, by interlacing grasses and weed stems amid surrounding vegetation. Eggs: 3–7, usually 5; white or very pale pink or green, profusely peppered, spotted, and blotched with browns. Incubation: 13–14 days, by the female; usually raises 2 broods. Age at 1st flight: 11–12 days. Food: Insects and other small invertebrates when these are available; grain, weed seeds, berries, and other fruit mainly in late fall, winter, and early spring. Growing grain is seldom disturbed, and grain seed is gleaned almost entirely after the harvest when insects are becoming scarce.

Suggested reading: W. E. Lanyon, *The Comparative Biology of the Meadowlarks (Sturnella) in Wisconsin*, Publ. Nuttall Ornith. Club, no. 1, Cambridge, Mass., 67 pp., 1957.

WESTERN MEADOWLARK (*Sturnella neglecta*)

Appearance: Small (8½–11 in.). Somewhat paler in coloration than the Eastern Meadowlark, but safely separated from it only by the song.

Voice: The song is more musical and less slurred than that of its congener, although there is some resemblance. There are many individual variations, but the song of the Western Meadowlark is much lower-pitched than that of the Eastern. A variation has been transliterated as *"Oh yes, I am a pretty little bird,"* trilling off at the end. The call notes are a low *tuck* and a rolling chatter.

Range and status: Breeds from sw. and c. B.C., c. Alta., c. Sask., s. Man., and w. and s. Ont. south to Baja Calif., c. and ne. Mexico, c. Tex., and La. Winters from sw. B.C., s. Alta., s. Sask., s. Man., and s. Wis. south to s.-c. Mexico. There is a considerable area of hybridization with the Eastern Meadowlark east of these limits. Common.

Habitat: Open grasslands and prairies.

Seasonal movements: Moves north late Feb.–early May and south Sept.–early Dec.

Biology: So similar to that of the Eastern Meadowlark that the description of that species will suffice here.

Suggested reading: W. E. Lanyon, "Specific Limits and Distribution of Meadowlarks of the Desert Grassland," *Auk*, vol. 79, pp. 183–207, 1962.

YELLOW-HEADED BLACKBIRD (*Xanthocephalus xanthocephalus*)

Appearance: Small (8–11 in.). Head, neck, and upper breast are yellow. The rest of the plumage (including feathers between the bill and eye and on the chin next to the bill) is sooty black, except for small patches of white near the bend of the wing and a spot of buffy yellow on the undertail feathers. In fall and winter the yellow feathers are mottled with black. The female and the immature male are fuscous, except for a buffy yellow face, throat, and upper breast and whitish streaks from the upper breast over the lower. The female has a narrow fuscous eye streak. The bill, legs, and feet are black, and the eye is brown.

Voice: The call notes are low *kra-a-ack*'s or *ka-ack*'s. The song is an individually variable, cacophonous series of liquid and squawking notes delivered while the bird writhes in a head-down position on a reed perch; *klee-klee-klee, ko-kow-u-u-u*, the last series trailing into a buzz or squeal, suggests the rhythm.

Range and status: Breeds from nw. Ore., c. Wash.,

c. B.C., ne. Alta., n.-c. Sask., c. and se. Man., n. Minn., n.-c. Wis., and nw. Ohio south to s. Calif., ne. Baja Calif., s.-c. Nev., sw. Utah, c. and e.-c. Ariz., s. N.Mex., n. Tex., s. Kans., sw., c., and ne. Mo., c. Ill., and nw. Ind. Winters from c. Calif., c. Ariz., s. N.Mex., c. and se. Tex., and s. La. south to s. Baja Calif. and s.-c. Mexico. Straggles farther north and to the Atlantic Coast and has reached the Arctic Ocean, c. Que., N.S., s. Fla., Cuba, Barbados, Greenland, and Denmark. Common.

Habitat: Freshwater swamps and marshes and surrounding open areas.

Seasonal movements: Moves north mid-Feb.–early June and returns mid-July–late Nov.

Biology: Courtship is aerial pursuit of female by male, followed by contorting, posturing exhibition by cock near seemingly indifferent hen. Nest: In colonies of up to 25–30 nests in a 15-ft.-square area. Built in reeds

The Yellow-headed Blackbird is most commonly seen about freshwater swamps and marshes.

over water 2–4 ft. deep; nests may be from 6 in. to 3 ft. above the water. Made of water-soaked grasses, which contract on drying and draw the separate reed stems together into a firm base; lined with dry grass blades in a neat cup. Eggs: 3–5, usually 4; very pale gray to very pale green, profusely and commonly evenly peppered and blotched with browns and grays. Incubation: 12–13 days. Age at 1st flight: 9–12 days. Food: Grain and weed seeds; insects and other small invertebrates make up about 33% of diet (almost 100% in nestlings).

Suggested reading: R. W. Fautin, "Incubation Studies of the Yellow-headed Blackbird," *Wils. Bull.*, vol. 53, pp. 107–122, 1941.

RED-WINGED BLACKBIRD (*Agelaius phoeniceus*)

Appearance: Small (7–9½ in.); entirely a glossy black, except for a large shoulder patch of scarlet that has a lower border of buffy yellow. The female is sepia above, with very pale gray undersides, heavily streaked and spotted. A narrow streak through the eye is sepia, and the center of the throat is almost clear white. The immature male in fall is black, but the feathers above are rather broadly edged with buffy brown and brownish red; below, including the face, he is narrowly edged with pale buff, and the small shoulder patch is a pale scarlet-orange with a broad lower edge of pale flesh. The moderately long sharp-pointed bill and the legs and feet are black, and the eye is dark brown.

Voice: The common call is a *tsack;* when repeated again and again by the individuals in a large marsh-ensconced flock, it sounds like the clicking and cackling of numerous large printing presses. The alarm note is a down-slurring nasal *peeeah.* The familiar *konk-la-ree* song shows its bubbling, liquid quality best when performed (never in concert) by large numbers of males gathered in a roosting or breeding marsh.

Range and status: Breeds from nw. B.C., se. Yuk., c. Mack., n.-c. Man., n. Ont., s. Que., P.E.I., and c. N.S. south to s. Baja Calif., Costa Rica, w. Cuba, and the n. Bahamas. In winter it retreats to s. Canada and s. New England, but is common at this season only from the sw. states and the central tier of states east of the Rockies southward. It has straggled to Alaska and Wales. Very common to abundant; it is successfully invading habitats relatively new to the species.

Habitat: Marshes and swamps, spilling into hay-fields, meadows, and cultivated lands.

Seasonal movements: Northward movement of large flocks Feb.–mid-May, returning mid-Aug.–early Dec.

Biology: Courtship is usually close pursuit of female by the male and posturing displays near her. Nest: From 3 in. to 14 ft. above the ground in bushes, tangles of vegetation, rushes, and low trees, preferably near water but, especially in recent years, in dry situations near open fields and meadows. It is constructed of long dry leaves, rushes, and sedges tightly bound to the substratum with vegetable fiber; the interstices are filled with rotten wood, rootlets, mosses, and other swamp debris and finally lined with grasses and slender rushes in a neat cup. Eggs: 3–5, usually 4; pale bluish green, spotted, blotched, marbled, and scrawled with browns, purples, and black, with these colors mostly concentrated at the larger end. Incubation: 11–12 days (1 record of 10 days); commonly 2 broods raised each year, possibly 3 in some instances. Age at 1st flight: 10–11 days. Food: Insects and other small invertebrates are the major food item in spring and summer (almost the entire diet of the nestlings); in fall and winter grain, gleaned mainly from the already harvested fields, and seeds of wild plants are consumed in large quantities. Considerable damage is done to some farm crops at certain seasons, but the benefits accruing to the farmer from the immense numbers of insects destroyed far outweigh the damage done.

Suggested reading: A. A. Allen, "The Red-winged Blackbird," *Proc. Linn. Soc. N.Y.,* abs. nos. 24–25, pp. 43–128, 1911–1913. R. W. Nero, "A Behavior Study of the Red-winged Blackbird," *Wils. Bull.,* vol. 68, pp. 5–37, 129–150, 1956.

TRICOLORED BLACKBIRD (*Agelaius tricolor*)

Appearance: Small (7½–9 in.); differs from the Red-winged Blackbird in having a darker red epaulet that is edged with white rather than yellow or buff. The female is darker than the female Redwing.

Voice: The call is a nasal *kape;* the song is more nasal and much less liquid than the Redwing's and has been transliterated as *oh-kee-quay-ah.*

Range and status: Breeds from s. Ore. (east of the Cascades) to nw. Baja Calif. Winters within Calif. range. Locally common and abundant.

The familiar Red-winged Blackbird is one of the world's most common land birds.

Habitat: Cattail and tule marshes and into adjoining open areas.

Seasonal movements: Irregular; no schedule known.

Biology: More colonial than the Redwing, with 16–34 nests found in 10-ft.-square plots. Nest: Like that of the Redwing. Eggs: 4; very pale bluish green, with markings similar to those of Redwing eggs, but sparser. Incubation: 11(?) days. Age at 1st flight: 10–12 days. Food: Very similar to that of the Redwing, but because of concentration of such large numbers in agricultural areas this bird probably does more damage to farm products.

Suggested reading: D. Lack and J. T. Emlen, Jr., "Observations on Breeding Behavior in Tri-colored Redwings," *Condor*, vol. 41, pp. 225–230, 1939.

TAWNY-SHOULDERED   BLACKBIRD   (*Agelaius humeralis*)

About the same size (7½–8½ in.) as the Redwing, but has tawny shoulder patches with buffy yellow lower edging. The female is also black, but her shoulder patch

The Orchard Oriole almost always builds its neat nest with bleached grass or straw.

is much smaller and almost inconspicuous. It is a resident of Cuba and w.-c. Haiti and has strayed on at least 1 occasion to Key West, Fla.

ORCHARD ORIOLE (*Icterus spurius*)

Appearance: Small (6–7¼ in.). Entire head, upper half of the back, wings, and tail are sooty black; the rest of the body, including a shoulder patch on the wing, is bright tawny. There is 1 white wing bar. The cap, nape, upper half of the back, wing, and tail of the female are light olive, and the rest of her plumage is dark straw-yellow; she has 2 white wing bars. The 1st-year males resemble the females, but the throat and feathers between the eye and bill are black, and the wing is almost blackish gray. The fairly long, sharp-pointed bill is black, with the proximal half of the lower bill pale grayish blue. The eye is brown, and the legs and feet are medium bluish gray.

Voice: A rather long, low rattle and a sharp *chack* are the common call notes. The song, very variable in time and pitch, is a rapid series of musical notes mixed with a few guttural and liquid notes and usually ending in a down-slurred call, as *look-here, what cheer, what-cheer, whip-yo, what-cheer, wee-yeer.*

Range and status: Breeds from s. Man., c. and se. Minn., c. Wis., s. Mich., s. Ont., n.-c. Pa., c. and e.-c. N.Y., and c. and ne. Mass. south to ne. Mexico, the Gulf Coast, and n. Fla. Winters from s.-c. Mexico (and Yucatan) to nw. S. America. Migrates over the Gulf of Mexico and w. Cuba. It has straggled to Calif., N.Mex., Colo., Wyo., Que., N.B., and N.S. Common to locally common; generally rare along extremities of range.

Habitat: Orchards, suburbs, towns, agricultural areas, and near marshes.

Seasonal movements: Arrives within breeding range late Mar.–mid-May and departs Aug.–mid-Oct.

Biology: Nest: A pendulous structure of securely woven grasses, lined with finer grasses and plant down and hung between horizontally forking branches of bushes or trees 4–30 ft. above the ground, commonly 10–20 ft. Eggs: 3–7, usually 4–5; pale blue, spotted, blotched, and scrawled with browns, purples, and grays. Incubation: 12–14 days; the male will feed the female while she is incubating. Age at 1st flight: 11–14 days; the male helps feed the nestlings. Food: Over 90% insects, spiders, etc.; some berries and flower parts.

Suggested reading: J. V. Dennis, "Observations on the Orchard Oriole in the Lower Mississippi Delta," *Bird-banding*, vol. 19, pp. 12–20, 1948.

BLACK-HEADED ORIOLE (*Icterus graduacauda*)

Appearance: Small (8–9¼ in.). Entire head, upper breast, wing, and rounded tail are black; upper back and adjoining part of wing are dusky straw-yellow. The remainder of the plumage is bright yellow, with 1 thin white wing bar and white edges on a few of the flight feathers. The female and immature birds in fall are similar but somewhat duller-colored. The fairly long, sharp-pointed bill is black except for the basal half of the lower beak, which is grayish blue. The eye is brown, and the legs and feet are bluish gray.

Voice: Song is composed of low, rather disjointed whistled notes; some consider this bird an accomplished songster.

Range and status: Resident from w.-c. and ne. Mexico and s. Tex. to nw. Guatemala; occasionally wanders as far north as s.-c. Tex. in summer. Common in southernmost Tex.

Habitat: Forests and brushland.

Seasonal movements: Some dispersal at end of breeding season, but irregular in time and direction.

Biology: Nest: A semipensile structure of well-woven grasses lined with finer grasses, built 8–15 ft. above the ground in trees. Eggs: 3–5; pale bluish or pale gray, flecked and scrawled with dark browns and purples or blotched and streaked with these colors. Incubation period and age at 1st flight unknown. Food: Little known; probably mainly insects, etc.

SPOTTED-BREASTED ORIOLE (*Icterus pectoralis*)

Appearance: Small (8½–9½ in.). The wing, tail, center of the back, feathers between the eye and the bill, a broad stripe covering the throat and the center of the upper breast, and some spots on the side of the breast are black; the rest of the plumage is orange. The female is somewhat duller-colored. The basal half of the lower bill is grayish blue, and the rest of the bill black. The eye is brown, and the legs and feet are bluish gray.

Voice: Loud, clear whistles in a pleasing liquid melody.

Range and status: Resident from s. Mexico to Costa Rica; established, probably through escaped cage birds, in the area around Miami, Fla. Becoming common.

Habitat: Jungles and tropical woodlands.

Seasonal movements. None.

Biology: Nest: In Fla., a flimsy cup woven of fine plant fibers and cradled in the branches of a tree; elsewhere, a long, pendant structure woven of plant fiber. Eggs: Insufficient data; probably 3–5, pale blue, splotched and lined with dark colors. Generally 2 broods each year. Incubation period and age at 1st flight unknown. Food: No data available, but diet certainly includes insects and fruit; the bird possibly is destructive in citrus-fruit orchards.

Suggested reading: C. M. Brookfield and O. Griswold, "An Exotic New Oriole Settles in Florida," *Nat. Geog. Mag.*, vol. 109, pp. 261–264, 1956. A. Skutch, "Life Histories of Central American Birds," *Pacific Coast Avifauna*, no. 31, pp. 274–275, 1954.

The Hooded Oriole is locally common in many parts of the Southwest.

HOODED ORIOLE (*Icterus cucullatus*)

Appearance: Small (7–7¾ in.). Forehead, feathers between the eye and bill, throat, center of upper breast, upper part of back, the wing, and the rather long, rounded tail are all black. The rest of the plumage is orange, and there are 2 white wing bars. The female is medium olive-green above and yellow below, with a dark gray wing and 2 white wing bars. The immature male in fall resembles the female, but the throat and the feathers between the eye and bill are black. The bill is black, with the basal half of the lower beak grayish blue. The eye is brown, and the legs and feet are bluish medium gray.

Voice: The calls commonly heard are loud, liquid, chirping whistles interspersed with low, soft chatters. The song, seldom heard, is a pleasant but rather guttural warble alternating with a chatter.

Range and status: Breeds from c. Calif., s. Nev., c. and se. Ariz., s. N.Mex., and w. and s. Tex. south to s. Baja Calif., s. Mexico, and n. British Honduras. Winters casually from just north of the U.S.-Mexican border southward. Rare to locally common to common.

Habitat: More open forests, suburbs, city parks, thickets, and shade trees.

Seasonal movements: Flocks arrive in U.S. mid-Mar.–Apr.; most have departed by the end of Aug., although some linger until mid-Nov.

Scott's Oriole

woven of tough grasses and other vegetable fiber, and usually very conspicuous. The 3–4 white eggs are spotted and scrawled with browns. It eats insects, berries, and other fruit. Not much more is known of its biology.

Suggested reading: G. M. Sutton and O. S. Pettingill, Jr., "The Alta Mira Oriole and Its Nest," *Condor*, vol. 45, pp. 125–132, 1943.

SCARLET-HEADED ORIOLE (*Icterus pustulatus*)

A small (8½ in.) member of the family. The scarlet-orange of the head grades to a buffy yellow on the rump and undertail feathers. The feathers between the eye and bill, the throat, tail, and wing are black; there are 2 broad white wing bars. The rather wide edges on the flight feathers of the wing are white, and the upper half of the back is heavily spotted with black. The rather long and stout but sharp-pointed bill is black, except for the grayish blue basal half of the lower bill. The eye is brown, and the legs and feet are a medium bluish gray. The female and immature birds in fall are duller-colored, being buffy yellow where the male is scarlet-orange. It is resident from w.-c. and c. Mexico to sw. Mexico and has straggled to Calif. and Ariz.

SCOTT'S ORIOLE (*Icterus parisorum*)

Appearance: Small (7¼–8¼ in.). Entire head, breast, upper half of back, wing, and tail are black. Except for 1 narrow white wing bar, the rest of the plumage is bright yellow, including a broad upper wing bar and the proximal ⅔ of the outer tail feathers. The female is a medium streaky olive-green above and a dingy greenish yellow below, with 2 narrow white wing bars on a dark, almost olive, wing. The immature bird resembles the female but has a black throat that is somewhat spotted toward the breast. The basal half of the lower mandible of the otherwise black bill is grayish blue. The eye is brown, and the legs and feet are medium bluish gray.

Voice: The song is a loud, clear, rollicking carol, *ly-ti-ti-tee-to-ti-te-to*, sung over and over. The female also sings the same song, but softer and less often.

Range and status: Breeds from s. Nev., sw. Utah, n.-c. Ariz., n.-c. N.Mex., and w. Tex. south to s. Baja Calif. and nw. and n.-c. Mexico; it has bred in w.-c. Nev. and ne. Utah. Winters from n. Baja Calif. and nw. and n.-c. Mexico south to sw. and s.-c. Mexico. Fairly common.

Habitat: Dry mountain slopes and deserts with scrub, yucca, oak, piñon, etc.

Seasonal movements: Arrives in U.S. Mar.–May and departs Sept.–mid-Oct.

Biology: Nest: A semipensile structure woven from vegetable fiber and grasses, lined with soft grasses and plant down, and "sewn" to the leaves and branches of the supporting tree, commonly yuccas, 4–10 ft. above the

Biology: Courtship involves male's aerial pursuit of female and male's bowing and bobbing display on a horizontal limb near the female. Nest: A thick-walled cup woven of green wiry grasses or mosses and lined with plant down, built 10–45 ft. above the ground in a tree. Eggs: 3–5, usually 4; white, very pale yellow, or very pale blue, marked with irregular spots and blotches of browns, purples, and grays, mainly about the larger end. Incubation: 12–14 days; may have 2 broods each year. Age at 1st flight: About 2 weeks. Food: Insects, nectar, berries, and other fruit.

LICHTENSTEIN'S ORIOLE (*Icterus gularis*)

Larger (8¼–10 in.) than the Hooded Oriole and of the same color pattern, except that there is no black on the forehead and the upper wing bar is orange rather than white. The bill is much wider at the base. The sexes are alike. The song is a series of loud, disjointed whistles and the call a rather raucous *ike-ike-ike*. It is resident from southernmost Tex. to c. Honduras and nw. Nicaragua. It is rare and irregular in Tex. It is found most commonly in woodlands and groves. The cylindrical pendant nest, built high in the trees, is often more than 2 ft. long,

ground. Eggs: 2–4, usually 3; very pale blue, speckled, spotted, blotched, and scrawled with grays, browns, purples, and black. Incubation: About 14(?) days. Age at 1st flight: About 2 weeks. Food: Insects, fruit, and nectar; few accurate data are available.

BALTIMORE ORIOLE (*Icterus galbula*)

Appearance: Small (7–8 in.). Entire head, center of upper breast, upper ⅔ of back, wing, and tail are black. Except for a white wing bar and white edges of the small flight feathers of the wing, the rest of the plumage is orange, including 2 slashes on the upper wing and the distal ⅓ of the outer tail feathers. The female is olive to mottled medium olive above, including the face and tail, and buffy yellow below. Her breast is darker and more orangish, and her wing is almost black, with 2 white wing bars. There is much variation in the females; some have a black cheek patch, with some black at the lower edge of the throat; usually the tail, rump, undertail feathers, and abdomen are light tawny orange, with more distinct orange on the breast. In fall and winter both sexes are duller in color; the male has orange-tawny tipping among the black feathers and blackish tipping among the orange plumage, especially on the rump and breast. The bill is dark bluish gray, the eye is brown, and the legs and feet are bluish gray.

Voice: The call note, a whistled *hootlee* or *hoolee*, is

The wide-ranging Baltimore Oriole is equally at home in city parks and open forests.

often used to separate singing performances; the bird also makes a harsh rattle or chatter. The song is a variable series of clear, rich, melodious whistles, easily imitated by man and recognizable more from quality of tone than by consistency of refrain or rhythm.

Range and status: Breeds from c. Alta., c. Sask., s. Man., w. Ont., n. Mich., s. Ont., s. Que., c. Maine, c. N.B., and c. N.S. south to ne. Tex., c. and se. La., c. Miss., n. Ala., n.-c. Ga., w. S.C., w. N.C., c. Va., n. Md., and Del. Winters from s.-c. and e.-c. Mexico south to nw. S. America; occasionally individuals winter as far north as se. Ont., c. N.Y., and Mass. Rare in Cuba during migration. It hybridizes readily with Bullock's Oriole in Okla. and Nebr. It has straggled to Nfld., n. Man., Greenland, Bermuda, and Scotland. Common.

Habitat: More open forests, shade trees in cities, suburbs and agricultural lands, and parklands.

Seasonal movements: Arrives in U.S. late Mar.–mid-May and departs Aug.–early Nov.

Biology: In courtship, the male bows, scrapes, fluffs his plumage, and spreads his wings and tail before the female, usually uttering low, sweet, chortling notes during the performance. Nest: In maples or elms by preference but also in other trees; generally 25–30 ft. above the ground, very rarely as low as 6 ft. and infrequently as high as 60 ft. At the end of a drooping branch the female weaves the familiar gray, swinging, pendant basket of plant fibers, hair, and string (yarn when available), lining it inside with hair, wool, and fine grasses. Eggs: 4–6, commonly 4; very pale gray, streaked, scrawled, and blotched with browns and black, very rarely unmarked. Incubation: 12–14(?) days. Age at 1st flight: About 2 weeks. Food: Insects, spiders, snails, and other small invertebrates; wild berries, fruit, and other vegetable matter.

Suggested reading: A. C. Bent, *Life Histories of North American Blackbirds, Orioles, Tanagers, and Their Allies*, Dover, N.Y. (reprint of U.S. Nat. Mus. Bull. 211, 1958), 1965, pp. 247–270.

BULLOCK'S ORIOLE (*Icterus bullockii*)

Appearance: Small (7–8½ in.). Throat, a narrow eye streak, cap, nape, upper half of back, wing, and tail are black. The rest of the plumage (except for a very broad white wing bar and narrow white edging on some of the flight feathers of the wing) is bright orange-yellow, including the proximal ⅔ of the outer tail feathers. The female has an olive-green cap and nape and olive back, rump, and tail. Her face, throat, and upper breast are dusky yellow, and the rest of the under-parts white. Her dark gray wing has 2 narrow white wing bars. The immature bird resembles the female during his 1st winter, acquires a black throat for his 2nd winter, and adopts the full adult male plumage during his 3rd winter. The fairly long, sharp-pointed bill is black, with the base of the lower beak grayish blue. The eye is brown, and the legs and feet are grayish blue.

Voice: The calls are a brisk, loud chatter, a sharp *skip,* and a soft *chirp-trap.* The song is similar to that of the Baltimore Oriole but not so variable; it is composed of louder, clearer double whistled notes with several higher, sharper pipes.

Range and status: Breeds from s. B.C., s. Alta., sw. Sask., Mont., sw. N.Dak., and c. S.Dak. south to n. Baja Calif. and c. Mexico. Winters on the w. side of the Continental Divide from s. Mexico to nw. Costa Rica. It has straggled to N.Y., Mass., Maine, and Ga. Fairly common to common.

Habitat: More open deciduous forests and groves and shade trees in towns and on farms.

Rusty Blackbird

Seasonal movements: Arrives in breeding areas Mar.–late May and departs Oct.–mid-Nov.

Biology: Nest: Similar to but not so pensile as that of the Baltimore Oriole; some are merely well-woven bowls or cups supported by twigs and thin branches. Eggs: 3–6, usually 4–5; very pale gray or very pale flesh, peppered, spotted, blotched, and scribbled with browns, grays, and black. Incubation: About 14 days. Age at 1st flight: About 14 days. Food: Almost 80% insects and the other small invertebrates; also fruit, wild berries, nectar, and other vegetable matter.

RUSTY BLACKBIRD (*Euphagus carolinus*)

Appearance: Small (8½–9¾ in.); entirely black with a slight bronzy gloss. The female is dark gray above and somewhat lighter gray below, with barring of darker gray on the breast, abdomen, and undertail feathers. In fall and winter the cap and broad eye mask of the male are brownish red mottled with black. A stripe above, below, and in back of the eye mask is dark buffy yellow spotted with black. The feathers of the back and rump are edged with brownish red, and the feathers of the breast and abdomen are edged with smoke-gray. The female in fall and winter is similar, but she is dark gray instead of black. The brownish red of the immature birds extends over the back, and the buffy yellow mottling is more extensive below. The fairly long, sharp-pointed bill and the legs and feet are black; the eye is bright, pale yellow.

Voice: The call notes are a short *kick* and a guttural rattle. The songs are a rhythmical alternation of 2–3-note phrases with a high, squeaky note, as *tolalee–eek, tolalee–eek,* often continued for some time, and a rapid repetition of 2–3 notes in rising scale.

Range and status: Breeds from tree limit of N. America south to c. Alaska, c. B.C., s.-c. Alta., c. Sask., c. Man., s. Ont., ne. N.Y., n. Vt., n. N.H., c. Maine, s. N.B., and s. N.S. Winters east of the Rockies from the s. edge of the breeding range south to se. Tex., the Gulf Coast, and n. Fla. It has straggled to Siberia, islands in the Bering Sea, Baja Calif., Greenland, and Wales. Fairly common to abundant (as a migrant and in winter in se. U.S.).

Habitat: Tree-bordered marshlands, riparian groves, and muskeg.

Seasonal movements: Moves north mid-Feb.–mid-May and returns Sept.–mid-Nov.

Biology: Although gregarious at other seasons, it is mainly a solitary nester. Nest: A well-built bulky structure of mosses, twigs, lichens, and grasses, with a neat cup composed of mudlike rotting vegetable matter, which, when dry, is lined with grasses and very fine twigs; built 2–20 ft. above water level in a tree or bush. Eggs: 4–5; very pale bluish green with spots and blotchings of browns and grays, often densest at the larger end.

Like the similar Rusty Blackbird, the male Brewer's Blackbird is all black, with yellow eyes.

Incubation: 14(?) days. Age at 1st flight: 13–14 days. Food: A little over 50% insects and other small invertebrates and grain, weed seeds, fruit, and other vegetable matter.

Suggested reading: F. H. Kennard, "Notes on the Breeding Habits of the Rusty Blackbird in Northern New England," *Auk*, vol. 37, pp. 412–422, 1920.

BREWER'S BLACKBIRD (*Euphagus cyanocephalus*)

Appearance: Small (8–10 in.); entirely black with a purple gloss, especially about the head, and a greenish or bronzy gloss elsewhere. The eye is bright yellow. The female is medium gray above and a somewhat lighter gray below and has a brown eye. Fall and winter plumage resembles that of the Rusty Blackbird but is darker-colored. The fairly long, pointed bill is black, as are the legs and feet.

Voice: The call note is a coarse *check;* the songs are long, drawn-out *squeeee*'s or *schl-r-r-up*'s with long pauses between or shorter notes uttered in rhythmic series, as *kit-tit-tit-tit-tit.*

Range and status: Breeds from sw. and c. B.C., c. Alta., c. Sask., s. Man., n. Minn., w.-c. Ont., and n. Wis.

south to nw. Baja Calif., s.-c. and e.-c. Calif., s. Nev., sw. and c. Utah, c. Ariz., w. and s.c. N.Mex., n. Tex., Okla., n. Iowa, n. Ill., and sw. Mich. Winters from sw. B.C., Idaho, Mont., Kans., Ala., and Ga. south to s. Baja Calif., c. Mexico, the Gulf Coast, and casually to w. Fla. It has straggled to n. Ont., Keewatin, and Ohio. Fairly common to common.

Habitat: A variety of open country, lakeshores, etc.

Seasonal movements: Moves north late Feb.–Apr. and returns late July–Nov.

Biology: Courtship consists of posturing and fluffing of feathers by male. Nest: A strong, neat structure of interlaced twigs and grasses plastered inside with mud or cow dung and lined with rootlets, hair, etc.; in very loose colonies on the ground or 150 ft. high in trees. Eggs: 3–7, commonly 5; very pale gray or pale greenish gray, peppered, spotted, and blotched with grays, browns, and black. Incubation: 12–14 days. Age at 1st flight: 13–14 days. Food: Insects and other small invertebrates, seeds, and some berries and other fruit.

Suggested reading: L. Williams, "Breeding Behavior of the Brewer Blackbird," *Condor*, vol. 54, pp. 3–47, 1952.

BOAT-TAILED GRACKLE (*Cassidix mexicanus*)

Appearance: Medium-sized (12–13-in. female and 16–17-in. male); the largest member of the family in America. Entirely black, with a purple gloss on the head, back, rump, and tail that merges into greenish and bluish glosses elsewhere. The long, flaring tail is almost as long as the body. The bill, which is as long as the head, and the legs and feet are black. The male's eyes are bright yellow, and the female's brown. The female is blackish brown above and smoke-gray below, becoming much darker toward the tail. Immature birds resemble the adults but are duller, especially below.

Voice: Rapid clicking sounds; the song, if it merits this distinction, is a great variety of vigorous loud, clear whistles. In some parts of its range the bird produces a "wolf whistle" with startling effect.

Range and status: Breeds from s. Ariz., c. N.Mex., w.-c. and se. Tex., the Gulf Coast, n. Fla. and the Atlantic Coast from s. N.J. south to the coasts of Peru, nw. Venezuela, and s. Fla. Mainly resident, but usually winters south of the Mexican border, along the Gulf Coast, and south of Va. Locally common to abundant.

Habitat: Open areas, coasts, river groves, parks, and farmlands.

Seasonal movements: No regular schedule.

Biology: Nest: A bulky cup of twigs, sticks, and other debris, plastered inside with mud or dung and lined with rootlets and grasses; in colonies, generally near water in bushes, trees, or other coarse vegetation. Eggs: 2–4, usually 3; light bright blue to pale bluish gray, boldly marked, spotted, and scribbled with browns,

A spectacular tail accounts for nearly half the length of the Boat-tailed Grackle.

grays, purples, and black. Incubation: 13–14 days. Age at 1st flight: 20–23 days. Food: Practically omnivorous.

Suggested reading: B. M. Tutor, "Nesting Studies of the Boat-tailed Grackle," *Auk*, vol. 79, pp. 77–84, 1962.

COMMON GRACKLE (*Quiscalus quiscula*)

Appearance: Medium-sized (11–13½ in.); entirely black with a high metallic gloss, which varies geographically. Many along the Atlantic Coast have a distinct purple, violet, and ultramarine cast (formerly the Purple Grackle), grading into populations where the back, rump, breast, belly, and undertail feathers have a bronze or greenish bronze gloss, while the entire head and the upper breast have a bluish cast (formerly the Bronzed Grackle). The eye is a bright light yellow; the legs and feet and the sturdy, sharp-pointed bill, which is almost as long as the head, are black. The sexes are very similar, but the female is less glossy.

Voice: The common call is a loud *chak;* the songs, identified as such by the season and manner in which they are presented rather than by any musical quality, are a series of hemidemisemiquavers of alternating husky clacks and high squeals; these are compressed into a *kuwaaaaa* or stretched tortuously into a *kogubaleek.*

Range and status: Breeds from ne. B.C., s. Mack., c. Sask., c. and ne. Man., w. and ne. Ont., s. Que., sw. Nfld., and n. N.S. south, east of the Rockies, to c. and s.-c. Tex., the Gulf Coast, and s. Fla. Winters casually north to the Great Lakes region; commonly in the se. U.S. It has been recorded occasionally from west of the Rockies. Common to abundant.

Habitat: Agricultural, urban, and suburban areas and the sides of streams or rivers.

Seasonal movements: Moves north late Jan.–early May and returns Aug.–mid-Dec.

Biology: Nest: Usually in small colonies of about 20–30 nests, close to the ground or as high as 50 ft. in trees, bushes, tangled vegetation, on ledges, in holes in trees, or even in the edges of bulky stick nests of the Osprey. It is a rather loose, bulky structure of weed stalks, sticks, grasses, seaweed, and debris, often cemented with mud on the inside and lined with grasses, feathers, cloth, and other debris. Eggs: 4–7, commonly 5–6; very pale green or very pale tawny, blotched, streaked, scrawled, and spotted with dark browns and purples. Incubation: 11–12 or 14 days (possibly geographic variation); old statements that in the purple variety the male assists in the incubation have never been proved, while it is known that the male of the bronzed form never assists. Age at 1st flight: 18–20 days; the male helps feed the nestlings. Food: Omnivorous; any small animal or plant matter in abundance will become part of the grackle's diet. Thus it will help man by gobbling up large numbers of insects in a scourge and only later turn to the abundance of grain ripening in the fields.

Suggested reading: A. Peterson and H. Young, "A Nesting Study of the Bronzed Grackle," *Auk,* vol. 67, pp. 466–476, 1950.

BROWN-HEADED COWBIRD (*Molothrus ater*)

Appearance: About House Sparrow size (6–8 in.). The entire head, neck, and upper breast are a buffy or tawny brown, and the rest of the plumage is a metallic green-glossed black. The female is a dark buffy brown above and smoke-gray below, with a throat patch of white or pale gray that is sometimes very distinct. The conical, finchlike bill and the legs and feet are black; the eye is brown. The immature birds resemble the female.

Voice: A variety of call notes such as a *chuck,* a slurred *preeah,* and a loud, harsh rattle are described, but flocks in fall and winter keep up a continuous low "conversation" that sounds like a small hillside stream gurgling over a rocky bed. The seasonal utterances fill the biological if not the musical definition of song: they are a series of high-pitched squeaks followed by 2–3 lower-pitched hissing notes, as *wheeeeeee-tsi-tsi-tsi,* and a courtship song paraphrased as *glub-glub-kee-he-keek.*

Range and status: Breeds from c. and ne. B.C., s.-c. Mack., c. Sask., s. Man., c. Ont., sw. and e.-c. Que., N.B., and s. N.S. south to n. Baja Calif., n. Mexico, La., s. Miss., and S.C. Winters from s. Ore., c. Ariz., s. N.Mex., Tex., Ark., the s. Great Lakes region, c. N.Y., s. Vt., s. N.H., and s. Maine south to s.-c. Mexico, the Gulf Coast, and s. Fla. It has straggled to Bermuda. **Common to abundant.**

Habitat: Farmlands, forest edges, groves, and riparian woodlands.

Seasonal movements: Moves north late Jan.–early June and returns mid-July–early Dec.

Biology: This cowbird is a nest parasite, laying its eggs in the nests of other—sometimes very disparate—species. It is definitely known to have victimized 206 different species, although only 101 of these have been known to rear the young cowbirds successfully. The Yellow Warbler, Song Sparrow, Red-eyed Vireo, Chipping Sparrow, and Eastern Phoebe are parasitized most frequently. This cowbird and the Bronzed Cowbird have no special adaptations in form, growth, or habit for the parasitism, and even the commonly parasitized species often fail, for one reason or another, to raise the hatchling cowbird or even to hatch the egg. Nest: None. Eggs: The female has been known to lay up to 5 eggs, usually each in a different nest. The eggs are white or very pale gray,

Like all blackbirds, the Common Grackle has highly ritualized display postures.

rather evenly speckled with browns and dark greens, with these colors sometimes more heavily massed or gathered in a wreath at the larger end. Incubation: 11–12 days. Age at 1st flight: More than 19 days. Food: More than 75% vegetable matter, such as seeds, fruit, pulp, and grain; the animal matter is made up of insects, spiders, snails, and other small invertebrates. The young probably are raised most often on an insect diet by the foster parents.

Suggested reading: H. Friedmann, *Host Relations of the Parasitic Cowbirds,* U.S. Nat. Mus. Bull. 233, 276 pp., 1963.

BRONZED COWBIRD (*Tangavius aeneus*)

Appearance: Small (6½–8¾ in.); entirely black, with a green-bronze metallic glossing, sometimes more bluish or purplish on the wing. The female is a dusky brown with very little metallic glossing. The rather long but finchlike bill and the legs and feet are black; the eye is scarlet.

Voice: Similar to that of the Brown-headed Cowbird, but wheezier and more guttural; it also has a harsh *chuck* call, but not all the variations of calls or song are known.

Range and status: Breeds from c. Ariz., sw. N.Mex., n.-c. Mexico, s.-c. Tex., and Yucatan south to w. Panama. Generally resident, but rare even in s. Ariz. in winter. Fairly common.

Habitat: Farmlands, brushland, and open country with scattering of trees and shrubs.

Seasonal movements: No pronounced movements: flocks after breeding season.

Biology: Parasitic like the Brown-headed Cowbird. It is known to have victimized 52 species, but the orioles of the genus *Icterus* are the most frequent sufferers. Nest: None. Eggs: No data on number laid; immaculate, very pale blue-green. Incubation period and age at 1st flight not definitely known, but probably similar to those of the Brown-headed Cowbird. Food: Almost entirely granivorous; the existing data indicate a few insects may also be eaten.

Suggested reading: H. Friedmann, *Host Relations of the Parasitic Cowbirds,* U.S. Nat. Mus. Bull. 233, 276 pp., especially pp. 173–188, 1963.

THE TANAGERS (THRAUPIDAE)

Tanagers are small (3–12 in.) songbirds of largely arboreal habits and are most closely related to the blackbirds, weaverbirds, and finches. There are 222 species distributed throughout the W. Hemisphere from the n. limit of forests in N. America to n. Chile and n. Argentina. There are only 4 species in the U.S.; these and a few others are wholly or partially migratory. Most species sport very brightly colored plumage, usually in large, bold patterns; greens, blues, yellows, oranges, reds, purples, browns, black, and white predominate. A few species have very glossy feathers, and a few are crested. The wings vary from short to moderately long; the short to medium tails are commonly square- or round-tipped. The bills are short to medium, conical, and slightly hooked or notched. The legs are comparatively short. In all the U.S. and Canadian species the sexes are dissimilar, although in a few of the exotic species they are alike. Spring and summer plumages differ from the fall and winter plumages, and during the molts U.S. species may present highly variable appearances. Some species have creditable songs. Courtship is probably restricted to simple display. Tanagers are sometimes gregarious but never colonial. Nests are cuplike or domed structures of plant material, placed in trees, bushes, or shallow cavities in banks or trees. The 1–5 eggs are white, pale greens, or pale blues, marked with browns and seldom immaculate. They are incubated solely by the females. The young, which are hatched with a sparse covering of down, are fed primarily insects; the males do assist in the feeding. Food of the adults is fruit, flowers, and insects or combinations of these.

WESTERN TANAGER (*Piranga ludoviciana*)

Appearance: A medium-sized (6¼–7½ in.) tanager. Entire head and throat are scarlet-orange; back, wing, and tail are black, with a narrow white wing bar and white edging on the smaller flight feathers of the wing. The rest of the plumage is bright yellow, including a rather wide upper wing bar. The female is medium olive-green above and yellow below; her black wing has an upper yellow and a lower white wing bar. In fall and winter the male has a more yellowish head; the yellow above is mottled with olive-green, and the black with buff. The bill is buffy yellow, the eye is brown, and the legs and feet are bluish gray. The young male resembles the female and in his 1st year is somewhat like the winter-plumaged male.

Voice: The common call note is a low *prit-it* or *prit-tittick*, sometimes followed by a lower *chert-it*. The song has some of the deliberate rhythm of a Gregorian chant, with a rough, Robinlike quality rising and falling in pitch, as *pir-ri, pir-ri, pee-wi-pir-ri, pee-we.*

Range and status: Breeds from se. Alaska, n. B.C., sw. and s.-c. Mack., ne. Alta., and c. Sask. south to n. Baja Calif., s. Nev., c. and se. Ariz., sw. N.Mex., and w. Texas; bred once in Wis. Winters from s. Baja Calif. and n.-c. Mexico south, west of the Continental Divide, to El Salvador and nw. Costa Rica; very casually north to Calif., Ariz., and Tex. It has straggled as far as n. Alaska, Yuk., Que., Mo., Maine, Mass., Conn., and Miss. Locally common to common.

Habitat: Open mixed and coniferous woodlands, and during migration all types of forest.

Seasonal movements: Arrives in breeding areas late Mar.–early June and departs July–late Oct.

Biology: Nest: A substantial cup of coniferous twigs, rootlets, and mosses, lined with hair and plant down; built 6–50 ft. above the ground near the outer end of a limb of a coniferous tree. Eggs: 3–5, commonly 3; very pale blues, irregularly speckled, spotted, and blotched with browns, sometimes wreathed about or most concentrated at the larger end. Incubation: 13 days. Age at 1st flight unknown. Food: Over 80% insects; the remainder fruit, seeds, flowers, and flower buds.

Suggested reading: A. C. Bent, *Life Histories of North American Blackbirds, Orioles, Tanagers, and Their Allies,* Dover, N.Y. (reprint of U.S. Nat. Mus. Bull. 211, 1958), 1965, pp. 466–479.

SCARLET TANAGER (*Piranga olivacea*)

Appearance: Medium-sized (6½–7½ in.); wing and tail are black, and rest of plumage is scarlet. The female is medium olive-green above, with dark gray wing and tail, and straw-yellow below. In winter the male resembles the female, but wing and tail are black; in fall the scarlet feathers are replaced in bits and patches, leading an observer to refer to them as "green-and-red plaid." The buffy yellow bill is dusky at the tip and cutting edge. The eye is brown, and the legs and feet are smoke-gray.

Voice: The familiar call is a *chip-churrr;* the song, with its half-whistle, half-hum quality, has been transcribed as *querit, queer, queery, querit, queer,* the phrases alternating in pitch.

Range and status: Breeds from c. Nebr., e. N.Dak., se. Man., w.-c. Ont., n. Mich., s. Ont., s. Que., and N.B. south to se. Okla., c. Ark., nw. and c. Ala., n. Ga., nw. S.C., w. N.C., c. and w. Va., and Md. Winters from nw. to c. S. America; migrates through Yucatan and C. America, rarely the W. Indies. It has straggled to Alaska, B.C., Calif., Ariz., Wyo., and Bermuda. Common.

Habitat: Dense deciduous forests of oaks, tulip trees, etc.; other types of woodlands, parks, and wooded suburban areas.

Seasonal movements: Arrives Apr.–mid-May and departs July–early Nov.

Biology: Nest: A flimsy, rather flat structure of twigs and rootlets lined with weed stems and grasses; built 8–45 ft. above the ground on horizontal tree limbs. Eggs: 3–5, usually 4; pale blues or pale greens, irregularly peppered, spotted, and blotched with browns. Incubation: 13–14 days. Age at 1st flight: About 15 days. Food: Over 85% insects and other small invertebrates garnered from the forests; the remainder of the diet consists of wild berries and seeds.

Suggested reading: K. W. Prescott, *The Scarlet Tanager,* N.J. State Mus. Investigations, no. 2, Trenton, 159 pp., 1965.

HEPATIC TANAGER (*Piranga flava*)

Appearance: Medium-sized (7–7¾ in.). A dusky, medium scarlet; somewhat duskier above, on the cheek, wing, and tail. The female is medium olive above and on the cheek and a rather dusky orange-yellow below. In fall and winter both sexes are duller-colored. The dark gray bill is comparatively much heavier and thicker than the bills of other U.S. tanagers. The eye is brown, and the legs and feet are bluish gray.

Voice: Rather silent except for the much repeated *chuck, chuck* call notes. The only description of the song merely states that it is short, loud, and clear.

Range and status: Breeds from n. Ariz., n. N.Mex., and w.-c. and s. Tex. south to c. Peru, c. Argentina,

The male Scarlet Tanager takes no part in incubation but does help rear the young.

Hepatic Tanager

Uruguay, and s. Brazil. Mainly resident, but retreats south of se. Ariz. and the Mexican border in winter. Fairly common locally in mountains.

Habitat: Open montane woodlands of oak and pine.

Seasonal movements: Arrives in U.S. in Apr. and departs in Oct.

Biology: Nest: Constructed of grasses, weed stems, and flowers and lined with finer grasses; built 15–50 ft. above the ground in the fork of a horizontal limb of a tree. Eggs: 3–5, usually 4; pale blues or pale greens, speckled and spotted with browns. Incubation and age at 1st flight unknown. Food: Little known; probably mainly insects, with some berries, seeds, and other fruit.

SUMMER TANAGER (*Piranga rubra*)

Appearance: Medium-sized (7–7¾ in.); somewhat paled ruby, with a dusky ruby wing and tail. The female is medium brownish olive above and dusky yellow below. Both sexes are somewhat duller-colored in fall and winter. The immature bird at first resembles the female, but in the process of acquiring the full adult male plumage has a rufous-olive mottled aspect. The bill is a light buffy brown, the eye is buffy brown, and the legs and feet are fleshy gray.

Voice: Like that of the Scarlet Tanager, but more musical and with more liquid sounds, transcribed as *"hée para vée-er chewit terwee hée para vée-er"* (M. M. Nice). The common call is a rattling *chicky-tucky-tuck*.

Range and status: Breeds from se. Calif., s. Nev., c. Ariz., c. N.Mex., c. Tex., c. Okla., se. Nebr., s. Iowa, c. Ill., c. Ind., c. Ohio, W.Va., Md., and Del. south to n. Mexico, the Gulf Coast, and s. Fla. Winters from s. Baja Calif. and c. Mexico to s.-c. Peru, w. Bolivia, w.-c. Brazil, and w. Guyana. It has straggled to Bermuda, the Bahamas, Jamaica, and Trinidad, and as far north as Minn., Mich., Ont., N.Y., Maine, N.B., and N.S. Rather rare to fairly common locally.

Habitat: Riparian woodlands; open, dry upland forests of oak, hickory, chestnut, and/or pine.

Seasonal movements: Arrives in breeding areas Mar.–mid-May and returns mid-Aug.–early Nov.

Biology: Nest: A flimsy structure of weed stems, bark, leaves, and grasses, lined with fine yellow grasses; built on a horizontal branch of a tree 10–35 ft. above the ground. Eggs: 3–5, usually 4; pale blues or pale greens, speckled, spotted, and blotched with browns and light gray. Incubation: 12(?) days. Age at 1st flight unknown, but may be more than 10 days. Food: Insects (wasps and bees preferred), other small invertebrates, berries, and other fruit.

Suggested reading: H. S. and V. R. Fitch, "Observations on the Summer Tanager in Northeastern Kansas," *Wils. Bull.*, vol. 67, pp. 45–54, 1955.

Unlike the Scarlet Tanager, the Summer Tanager has no black in its plumage.

GROSBEAKS, BUNTINGS, FINCHES, AND SPARROWS (FRINGILLIDAE)

These small (3½–10¾ in.) songbirds are most closely related to the weaverbirds, tanagers, and blackbirds. There is considerable difference of opinion among the experts as to the true affinities of the family. Some major groups, called subfamilies, are shifted by some authorities to the weaverbirds or are considered separate families. Since the grouping here follows that of the *Check-list of North American Birds* (5th ed., 1957), the number of species listed as belonging to the finches differs from listings in other recent books. In general grosbeaks are those species with larger, somewhat swollen beaks. Besides those actually bearing "grosbeak" as part of their common name, we could include the cardinals, the Dickcissel, the Bullfinch, the Hawfinch, the Brambling, and the Pyrrhuloxia as grosbeaks. In America, buntings are the brighter-colored finches; in Afro-Eurasia the name refers to all species in the subfamily Emberizinae, separated from other subfamilies of the Fringillidae on anatomical characters independent of coloration or habitat. In America "finch" and "sparrow" are almost synonymous, while in Europe "sparrow" is restricted to the weaver finches (family Ploceidae) and to members of the Eurasian genus *Montifringilla*. Although "finch" may be used as a substantive name for any member of the entire family, in general practice, especially in Europe, it is applied to those species that are not definitely grosbeaks, buntings, or sparrows. The 425 species in the family are distributed throughout the world except Antarctica, Madagascar, and Australia and New Zealand; 86 of these occur in America. Many species are migratory and are found in many types of habitat, from tundra to tropical forests. They are common and prominent parts of the avifauna. Many species are modestly clad in streaked and spotted plumages of browns, grays, black, and white, while others are more conspicuous in contrasting color patterns of reds, yellows, blues, purples, greens, black, and white. Some species have prominent crests. The general design of the bill is conical, but some bills are large and swollen and, at the other extreme, tiny and sharp-pointed. The wings may be short and rounded or fairly long and pointed; the tail varies from short to long; and the legs are strong and of moderate length. The sexes are alike in many of the species, and the immature birds often differ from the adults. Flight varies from weak to strong. Courtship is commonly a simple affair, but some species perform aerial acrobatics or go through complicated posing and posturing activities. During the breeding season they are usually solitary, although many species are highly gregarious at this and other seasons. The nests are generally simple cups on the ground, in low vegetation, shrubs, or trees, and sometimes in holes in trees. The 2–8 eggs are of light pastel shades and are immaculate or marked with browns, grays, and/or black. In some species the female alone incubates. The young on hatching are covered with sparse down; both sexes attend to the needs of the nestlings. Food fed the nestlings in almost all species consists of insects and other small arthropods, but the primary food of the adults is seed. Other items of the adults' diet are fruit, flowers, and some insects.

CARDINAL (*Richmondena cardinalis*)

Appearance: A large (7½–9 in.) sparrow, almost entirely scarlet. It is dusky scarlet on nape, back, rump, wing, and tail, with the area between the eye and the bill, the chin, and upper edge of the throat black. Both sexes have a prominent crest. The tip of the crest, the tail, and much of the wing of the female are like those of the male; otherwise she is a light buffy brown above and a dusky buffy yellow below, including the face; this fades to almost white on the center of the abdomen and on the undertail feathers. In winter both sexes are somewhat duller-colored. The rather large, conical bill is scarlet-orange, the eye is dark brown, and the legs and feet are dusky brown.

Voice: The common call note is a weak *tsink*. The song varies from individual to individual, but commonly consists of a series of loud, clear, rather husky whistled phrases repeated 2–3 times, followed or preceded by a faster or slower series of shorter, less emphatic notes. A common song may be transliterated as *che-eer, che-eer, che-eer, ti-ti-ti-ti-ti-ti-ti*, a cheering sound in early spring.

Range and status: Resident from se. S.Dak., c. Minn., s. Ont., w. and c. N.Y., and Mass. south to the

Gulf Coast and s. Fla. and from s. Calif., c. Ariz., s. N.Mex., and n. Tex. south to s. Baja Calif., s. Mexico, and British Honduras. Introduced and established on Kauai, Oahu, and Hawaii Is., Hawaii, and on Bermuda. Common; it is extending its range northward, especially in ne. U.S. and Ont.

Habitat: Forest edges, thickets, groves, suburbs, towns, and city parks.

Seasonal movements: None; range expansion is apparently the result of the progeny of successful breeding in adjoining areas moving into unoccupied territory insofar as climate and food supply permit.

Biology: Nest: A loosely built structure of twigs, leaves, bark, grasses, weed stalks, and rootlets, lined with fine grasses and hair; 3–30 ft. (commonly below 10 ft.) above the ground in bushes, low trees, thickets, or tangles of vegetation. Eggs: 3–6, usually 3–4; white, pale gray, or pale blues or greens, peppered, spotted, and blotched with browns, grays, and purples. Incubation: 12(?) days, perhaps by both sexes; 2–3 broods, sometimes more, yearly. Age at 1st flight: About 2 weeks.

The Cardinal is gradually extending its range northward in the northeastern states.

South America's Red-crested Cardinal has been successfully introduced in Hawaii.

Food: More than 70% vegetable matter (weed seeds, wild berries, and less than 10% grain) with somewhat less than 30% of diet made up of insects, spiders, and other small invertebrates.

Suggested reading: B. G. Beddall, "Range Expansion of the Cardinal and Other Birds in the Northeastern States," *Wils. Bull.*, vol. 75, pp. 14–158, 1963. A. R. Laskey, "A Study of the Cardinal in Tennessee," *Wils. Bull.*, vol. 56, pp. 27–44, 1944.

RED-CRESTED CARDINAL (Brazilian Cardinal) (*Paroaria cristata*)

Appearance: Medium-sized (ca. 7½ in.). Forehead, prominent crest, entire face, and throat are scarlet; the border between this and the medium gray upperparts (including somewhat darker wing and tail) and the remainder of the underparts are white. The immature bird is similar to the adults, but the scarlet is replaced by buffy brown. The fairly large, conical bill is straw-yellow, the eye is brown, and the legs and feet are buffy brown.

Voice: The song is of somewhat slurred, Robinlike phrases.

Range and status: Resident from e. Bolivia and s.-c. Brazil south to n.-c. Argentina and Uruguay. Successfully introduced in Oahu, Kauai, and Maui Is., Hawaii. Common and widespread on Oahu. It is popular as a cage bird, and escaped pets have been known to survive the winters in N.Y.

Habitat: In Hawaii in lowland thickets, brush, and shrubbery of suburbs and small towns.

The Cardinallike Pyrrhuloxia is fairly common in parts of the Southwest.

Seasonal movements: None.

Biology: Nest: In bushes and low trees; similar in structure to that of the Cardinal. Eggs: 3–4; white or pale gray, spotted with browns and grays. Incubation period and age at 1st flight unknown. Food: Mainly seeds, berries, and other fruit, with some insects and other small invertebrates.

PYRRHULOXIA (*Pyrrhuloxia sinuata*)

Appearance: A large-sized (7½–8¼ in.) Cardinal-like bird. Light gray above and pale gray below, with a scarlet tip on the long, Cardinallike crest. The feathers between the red-ringed eye and the bill, the throat, the center of the breast and abdomen, some of the larger flight feathers of the wing, and the proximal third of the outer tail feathers are also scarlet. The rest of the tail and most of the wing are dark, grayish brown. The female is similar but much browner above and below; she lacks the scarlet below. The stout, rounded, conical bill is buffy yellow, the eye is brown, and the legs and feet are dusky pink. The young in fall resemble the female.

Voice: The song is a series of 5–7 loud, clear *kwink*'s, usually on 1 pitch, and a rather thin *wha-cheer*, repeated several times.

Range and status: Resident from c. Baja Calif., s.-c. and se. Ariz., s. N.Mex., and w., c., and se. Tex. south to s. Baja Calif. and c. Mexico. Fairly common.

Habitat: Arid and semiarid areas with mesquite and thorn scrub.

Seasonal movements: None.

Biology: Nest: A neat cup of grasses, twigs, and bark fibers lined with finer grasses, constructed fairly high in low tree or thorn bush. Eggs: 2–5, usually 3–4; white, peppered and finely spotted with browns. Incubation period and age at 1st flight not recorded, but probably similar to those of the Cardinal. Food: Seeds and some insects.

Suggested reading: P. J. Gould, "Territorial Relationships Between Cardinals and Pyrrhuloxias," *Condor*, vol. 63, pp. 246–256, 1961.

ROSE-BREASTED GROSBEAK (*Pheucticus ludovicianus*)

Appearance: A large (7–8½ in.) sparrow. Head, neck, back, wing, and tail are white, as are 2 wide wing bars, several spots on the wing, a few spots near the tip of the outer tail feathers, and the rump. A triangular breast patch, with the apex pointed down, and feathers under and hidden by the wing are ruby or rose-colored. The rest of the underparts are white. The female is dark buffy brown above, including the face. Her back is streaked with lighter and darker browns, and she has 2 white wing bars. Her throat, abdomen, undertail feathers, and a broad stripe down the center of her head and another just above the eye are also white; the breast and flank are pale buffy brown streaked with dark buffy brown; and the smaller feathers on the underside of the wing and the tips of some of the rump feathers are orange-yellow. The head, neck, and back of the adult male in winter are heavily streaked with buffy brown, with a dusky buffy yellow median streak and stripe just above the eye; the underparts are pale brownish, and the chest is pinkish. The 1st-year male is similar but grayer, with less black. The stout, conical dark-tipped bill is straw-yellow, the eye is buffy brown, and the legs and feet are dusky brown.

Voice: The common call is a short, high-pitched *kink*. The Robinlike song is variable, but generally contains 15–25 notes in a clear, whistled series alternating between single notes and liquid phrases and at least 1 phrase like *whip-poor-will*.

Range and status: Breeds from ne. B.C., n. Alta., c. Sask., s. Man., w. and s. Ont., sw. Que., P.E.I., and N.S. south to se. Alta., s. Sask., n.-c. N.Dak., e. Nebr., sw. and c. Mo., c. Ind., n. Ohio, through the Appalachians to e. Tenn. and n. Ga., se. Pa., and s. N.J.; casually to e. Md. and once in Colo. Winters from s. Mexico to nw. S. America; rarely s. La. and w. Cuba. It has straggled west of the Rockies and to Nfld., Bermuda, the Bahamas, Hispaniola, Jamaica, and Dominica I. Common.

Habitat: Rather open deciduous forests, thickets, groves, and arboreal suburbs and parks.

Seasonal movements: Moves north mid-Mar.–mid-May and south mid-Aug.–early Nov.

Biology: Nest: Loosely constructed of twigs, grasses, and vegetable fibers and lined with finer grasses, rootlets, and pine needles; built 6–26 ft. high in tree. Eggs: 3–6, usually 3–5; very pale gray, pale green, pale blue, or pale bluish green, spotted and blotched with browns and purples. Incubation: 14(?) days, with some assistance by male; usually only 1 brood raised each year. Age at 1st flight: About 2 weeks. Food: At least in the summer, slightly more than 50% of the diet consists of insects, spiders, etc., and the remainder of wild seeds and fruit.

Suggested reading: G. Sutton, "The Nesting Fringillids of the E. S. George Reserve," *Jack Pine Warbler*, vol. 37, pp. 86–89, 1959.

BLACK-HEADED GROSBEAK (*Pheucticus melanocephalus*)

Appearance: Slightly smaller (6½–7¾ in.) than the Rose-breasted Grosbeak. Cap, face, wing, tail, and stripes down the back are black. The pattern of white on wing and tail is like that of the Rose-breasted, but lower wing bar is obscure. The rest of the plumage is medium tawny, lighter on abdomen and undertail feathers. The female is very similar to the female Rose-breasted, except that the underparts are a medium buffy brown and are streaked only on the flank. The 2 species hybridize where their ranges overlap. The stout, rounded, conical bill is pale straw-yellow, the eye is brown, and the legs and feet are bluish gray.

Voice: Very similar to that of the Rose-breasted Grosbeak; a practiced ear can separate the two, but the description of one fits the other.

Range and status: Breeds from s. B.C., s. Alta., s. Sask., and c. Nebr. south to n. Baja Calif. and sw. and s.-c. Mexico. Winters south of s. Baja Calif., n. Mexico, and sw. La. It has straggled to Conn. and Mass. Common.

Habitat: Open, brushy woodlands and edges of forests, preferably deciduous or mixed, and chaparral, orchards, riparian groves, parks, and suburbs.

Seasonal movements: Arrives in U.S. Mar.–mid-May and departs mid-Aug.–Nov.

Biology: Nest: A shallow cup loosely woven of twigs, weed stems, grasses, and/or rootlets, with little or no lining; built 4–25 ft. high in tree, usually on side facing open area. Eggs: 2–5, commonly 3–4; very pale blue or green, rather evenly spotted with browns. Incubation: 12 days, by both sexes. Age at 1st flight: 12 days. Food: Seeds, fruits, berries, buds, and flowers; in summer mainly insects.

Suggested reading: H. G. Weston, Jr., "Breeding

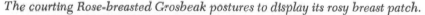

The courting Rose-breasted Grosbeak postures to display its rosy breast patch.

A young male Black-headed Grosbeak still has some of the immature striping on its head.

Behavior of the Black-headed Grosbeak," *Condor*, vol. 49, pp. 54–73, 1947.

BLUE GROSBEAK (*Guiraca caerulea*)

Appearance: Medium-sized (6–7½ in.); almost entirely cobalt-ultramarine, with black on chin and between the bill and the eye. The wing and tail are darker, almost blue-black, and there are 2 tawny wing bars and tawny edging on the 2 innermost flight feathers of the wing. The female is sepia above and light buffy brown below, with a light streak above and a dark streak through the eye and 2 buffy yellow wing bars on a bluish gray wing. In the winter the male acquires a buffy brown edging on the feathers that more or less obscures his general blue coloration. The young resemble the female; immature males are variously pied combinations of the adults. The stout, conical bill is black above and bluish gray below. The eye is brown, and the legs and feet are dusky brown.

Voice: The call notes are sibilant *tsink*'s or *zieeet*'s. The song is a melodious but rather slow and guttural composition of single notes, trills, and warbles, with considerable individual variation.

Range and status: Breeds from c. Calif., s. Nev., s. and e. Utah, s. Colo., c. S.Dak., c. Mo., s. Ill., c. Ky., n. Ga., se. Pa., and s. N.J. south to Costa Rica. Winters from s. Baja Calif., n.-c. Mexico, and Cuba south to w. Panama. It has straggled as far north in summer as Wis., Ont., Que., N.B., and N.S. and in migration to the Bahamas and the Greater Antilles. Fairly common to common.

Habitat: Brushy areas, woodland edges, groves, and river thickets.

Seasonal movements: Arrives in U.S. Apr.–mid-May and departs mid-Aug.–Oct.

Biology: Nest: Constructed of grasses, bark strips, leaves, and weed stems, lined with rootlets and sometimes hair and often with a snakeskin or cellophane or similar plastic incorporated into the base; usually in low trees, bushes, or tangled vegetation at edge of open area 3–14 ft. above the ground. Eggs: 3–5, commonly 4; white or pale blue (color fades on exposure to light),

The strikingly patterned Bullock's Oriole is the most common oriole over much of the western United States, but stragglers have been sighted as far east as Maine.

Of the 222 species of tanagers distributed throughout the Western Hemisphere, the colorful Western Tanager is one of the four species found in the United States.

Despite its gaudy plumage and relative abundance, the Painted Bunting is rather difficult to see, since it is shy and tends to remain hidden in dense foliage.

very rarely sparsely spotted with browns. Incubation period uncertain; probably about 2 weeks. Usually 2 broods raised each year. Food: Seeds, wild berries, and fruit; in summer a very considerable proportion of insects.

Suggested reading: R. M. Stabler, "Nesting of the Blue Grosbeak in Colorado," *Condor*, vol. 61, pp. 46–48, 1959.

INDIGO BUNTING (*Passerina cyanea*)

Appearance: Smaller (5¼–5¾ in.) than the House Sparrow; almost completely cobalt, with a purplish cast. The flight feathers of the wing and tail are dark gray, and there is some blackish plumage at the base of the bill. The female is buffy brown above and pale buffy brown below (somewhat darker on breast and flank), with some bluish gray on the wing and tail. The young birds resemble the female. The stout, conical bill is black above and bluish gray below, the eye is brown, and the legs and feet are blackish brown.

Voice: The call note is a sharp *tsick* like that produced by knocking quartz pebbles together. The common characteristic of the variable song is the combination of rather high-pitched, sibilant notes and phrases into rhythmic groups. The pitch is the same within each

The Indigo Bunting usually nests in tangled vegetation within 12 feet of the ground.

The female Blue Grosbeak is brownish, with only traces of blue on its wings and tail.

group but differs from group to group, and each group lasts about the same length of time.

Range and status: Breeds from s. Man., sw. and s. Ont., s. Que., s. Maine, and s. N.B. south to s.-c. and se. Tex., s. La., s. Miss., and n. Fla.; has bred in Ariz. and Colo. Winters from s.-c. Mexico, Cuba, Jamaica, Puerto Rico, and the Bahamas to c. Panama; rarely along the Gulf Coast and in Bermuda. It has straggled to Baja Calif., Calif., Ore., Alta., Nfld., and Iceland. Common; rare along n. edge of breeding range.

Habitat: Brushy fields, resprouting burned-out areas.

Seasonal movements: Arrives in U.S. Mar.–mid-May and departs Sept.–mid-Dec.

Biology: Nest: A rather shallow cup of twigs, leaves, weeds, and coarse grasses, lined with fine grasses and sometimes hair or feathers; built in brush, shrub, low tree, or tangled vegetation 2–12 ft. above the ground. Eggs: 3–6, commonly 3–4; white or very pale blue or blue-green, usually immaculate but sometimes mottled with brown. Incubation: 12(?) days; the male is said to assist, but this is not proved; 1 or 2 broods raised each year. Age at 1st flight unknown, but probably about 12 days. Food: Seeds, some grain, and other vegetable matter; in summer largely insects; the young are fed insects almost exclusively.

Suggested reading: A. A. Allen, *The Golden Plover and Other Birds*, Comstock, Ithaca, N.Y., 1939, pp. 77–84.

LAZULI BUNTING (*Passerina amoena*)

Appearance: Slightly smaller (5–5½ in.) than the Indigo Bunting. Head, neck, back, and rump are cobalt blue, with dusky brown streaks on the back; wing and tail are black. There is 1 wide white wing bar and a broad tawny band across the chest, just below the neck. The flank is tawny, and the rest of the underparts are white. The female is buffy brown above, tinged with bluish on the rump, and very pale gray below, with a pale buffy brown band across the chest and 2 white wing bars on the blackish wing; the tail is also blackish. The young resemble the female, and on the immature males the blue of the upperparts is clouded with buffy brown. The stout, conical bill is black above and bluish gray below, the eye is brown, and the legs and feet are black.

Voice: The call note is a sharp *tsip;* the song is a strident, fast-tempoed series of sibilant notes in groups of 2–4, each varying rather abruptly in pitch from the preceding combination.

An inhabitant of bushy areas, the Lazuli Bunting seldom ventures into dense forests.

Range and status: Breeds from s. B.C., nw. and c. Mont., s. Sask., c. N.Dak., and ne. S.Dak. south to nw. Baja Calif., se. Calif., s. Nev., sw. Utah, c. Ariz., n. N.Mex., and w. Okla. Winters from s. Baja Calif. and s. Ariz. to s.-c. Mexico. It has straggled to Alta., Minn., Mo., and Mack. Locally common.

Habitat: Brushy fields, thickets bordering fields, sprouting burned-out areas, and sage growth.

Seasonal movements: Moves north Apr.–mid-May and south mid-Aug.–Oct.

Biology: Nest: A cup of grasses and weed stems lined with fine plant fibers, built low in bushes or tangled vegetation. Eggs: 3–4; very pale blue-green, usually immaculate but sometimes peppered with dark brown. Incubation: 12 days. Age at 1st flight unknown. Food: Seeds and, especially in spring and early summer, a considerable proportion of insects.

VARIED BUNTING (*Passerina versicolor*)

Appearance: Small to medium (4½–5½ in.). Upper nape, throat, and center of upper breast are ruby; rump is pale ultramarine, wing and tail are blackish violet. The rest of the plumage is a dusky violet. The female is buffy brown above and smoke-gray below (lighter on throat and abdomen), with an almost brownish olive wing and tail. The strong conical bill is black above and bluish gray below, the eye is brown, and the legs and feet are blackish brown. In winter much of the body color of the adult male is obscured by buffy brown tips on the feathers. The young resemble the female.

Voice: The song is similar to those of the other buntings, but much less strident.

Range and status: Breeds from s. Baja Calif., s.-c. Ariz., n.-c. Mexico, and w. and s. Tex. south to s.-c. Mexico, with an isolated colony in Guatemala. Winters from n.-c. Mexico and s. Tex. south. Locally common.

Habitat: Shrubby fields and pastures, especially near streams, tangles of vegetation near open areas, mesquite, and chaparral.

Seasonal movements: Data insufficient to establish schedule.

Biology: Nest: Built of grasses, barks, and rootlets, low in shrub or thicket. Eggs: 3–4, immaculate pale blue. Incubation: No data, but probably about 12 days. Age at 1st flight unknown. Food: Seeds and insects.

PAINTED BUNTING (*Passerina ciris*)

Appearance: Smaller (5–5½ in.) than the House Sparrow. Cap, face, side of neck, and nape are violet; back and broad bar across wing are lime-green; wing and tail are sooty black; and rest of plumage, including an eye-ring, is ruby. The female is olive above, her wing and tail somewhat more dusky, and dusky yellow below, tinged with olive on the chest and flank. The young

The Black-faced Grassquit, a West Indian species, has appeared accidentally in Florida.

resemble the female. The upper bill is black, and the lower is bluish gray; the eye is brown, and the legs and feet are dusky brown.

Voice: The call notes are 2–3 chirps. The song has been described as a bright, pleasing warble and a loud, clear chant. Saunders says it is "a high-pitched, sweet, but thin, tinkly song" and that "abrupt two-note phrases are common."

Range and status: Breeds from se. N.Mex., c. Okla., e.-c. Kans., s. Mo., sw. Tenn., and se. N.C. south to n.-c. Mexico, s. Tex., the Gulf Coast, and c. Fla. Winters from n.-c. Mexico, s. La., c. Fla., and the Bahamas south to w. Panama and Cuba. Before capture was forbidden by law, this was a popular cage bird; many of the extralimital appearances of this species, particularly in the ne. U.S., were probably due to escaped pets. Fairly common, but shy and difficult to see.

Habitat: Brushy fields, forest edges, fencerows, and shrubby streamsides.

Seasonal movements: Arrives in breeding areas mid-Apr.–mid-May and departs Aug.–early Oct.

Biology: Nest: A shallow cup made of grasses, weed stems, barks, and leaves, lined with rootlets, hair, and fine fibers; built 2–14 ft. high in bushes, low trees, or tangles of vegetation. Eggs: 3–4; white or pale blue, spotted with brownish red. Incubation: 12(?) days. Age at 1st flight unknown. Food: Seeds and insects, the latter predominating in spring and early summer.

Suggested reading: D. F. Parmelee, "The Breeding Behavior of the Painted Bunting in Southern Oklahoma," *Bird-banding*, vol. 30, pp. 1–17, 1959.

BLACK-FACED GRASSQUIT (*Tiaris bicolor*)

A small (ca. 4½ in.), stout-billed sparrow. Grayish green above and very pale gray below, with black face, throat, and breast. The female lacks the black pattern. Native of the W. Indies and n.-c. and nw. S. America; has straggled once to Miami, Fla.

MELODIOUS GRASSQUIT (*Tiaris canora*)

A small (ca. 4½ in.), thick-billed sparrow. Grayish green above and pale gray below, with face, throat, and breast black as in the Black-faced Grassquit, but with a broad bright yellow bar on the side of the neck that thins and arches over the face just above the eye. The female is dull grayish green above and pale gray below. Resident in Cuba. Has straggled to s. Fla.

DICKCISSEL (*Spiza americana*)

Appearance: Slightly larger (6–7 in.) than the House Sparrow. Cap, face, nape, and side of neck are light gray. The rest of the upperparts, including the wing and tail, are a light, grayed buffy brown, the upper back

The Dickcissel feeds heavily on insects, especially during the nesting season.

is streaked with black and pale buffy yellow, and the shoulder of the wing is brownish red. A streak above the eye, a streak from the base of the lower bill terminating in a white spot at the side of the neck, and the chest are yellow. A broad black "necklace" separates the white chin from the breast; the rest of the underparts are white. The female is similar, but lacks the black necklace, the brownish red shoulder is lighter-colored, and there is just a tinge of yellow on the chest. The young bird resembles the female.

Voice: The call notes are a buzzy *gzzzzt* and a ratchety *ka-ka-kakakakakaka*. The song is a chatting, stuttering, unmusical, sibilant, lengthened rendition of its name, *dik-dik-dik-sisisis-klip-klip-sisisis-tsit-tsit-tsit-zi-zi-zi*.

Range and status: Breeds from e. Mont., nw. N.Dak., s. Man., nw. and c. Minn., n. Wis. s. Mich., s. Ont., c. N.Y., and Mass. south to Tex., s. La., c. Miss., c Ala., c. Ga., and S.C.; generally away from the coastal plain. Winters from c. Mexico to nw. and n.-c. S. America; casually and irregularly farther north to the Ohio River Valley and se. N.Y. It is rare to irregularly locally common as a breeder east of the Appalachians,

where it was formerly common; it is fairly common in the Midwest. It has straggled to Calif., Ariz., B.C., N.Mex., Que., Maine, Nfld., the Bahamas, and Jamaica.

Habitat: Prairies, meadows, hayfields, etc.

Seasonal movements: Arrives in breeding areas Apr.–mid-May and departs Aug.–Oct.

Biology: Nest: A shallow cup of leaves and grasses lined with finer grasses and hair built on the ground or close to it, in matted grasses or herbage, bushes, or low trees. Eggs: 3–5, commonly 4; pale blue or light green-blue. Incubation 12(?) days; 2 broods yearly. Age at 1st flight unknown. Food: Weed seeds, some grain, and, particularly in spring and early summer, a considerable number of insects.

Suggested reading: A. O. Gross, "The Recent Reappearance of the Dickcissel in Eastern North America," *Auk,* vol. 73, pp. 66–70, 1956.

BRAMBLING (*Fringilla montifringilla*)

Of House Sparrow size (ca. 5¾ in.), with black cap, face, back, wing, and tail. The throat, breast, shoulder of wing, lower wing bar, and flank are rufous to tawny, and the upper wing bar, rump, and remainder of underside are white. In winter the black feathers are edged with tawny. The female is browner, with gray cheek and black shoulder on wing. It breeds in n. Eurasia and winters through s. Eurasia; has straggled to Alaska and the Philippines.

HAWFINCH (*Coccothraustes coccothraustes*)

A large (6–7 in.), big-billed sparrow with a tawny crown, rufous cheek, smoke-gray neck and undersides, and chestnut back, rump, wing, and tail. The throat and flight feathers of the wing are black, and the broad wing bar is white. The female is duller, with crown and face smoke-gray. It breeds in n. Eurasia and winters south through c. Eurasia. It has straggled to Alaska.

EVENING GROSBEAK (*Hesperiphona vespertina*)

Appearance: Large (7–8½ in.). The forehead and conjoining streak just above the eye are yellow, and the cap, tail, and most of the wing are black. The rest of the head and neck is medium fuscous, grading into the bronzy yellow of the remainder of the body plumage. The proximal flight feathers of the wing are white. The female differs in being dark smoke-gray above and light smoke-gray below, with some white on the throat and rump. The young resemble the females, but the immature males gradually acquire more yellow and bronzy yellow, so that there is considerable plumage variation in a wintering flock. The large, prominent, conical bill is straw-yellow, the eye is brown, and the legs and feet are dusky flesh.

In winter Evening Grosbeaks are easily attracted with offerings of sunflower seeds.

Voice: The common calls are a loud *kle-eer* and *klee-ip*. The song is a series of short, not unpleasant warbles, the last terminating in a sharp whistle.

Range and status: Resident from n.-c. B.C., ne. Alta., c. Sask., s. Man., w. and c. Ont., w.-c. Que., and n. N.B. south to c. Calif., n. Nev., c. Ariz., the mountains of w.-c. and ne. Mexico, n. Minn., n. Mich., s. Ont., n. N.Y., and Mass. In winter the range is extended south to s. Calif., Okla., Ark., Tenn., and S.C., at least sporadically. Common, sometimes abundant.

Habitat: Coniferous woodlands; in migration and winter into deciduous forests.

Seasonal movements: Limited to somewhat irregular southward winter incursions.

Biology: Nest: A shallow cup loosely woven of twigs and lined with rootlets, built in conifer 20–60 ft. above the ground. Eggs: 3–4, light blue-green. Incubation period not recorded. Age at 1st flight unknown. Food: Seeds (it is one of the most efficient sunflower-seed huskers in existence); also leaves, other plant matter, and insects. Its fondness for sunflower seeds coupled with the popularity of winter bird-feeding trays has probably had a great influence on its increasing numbers and range over the last decade.

Suggested reading: G. H. and H. C. Parks, "Some Notes on a Trip to an Evening Grosbeak Nesting Area," *Bird-banding*, vol. 34, pp. 22–30, 1963.

BULLFINCH (*Pyrrhula pyrrhula*)

About House Sparrow size (5½–6½ in.). Cap, wing, and tail are black; nape and back are medium gray; rump, undertail feathers, and a broad wing bar are white; and the rest of the plumage is light ruby. The female is similar, but in place of the light ruby she has dusky cinnamon. The young resemble the female, but the cap, nape, and back are dark tawny. The stout, conical bill and the legs and feet are black. It is resident in n. and c. Eurasia and has straggled several times to Alaska.

PURPLE FINCH (*Carpodacus purpureus*)

Appearance: About the size (5½–6¼ in.) of the House Sparrow. The head, neck, breast, back, rump, and smaller feathers of the wing are a dusky magenta or Tyrian purple, with the cheek, nape, back, and wing streaked or mottled with buffy brown. The wing and tail are fuscous, and the rest of the plumage is white, tinged with pink on the flank and toward the breast. The female is dusky smoke-gray above, with streaks and mottlings of

Like all its kind, the Purple Finch has a stout bill well suited to cracking seeds.

darker grayish brown. She is white below, with a small, triangular patch of dark grayish brown at the side of the throat and streaks of the same color on the chest and flank. The immature bird resembles the female. The rather stout, conical bill is pale smoke-gray, almost brownish olive, especially near the tip in the female. The eye is brown, and the legs and feet are buffy brown.

Voice: Calls vary from a single sharp *pit* in flight or a *chip-chee* or *pe-wee* while the bird is feeding to a scolding chatter. Song is very variable; it has a rapid, vigorous warble in the spring, often finished in flight; a clear, slower series of accented double liquid notes in summer; and a measured series of 2–3-note phrases in a cadence like the Red-eyed Vireo's.

Range and status: Breeds from n. B.C., n.-c. Alta., c. Sask., c. Man., n. Ont., c. Que., and Nfld. south to n. Baja Calif., c. B.C., c. Alta., s. Sask., N.Dak., c. Minn., c. Wis., c. Mich., ne. Ohio, W.Va., ne. Pa., and se. N.Y. In winter in the West from sw. B.C. to c. Baja Calif. and s. Ariz. and from s.-c. and se. Canada to se. Tex., the Gulf Coast, and c. Fla. It is common but erratic, as it may be common both summer and winter in an area for several years then suddenly become rare during either or both seasons for several years.

Habitat: Mixed forests; definitely a woodland species.

Seasonal movements: Dispersal after breeding is erratic in time and direction.

Biology: Nest: A fairly neat, shallow cup of twigs, grasses, weed stems, bark strips, and rootlets, generally lined with fine grasses and hair; most often built in coniferous trees from 5–60 ft. above the ground. Eggs: 3–5, commonly 4; pale green-blue, spotted and scrawled with dark browns and black, with these markings usually most concentrated in a wreath about the larger end. Incubation: 13(?) days, entirely by the female. Age at 1st flight unknown. Food: Over 70% weed seeds and other plant matter; the remainder of the diet is composed of insects, spiders, and other small invertebrates.

Suggested reading: R. L. Weaver, "The Purple Finch Invasion of Northeastern United States and the Maritime Provinces in 1939," *Bird-banding*, vol. 11, pp. 79–105, 1940.

CASSIN'S FINCH (*Carpodacus cassinii*)

Appearance: Slightly larger (6–6½ in.) than the Purple Finch, which it resembles closely except that the purple of the male is much paler, almost a pink, and the female is somewhat lighter-colored.

Voice: Very similar to that of the Purple Finch, but the song is more distinctly separated into phrases.

Range and status: Breeds from s.-c. B.C., sw. Alta., nw., c., and sw. Mont., and n. Wyo. south to n.-c. and se. Calif., the mountains of n. Baja Calif., s. Nev., n. Ariz., and n.-c. N.Mex. Mainly resident, but retires from

Cassin's Finch

n. edge and higher altitudes of breeding range and extends south through the mountains to se. Ariz. and c. Mexico. Fairly common.

Habitat: More open montane coniferous forests.

Seasonal movements: Somewhat erratic; generally moves out of breeding areas Sept.–Nov. and returns Mar.–Apr.

Biology: Nest: A bulky structure of twigs lined with grasses, built in a conifer 10–80 ft. above the ground. Eggs: 4–5; pale blue-green, sparsely spotted with purplish gray. Incubation period and age at 1st flight unknown. Food: Seeds, berries, buds, etc., and in late spring and summer a large percentage of insects.

HOUSE FINCH (*Carpodacus mexicanus*)

Appearance: Somewhat smaller (5–5¾ in.) than the very similar Purple Finch. The bright color is closer to ruby and more restricted to the head, throat, breast, and rump; the flank is strongly streaked with dark brown. The female is duller-colored than the female Purple Finch and less distinctly patterned, especially about the head and below.

Voice: The call note is a dull *chip;* the song, although rather long and disconnected, is cheerful and musical despite a harsh *wheer* or *che-urr* ending.

Range and status: Mainly resident from sw. and s.-c. B.C., w.-c. and s. Idaho, n.-c. and se. Wyo., and w. Nebr. south to s. Baja Calif. and s.-c. Mexico. Introduced and now established on most of the main islands of Hawaii and in se. N.Y. and sw. Conn. (in 1963–64 it was apparently starting to spread out from this area). Casual in winter to s. Tex. Common.

Habitat: Varied; open woods, suburbs, towns, deserts, scrub-growth areas, ranches, and farmlands.

Seasonal movements: Some altitudinal movements from high areas in winter, returning in spring.

Biology: Nest: In sheltered places such as tree cavities, birdhouses, ledges in buildings, matted vines and other vegetation, deserted woodpecker and Bank Swallow holes, and old oriole nests. Almost any available soft material is used, including fine twigs and grasses. Eggs: 4–5; pale blue-green, sparsely spotted with black. Incubation: 12–16 days. Age at 1st flight: 11–19 days. Food: Seeds, berries, and other fruit and a large percentage of insects in spring and early summer.

Suggested reading: P. Bailey, "Home Life of the House Finches," *Nature Mag.*, vol. 46, pp. 262–264, 1953.

WHITE-COLLARED SEEDEATER (*Sporophila torqueola*)

Appearance: Small (4–4½ in.). Cap, nape, back, face, wing, a thin band separating the throat and chest, and tail are black; in some individuals the cap, nape,

The adaptable House Finch builds its messy nest in almost any sheltered spot.

back, and rump are medium gray. The 2 wing bars and a prominent spot below these are white, and the rest of the plumage, including an almost complete collar about the neck, is a very pale straw-yellow. The female is medium brownish gray above, with wing and tail like those of the male, and dusky straw-yellow below. The small but stout, conical bill is dark smoke-gray, the eye is brown, and the legs and feet are buffy brown.

Voice: A loud, musical song of several high notes followed by 2–4 lower notes, as *sweet-sweet-sweet, cheer-cheer-cheer.*

Range and status: Resident from w.-c. and n.-c. Mexico and s. Tex. south to Costa Rica. Common.

Habitat: Brushy and weedy borders of agricultural lands.

Seasonal movements: None; more gregarious in non-breeding seasons.

Biology: Nest: Made of grasses and rootlets, sometimes lined with hair; partly suspended between branches of a bush, close to the ground. Eggs: 2–3, usually 2; blue-green, evenly speckled with browns, sometimes blotched with black or dark brown. Incubation: 13 days, by female alone; possibly 3 broods each year. Age at 1st flight: 10–11 days. Food: Seeds, some insects.

Suggested reading: A. F. Skutch, "Life Histories of Central American Birds," *Pacific Coast Avifauna*, no. 31, pp. 33–37, 1954.

The Pine Grosbeak typically builds its nest with coarse coniferous twigs.

PINE GROSBEAK (*Pinicola enucleator*)

Appearance: About Robin size (8–10 in.). Head, neck, breast, abdomen, rump, and edges of black feathers of back are rose; flank and undertail feathers are light gray; and wing and tail are black, with 2 white wing bars. The female's head, neck, upper chest, and rump are dusky yellow mottled with light gray, her tail and wing are like those of the male, and the rest of her plumage is light gray mottled with medium gray. Immature males start acquiring the rose color on the top of the head and on the rump. The rather large, stout, conical bill is black above and gray below, the eye is brown, and the legs and feet are black.

Voice: The call is 2–3 loud, resonant whistles. The song is a rather long, melodious composition of single whistled notes, warbles, and trills.

Range and status: Breeds south of the tree limit of n. Eurasia and N. America south to c. Scandinavia, Finland, n. Russia, s. Siberia, Sakhalin I., the Kuriles, c. Calif., s. Idaho, e.-c. Ariz., n.-c. N.Mex., c. Man., n. edge of the Great Lakes, c. Ont., n. N.H., c. Maine, and N.S. Winters in s. parts of breeding range south sporadically to c. Europe, c. Asia, N.Mex., Ky., and Va. It has straggled to Greenland and Bermuda. Common; sporadically and locally common in winter in parts of U.S.

Habitat: Coniferous forests, subarctic birch regions, and mixed and deciduous woodlands during some winters.

Seasonal movements: None regular.

Biology: Nest: A somewhat bulky structure of mosses and twigs lined with hair, built rather low in coniferous trees or underbrush of coniferous forests. Eggs: 3–6, usually 3–4; pale grayish green, spotted and blotched with browns and purples. Incubation: 13–14 days, by hen alone; probably a single brood each year. Age at 1st flight unknown. Food: Seeds, buds, etc., and some insects, particularly in spring and early summer.

Suggested reading: D. Allen, "Pine Grosbeaks Nesting in Connecticut," *Auk*, vol. 50, pp. 442–443, 1933.

GRAY-CROWNED ROSY FINCH (*Leucosticte tephrocotis*)

Appearance: Small to medium-sized (4¾–6¾ in.). The rump, abdomen, undertail feathers, and shoulder of wing are light rose, forehead and fore half of cap are black, and remainder of cap, nape, and extension from this area to the eye are pale gray. (Birds of the Coast Ranges have a pale gray face.) The rest of the plumage, including the wing and tail, is medium to light fuscous. The females are duller, with a much smaller gray patch.

The rather stout, conical bill is buffy yellow, with a blackish tip (described in some works as completely black), the eye is buffy brown, and the legs and feet are dusky brown.

Voice: Call notes are short twitters and a high-pitched *zee-o*. The song is a series of chirps of varying length and intensity, sounding much like a flock of House Sparrows.

Range and status: Breeds from n. Alaska (including islands in the Bering Sea and the Aleutians, where it is resident), c. Yuk., and w. Mack. south through the mountains to n.-c. Calif., Idaho, and nw. Mont. Winters from s.-c. Alaska, c. B.C., and c. Mont. south to e.-c. Calif., c. Nev., c. Utah, n. N.Mex., and nw. Nebr. Fairly common, but rarely seen because of remote habitat.

Habitat: Mountains, arctic and alpine meadows, edges of and on snowfields, moving down to lower open areas in winter.

Seasonal movements: Irregular in time and direction.

Biology: Nest: A bulky structure of mosses and grasses lined with fine grasses and often feathers, well hidden on ground among or under boulders or in rock crevices. Eggs: 3–5, usually 4–5; pure white. Incubation period and age at 1st flight unknown. Food: Seeds and insects.

Suggested reading: W. T. Shaw, "Winter Life and Nesting Studies of Hepburn's Rosy Finch in Washington," *Auk*, vol. 53, pp. 9–16, 133–149, 1936.

BLACK ROSY FINCH (*Leucosticte atrata*)

Appearance: Small (ca. 6 in.). Many ornithologists consider all Rosy Finches geographical variations of 1 species; the Black Rosy Finch differs from the preceding finch only in that the brown (light fuscous) is replaced with blackish brown.

Voice: A much reiterated, querulous *cheeoo*; otherwise like that of the Gray-crowned.

Range and status: Breeds above the timberline in the mountains of c. Idaho, sw. Mont., n. Nev., n. Utah, and w. Wyo. Winters at lower altitudes and south to ne. Calif., n. Ariz., and n.-c. N.Mex. Apparently rare, but possibly only because of remote habitat.

Habitat: Above the timberline of the mountains in summer and in open areas at lower altitudes in winter.

Seasonal movements: Irregular and erratic.

Biology: No noticeable difference from that of the Gray-crowned Rosy Finch. Incubation: 12–14 days. Age at 1st flight: 18–20 days.

Suggested reading: N. R. French, "Life History of the Black Rosy Finch," *Auk*, vol. 76, pp. 159–180, 1959.

BROWN-CAPPED ROSY FINCH (*Leucosticte australis*)

Appearance: About the same size (5¾–6¼ in.) as the other Rosy Finches. Very similar to the Gray-crowned, but head is all light sepia with no gray.

Voice: Like that of the other Rosy Finches.

Range and status: Breeds in the mountains of se. Wyo., Colo., and n.-c. N.Mex. and winters at lower altitudes.

Habitat: Above the timberline in summer.

Seasonal movements: Irregular and erratic; at lower altitudes in winter.

Biology: Like that of the other Rosy Finches.

EUROPEAN GOLDFINCH (*Carduelis carduelis*)

Appearance: Small (5½ in.). Forward half of face, chin, and forehead are scarlet; nape, flank, a broad band across upper chest, back, and rump are buffy brown; crown, rear edge of face, wing, and tail are black. A broad band of orange-yellow crosses the wing. The rest of the plumage is white, including the back half of the face, the lower edge of the throat, and white spots on the tips of the central tail feathers and near the tips of the flight feathers of the wing. The sexes are alike, but the immature birds are buffy brown above, with light buffy brown on the throat, chest, and flank and streaks of

Black Rosy Finch

darker brown on the back and flank. The sharp-pointed, conical bill is pale straw-yellow, the eye is brown, and the legs and feet are dusky flesh.

Voice: A short, coarse, rasping *geez* and a liquid, twittering, much lengthened and repeated *tswit-wit-wit-wit,* which, with variations and modulations, becomes the song in spring.

Range and status: Resident from n. Europe and c. Siberia south to n. Africa and c. and sw. Asia. Introduced successfully in N.Y. (Long I.) and Bermuda; unsuccessfully in Ore., Mo., Ohio, N.J., and Mass. Locally common at times on Long I.

Habitat: Gardens, orchards, and open lands with a few trees.

Seasonal movements: None.

Biology: Nest: A neat structure of rootlets, mosses, and lichens, well lined with plant down and wool; built far out in the branches of trees or shrubs. Eggs: 3–7, usually 5–6; very pale blue, sparsely spotted and streaked with browns. Incubation: 15–18 days, by hen alone; 2 broods each year. Age at 1st flight: 13–14 days. Food: Mainly seeds, some insects.

Suggested reading: J. Bull, *Birds of the New York Area,* Harper & Row, N.Y., 1964, pp. 433–434.

European Goldfinch

CANARY (*Serinus canaria*)

The familiar caged canary, a pale yellow variety, has become established as a breeding bird on Sand I. off Midway I. of Hawaii.

HOARY REDPOLL (*Acanthis hornemanni*)

Appearance: Small (5¼–5½ in.). Forehead and front half of cap are dusky ruby; nape, face, and back are very pale smoke-gray streaked with dark smoke-gray. It has a black chin and wing and 2 whitish wing bars; tail is dark brown. Breast and lower part of face are light pink; rest of underparts and rump are white; and the flank is streaked with smoke-gray. The female usually lacks the pink on the breast. The sharp-pointed, conical bill is very pale straw-yellow, the eye is brown, and the legs and feet are black.

Voice: Like that of the Common Redpoll, but call is said to be somewhat higher-pitched.

Range and status: Breeds in the high Arctic and, in winter, moves irregularly and erratically south to n. and c. Europe, s. Siberia, s. Alaska, s. B.C., e. Mont., S.Dak., Minn., n. Ill., n. Ohio, and once to Md. Rare in the U.S. and s. Canada.

Habitat: Tundra and scrubby s. edges; in winter open areas, roadsides, etc.

Seasonal movements: Erratic; most U.S. records from late winter.

Biology: Nest: Made of twigs and plant stalks and lined with hair, down, and other feathers; built on or near ground in shelter of rocks or dwarf plants. Eggs: 5–6; blue, spotted and streaked with light brown, occasionally unmarked. Incubation period and age at 1st flight unknown, but probably like those of the Common Redpoll. Food: Seeds and some insects.

COMMON REDPOLL (*Acanthis flammea*)

Appearance: Small (5–5½ in.); very similar to the Hoary Redpoll, but brown of upperparts is darker, rump is a light smoke-gray streaked with darker smoke-gray, and black of chin is more extensive.

Voice: Calls are a plaintive *tsoo-eet,* a harsh *geez,* and in flight a metallic, twittering *chet-et-et-et-et.* The song consists of the notes of the flight call interspersed with a brief rippling trill, usually sung from the highest available perch.

Range and status: Breeds from n. continental edges of Eurasia (including the British Isles) and N. America south to c. Europe, c. and se. Siberia, s. Alaska, n. B.C., n. Alta., n. Sask., n. Man., n. Ont., c. and se. Que., and Nfld. Winters from s. parts of breeding range (sometimes throughout) south to s.-c. and se. Europe, c. Asia, Japan, n. Calif., n. Nev., n. Utah, c. Colo., Kans., s. Ind., Ohio, n. W.Va., and S.C. Common to abundant some years.

PINE SISKIN (*Spinus pinus*)

Appearance: Small (4½–5½ in.). Light buffy brown above and pale smoke-gray below, streaked all over with dark brown. The wing and tail are blackish brown, with a rather broad wing bar and the proximal ⅔ of the outer tail feathers yellow. The sexes are alike. The sharp-pointed, rather long conical bill is pale smoke-gray, the eye is brown, and the legs are dusky flesh. Flight is undulating.

Voice: The call notes are a husky *swi-sieee* and a flight call, *tit-a-tit, tit-a-tit,* coordinated with the undulations of flight. The song is a series of husky whispering trills, long down-slurring notes, rolls, and short ascending notes, similar to the song of the American Goldfinch but lower and huskier.

Range and status: Breeds from s. Alaska, c. Yuk., s. Mack., c. Sask., s. Man., n. Ont., c. and se. Que., s. Lab., and Nfld. south to n. Baja Calif., the highlands of Mexico and Guatemala, Kans., Iowa, n. Wis., c. Mich., s. Ont., n. Pa., se. N.Y., and Conn. Winters at lower altitudes and south to the Gulf Coast and s. Fla. Fairly common to locally common; somewhat irregular.

Habitat: Coniferous and mixed woodlands, alder thickets, and weedy areas near forests.

Seasonal movements: Irregular in se. U.S. Oct.–May.

Biology: Nest: A shallow saucer constructed of twigs, grasses, mosses, lichens, and bark strips and lined with rootlets, plant fibers, hair, fur, and feathers; saddled

In winter the Common Redpoll moves erratically south of its arctic breeding range.

Hoary Redpoll

Habitat: Edges of tundra, scrub willow and birch; brushy areas, roads and tree- or brush-girt open areas in winter.

Seasonal movements: Somewhat irregular and erratic; usually in U.S. late Oct.–Apr.

Biology: Flocks seem constantly on the move, but are sometimes remarkably tame, allowing close approach. Nest: Made of twigs and grasses and well lined with fine grasses, hair, down, and other feathers; built low in bushes or scrub growth to high in conifers. Eggs: 3–7, usually 4–5; blue, spotted and streaked with light brown, sometimes unmarked. Incubation: 10–11 days (some longer periods recorded), by hen alone; sometimes raises a 2nd brood. Age at 1st flight: 11–14 days. Food: Seeds and some insects.

Suggested reading: L. I. Grinnell, "Nesting of the Common Redpoll," *Wils. Bull.*, vol. 55, pp. 155–163, 1943.

on a branch in conifer 8–40 ft. above the ground. Eggs: 3–6, usually 4–5; pale bluish green, spotted and peppered with browns and some black, commonly most heavily about larger end. Incubation: Not certainly known, but probably 12–14 days; by hen alone. Age at 1st flight unknown. Food: Seeds, primarily of evergreens in summer, and insects. Fond of seeds offered at winter feeding trays.

Suggested reading: R. L. Weaver and H. L. West, "Notes on the Breeding of the Pine Siskin," *Auk*, vol. 60, pp. 492–503, 1943.

AMERICAN GOLDFINCH (*Spinus tristis*)

Appearance: Smaller (4½–5½ in.) than the House Sparrow. Forehead, fore part of crown, wing, and tail are black; 1 wing bar, spots on the flight feathers of the wing, the undertail feathers, and edges of the rump feathers are white; and the rest of the plumage, including a patch on the shoulder of the wing, is yellow. The female is light olive above (almost a dark smoke-gray on the back) and light smoke-gray below, with a blackish brown tail and wing; 2 wing bars and spots near the tip of the flight feathers of the wing are white. The male in winter resembles the female, but usually retains the yellow shoulder patch. The eye is brown; the bill, legs, and feet are pale flesh. Undulating flight is typical of the species.

Voice: The song is similar to that of many pet canaries, but with fewer trills and no rolling notes. It is a series of single or 2-note phrases interspersed with a few trills and slurred notes, usually quite long. The flight call has been described as *per-chic-o-ree;* calls from perches are a clear *chee* or *chee-chee-chee-wee.*

Range and status: Breeds from s.-c. B.C., c. Alta., c. Sask., s. Man., c. Ont., s. Que., P.E.I., and n. N.S. south to n. Baja Calif., c. Utah, s. Colo., c. Okla., ne. Tex., n. La., n. Miss., c. Ala., c. Ga., and S.C. Winters from s. B.C., the n. U.S., and se. Canada south to n. Mexico, the Gulf Coast, and s. Fla. It has straggled to Lab., Nfld., and Bermuda. Common.

Habitat: Farms, fields, villages, groves, parks, and riparian woodlands.

Seasonal movements: Rather irregular and erratic; most conspicuous Apr.–Oct.

Biology: Gregarious; not a colonial nester, but nesting territories of single pairs are small enough so that quite a few pairs may occupy suitable fields. Nest: 1–90

The Pine Siskin feeds primarily on the seeds of conifers.

During incubation, the male American Goldfinch often brings food to the female.

ft. (commonly 3–40 ft.) high in trees scattered through open country, usually in a fork near the end of a branch. The bird nests rather late when larger amounts of thistle-down and other fine vegetable fibers are available; these are woven so tightly into a neat cup shape that the nests will often hold water. Eggs: 4–6, usually 5, very pale blue. Incubation: 12–14(?) days, by hen alone. Age at 1st flight: 10–16 days, usually about 12. Food: Seeds; insects in spring and during nesting.

Suggested reading: A. W. Stokes, "Breeding Behavior of the Goldfinch," *Wils. Bull.*, vol. 62, pp. 107–127, 1950. W. P. Nickell, "Studies of Habitats, Territory, and Nests of the Eastern Goldfinch," *Auk*, vol. 68, pp. 447–470, 1951. J. M. Linsdale, "Goldfinches on the Hastings Natural History Reservation," *Amer. Midland Naturalist*, vol. 57, pp. 1–119, 1957.

LESSER GOLDFINCH (Arkansas Goldfinch, Green-backed Goldfinch) (*Spinus psaltria*)

Appearance: Smaller (3¾–4½ in.) than the American Goldfinch. Varies geographically from a form that is entirely blackish brown above, including face, wing, and tail, with white wing bar and white spots on flight feathers of the wing, and yellow below, to a form that has a light olive face, nape, back, and rump, with some brownish streaking on the back. The female, very similar to the female of the American Goldfinch, is pale olive above and straw-yellow below, with dusky brown tail and wing and 2 white wing bars. There is no seasonal change. The eye is brown, and the legs, feet, and bill are pale, dusky flesh.

Voice: Notes are a rather querulous *tee-ee* or *tee-err;* the song resembles that of the American Goldfinch but has a more regular cadence and more frequently paired notes.

Range and status: Resident from sw. Wash., w. Ore., n. Nev., n. Utah, n. Colo., nw. Okla., and c. Tex. south through Mexico and C. America to nw. Peru, c. Colombia, and n. Venezuela. Introduced in w. Cuba. Fairly common.

Habitat: Brushy fields, open woodlands, gardens, farms, edges of groves, and wooded streamsides.

Seasonal movements: None regular, but more widely scattered in winter.

Biology: Nest: A deep, tightly woven cup of fine grasses, plant fibers, and down, built in low trees, bushes, or tangles of vegetation 1–40 ft. above the ground. Eggs: 4–5, very pale blue-green. Incubation: Probably about 13–14 days. Age at 1st flight unknown, but about 14 days. Food: Seeds and some insects.

Suggested reading: J. M. Linsdale, "Goldfinches on

The Red Crossbill's distinctive beak structure is obvious only at close range.

the Hastings Natural History Reservation," *Amer. Midland Naturalist*, vol. 57, pp. 2–60, 1957.

LAWRENCE'S GOLDFINCH (*Spinus lawrencei*)

Appearance: Small (4–4½ in.). Forehead, cap, area between the eye and the bill, chin, and throat are black, and the rest of head, back, and flank are light gray. Breast, 2 wing bars, and rump are yellow. The proximal third of the tail is light gray, and the remainder black. The wing is dark brownish olive, and the abdomen and undertail feathers are white. The female is similar, but her head is entirely light gray, the yellow is much duller, and the wing is darker, almost black. There is no seasonal change. The eye is brown, and the bill, legs, and feet are dusky, light flesh.

Voice: The flight call consists of 1–3 high-pitched tinkling notes, and from a perch the bird gives a loud, harsh *kee-yerr*. The song is very similar to that of the American Goldfinch.

Range and status: Breeds west of the Sierra Nevadas from n.-c. Calif. south to the mountains of n. Baja Calif.; mainly resident, but in winter found at lower altitudes in the North and into nw. Mexico and to w. Tex. Rare to locally common.

Habitat: More open oak and oak-pine woodlands, burned-over areas with scattered scrub, and chaparral; sometimes in heavy growths along streams in more arid regions.

Seasonal movements: Irregular and erratic.

Biology: Gregarious, sometimes nesting in loose colonies. Nest: A neat cup woven of grasses, weed stems, and other plants with some wool and feathers, built 1–25 ft. above the ground, usually in the dense foliage of a bush or low tree. Eggs: 4–5, white. Incubation period unknown. Age at 1st flight: About 13 days. Food: Seeds, mainly small weed seeds; some insects.

Suggested reading: J. M. Linsdale, "Observations on the Lawrence Goldfinch," *Condor*, vol. 52, pp. 255–259, 1950.

RED CROSSBILL (*Loxia curvirostra*)

Appearance: About the size (5½–6½ in.) of the House Sparrow. A dusky scarlet, with mottlings of brown on crown, face, breast, and back and a dusky brown wing and tail. The female is a dark, dusky buff yellow, with medium brownish gray wing and tail and mottlings of this color on the crown, nape, and upper back. The immature male resembles the female, with patches and mottling of dusky scarlet, most concentrated and appearing first on the crown, back, rump, and breast. The eye is brown, and the legs and feet are dusky brown. The black-tipped, dusky straw-yellow bill starts out like a normal, cone-shaped finch's bill, but the tip of the upper bill soon starts curving downward and to either side, the lower curving upward and to the other side, so that they cross shortly before the sharp tips. This peculiarity enables the bird to pry apart the scales of evergreen tree cones and extract the seeds. The bird must be quite close and in good light before the odd structure of the bill is noticeable; fortunately for bird watchers, the crossbills are remarkably tame, allowing rather close approach.

Voice: The common call is a coarse *yip* or *jip* repeated 1–3 times and sometimes a peculiar hollow-whistled trill. The song originates in a series of common call notes, then breaks into more drawn-out notes mixed with warbles and chattering notes; it also has a similar flight song.

Range and status: More or less resident from n.-c. Scandinavia, n. Russia, n.-c. Siberia, se. Alaska, sw. Yuk., c. B.C., s. Mont., sw. Sask., n. Minn., c. Ont., sw. Que.,

N.B., and Nfld. south (mainly through the mountains and over large unoccupied areas to detached local populations) to sw. Europe, Algeria, Tunisia, the Balkans, Asia Minor, Cyprus, the Himalayas, w. China, Manchuria, n. Philippines, c. Japan, n. Baja Calif., n. Nicaragua, n. Wis., e. Tenn. and w. N.C., se. N.Y., e. Mass., and Maine. Erratic and irregular winter (but sometimes at any season) dispersal may bring the species to any state of the continental U.S. It has straggled to Bermuda, Greenland, Iceland, and other places farther north. Common to locally abundant.

Habitat: Mainly coniferous forests, especially for breeding, but at times into other woodlands.

Seasonal movements: Highly erratic and irregular, even to season and place of nesting.

Biology: Probably abundance of food governs choice of nesting localities. Nest: Made of twigs, rootlets, and bark strips and well lined with mosses, feathers, fur, and fine grasses; usually built well out on the branch of a conifer 5–80 ft. above the ground, but commonly quite low. Eggs: 4–5; very pale blue or bluish green, spotted with browns and purples, mostly concentrated about larger end. Incubation: Probably 12–14 days; by hen alone. Age at 1st flight: 1 nestling reported still unable to fly at 24 days. Food: Predominantly seeds of conifers, but also buds, fruits, and seeds of beech, maple, alder, etc., and some insects. Very fond of salt.

Suggested reading: T. Kemper, "Notes on the Breeding Cycle of the Red Crossbill in Montana," *Auk*, vol. 76, pp. 181–189, 1959.

WHITE-WINGED CROSSBILL (*Loxia leucoptera*)

Appearance: Somewhat larger (6–6¾ in.) than the Red Crossbill; predominantly a dusky rose color, with black wing and tail. There are 2 broad white wing bars and white edging at the tips of the innermost flight feathers of the wing. The female and the immature males resemble those of the Red Crossbill, but each displays the prominent white markings of the wing. The dark-tipped, dusky straw-yellow bill is distinctly crossed, the eye is brown, and the legs and feet are dusky brown.

Voice: The call is a simple, whistled *cheep* or *peet*, a loud series of 3–4 *wheet*'s, or rolling twitters. The song is an alternating series of whistles, trills, and twitters, somewhat like the song of the American Goldfinch.

Range and status: Mainly resident south of the tree limit in n. Scandinavia, n. Russia, and in nw. and c. Siberia and from the tree limit in N. America south to c. Alaska, c. B.C., c. Alta., n. Minn., n. Wis., n. Mich., s. Ont., s. Que., s. N.B., and s. N.S. Casually and erratically farther south to Wash., Mont., N.Y., Vt., and Maine. An isolated subspecies occurs in Hispaniola. Wanders farther south, particularly in winter, to c. Europe and the c. U.S.; it has straggled to Bermuda, Greenland, and the British Isles. Locally common to common.

Habitat: Coniferous forests; mainly spruce, rarely pine.

Seasonal movements: Like the Red Crossbill, highly erratic and irregular.

Biology: Nest: Constructed of twigs, rootlets, mosses, and bark strips and lined with fine grasses, feathers, and hair; built 5–70 ft. up in the branches of a conifer, but usually fairly low. Eggs: 2–5, usually 3–4; very pale bluish green or white, spotted and blotched, sometimes scrawled, with browns and purples. Incubation period unknown, but probably similar to that of the Red Crossbill. Age at 1st flight unknown. Food: Seeds, largely of coniferous trees, berries, other fruit, and some insects.

Suggested reading: D. A. Bannerman, *Birds of the British Isles*, Oliver and Boyd, Edinburgh, vol. 1, 1953, pp. 203–206.

OLIVE SPARROW (Texas Sparrow) (*Arremonops rufivirgata*)

Appearance: About the size (5½–6 in.) of the House Sparrow. Nape, back, rump, wing, and tail are grayish olive-green. A broad median stripe on the crown and a narrower stripe just above the eye are grayish buffy yellow; a rather broad stripe separating these and another narrow streak through the eye are dull buffy brown. The face is light gray, the breast and flank are smoke-gray, and the remainder of the underparts are white. The forward edge of the wing is light yellow. The bill, legs, and feet are pale buffy brown, and the eye is dark brown. The immature birds are dull brown above and similar to the adults below; the sexes are alike.

Voice: The common call is a loud, clear *clink* like the Cardinal's, and the song is a similar note repeated slowly, then increasing in cadence to a climactic trill.

Range and status: Resident from w.-c. and c. Mexico and s. Tex. south, mainly along the coasts, to Costa Rica on the Pacific and the Yucatan Peninsula on the Caribbean. Irregularly rare to abundant; rather secretive and difficult to see.

Habitat: Moist to arid weedy fields, thickets, and brushy areas.

Seasonal movements: None.

Biology: Nest: Made of twigs, grasses, weed stalks, and leaves and domed and lined with finer materials; usually built 2–5 ft. above the ground in a bush, low tree, or cactus plant. Eggs: 3–4, commonly 4, white. Incubation period and age at 1st flight unknown. Food: Seeds and some insects.

GREEN-TAILED TOWHEE (*Chlorura chlorura*)

Appearance: Larger (6¼–7 in.) than the House Sparrow. Cap and nape are tawny; back, rump, wing, and tail are a light, grayish olive-green; face, upper chest, and flank are medium gray; and the forehead, a short "mustache," throat, and remainder of the underparts are white. The lower side and edge of the wing are bright yellow. The tail is relatively long and prominent. The sexes are alike, although the female may be slightly duller; the immature birds are rather streaked above and below. The bill is black, the eye is brown, and the legs and feet are light fuscous.

Voice: The common call is a low, querulous *mew,*

The Green-tailed Towhee lives on dry brushy foothills and mountain slopes in the West.

repeated 2–6 times, and sometimes a nasal *chink.* The song, which may be easily mistaken for that of the Fox Sparrow, usually starts with a *wee-chur-r-r* followed by a series of rather high notes or more burry *chur-r-r's,* ending in a weak trill.

Range and status: Breeds from sw. and c. Ore., se. Wash., s. Idaho, sw. Mont., and nw., c., and se. Wyo. south through the interior mountains to s. Calif., s. Nev., c. Ariz., and s. N.Mex. Winters from s. Calif., s. Ariz., and w. and s. Tex. south to s. Baja Calif. and n.-c. Mexico. It has straggled to Sask., Mass., N.J., Va., S.C., and La. Fairly common.

Habitat: More arid, brushy foothills and mountain slopes, more open pine forests, chaparral, etc.

Seasonal movements: Moves north Mar.–mid-May and returns mid-Aug.–late Nov.

Biology: Nest: A deep-cupped mass of twigs, grasses, and weed stems, lined with rootlets and hair; built near the ground in a dense-foliaged bush. Eggs: 3–4, commonly 4; white or very pale blue, evenly spotted with reddish brown. Incubation period and age at 1st flight apparently unrecorded. Food: Weed seeds and insects gathered on or near the ground.

RUFOUS-SIDED TOWHEE (Spotted Towhee, White-eyed Towhee, Red-eyed Towhee, Chewink) (*Pipilo erythrophthalmus*)

Appearance: Larger (7–8½ in.) than the House Sparrow; sometimes mistaken for a small blackish Robin. Entire head, neck, chest, back, rump, tail, and wing are black; flank is rufous. Rest of underparts, 2 wing bars, in some areas numerous spots on the upper wing and back, and edge of the outermost and tips of the outer 3–4 tail feathers are white. The female is similar, but the black is replaced with fuscous or buffy brown. The immature birds resemble the adults, but are lighter or duller in color. The bill is black, the legs and feet are dusky brown, and the eye varies from whitish (se. U.S.) and scarlet (n.e. U.S.) to brownish red (w. U.S. and w. Canada). It is very variable throughout its range, being divided into more than 16 subspecies in U.S. and Canada.

Voice: The familiar call is a loud *che-wink* or *to-whee;* also occasionally a low *screee.* The song varies considerably, both locally and geographically, but commonly in the East consists of 1–2 fairly loud notes followed by trills or a series of swift-cadenced fluttering notes; in the West, it is a buzzy *schreee-e-e,* sometimes preceded by 2–3 *chup's.*

Range and status: Breeds from s. B.C., c. Alta., c. Sask., s. Man., n. Minn., n. Mich., s. Ont., n. N.Y., n. Vt., c. N.H., and sw. Maine south to Guatemala, n. Okla., s.-c. La., the Gulf Coast, and s. Fla. Winters fairly often north to s. B.C., Utah, Colo., Nebr., Iowa, the s. Great Lakes area, and Mass. It has straggled to Que., N.B., and N.S. Fairly common to abundant.

Habitat: Brushy fields, thickets, forest edges, chaparral, and shrubby suburban areas and city parks.

Seasonal movements: There is considerable migratory movement northward Mar.–early May and southward Sept.–early Nov.

Biology: Forages vigorously on the ground among natural litter. Nest: Built up of leaves, bark strips, weed stalks, twigs, and grasses and lined with fine grasses, pine needles, and hair; commonly on the ground under a bush or tussock of grass, sometimes 3–4 ft. above the

In winter the Rufous-sided Towhee often remains in rather northerly areas.

ground in a low bush or brush pile. Eggs: 4–6; white, peppered with reddish browns, occasionally with a few larger spots. Incubation: 12–14 days, mainly by the hen. Age at 1st flight: 10–12 days. Food: Seeds, wild fruit, and insects.

Suggested reading: J. Davis, "Nesting Behavior of the Rufous-sided Towhee in Coastal California," *Condor,* vol. 62, pp. 434–456, 1960.

BROWN TOWHEE (*Pipilo fuscus*)

Appearance: Large (8¼–10 in.) and Robin-sized. In the Rocky Mountain area this species is dark smoke-gray above, with tawny cap, a light buffy yellow throat fringed with buffy brown streaks, smoke-gray flank, white lower chest and abdomen, and light tawny undertail feathers. There are forms on the Pacific Coast that are entirely fuscous above and somewhat darker below than the variety found in the Rockies. The bill, legs, and feet are a light buffy brown, and the eye is light tawny. The sexes are alike.

Voice: The call is a brassy *chink* and the rather variable song is commonly a monotonous series of *chink's,* sometimes speeding up to a trill at the end, or a similar series of liquid *chip's.*

Range and status: Resident from sw. Ore., w. and c. Ariz., n. N.Mex., se. Colo., extreme w. Okla., and w. and c. Tex. south to s. Baja Calif. and sw. and s.-c. Mexico. Fairly common to common.

Habitat: Rather open brushy areas, also canyons, chaparral, woodlands, lawns, and gardens where there are sizable open spots.

Seasonal movements: None.

Biology: During courtship and breeding seasons, there is considerable bowing, scraping, and posturing between the sexes. Nest: A fairly thick, deep cup of grasses and fine plant stems, built 2–25 ft. above the ground in hedges, shrubs, trees, or other plant growth. Eggs: 3–4, most commonly 4; very pale blue, sparsely spotted and blotched with blackish browns and blackish reds. Incubation period and age at 1st flight apparently unrecorded. Commonly 2 broods each year. Food: Seeds, wild fruit, buds, and insects vigorously scratched from ground litter by 2-footed, leapfrogging actions.

Suggested reading: F. F. Gander, "The Brown Towhee," *Aud. Mag.,* vol. 59, pp. 124–126, 1957.

ABERT'S TOWHEE (*Pipilo aberti*)

Appearance: Somewhat smaller (8–9 in.) than a Robin; largely smoke-gray (darker on wing and on large, long tail), with tawny undertail feathers. The face is splashed with blackish, reminding one of a small boy who, after a raid on the blackberry jam, has just managed to wipe his mouth clean, but not his eyes, forehead, chin, and face. The bill is light buffy brown, the legs and

Abert's Towhee

feet are buffy brown, and the eyes are a yellowish buffy brown. The sexes are alike.

Voice: The only note recorded is a single, loud *peek*.

Range and status: Resident, mainly in the river and stream valleys, from se. Nev., sw. Utah, c. Ariz., and sw. N.Mex. south to ne. Baja Calif., nw. Mexico, and se. Ariz. Rather rare to fairly common, becoming more common near towns, villages, and cities.

Habitat: Brushy borders of flowing waters in arid and semiarid areas and into other scrubby regions and shrubby suburbs.

Seasonal movements: None.

Biology: Nest: A deep cup made of grasses and weed stems and lined with finer grasses, built 2–20 ft. high in tree or bush. Eggs: 3–4; pale blue-green, scrawled and splashed with dark browns commonly massed at the larger end. Incubation period and age at 1st flight unknown. Food: Seeds and probably insects.

Suggested reading: W. R. Dawson, *Temperature Regulation and Water Requirements of the Brown and Abert Towhees*, Univ. Calif. Publ. Zool., vol. 59, pp. 81–124, 1954.

LARK BUNTING (*Calamospiza melanocorys*)

Appearance: Larger (6–7½ in.) than the House Sparrow. Sooty black, with a large white patch near the shoulder of the wing, white edges on the proximal flight feathers, and small white patches near the tip of the outer tail feathers. The female is smoke-gray above and white below, with the large white wing patch somewhat obscured by brownish streaks; she has a blackish brown tail and a whitish streak just above the eye. The male in winter has a black chin but otherwise resembles the female; the immature birds resemble the female. The bill is black, the eye is dark brown, and the legs and feet are dusky flesh.

Voice: The call is a low, sweet *hoo-ee*. The song, sometimes delivered from a high perch but more often heard during what has been described as a courtship flight, is a series of clear, high notes interspersed with pleasant trills and warbles. Other notes in songs have been described as slurs like the Cardinal's and *chug*'s like the Chat's.

Range and status: Breeds from s. Alta., s. Sask., sw. Man., se. N.Dak., and sw. Minn. south to s.-c. Mont., se. N.Mex., n. Tex., and s.-c. and e.-c. Kans.; locally and sporadically in Utah and sw. Colo. Winters from s. Calif., s. Nev., c. Ariz., s. N.Mex., and n.-c. Tex. south to s. Baja Calif., c. Mexico, and s. La. It straggles, primarily in migration, to B.C., c. Calif., Ont., N.B., Mass., N.Y., Va., S.C., and Ga. Sometimes travels in huge flocks; locally common to fairly common.

Habitat: Grasslands; during nonbreeding seasons into arid scrub areas.

Seasonal movements: Moves northward Apr.–June and returns late July–Oct.

Biology: Gregarious; not colonial in the strict sense, but many may nest within 100 ft. of each other. Nest: A fairly shallow cup made of grasses and weed stems and sometimes fine rootlets, sometimes lined with hair; built in a slight hollow in the ground, commonly sheltered by a bunch of weeds, grasses, or scrub growth. Eggs: 4–5; very pale blue, sometimes spotted or scrawled with light reddish browns. Incubation period and age at 1st flight apparently unknown. Food: Weed seeds, sometimes grain, and insects. Seems particularly fond of grasshoppers.

IPSWICH SPARROW (*Passerculus princeps*)

Appearance: About the size (6–6¼ in.) of the House Sparrow; smoke-gray above and white below. Dark brown and blackish spots on the breast, flank, crown, nape, and back merge into thin "mustaches." A streak just above the eye is light buffy yellow at the bill, fading to white at the eye and behind it. The cheek and the edges of some of the wing feathers are pale tawny, and a streak down the center of the crown is white; the wing and tail may be somewhat darker in some individuals. The upper bill is dark brown or blackish, and the lower bill is usually paler; the eye is dark brown, and the legs and feet are dusky flesh. The sexes are alike.

In spring the male Lark Bunting is unmistakable, but in winter it is streaked like the female.

Voice: The call is a short, crisp *tsit*. The song is like that of the Savannah Sparrow, but said to be more tuneful, a trifle lower, and ending in more of a trill; it has been transliterated as *tsip-tsip-tsee-ee-ee-ee-ee-pr-ree-ah*.

Range and status: Breeds only on Sable I. off sw. N.S.; winters along coasts from Mass. to Ga. It has straggled inland in Mass. and Conn. It is increasingly rare because the island on which it breeds has been decreasing in size yearly.

Habitat: Most common among beach grasses in dune areas.

Seasonal movements: Found in wintering areas mid-Oct.–early Apr.

Biology: Walks and runs over the ground, very rarely hopping; often flies up into the air from the ground after insects. Nest: A hollow dug in the sand in grass or under bushes and filled with seed stems, coarse grasses, sedges, mosses, etc., and lined with finer grasses and hair. Eggs: 4–5; pale blue, very pale gray, or light olive, usually heavily spotted, blotched, and splashed with browns. Incubation period and age at 1st flight unknown. Food: In the summer over 75% of the diet is insects and other small beach invertebrates and in the winter only a little more than 10%; the remainder of the diet is composed of seeds and other vegetable matter, mainly grass seeds.

Suggested reading: J. J. Elliott, "The Ipswich Sparrow on the Northeastern Seaboard," *Kingbird*, part 1, vol. 4, pp. 91–96, 1954; part 2, vol. 6, pp. 3–10, 1956.

SAVANNAH SPARROW (*Passerculus sandwichensis*)

Appearance: A small- to medium-sized (4½–6 in.) sparrow, very similar to the Ipswich Sparrow but considerably darker, with more prominent spots below. The cheeks are browner and uniformly spotted, the eye is ringed with light orange-yellow matching the fore half of the light streak just above the eye, and the back and

The Savannah Sparrow nests on the ground in hayfields, on prairies, and in other open areas.

rump are more spotted with blackish. There are rather prominent buffy streaks on the back. There is considerable variation from lighter to darker throughout the extensive geographic range.

Voice: Common calls are a sharp *tsip* and a harsh *b-z-z-s*. The song, somewhat slow and sibilant, is described as *tseet-tseet, tseet, tsee-ee-ee, tsay-ay-ay-ay*, the middle section often referred to as a grasshopperlike trill and the last as a more musical trill; due to the high pitch, many people hear only the 1st part, and that but faintly.

Range and status: Breeds from n. continental N. America south (locally and in disconnected areas to the south) to Guatemala. Winters from s. B.C., s. Nev., s. Utah, c. N.Mex., Okla., n. Gulf States, and coastally from Mass. south to El Salvador, Swan Is., Grand Cayman I., Cuba, and n. Bahamas; casually farther n. to Great Lakes region. Resident over a large part of its range. Locally common; sometimes rather scattered and often mistaken by the casual bird watcher for a Song Sparrow or Vesper Sparrow or overlooked because its high-pitched song simply is not heard.

Habitat: All types of open country; prairies, tundra, marshes, fields, beaches, etc.

Seasonal movements: Irregular; migrants move north Feb.–mid-May and return Sept.–Nov.

Biology: Nest: A hollow scratched in the ground, hidden by grass tussocks, etc., filled with grasses and rootlets and sometimes lined with hair and fine rootlets. Eggs: 4–6, usually 4–5; very pale green or blue, heavily spotted and blotched with browns (sometimes hiding the ground color), which coalesce into a ring about the larger end. Incubation period unknown; by female alone. Age at 1st flight unknown. Food: Grass and weed seeds, insects, and, along beaches and at other aquatic environments, other small invertebrates.

Suggested reading: T. E. Shields, "A Study of the Savannah Sparrow in West Virginia," *Wils. Bull.*, vol. 47, pp. 35–42, 1935.

GRASSHOPPER SPARROW (*Ammodramus savannarum*)

Appearance: Smaller (4½–5¼ in.) than the House Sparrow. The chestnut crown is heavily spotted with blackish brown and divided lengthwise medially by a streak of light smoke-gray. Nape, back, rump, wing, and tail are largely dark smoke-gray, but the tail and parts of the wing are darker, almost black, the nape is spotted with tawny and the rump with tawny and black, and the back is streaked with tawny, whitish, and black. It is white or whitish below, with the face, throat, breast, a stripe above the eye, and flank a dusky, buffy yellow. The breast is sometimes lightly suffused with pale tawny. The leading edge of the wing is yellow. The upper bill is dark brown, and the lower pinkish brown; the eye is brown, and the legs and feet are light buffy brown. The sexes are alike; the immature birds are more streaked and duller-colored.

Voice: Call note a *tilik*, rather high-pitched and repeated several times. The song is much like the sounds produced by grasshoppers, but usually louder and sometimes higher-pitched; described in 1 version as *tip-zee-e-e-e-e-e, tip-tupa-zee-e-e-e-e-e*. Because of pitch, the song is indiscernible to many humans; some hear it only as faint clicks or buzzes.

Range and status: Breeds from nw. Calif., e. Wash., se. B.C., s. Alta., s. Sask., s. Man., n. Minn., s. Ont., sw. Que., n. Vt., c. N.H., and Maine south to s. Calif., c. Nev., n. Utah, c. Colo., c. Tex., c. Gulf States, and Fla. and from s. Mexico to nw. S. America and in Jamaica, Hispaniola, Puerto Rico, Curaçao, and Bonaire. The n. subspecies winter from across the s.-c. U.S. south to El Salvador, Cuba, and the Bahamas. It has straggled to P.E.I., N.B., and Nfld. and occasionally occurs farther north in winter than noted. Fairly common; more common than indicated by records, as it is secretive and the song, if heard at all, is apt to be mistaken for that of an insect.

Habitat: Prairies, grasslands, hayfields, meadows, etc.

Seasonal movements: Migrates northward Mar.–mid-May and southward late Aug.–mid-Nov.

Biology: Nest: Built of dried grasses on the ground, usually in a hollow concealed by grasses or other vegetation, and commonly lined with hair or fine rootlets. Eggs: 3–6, usually 4–5; white, pale green, or pale buff, sparingly spotted and blotched with browns and purples, mostly toward larger end. Incubation: Estimated as about 12–13 days, by female alone; commonly 2 broods. Age at 1st flight: 9 days. Food: Seeds and a larger percentage of insects than in the case of most other sparrows.

Suggested reading: R. L. Smith, "Some Ecological Notes on the Grasshopper Sparrow," *Wils. Bull.*, vol. 75, pp. 159–165, 1963.

BAIRD'S SPARROW (*Ammodramus bairdii*)

Appearance: Smaller (5–5½ in.) than the House Sparrow. Buffy brown above and white below; face, a broad band across the chest, stripes down the back, and a medial streak down the center of the crown are buffy yellow. Spots on the sides of the crown, nape, and wing, streaks on the back, short heavy streaks on the breast and flank, and 2 "mustaches" are blackish brown. The bill is light buffy brown, the eye is brown, and the legs and feet

are dusky, pale flesh. The sexes are alike; the immature birds are somewhat buffier and duller-colored.

Voice: Calls apparently not recorded. The song is similar to that of the preceding species in pitch and rhythm, but said to be more musical; it starts with 2–3 *zip*'s and ends in lower-pitched trills.

Range and status: Breeds from the s. Prairie Provinces of Canada south to Mont., nw. and c. S.Dak., se. N.Dak., and w.-c. Minn. Winters from se. Ariz. and s. N.Mex. south to n.-c. Mexico. It has straggled to N.Y. Common.

Habitat: Drier parts of prairies with scattering of brush.

Seasonal movements: Moves north Apr.–May and south Aug.–Nov.

Biology: Nest: On the ground sheltered by grass clump or other vegetation; a shallow cup of grasses and weed stems lined with finer grasses. Eggs: 3–5, usually 4–5; white, blotched, spotted, and scrawled with dark browns. Incubation: More than 11 days; 2 broods are raised each year. Age at 1st flight: About 9 days. Food: Seeds and some insects.

Suggested reading: B. M. Cartwright, T. M. Shortt, and H. D. Harris, "Baird's Sparrow," *Trans. Royal Can. Inst.*, vol. 21, pp. 153–199, 1937.

LE CONTE'S SPARROW (*Passerherbulus caudacutus*)

Appearance: Small (4½–5¼ in.). Crown fuscous, with a medial white stripe; nape a dusky, buffy yellow streaked with light tawny; back streaked with fuscous and pale buffy yellow. Tail and wing are buffy brown; the wing is marked with fuscous, and the tail feathers are noticeably sharp-pointed. The cheek is light gray, and the chest, flank, and a stripe above the eye are buffy yellow. Streaks at the side of the chest and on the flank and a streak starting just behind the eye are fuscous. The chin and the rest of the underparts are white. The bill is light buffy brown, the eye is dark brown, and the legs and feet are light flesh. The sexes are alike; the immature birds are similar to the adults but buffier.

Voice: Call notes not yet reported. The song, high-pitched and barely audible, is described as a short squeak followed by an insectlike buzz and ending in a chip.

Range and status: Breeds from s. Mack., ne. Alta., c. Sask., c. Man., and n. Ont. south to n.-c. Mont., se. Alta., s. Sask., n. N.Dak., nw. and e. Minn., ne. Wis., and n. Mich.; casually farther south. Winters from w.-c. Kans., c. Okla., nw. Ark., c. Ala., s.-c. Ga., and S.C. south to s. Tex., the Gulf Coast, nw. Fla., and se. Ga. It has straggled to Idaho, Utah, N.Mex., N.Y., N.C., and s. Fla. Status uncertain due to secretive habits and almost indiscernible song.

Habitat: Grasslands such as tall-grass prairies, open meadows, and marshlands.

Grasshopper Sparrow

Seasonal movements: Moves north Mar.–May and south Sept.–Nov.

Biology: Nest: On the ground in shelter of grass, a shallow cup of grasses lined with hair. Eggs: 3–5, usually 4–5; pale pink, lightly spotted with brown and black, mainly near larger end. Incubation period and age at 1st flight unknown. Food: Seeds and insects. Raillike, it prefers to escape intruders by running on ground rather than flying.

Suggested reading: L. H. Walkinshaw, "Leconte's Sparrow Breeding in Michigan and South Dakota," *Auk,* vol. 54, pp. 309–320, 1937.

Le Conte's Sparrow

HENSLOW'S SPARROW (*Passerherbulus henslowii*)

Appearance: Smaller (4¾–5¼ in.) than the House Sparrow and very similar to Le Conte's Sparrow, except that the wing and rump are more reddish (tawny), the chest and flank are less yellowish (more of a smoke-gray), and the spotting and streaking below cover much more of the chest. Separation in the field by sight alone, especially in fall, is almost impossible.

Voice: No calls have been recorded. The song is short enough to double as a call and sounds more like the "sneeze" of a large grasshopper than what we normally consider a bird song; 1 rendition into phonetics is *tsezick,* but some insist it says *schlitz.* It is rather loud, but because it is high-pitched, it is apt to be unheard or unnoticed by many.

Range and status: Breeds from e. S.Dak., c. Minn., Wis., c. Mich., s. Ont., s. Vt., and s. N.H. south to e. Kans., c. Mo., s. Ill., n. Ky., W.Va., and N.C. Winters in the Gulf states and from S.C. to c. Fla. May be locally common, probably more common than records indicate.

Habitat: Prefers well-watered meadows, but may be found in many fields where the grasses grow thickly.

Seasonal movements: Moves northward Apr.–mid-May and southward Aug.–Oct.

Biology: Nest: Made of grasses and lined with finer grasses and hair, commonly well hidden on the ground in a clump of grass. Eggs: 4–5; very pale gray, thickly and evenly peppered with pale brownish red. Incubation: 11 days; sometimes 2 broods. Age at 1st flight: 9–10 days. Food: Seeds and insects.

Suggested reading: A. S. Hyde, *The Life History of Henslow's Sparrow,* Misc. Publ. Zool. Univ. Mich., vol. 41, pp. 1–72, 1939.

SHARP-TAILED SPARROW (*Ammospiza caudacuta*)

Appearance: Somewhat smaller (5–6 in.) than the House Sparrow. A median stripe down the center of the crown and the cheek, nape, sides of the neck, back, and rump are medium gray (somewhat brownish toward the rump in some geographic areas). The wing and tail are buffy brown, with some darker browns and tawny markings on the wing. With a streak just above the eye forming the upper border, the cheek is completely edged with light tawny. A band across the chest and the flank is also light tawny, but this color varies to a pale buffy yellow in some regions. The breast and flank are streaked with fuscous, and there are 4 fuscous-edged stripes on the back and upper wing. The rest of the underparts are white. The upper bill is blackish gray, the lower bill dusky, light flesh; the eye is dark brown, and the legs and feet are pale flesh. The tail is not sharp-pointed as the common name implies, but the component feathers of the tail are sharp-tipped.

Voice: The calls are sharp *chip*'s or *chuck*'s. The

song starts or ends with 2 soft, high-pitched, and barely discernible *tick*'s, followed or preceded by a bubbling, hissing *gshshshhh.*

Range and status: Breeds from ne. B.C., s. Mack., c. Sask., and c. Man. to s. Alta. and N.Dak.; in the James Bay area; and along the Atlantic Coast from s. Que., P.E.I., and N.S. south to N.C. Winters along the coasts from Tex. and N.Y. to s. Fla. May be locally common.

Habitat: Inland in summer in the lush, reedy margins of marshes and muskegs. In winter and along coasts during the breeding season in saltwater and brackish marshes near the sea.

Seasonal movements: Moves north Apr.–May and returns mid-Aug.–Oct.

Biology: Nest: Made of dried, coarse grasses and lined with finer grasses; built on or in tussock of grass or sedge, among driftwood or dried seaweeds, or in grasses in boggy part of marsh. Eggs: 3–6, usually 4–5; very pale blue, pale green, or pale gray, peppered, sometimes spotted (often most heavily about larger end) with pale grayish purples. Incubation period and age at 1st flight unknown. Food: A May–Oct. examination of stomach contents showed that insects, spiders, snails, and other small invertebrates make up more than 80% of the diet and weed and grass seeds the remainder.

Suggested reading: J. J. Elliott, "Sharp-tailed and Seaside Sparrows on Long Island, N.Y.," *Kingbird*, vol. 12, pp. 115–123, 1962.

SEASIDE SPARROW (*Ammospiza maritima*)

Appearance: About the size (5½–6½ in.) of the House Sparrow; rather gray in general appearance. Crown, face, nape, side of neck, back, flank, and streaks on pale buffy chest are medium gray, and the tail and rump are a light buffy brown. The wing is largely tawny, with the proximal blackish brown flight feathers narrowly edged with light gray. A stripe just above the eye and a small patch at the lower rear angle of the cheek are buffy yellow, and the throat and the rest of the underparts are white. There is a black "mustache" near the edge of the throat. Sometimes the edge of the crown is fuscous. The upper bill is blackish gray, the lower bill dusky flesh; the eye is dark brown, and the legs and feet are light buffy brown. The sexes are alike; the immature birds are browner above than the adults.

Voice: The call is a squeaky *cheep*. The 1st part of the song is a gurgling trill and the 2nd part a grasshopperlike, high-pitched trill; some songs resemble those of the Sharp-tailed Sparrow, but start more emphatically; as *tup-tup-tup-tse-tr-r-r-r.*

Range and status: Salt marshes of Gulf and Atlantic Coasts from Tex. to w.-c. Fla. and from Mass. to ne. Fla. It has straggled to Maine. Locally common.

Habitat: Tidal salt marshes, particularly those with scattered shrubs.

Seasonal movements: There is some migration, as populations in n. parts of range are much reduced in winter.

Biology: Nest: A structure of grasses lined with finer grasses, on ground among fine marsh grasses or in grasses over water above high-water line. Eggs: 3–6, commonly 4–5; very pale gray, coarsely spotted with brownish red. Incubation period unknown, but by female only; only 1

Henslow's Sparrow is best identified by its insectlike song.

brood each year. Age at 1st flight unknown. Food: Insects and small invertebrates and seeds.

Suggested reading: J. J. Elliott, "Sharp-tailed and Seaside Sparrows on Long Island, N.Y.," *Kingbird*, vol. 12, pp. 115–123, 1962.

DUSKY SEASIDE SPARROW (*Ammospiza nigrescens*)

Appearance: The size (ca. 6 in.) of the House Sparrow. Very similar to the Seaside Sparrow, but much darker gray above and more heavily spotted with dark gray below; the brown on wing is almost fuscous.

Voice: Similar to that of the Seaside Sparrow, but usually only 1 bubbling note followed by the buzzy trill.

Range and status: Resident in the salt marshes of e.-c. Fla. Fairly common.

Habitat: Salt marshes.

Seasonal movements: None.

Biology: What little is known is much like the information on the Seaside Sparrow, of which many experts feel the Dusky Seaside Sparrow is but a geographic variation.

CAPE SABLE SPARROW (*Ammospiza mirabilis*)

Appearance: About the size (6 in.) of the House Sparrow. Resembles the 2 preceding species closely, except that it is a darker gray above than the Seaside Sparrow and less streaked than the Dusky Seaside Sparrow; below, it is whiter, with less pale buffy yellow on chest and flank.

Voice: No differences noted from that of the Dusky Seaside Sparrow.

Range and status: Coasts of sw. Fla. Formerly extended to Cape Sable; locally common.

Habitat: Salt marshes.

Seasonal movements: None.

Biology: Very similar to that of the Seaside and Dusky Seaside Sparrows; probably just a geographic variation of those species.

Suggested reading: A. Sprunt, Jr., *Florida Bird Life*, Coward-McCann, N.Y., 1954, pp. 478–481.

VESPER SPARROW (*Pooecetes gramineus*)

Appearance: About the size (5–6½ in.) of the House Sparrow; generally dark smoke-gray above and white below, with blackish brown spots on back, crown, face, nape, and below. There is a patch of brownish red at the shoulder of the wing, and some of the proximal flight feathers of the wing are chestnut with pale edges. The outer tail feathers and a stripe above the eye are white. The throat is usually immaculately white, with a blackish brown "mustache" near the edge. The upper bill is buffy brown, the lower bill dusky flesh; the eye is dark brown, and the legs and feet are pale dusky pink. The

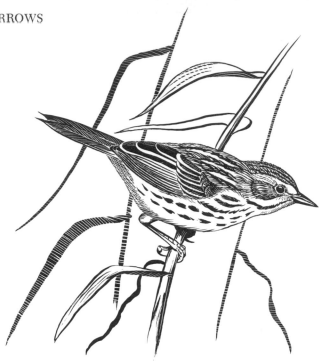

Cape Sable Sparrow

sexes are alike; the immature birds are somewhat duller-colored than the adults.

Voice: The call is a *chip*. The song, often sung in the evening, which led to the common name, is best described as 2 long, low whistled notes followed by 2 higher notes and trailing off in chippering trills.

Range and status: Breeds from c. B.C., sw. Mack., c. Sask., s. Man., c. and ne. Ont., s. Que., and N.S. south to sw. Ore., e.-c. Calif., c. Nev., sw. Utah, c. Ariz., c. N.Mex., Colo., Mo., Tenn., and N.C. Winters from c. Calif., s. Utah, c. N.Mex., c. Tex., Ark., s. Ill., Ky., W.Va., s. Pa., and Conn. south to s. Baja Calif., s. Mexico, the Gulf Coast, and c. Fla.; casually farther north. It has straggled to Yucatan and Bermuda. Fairly common.

Habitat: Open grasslands with scattering of brush, sagebrush; meadows, etc.

Seasonal movements: Wintering individuals make it difficult to determine the migration schedule; major movements northward Mar.–early May, returning Sept.–Nov.

Biology: Nest: Made of dry grasses and rootlets and lined with finer grasses and rootlets; built on the ground or in hollow in the ground, sheltered by nearby grass clumps or other small plant growth, or in tussock of grass. Eggs: 4–5; pale green or very pale gray, peppered and spotted with brownish red and dark brown. Incubation: 11–13(?) days; mainly by the female, but cock reported once or twice. Age at 1st flight not recorded.

Food: Seeds, mainly weed seeds, but some grain; nearly 33% of diet consists of insects and other small invertebrates.

Suggested reading: L. Bryant, Jr., "Some Notes on the Breeding of the Vesper Sparrow," *Bird-banding*, vol. 2, pp. 178–184, 1931.

LARK SPARROW (*Chondestes grammacus*)

Appearance: Medium-sized (5½–6¾ in.). Crown and cheek are brownish red; the side of the neck, upper chest, and flank are pale gray. The rest of the underparts, throat, lower part of the face, a median stripe down the crown, a streak just above the eye, the lower eyelid, and the exposed webbing of the outermost and the tips of the outer 3–4 tail feathers are all white. A spot in the center of the breast, a "mustache" separating the throat and face, and the rear edge of the cheek are black. The back, rump, and wing are a light buffy brown, with streaking of blackish brown on the back and 2 indistinct whitish wing bars; the tail is dark brown, becoming almost black toward the edge. The dark-tipped bill is dusky, buffy yellow, the eye is dark brown, and the legs and feet are light buffy brown. The sexes are alike. The immature birds lack the black spot on the chest and have the upper breast and the brownish red on the head streaked with dark brown.

Voice: The song, often sung on the wing, is a variable, rich, gay, melodious composition of series of short notes, 2-note phrases, trills, and churring cadenzas, reportedly somewhat like the songs of the Indigo Bunting.

Range and status: Breeds from nw. Oregon, s.-c. B.C., s. Alta., s. Sask., s. Man., nw. and c. Minn., n.-c. Wis., s. Ont., w. N.Y., and c. Pa. south to s. Calif., n.-c. Mexico, s. Tex., La., and c. Ala. Winters from c. Calif., s. Ariz., and c. Tex. to El Salvador and from the e. Gulf Coast to s. Fla. Rare to common and even abundant; rather irregular and erratic.

Habitat: Prairies, old fields, open woods, and agricultural lands.

Seasonal movements: Moves north Mar.–mid-May and returns Aug.–Nov.

Biology: Nest: Made of grasses and lined with rootlets, fine grasses, and hair; on the ground or in a low tree or bush. Eggs: 3–5; white or pale pink, spotted,

Removed from their ground nest, young Lark Sparrows pose on a low branch.

blotched, and scrawled with dark browns or black, sometimes purple. Incubation: About 12 days, mainly by the female. Age at 1st flight unknown. Food: Weed, grass, and other seeds, including some grain; grasshoppers and other insects.

Suggested reading: M. Brooks, "The Eastern Lark Sparrow in the Upper Ohio Valley," *The Cardinal*, vol. 4, pp. 181–200, 1938.

RUFOUS-WINGED SPARROW (*Aimophila carpalis*)

Appearance: Smaller (5–5½ in.) than the House Sparrow. Crown is pale rufous, with a median streak of smoke-gray; face, nape, back, and rump are smoke-gray; and wing and tail are dark smoke-gray mottled with rufous at the shoulder of the wing. A short "mustache" and streaks on the back are dark buffy brown. There is a narrow streak of pale rufous through the eye, and the rest of the underparts are white. The bill is dusky yellow, the eye is dark brown, and the legs and feet are light buffy brown.

Voice: 1–2 pleasant notes followed by a rapid chippering.

Range and status: Resident in s.-c. Ariz. and nw. Mexico. Locally common.

Habitat: Tall grasses and thorny scrub areas of semiarid region.

Seasonal movements: None.

Biology: Nest: Low in shrub, made of long grass stems woven into a strong, thin, shallow cup. Eggs: 3–4, pale blue. Incubation period and age at 1st flight unknown. Food: Seeds and some insects.

Suggested reading: R. T. Moore, "The Rufous-winged Sparrow: Its Legends and Taxonomic Status," *Condor*, vol. 48, pp. 117–123, 1946.

RUFOUS-CROWNED SPARROW (*Aimophila ruficeps*)

Appearance: Somewhat smaller (5–6 in.) than the House Sparrow. Crown and a narrow streak through the eye are brownish red; rest of face, neck, breast, and upper back are light gray; shoulder of wing, streaks on back, and rump are dusky cinnamon; and rest of wing and the tail are light fuscous. There is a distinct black "mustache" at the side of the throat. The rest of the underparts are white. The bill is a dusky, buffy yellow, the eye is dark brown, and the legs and feet are buffy yellow. The sexes are alike; the immature bird is finely streaked on the crown and breast with dark brown.

Voice: The calls are double *chip*'s and *mew*'s of alarm; the song starts with 1–3 clear notes followed by a series of rapid warbles interspersed with trills (rather like wren song in quality).

Range and status: Mainly resident from c. Calif., n.-c. Ariz., sw. N.Mex., se. Colo., and nw. and c. Okla.

south, discontinuously, to s. Baja Calif. and s.-c. and nw. Mexico; east of the Rockies retires to south of n. Tex. and c. Okla. in winter. Locally common.

Habitat: Open pine-oak forests and grassy and rocky slopes with a scattering of low bushes and trees.

Seasonal movements: Not pronounced.

Biology: Usually found in small, rather loose colonies. Nest: A cup made of grasses and lined with fine grasses; built on or near the ground in a bush, usually sheltered by grass or other vegetation. Eggs: 5–6, pale blue-green. Incubation period and age at 1st flight unknown. Food: Seeds, probably some insects.

Suggested reading: J. T. Marshall, Jr., "Birds of Pine Oak Woodland of Southern Arizona and Adjacent Mexico," *Pacific Coast Avifauna*, no. 32, pp. 119–120, 1957.

BACHMAN'S SPARROW (Pine Woods Sparrow) (*Aimophila aestivalis*)

Appearance: Smaller (ca. 5¾ in.) than the House Sparrow. Smoke-gray above, darker on wing and tail, with fine streaking of chestnut on side of crown and broader streaking of blackish brown on back, rump, and wing. The face, breast, and flank are smoke-gray, a narrow streak of dusky brown runs through the eye, and the throat and rest of the underparts are very pale gray. The upper bill is dusky brown, the lower bill light dusky brown; the eye is dark brown, and the legs and feet are pale flesh or dusky buffy yellow. The sexes are alike. The immature birds resemble the adults but are finely streaked below, especially on the chest, with dark smoke-gray.

Voice: Makes a hissing sound when disturbed. The song is a pleasant, thrushlike series of 5–12 varied phrases with distinct pauses between; each phrase usually starts with a long, sweet note, followed by a trill or series of rapid notes on a different pitch.

Range and status: Breeds from se. Mo., ne. Ill., c. Ind., sw. and n.-c. Ohio, sw. Pa., and c. Md. south to c. Tex., the Gulf Coast, and c. Fla. Winters from ne. Tex., c. Miss., c. Ala., n. Ga., and N.C. south. It has straggled to Mich., Ont., N.Y., and N.J. Rather rare to locally common.

Habitat: Weedy, abandoned fields with scattered brush, pines, or other trees, and old weed-grown orchards.

Seasonal movements: Reaches n. breeding areas Apr.–mid-May and departs mid-July–Aug.

Biology: Nest: Built of fine grasses, on the ground beneath brush or scrub trees. Eggs: 3–5, white. Incubation period and age at 1st flight unknown. Food: Seeds and insects.

Suggested reading: M. Brooks, "Bachman's Sparrow in the North-central Portion of Its Range," *Wils. Bull.*, vol. 50, pp. 86–103, 1938.

BOTTERI'S SPARROW (*Aimophila botterii*)

Appearance: About the size (5¼–6¼ in.) of the House Sparrow and somewhat resembling the female of that species. It is smoke-gray (paler below to almost whitish on the abdomen and undertail feathers), with tawny markings and streaks on the crown, nape, side of neck, wing, and tail. The wing and tail are mainly brownish olive, and there are blackish brown spots and streaks on the back, rump, and wing. The sexes are alike. The immature birds are narrowly streaked with dusky brown below. The upper bill is dark buffy brown, the lower bill light buffy brown; the eye is dark brown, and the legs and feet are dusky flesh.

Voice: The song is a canarylike series, roughly similar to the song of Bachman's Sparrow, starting with 1–2 long notes followed by a trill, then a slow-cadenced series of notes.

Range and status: Breeds from southernmost Ariz., n.-c. Mexico, and southernmost Tex. south to Guatemala. Not found in the U.S. in winter. Rather rare; any alteration of preferred habitat causes desertion of area by birds.

Habitat: Tall grasses in semiarid regions and in coastal regions of Tex. with scattering of brush.

Seasonal movements: No schedule set because of lack of data.

Biology: Little is known of this secretive species, which seldom takes flight but scurries over the ground more in the manner of small field mice than birds. Nest: On the ground, made of grasses. Eggs: 3–5, white. Incubation period and age at 1st flight unknown. Food: Probably seeds and some insects.

Suggested reading: F. Harper, "A Historical Sketch of Botteri's Sparrow," *Auk*, vol. 47, pp. 177–185, 1930.

CASSIN'S SPARROW (*Aimophila cassinii*)

Appearance: Smaller (5¼–5¾ in.) than the House Sparrow. Very similar to Botteri's Sparrow, but whiter below and grayer above, with no tawny except for a small touch on the wing.

Voice: The song is pleasant but rather high-pitched, starting with 2 short, clear notes followed by a trill and then 2 lower-pitched notes. Many people are unable to hear the first 2 notes because of pitch.

Range and status: Breeds from se. Ariz., sw. N. Mex., c. Colo., w.-c. Kans., w. Okla., and w. and c. Tex. south to n. Mexico. Winters from sw. Ariz., n.-c. Mexico, and w. and s.-c. Tex. south to n.-c. Mexico. It has straggled to Nev. Rather rare, but possibly not often seen because of secretive habits and inhospitable haunts.

Habitat: Arid and semiarid short-grass areas with scattered desert shrubs; rocky, dry slopes with sparse vegetation; and edges of dense desert scrub.

The Black-throated Sparrow is locally common in brushy semiarid areas in the Southwest.

Seasonal movements: Moves north Apr.–May and returns Aug.–early Oct.

Biology: Nest: A deep cup made of coarse grasses, weed stems, bark, and vegetable fibers and lined with finer grasses; built on the ground, in low bushes, or on tufts of grass. Eggs: 3–5; white or very pale blue. Incubation period and age at 1st flight unknown. Food: Seeds and insects.

Suggested reading: A. R. Phillips, "Status of Cassin's Sparrow in Arizona," *Auk*, vol. 61, pp. 409–412, 1944.

BLACK-THROATED SPARROW (*Amphispiza bilineata*)

Appearance: Smaller (4¾–5¼ in.) than the House Sparrow. Crown, nape, side of neck, back, rump, and tail are light gray; flank is pale gray; and forehead, throat, upper part of breast, and spot between the eye and bill are black. Streak just above the eye, another bordering the throat, the rest of the underparts, and the edge of the tail are white. The sexes are alike. The immature birds are similar to the adults, but are gray instead of black, with a white throat sometimes flecked with gray and with some gray streaking on the chest. The dark-tipped bill is grayish blue, the eye is dark brown, and the legs and feet are dusky brown.

Voice: The call is a soft, metallic *weet*. The song is variable, with the same metallic quality as the call; 1 variation starts with 2 long and 1 short note followed by a waveringly pitched trill, and another version starts with 6 ascending-descending notes followed by the trill.

Range and status: Breeds from ne. Calif., n. Nev., n. Utah, sw. Wyo., w. and se. Colo., nw. Okla., and n.-c. Tex. south to s. Baja Calif. and n.-c. Mexico. In winter retreats south of se. Calif., s. Nev., c. Ariz., and sw. N.Mex. Locally abundant to fairly common.

Habitat: Brushy arid and semiarid regions.

Seasonal movements: Absent from more northerly parts of range from Nov.–Mar.

Biology: Nest: A loosely made cup of grasses, sage bark, and fine plant stems, lined with wool or hair; built in desert bushes, scrub growth, and low vegetation. Eggs: 3–4; pale blue or pale pink. Incubation period and age at 1st flight apparently unknown. Food: Seeds and insects.

SAGE SPARROW (*Amphispiza belli*)

Appearance: Somewhat smaller (5–6 in.) than the House Sparrow. Crown, face, nape, side of neck, and upper back are light gray. The blackish brown tail has white "corners." The lower part of back, rump, and wing are dark smoke-gray; a stripe just above the eye, another at the lower border of the face, and the undersides are white; and a prominent, roundish spot in the center of the chest is dusky brown. Tear-shaped spots at the side of the throat, the side of the breast, and the flank, back, and wing are also dusky brown. It has 2 somewhat indistinct, whitish wing bars. The sexes are alike; the immature birds are similar to the adults, but more brownish and more heavily streaked, and with a pale straw-yellow eye-ring. The upper bill is blackish blue, the lower bill pale grayish blue; the eye is brown, and the legs and feet are dark buffy brown. Birds in the sw. part of the range are generally darker-colored and were formerly considered a separate species.

Voice: The call note is a barely discernible *tik*, which becomes slightly louder when the bird is alarmed. The song is a rocking crescendo-diminuendo of rapid-cadenced, somewhat deadened, tinkling notes.

Range and status: Breeds from c. Wash., s. Idaho, sw. Wyo., and nw. Colo. south to c. Baja Calif., s. Nev., n. Ariz., and nw. N.Mex. Winters from c. Calif., c. Nev., sw. Utah, n. Ariz., and c. N.Mex. south to c. Baja Calif., nw. and n.-c. Mexico, and w. Tex. Common, but difficult to see and observe.

Habitat: Arid and semiarid regions of dry brushy foothills, open sagebrush, and chaparral.

Seasonal movements: Moves north Mar.–mid-May and returns Aug.–Nov.

Biology: In winter is found in flocks of 25–50. Nest: A cup of shredded bark, coarse grasses, and weed stems,

White-winged Junco

lined with finer plant materials and hair; built on the ground or in low brush. Eggs: 3–4; white, very pale blue or green, peppered with reddish browns, chiefly about larger end. Incubation: 13 days; sometimes 2 broods each year. Age at 1st flight unknown. Food: Seeds and some insects.

WHITE-WINGED JUNCO (*Junco aikeni*)

Appearance: Slightly larger (6–6¾ in.) than the House Sparrow. Head, neck, upper breast, back, rump, and central tail feathers are blackish gray; wing is a slightly darker gray; and the rest of the plumage is white, including 2 wing bars, which may be distinct or indistinct. The bill is a pale, somewhat dusky pink, the eye is dark brown, and the legs and feet are pale flesh. The sexes are much alike, but the hen is usually a slightly paler gray. The immature birds, and some of the adults in winter, are tinged with brownish, especially on the back.

Voice: Similar to those of other juncos; a rather loose, musical trill or chippering.

Range and status: Breeds from se. Mont. and w. S.Dak. south to ne. Wyo. and nw. Nebr. Winters near breeding grounds south to sw. Colo., n.-c. N.Mex., w. Okla., and w. Kans.; casually to n. Ariz. Locally common.

Habitat: More open pine woodlands.

Seasonal movements: Found outside breeding range Oct.–Mar.

Biology: Travels in flocks during nonbreeding seasons. Nest: Made of grasses, rootlets, bark shreds, etc., and lined with finer grasses and rootlets and often with hair; built on the ground, often near running water, under exposed tree roots, in shelter of logs, or on rock ledges. Eggs: 4–6; pale blue, pale green, or very pale gray, rather thickly spotted with browns and purples. Incubation: Probably 11–12 days, like the Slate-colored Junco; sometimes 2 broods in a year. Age at 1st flight unrecorded. Food: About 50% seeds and 50% insects in summer; mostly seeds in winter.

SLATE-COLORED JUNCO (*Junco hyemalis*)

Appearance: Somewhat smaller (5½–6¼ in.) than the House Sparrow. Sooty black above, including entire head, neck, upper breast, flank, wing, and central tail feathers. The rest of the plumage is white. The bill is a somewhat dusky pale pink, the eye is dark brown, and the legs and feet are pale flesh. The sexes are alike, but the females may be a lighter gray. Immature birds and some females in winter may have some brownish on the back; immature birds may also be streaked on the chest and flank and may even have pale flesh color on the flank.

Voice: The calls are a variety of chirps. The songs are a series of chippering notes, sometimes run into a trill, and soft, "whispering" warbles.

Range and status: Breeds from the tree limit of N. America south to n. B.C., the c. Prairie Provinces of Canada, c. Minn., Wis., c. Mich., s. Ont., N.Y., and Conn. and through the Appalachians to n. Ga. Winters from s. Canada south to n. Baja Calif., n. Mexico, the Gulf Coast, and n. Fla. It has straggled to Siberia, the Canadian Arctic Archipelago, Bermuda, Ireland, and Italy. Common.

Habitat: Mixed and coniferous forests; in winter, mixed woods, forest edges, wooded lanes, etc.

Seasonal movements: Moves north Mar.–Apr. and returns Sept.–Nov.

Biology: Often called the snow bird, as its arrival indicates the approach of the winter season and storms; these juncos are frequently seen taking "snow baths" in the loose, powdery snow, much as other birds take dust baths. Nest: Made of grasses, rootlets, bark shreds, etc., with a lining of finer grasses, rootlets, and hair; built on the ground, under exposed tree roots, in the shelter of

Even in flight, white outer tail feathers are the Slate-colored Junco's best field marks.

In winter, flocks of Oregon Juncos wander far beyond their normal breeding range.

fallen trees or logs, on rock ledges, etc. Eggs: 4–6; pale blue, pale green, or very pale gray, thickly spotted with brownish reds and light purples. Incubation: 11–12 days; sometimes 2 broods in a year. Age at 1st flight unknown. Food: Seeds and almost 50% insects in summer; mainly seeds in winter, when the grain consumed is almost entirely the waste gleaned from the winter-idle fields.

Suggested reading: W. P. Smith, *The Partial History of a Pair of Nesting Juncos*, Bull. N.E. Bird-banding Assn., vol. 4, pp. 137–141, 1928.

OREGON JUNCO (Pink-sided Junco) (*Junco oreganus*)

Appearance: Slightly smaller (5–6 in.) than the Slate-colored Junco. Head and neck vary from sooty black to medium gray. The rump and white-sided tail are medium brownish gray to medium gray, the back and wing are bright to pale tawny, and the flank is a light flesh. The rest of the underparts are white. The bill is a somewhat dusky, pale pink; the eye is dark brown, and the legs and feet are dusky, light flesh. There is much geographical variation; a paler form, known as the Pink-sided Junco, is found mainly east of and in the c. Rocky Mountains. The sexes are alike, although the female may be lighter-colored; the immature bird is usually streaked with blackish on the head, nape, and back, and on the smoke-gray throat, upper breast, and flank.

Voice: The calls consist of snapping noises and soft twitterings. The song is a rather slow and monotonous but musical trill or chippering.

Range and status: Breeds from se. Alaska, c. B.C., w.-c. and s. Alta., and sw. Sask. south to w.-c. Calif., the mountains of n. Baja Calif., w. Nev., ne. Ore., s. Idaho, and nw. Wyo. Winters from se. Alaska, s. B.C., n. Idaho, w. Mont., Wyo., and S.Dak. south to n. Baja Calif., n. Mexico, and c. Tex. It wanders widely in nonbreeding seasons and has reached Banks I. in the Canadian Arctic Archipelago, Ont., Mass., Md., La. and points between. Common.

Habitat: Coniferous and mixed woodlands; also forest edges, wooded lanes, etc., in winter.

Seasonal movements: Migrating and wintering flocks most common Sept.–Mar.

Biology: Like that of the Slate-colored Junco; nest may be higher.

Suggested reading: W. S. Sabine, "The Winter Society of the Oregon Junco: The Flock," *Condor*, vol. 57, pp. 88–111, 1955.

GRAY-HEADED JUNCO (Red-backed Junco) (*Junco caniceps*)

Appearance: Same size (5½–6 in.) as the Oregon Junco. Entire head, neck, upper chest, flank, rump, lower back, wing, and central tail feathers are light to medium gray (somewhat darker on wing); upper back is tawny to light brownish red; and rest of the plumage is white. The bill is a pinkish buffy yellow (in some areas the upper bill is blackish), the eye is brown, and the legs and feet are dusky, light flesh. The sexes are alike. The immature birds are streaked with grayish and black on the crown and nape and are brownish gray on the breast and flank.

Voice: A monotonous trill or chippering.

Range and status: Breeds from n.-c. Nev., n. Utah, and s. Wyo. south to c. Ariz., s. N.Mex., and w. Tex. Winters at lower altitudes and south to s. Calif. and nw. Mexico. It has straggled to Mont., Calif., and Nebr. Fairly common.

Habitat: Forested mountains; in winter, mixed and coniferous woodlands, forest edges, etc.

Like all its relatives, the Gray-headed Junco usually nests on the ground.

Seasonal movements: In migrating and wintering flocks Sept.–Mar.

Biology: Little different from that of other juncos.

MEXICAN JUNCO (Arizona Junco) (*Junco phaeonotus*)

Appearance: Somewhat larger (5½–6½ in.) than the other juncos; very similar to the Gray-headed Junco, but the grays are tinged with brownish to almost a fuscous on the wing, rump, and central tail feathers. The grays on the underside are very pale, the eye is yellow, and the bill is black above and pale, pinkish, buffy yellow below.

Voice: The call is a fairly loud *tik* or *chip;* the song, unlike those of the other juncos, is variable and musical, starting with 2–3 short notes followed by 2 liquid double notes and ending in a slow trill.

Range and status: Resident from se. Ariz., sw. N.Mex., and n.-c. Mexico south to s. Mexico. Common; a sprightly visitor to the picnic tables in the national forests within its range on a "help itself and family" basis.

Habitat: Coniferous mountain forests and the more mature pine-oak woodlands in the foothills and mountains.

Seasonal movements: None; gathers in larger flocks during nonbreeding seasons.

Biology: Nest: A cup made of bark fibers lined with felted plant down; built on the ground under logs or vegetation. Eggs: 3–4, very pale green. Incubation period and age at 1st flight unknown. Food: Seeds and insects.

TREE SPARROW (*Spizella arborea*)

Appearance: About the size (5½–6½ in.) of the House Sparrow. The crown is bright tawny, as is a mark at the side of the breast, just above the shoulder of the wing. A bright tawny streak through the eye broadens somewhat toward the back of the head and curves down and back on itself. A stripe just above the eye and the face, throat, and neck are light gray; the back, rump, and flank are light buffy brown to smoke-gray; the tail is blackish brown, with the proximal half of the outer feathers whitish; and the wing is largely dark buffy brown, with patterns of blackish brown and tawny. The rest of the plumage, including 2 wing bars, is white. The upper bill is blackish brown, the lower bill yellow, tipped with dusky; the eye is dark brown, and the legs and feet are fuscous. The sexes are alike. The immature birds, at least early in the winter, have fine, dark brown streaks on the crown and the sides of the chest and on the flank.

Voice: The alarm note is a low *tsip;* the soft *teel-wet* uttered by each bird in a flock combines into a pleasant twittering. It starts singing before migrating northward, so many of us are able to hear its pleasant, varied series of long and short high-pitched notes if our ears are so attuned. A version has been paraphrased as *eee, eee, tay, titititee, tay, toowee, tee, tah-ta-ta-tay-ta-ta, toh.*

Range and status: Breeds from n. Alaska, n. Yuk., Mack., c. Keewatin, n. Man., n. Ont., n. Que., and Lab. south to c. Alaska, n. B.C., n. Sask., and c. Que. Winters from s. Canada south, rarely to n. Calif., c. Nev., c. Ariz., c. N.Mex., c. Tex., Ark., Tenn., and N.C. Generally an abundant winterer in s. Canada and n. U.S.

Habitat: Subarctic areas with low stunted trees and shrubs; in winter, brushy areas, weedy fields, and woodland roads; a common, friendly visitor at feeding trays.

Seasonal movements: Arrives in wintering areas from subarctic breeding areas sometimes as early as Sept. and may linger to late Apr.

Biology: Travels in flocks of 30–40 birds in non-breeding season. Nest: A bulky structure of grasses, rootlets, weed stems, and bark strips, lined with fur and hair; built on the ground or in low brush in bushy areas near water. Eggs: 4–5; very pale blue or pale grayish green, peppered and flecked with light brown. Incubation: 12–13 days. Age at 1st flight unknown. Food: Seeds and some insects; in winter almost entirely seeds.

Suggested reading: A. M. Baumgartner, "Nesting Habits of the Tree Sparrow at Churchill, Manitoba," *Bird-banding*, vol. 8, pp. 99–109, 1937.

The friendly Chipping Sparrow often nests in city and suburban gardens and lawns.

CHIPPING SPARROW (*Spizella passerina*)

Appearance: Smaller (5–5¾ in.) than the House Sparrow. The crown is brownish red; a stripe just above the eye, the chin, and 2 wing bars are white; and the back, rump, wing, and tail are dark smoke-gray, with blackish brown streaks on the back and fuscous edges and centers to some of the wing feathers. There is a thin streak of black through the eye, and the rest of the plumage is light gray (almost white on the abdomen and undertail feathers). The bill is blackish brown, the eye is brown, and the legs and feet are light buffy brown. The sexes are alike. The immature birds have a brown, streaky crown, more brownish underparts, and grayish rump. When first out of the nest the young are more streaked above, and most of the underparts are finely streaked with blackish brown.

Voice: A *tsip* or *chip* of alarm and some rather pleasant twittering notes. The song is a series of *chip*'s, sometimes at a slow cadence, often rapid, many times speeding into a trill.

Range and status: Breeds from e.-c. Alaska, c. Yuk., s. Mack., n. Sask., n. Man., n. Ont., s. Que., and sw. Nfld. south to n. Baja Calif., n. Nicaragua, the Gulf Coast, and n. Fla. Winters from s. Calif., s. Nev., c. Ariz., s. N.Mex., and w. Tex. south; a rare winterer farther north to c. tier of states in the U.S. Common.

Habitat: All types of open woodlands, farms, orchards, suburbs, and towns.

Seasonal movements: Moves north mid-Mar.–mid-May and returns Aug.–early Nov.

Biology: Nest: Made of fine grass and rootlets, lined with hair and sometimes plant down or fibers; built in tree, bush, or vine 1–25 ft. above the ground, rarely on the ground. Eggs: 3–5; pale bluish green, peppered, spotted, and scrawled with blackish and pale purple, mainly about the larger end. Incubation: Listed as 10–12 days, but probably 11–12; mainly by female; sometimes 2 broods a year. Age at 1st flight not recorded. Food: Seeds, mainly of grasses, and almost 50% insects in the summer. Perhaps this would be the common small bird about our habitations, even in the cities, if the House Sparrow had not been introduced in America; it is still friendly and relatively unafraid of man. It seems to like to build its nest in rosebushes and other ornamental shrubs near our houses.

Suggested reading: L. H. Walkinshaw, "The Eastern Chipping Sparrow in Michigan," *Wils. Bull.*, vol. 56, pp. 193–205, 1944.

CLAY-COLORED SPARROW (*Spizella pallida*)

Appearance: About the size (5–5½ in.) of the Chipping Sparrow. Crown, cheek, back, rump, wing, and tail are smoke-gray. The side of the crown and nape are finely streaked, the back striped, and the central parts of

The White-winged Crossbill uses its crossed mandibles to pry apart the scales on the cones of spruces and other conifers, then extracts the seeds with its tongue.

The Tree Sparrow is a common and friendly visitor at feeding trays throughout its winter range in southern Canada and the northern United States.

Although the female Chestnut-collared Longspur is a rather drab, brown-streaked sparrow, her mate is handsomely patterned with chestnut, black, and white on head and breast.

the larger feathers of the wing solid with blackish brown. A stripe just above the eye, 2 wing bars, and the underparts are white. This sparrow has a double "mustache" of blackish brown, one at the lower edge of the cheek and the other at the side of the throat. The nape and side of the neck are light gray. The upper bill is a darker brown than the lower, and both are tipped with blackish; the eye is dark brown, and the legs and feet are pale buffy brown. The sexes are alike. The immature birds are generally buffier and in the fall are streaked below with blackish brown.

Voice: The song is 3–4 low, slow, insectlike buzzes.

Range and status: Breeds from ne. B.C., s.-c. Mack., c. Sask., c. Man., w. Ont., and n. Mich. south to sw. Alta., se. Wyo., se. Colo., s. Nebr., n. Iowa, s. Wis., c. Mich., and s. Ont; locally and rarely west to c. B.C., south to n. Tex., and possibly east to Ill. and Ind. Winters from s. Baja Calif., n.-c. Mexico, and s. Tex. to s. Mexico, casually to Guatemala. It has straggled to Utah, n. Ont., Ohio, N.Y., Mass., Miss., Fla., and S.C. Locally common.

Habitat: Fields and meadows with scattered brush and parklands with scattered shrubs.

Seasonal movements: Moves north Apr.–mid-May and returns Aug.–Sept.

Biology: Nest: A bulky structure of grass and weed stems, lined with hair; built on ground in clump of grass or up to 5 ft. high in bush or low tree. Eggs: 3–5, usually 4; pale blue-green, spotted with black and browns. Incubation: 11–11½ days. Age at 1st flight: 7–9 days. Food: Seeds and insects.

Suggested reading: G. A. Fox, "A Contribution to the Life History of the Clay-colored Sparrow," *Auk*, vol. 78, pp. 220–224, 1961. W. R. Salt, "A Nesting Study of *Spizella pallida*," *Auk*, vol. 83, pp. 274–281, 1966.

BREWER'S SPARROW (*Spizella breweri*)

Appearance: Slightly smaller (5–5¼ in.) than the Chipping Sparrow. Very similar to the Clay-colored Sparrow, but it has no gray on nape or side of neck and is less white, more pale smoke-gray below.

Voice: Call is a weak *tseet*. The song is a series of *chip*'s similar to those of the Chipping Sparrow, but more varied in pitch and rhythm; somewhat like the chopping song of a canary.

Range and status: Breeds from sw. Yuk., nw. B.C., w.-c. Alta., sw. Sask., and sw. N.Dak. south to s. Calif., c. Ariz., and nw. N.Mex. Winters from s. Calif., s. Nev., c. Ariz., s. N.Mex., and c. Tex. south to s. Baja Calif. and s.-c. Mexico. It has perhaps straggled to Mass. Common to abundant.

Habitat: Sagebrush, brushy and weedy fields, and edges of timberline in mountains; adaptable to many types of open areas with scattering of dense patches of vegetation.

Open fields with scattered brush are the Clay-colored Sparrow's preferred habitat.

Seasonal movements: Migrants move north Mar.–May and return Aug.–Nov.

Biology: Nest: A small cup constructed of twigs, weed stems, and rootlets and lined with horsehair; built in a shrub, sagebrush, etc. Eggs: 3–4; pale bluish green, peppered with bright brownish red. Incubation: 13 days. Age at 1st flight unknown. Food: Mostly insects in the summer and some seeds; proportions probably reversed in winter.

FIELD SPARROW (*Spizella pusilla*)

Appearance: About the size (5¼–6 in.) of the House Sparrow. Crown, nape, back, wing, side of breast, and flank are tawny. A narrow tawny streak through the eye angles sharply down at the back of the head, and the same color tinges the pale gray underparts. The face and throat are pale gray, the rump is light buffy brown, the tail is dark smoke-gray, and the back is striped with fuscous and light smoke-gray. There are 2 rather indistinct whitish wing bars, and the webbings of the larger flight feathers of the wing are fuscous. The bill is light flesh, the eye is brown, and the legs and feet are dusky, pale flesh. The sexes are alike. The immature birds are similar but have some dark, fine streaks on the breast and flank.

Voice: The calls are a short *tsip* and a high-pitched *tsee*. The song is a series of simple, sweet, whistled notes starting slow and long and becoming faster and shorter, usually ending in a trill. There are considerable variations, some on a single pitch and others rising and falling.

Range and status: Breeds from se. Mont., n. N.Dak., c. Minn., n. Wis., n.-c. Mich., s. Ont., sw. Que., and s. Maine south to c. Tex., La., s. Miss., and s. Ga.; casually to nw. Mont. Winters casually from Kans., Mo., Ohio, W.Va., s. Pa., and Mass. south to ne. Mexico, the Gulf Coast, and c. Fla. Fairly common.

Habitat: Meadows, old abandoned hayfields, formerly grassy areas that have gone to weed and brush, and edges of woods.

Seasonal movements: Moves north Mar.–early May and returns Sept.–Nov.

Biology: Nest: Made of grasses and weed stems and often lined with hair; built 8–10 ft. high in a low bush or tree or on the ground. Eggs: 3–5, usually 4–5; pale gray or pale blue, spotted with light brownish red and pale purples. Incubation: 13 days, mainly by hen; 2 broods yearly, sometimes 3, over much of range. Age at 1st flight: 9–10 days, but young are able to flee on foot from danger at 5–6 days. Food: Seeds and, in summer, over 40% insects.

Suggested reading: L. H. Walkinshaw, "Nesting of the Field Sparrow and Survival of the Young," *Bird-banding*, vol. 10, pp. 107–114, 149–156, 1935.

WORTHEN'S SPARROW (*Spizella wortheni*)

Smaller (5¼ in.) than the House Sparrow. The blackish brown feathers of the wing are broadly edged with smoke-gray; the smoke-gray back is dashed with stripes of blackish brown; the tail is dark smoke-gray; and the crown is tawny. The rest of the plumage is pale gray. The bill is buffy yellow, the eye is brown, and the legs and feet are dusky straw-yellow. It ranges through much of the Mexican plateau and may have occurred formerly in s. N.Mex., where the 1st specimen of this rather rare species was taken.

BLACK-CHINNED SPARROW (*Spizella atrogularis*)

Appearance: Smaller (5–5½ in.) than the House Sparrow. Head, neck, breast, flank, and rump are medium gray; forehead, area between the bill and eye, and the chin are black; tail is dark gray; and larger feathers of the wing are blackish brown, with light tawny edges. The back is light tawny with irregular blackish stripes, and the abdomen, undertail feathers, and 2 thin wing bars are white. The bill is yellow, the eye is dark brown,

Like other birds, the Field Sparrow cleans its nest of fecal sacs dropped by the young.

and the legs and feet are blackish. The female is generally a paler gray, with no black on head and chin; the young birds resemble the hen, but usually have some indistinct streaking on the breast and flank.

Voice: The song starts with a series of high, slow, wiry notes followed by a swift tumbling of similar notes running into a trill on 1 pitch or with some variation.

Range and status: Breeds from c. Calif., s. Nev., sw. Utah, c. Ariz., s. N.Mex., and w. Tex. south to n. Baja Calif. and s.-c. Mexico. Winters south of s. Calif., s. Ariz., n.-c. Mexico, and w. Tex. Fairly common, but secretive and difficult to find.

Habitat: Mountain slopes overgrown with sagebrush, chaparral, and other brush.

Seasonal movements: Northward movement Mar.–mid-May; southward Sept.–Nov.

Biology: Nest: A tight cup of grasses and weed stems, often lined with hair; built in low bush 6 in. to 4 ft. above the ground. Eggs: 3–4; very pale blue, immaculate or evenly spotted with browns. Incubation: 13 days. Age at 1st flight unknown. Food: Seeds and some insects.

HARRIS' SPARROW (*Zonotrichia querula*)

Appearance: Larger (7–7¾ in.) than the House Sparrow. Crown, face in front of the eye, throat, and upper chest are black; wing, rump, and tail are buffy brown (darker toward center of each wing feather). Back and flank are smoke-gray, with jagged blackish stripes on back and rounded blackish dashes on side of breast and flank. Face, nape, and side of neck are very pale gray, and rest of underparts are white. The fairly husky bill is light orange-yellow, the eye is dark brown, and the legs and feet are buffy yellow. The sexes are alike. The immature birds in the 1st winter have a smoke-gray face, crown, and nape, with blackish barring on the crown; the throat is white; and a bib of fairly large blackish brown spots marks the edge of the throat.

Voice: The call is a loud, nasal *spink*. The song begins with a series of long, thin, tremulous whistles, then the tempo quickens and the notes shorten until the song ends in a trill, which may rise and fall in pitch. These sparrows often sing in groups during winter.

Range and status: Breeds from nw. and e.-c. Mack. and s. Keewatin south to ne. Sask. and n. Man. Winters from s. B.C., s. Idaho, n. Colo., n. Nebr., and c. Iowa south to s. Calif., s. Nev., c. Ariz., s.-c. Tex., n. La., and Tenn. Has straggled to Ont., Wis., Ohio, Mass., Miss., and Ga. Rather rare to locally common.

Habitat: Breeds in scrubby, subarctic woodlands; in winter in open forests and brushy forest edges.

Seasonal movements: Moves north Mar.–early May and south Sept.–Nov.

Biology: Nest: Made of mosses, leaves, and weed stems and lined with fine grasses; built on the ground at the base of a tree or mossy hummock in a damp spot. Eggs: 3–5; very pale blue, spotted and blotched with browns. Incubation period unknown, but by hen alone; 1 brood yearly. Age at 1st flight unknown. Food: Seeds, other vegetable matter, insects, and other small invertebrates.

Suggested reading: J. B. Semple and G. M. Sutton, "Nesting of Harris's Sparrow at Churchill, Manitoba," *Auk*, vol. 49, pp. 166–183, 1932.

WHITE-CROWNED SPARROW (*Zonotrichia leucophrys*)

Appearance: Size (5½–7 in.) varies from smaller to larger than the House Sparrow. Crown has a broad medial stripe of white bordered at the side with black and joining a white stripe just above the eye at the back of the head. There is a black streak through the eye. The rest of the head, the neck, and breast are light gray (lighter at throat and lower breast); the back, rump, flank, and undertail feathers are dark smoke-gray; and the tail and much of the wing are dusky brown. Some of the wing and jagged stripes down the back are tawny. There are 2 white wing bars and some whitish streaks on the back. In the East, the white stripe above the eye starts just at the eye; west of Hudson Bay it starts at the bill. The dusky-tipped bill is light cinnamon, the eye is brown, and the legs and feet are light flesh. The female is commonly slightly duller-colored. In immature birds, the white on the head is replaced with light buffy brown, the black with tawny, and the grays with light buffy brown and smoke-gray; the nape and back are streaked with fuscous.

Harris' Sparrow

The White-crowned Sparrow forages on the ground for seeds and insects.

Voice: The calls are a *chink* or *tsip* and a sharp *chip* of alarm. The song is a series of 5–7 notes (sometimes more short notes are added), the first long and clear but shortening and ending with 2 rather blurred notes.

Range and status: Breeds from n. Alaska, n. Yuk., nw. and e.-c. Mack., c. Keewatin, n. Man., n. Ont., n. Que., and Lab. south to s.-c. Calif., Nev., c. Ariz., n. N.Mex., c. Man., se. Que., and n. Nfld. Winters from s. B.C., se. Wash., Kans., Mo., Ky., and w. N.C. south to s. Baja Calif., s.-c. Mexico, the Gulf Coast, and Cuba. Rather rare to locally common.

Habitat: Thickets and areas of low, scattered brush and scrub trees; in winter open areas with scattered bushes and trees, gardens, suburbs, etc.

Seasonal movements: Apr.–May and Sept.–mid-Nov., usually in fast-moving waves.

Biology: Nest: Made of grasses, mosses, and rootlets and lined with finer rootlets, hair, and fur; built on the ground among mosses sheltered by some higher vegetation. Eggs: 3–5; pale blue or pale green, thickly spotted with browns and black. Incubation: 11½–12 days; chiefly, if not entirely, by female. Age at 1st flight: 8–10 days, commonly 10. Food: Insects and seeds in spring and summer; in winter probably a larger percentage of seeds.

Suggested reading: B. D. Blanchard, *The White-crowned Sparrows of the Pacific Seaboard,* Univ. Calif. Publ. Zool., vol. 46, pp. 1–178, 1941. B. B. Oakeson, "The Gambel's Sparrow at Mountain Village, Alaska," *Auk,* vol. 71, pp. 351–365, 1954.

GOLDEN-CROWNED SPARROW (*Zonotrichia atricapilla*)

Appearance: Larger (6–7 in.) than the House Sparrow. The crown is orange-yellow (becoming white toward the back of the head), with a broad black edge extending on the side of the head to the eye. The rest of the head, the neck, and breast are light gray, the rest of the undersides and 2 wing bars are whitish, and the tail is sepia. The dusky brown wing feathers are edged with dark tawny. The back and rump are smoke-gray, with jagged stripes of dusky brown on the back. The bill is buffy brown, the eye is dark brown, and the legs and feet are flesh. The sexes are alike. The immature birds in the 1st winter have a dark, buffy brown cap streaked with fuscous, a smoke-gray stripe just above the eye, and a light buffy brown face; otherwise they resemble the adults in duller plumage.

Voice: The song is a series of 3–4 querulous, piping notes somewhat in the cadence of "Three Blind Mice" (Pough).

Range and status: Breeds coastally in Alaska and from s.-c. Yuk. to s. B.C., the Cascade Range of extreme n. Wash., and sw. Alta. Winters west of the Cascades from sw. B.C. to n. Baja Calif. and in the Sierra Nevadas; casually to s. Baja Calif., Ariz., nw. Mexico, Utah, Colo., and N.Mex. It has straggled to Sask., Wis., Ill., Mass., Pa., Tex., La., and Japan. Fairly common to locally abundant, especially in winter.

Habitat: Spruce forests, stunted forests of arctic and mountain slopes; in winter, denser thickets and scrub growth.

Seasonal movements: Arrives in wintering areas in Sept. and departs by early May.

Biology: Nest: Made of twigs and mosses and lined with fine grasses; built in low bush or scrub trees near the ground, or on the ground in shelter of such plants. Eggs: 4–5, commonly 5; pale green or light buffy yellow, peppered with brown. Incubation period and age at 1st flight unknown. Food: Seeds and insects; not much more is known.

WHITE-THROATED SPARROW (*Zonotrichia albicollis*)

Appearance: Larger (6–7 in.) than the House Sparrow. A median stripe on the crown, a stripe just above the eye (yellow near the bill), 2 wing bars, and small throat patch are white. There is a black lateral stripe on the crown and a black streak through the eye; rest of head is light gray. The bird is light gray below (lightest on abdomen). The nape, back, wing, rump, and tail are tawny to buffy brown, with spots on the nape and jagged streaks on the back blackish. The bill is blackish, the eye is dark brown, and the legs and feet are flesh. The sexes are alike. Immature birds have black-stippled tawny lateral crown stripes instead of black, and the flank is smoke-gray with medium gray spots.

Voice: Calls vary from a brisk *chip* and a sibilant *sst* to a peculiar clinking note. The song has been paraphrased so commonly as *poor Sam Peabody-Peabody-Peabody* that this sparrow is called the Peabody Bird in New England; the first 2 notes are slower and somewhat lower than the rather high-pitched faster notes that follow. It also sings a longer song.

Range and status: Breeds from s. Yuk., c. Mack., n. Man., n. Ont., w.-c. and se. Que., s. Lab., and Nfld. south to c. B.C., c. Alta., s. Sask., n.-c. N.Dak., c. Minn., c. Mich., n. Ohio, n. W.Va., ne. Pa., se. N.Y., nw. Conn., and Mass. Winters from n. Calif., s. Ariz., s. N.Mex., e.

Until it matures, the Golden-crowned Sparrow lacks the distinctive yellow crown.

Kans., s. Ill., n. Ky., and se. N.Y. (rarely farther north) south to n. Mexico, the Gulf Coast, and s. Fla. It has straggled to the British Isles. Common.

Habitat: Coniferous forests with undergrowth, brush, and woodland edges.

Seasonal movements: Moves north Mar.–May and returns Aug.–Nov.

Biology: Nest: Made of grasses, rootlets, and leaves, sometimes mosses and bark fibers, and lined with fine grasses and/or hair; built on or close to the ground in hummock of grass or brush pile. Eggs: 4–5; pale blue, pale green, or very pale gray, peppered and heavily spotted with browns, sometimes scrawled with black, mainly at larger end. Incubation: 12–14 days, by female alone; commonly 2 broods yearly. Age at 1st flight: 12–14 days. Food: Weed seeds and insects.

Suggested reading: R. B. Fischer and G. Gills, "A Cooperative Study of the White-throated Sparrow," *Auk*, vol. 63, pp. 402–418, 1946.

FOX SPARROW (*Passerella iliaca*)

Appearance: Larger (6¼–7½ in.) than the House Sparrow. Color varies geographically, but in general the Fox Sparrow is brown or brown and gray above and white below, more or less heavily streaked with brown.

In the East the brown is a bright tawny or a light brownish red, above and below, and a stripe just above the eye, the nape, sides of the neck, and the back are light grayish, with jagged brown stripes on the back. In the West 1 form is a dull tawny and a darker gray and has 2 thin whitish wing bars; another variety has a dark gray crown, face, nape, and back, and the brown is fuscous; and yet another is entirely dusky brown above, including the face, and the heavy, dusky brown spots below almost obscure the white. The generally reddish tail is relatively long, which often leads the inexperienced bird watcher into thinking it is a thrush. The bill varies from buffy brown to blackish brown above and light buffy brown below. The eye is dark brown, and the legs and feet are light buffy brown. The sexes are alike; the immature birds resemble the adults, but are somewhat duller-colored.

Voice: Call notes are a loud *smack* or *chek,* a thin, long-drawn *stssp,* and a short *chip.* The song varies in time and pitch, but is composed of loud, clear, melodious notes followed by down-slurring notes and a variety of shorter notes, as *wee-weeoh-ay-ah-eee-tata-ayoo.*

Range and status: Breeds from nw. and c. Alaska, n. Yuk., nw. and e.-c. Mack., n. Man., n. Ont., n. Que., and Lab. south to nw. Wash. (along coasts), s. Calif., c. Nev., c. Utah, c. Colo., c. Alta., c. Sask., s. Man., c. Ont.,

Because of its song, the White-throated Sparrow is sometimes called the Peabody Bird.

*Its long reddish tail accounts for the Fox
Sparrow's name.*

LINCOLN'S SPARROW (*Melospiza lincolnii*)

Appearance: Slightly smaller (5–6 in.) than the
House Sparrow. Median crown streak, stripe just above
the eye, side of neck, and back are smoke-gray, with
blackish streaks on the back. The sides of the crown are
brownish red, finely streaked with black. Rump, tail, and
wing are tawny, with some dusky brown centers on wing
feathers. The chest, upper breast, and flank are pale
tawny, with a fine, short streaking of blackish that
extends along side of throat, and the throat and rest of
the underparts are very pale gray or white. The sexes are
alike; the immature birds are similar to the adults but
somewhat duller, with less distinct markings. The bill is
dusky brown above and smoke-gray below, the eye is
dark brown, and the legs and feet are pale buffy brown.

Voice: The calls are a faint *tsick* and a louder but
lower-pitched *tschuck*. The song is a sweet, musical
composition of low, clear notes and true, liquid trills,
starting low and then rising and finally falling; it is more
reminiscent of a wren's song than that of a sparrow.

Range and status: Breeds from n. Alaska and n.-c.
Canada south to s. Calif., c. Ariz., n. N.Mex., s. Man., n.
Minn., n. Wis., n. Mich., s. Ont., n. N.Y., c. Maine, and
N.S. Winters from n. Calif., c. Ariz., Okla., c. Mo., the

*Although it breeds over a wide range, the shy
Lincoln's Sparrow is rather rare.*

s. Que., and Nfld. Winters from sw. B.C., c. Calif., s.
Utah, c. Colo., s. Iowa, s. Wis., s. Mich., s. Ont., and s.
N.B. (but east of the Rockies it is rather rare north of the
central tier of states of the U.S.) south to s. Baja Calif., s.
Ariz., w. and s. Tex., the Gulf Coast, and c. Fla. It has
straggled to Bermuda, Iceland, Greenland, Japan, and
Europe. Fairly common.

Habitat: Scrubby subarctic woodlands, chaparral-
covered mountain slopes, and forest undergrowth; in
migration and winter, undergrowth, thickets, scrubby
areas, parks, gardens, and farmlands.

Seasonal movements: Moves north Mar.–May and
south Aug.–Nov.

Biology: Nest: A large structure of grasses, mosses,
leaves, and rootlets, usually lined with hair or feathers;
built on the ground, sheltered by branches of trees or
shrubs, or close to the ground in tree or bush. Eggs: 3–5,
commonly 3–4; pale blue or pale green, thickly spotted
with reddish brown. Incubation: 12–14(?) days. Age at
1st flight apparently unrecorded. Food: Seeds and insects; in summer mainly insects, at other seasons mostly
seeds.

Suggested reading: J. M. Linsdale, *Variations in the
Fox Sparrow (Passerella iliaca) with Reference to Natural History and Osteology*, Univ. Calif. Publ. Zool., vol.
30, pp. 251–392, 1928.

*The well-named Swamp Sparrow generally
frequents marshes, muskegs, and swamps.*

Gulf states, and c. Ga. south to El Salvador, .Guatemala,
the Gulf Coast, and c. Fla. It has straggled to Greenland
and Jamaica. Difficult to see because of habits and
habitat, but only locally common to rare according to
records.

Habitat: Boggy and wet thickets of willow and
alder, muskeg, hedgerows, and woodland margins.

Seasonal movements: Moves north Apr.–May and
returns late Aug.–early Nov.

Biology: Nest: A fairly neat cup of grasses, lined
with finer grasses; built in a tussock of grass or sedges,
usually surrounded by water. Eggs: 4–5; white or pale
greens, heavily peppered and spotted with browns. Incubation period and age at 1st flight unknown. Food: In

spring and summer more than 65% insects and other
small invertebrates and seeds; at other seasons about 90%
seeds, mainly of weeds and grasses.

Suggested reading: William Brewster, "Notes on
Lincoln's Finch," *October Farm,* Harvard Univ. Press,
Cambridge, Mass., 1936, pp. 138–143.

SWAMP SPARROW (*Melospiza georgiana*)

Appearance: Smaller (5–5¾ in.) than the House
Sparrow. Cap is bright tawny; back, rump, wing, and tail
are duller tawny, with rough-edged black stripes on the
back and dusky brown centers in the flight feathers of
the wing. The throat, abdomen, and undertail feathers
are white. A pale gray streak just above the eye merges
with the darker gray of the nape, side of neck, and
breast, and a narrow streak behind the eye is blackish.
The cheek is very pale smoke-gray, and the flank is light
tawny. The bill is dusky brown, the eye is dark brown,
and the legs and feet are pale flesh. The sexes are alike.
Immature birds resemble the adults, but the chestnut
crown is finely streaked with black, the face and chest
are darker and browner, and the flank is slightly streaked
with black.

Voice: The call is a metallic *chink* or *chip.* The song
is a much repeated *weet,* at slow or fairly rapid cadence,
sometimes mingled with a series or variety of twittering
notes and sometimes a series of double notes.

Range and status: Breeds from sw. and s.-c. Mack.,
n. Man., n. Ont., c. Que., and Nfld. south to ne. B.C., c.
Alta., s. Sask., e. Nebr., n. Mo., n. Ill., n. Ind., c. Ohio, s.-
c. W.Va., Md., and Del. Winters from e. Nebr., Iowa, s.
Great Lakes region, c. N.Y., and Mass. south to s. Tex.,
the Gulf Coast, and s. Fla. It has straggled to Bermuda.
Fairly common.

Habitat: Brushy marshes, muskegs, swamps, etc.; in
migration weedy gardens and fields.

Seasonal movements: Migrates in small flocks Mar.–
Apr. and Sept.–Nov.

Biology: Nest: In tussock of grasses or sedges or low
in a bush, sometimes with nearby grasses arched over the
site; made almost entirely of grasses. Eggs: 4–5; pale
green, pale pink, or pale blue, heavily peppered and
spotted with browns, sometimes with light purple
blotches. Incubation: 12–15 days, by female alone; sometimes 2 broods each year. Age at 1st flight: 12–13 days.
Food: Over 80% insects in spring and early summer, in
late summer and fall more than 90% seeds (mainly
weeds and grasses), and in winter 50% seeds and 50%
insects.

SONG SPARROW (*Melospiza melodia*)

Appearance: Size (5–7 in.) varies geographically,
as does general color but not pattern. Most widespread
variety is dark buffy brown above, including wing, tail,

Across its wide range, the Song Sparrow varies greatly in size, color, and even song.

eating, so persistent a songster is the male. Its songs are even more variable than its color and size, but the pattern is commonly 2–3 long, loud whistled notes, followed by a swifter-paced series and ending in liquid trills and flutters. Thoreau composed this lyric for the merry music: *"Maids! maids! maids! hang up your tea-kettle-ettle-ettle."* In late summer and autumn, as if regretting lost summer days, it sings a lower, slower, more warbled concert.

Range and status: Breeds from the Aleutian Is. of Alaska, s. Alaska, s. Yuk., s. Mack., n. Sask., n. Man., n. Ont., c. Que., and Nfld. south to s.-c. Baja Calif., c. Mexico, n. N.Mex., ne. Kans., n. Ark., se. Tenn., n. Ga., nw. S.C., c. Va., and Md. Winters from s. Alaska, s. B.C., lower altitudes of the n. Rockies, se. Mont., S.Dak., s. Minn., s. Wis., s. Mich., s. Ont., s. Que., c. N.B., and N.S. south to c. Mexico, the Gulf Coast, and s. Fla. Common to abundant; rare and local north of the Mason-Dixon line in winter.

Habitat: Brushy areas, swamps, thickets, hedgerows, gardens, woodlot edges, and beaches.

Seasonal movements: Migrants swell the ranks of the local residents late Feb.–early May and Sept.–Nov.

Biology: Nest: Made of grasses, weed stems, leaves, and bark fibers and lined with finer materials, sometimes rootlets and hair; usually well hidden on the ground or low in bushes, very rarely in trees, in hollow logs, or in buildings. Eggs: 3–7, commonly 4–6; white, pale blue, pale green, or pale pink, heavily peppered and spotted with browns, often blotched with purples. Incubation: 12–15 days, usually 12–13 days; by hen alone; 2–3 broods yearly, at least in most of U.S. Age at 1st flight: 10 days. Food: Mainly grass and weed seeds, but considerable numbers of insects in spring and summer.

Suggested reading: M. M. Nice, "Studies in the Life History of the Song Sparrow," *Trans. Linn. Soc. N.Y.*, part I, vol. 4, 247 pp., 1937; part II, vol. 6, 329 pp., 1943. (Reprinted in 1964 by Dover, N.Y.)

McCOWN'S LONGSPUR (*Rhynchophanes mccownii*)

Appearance: Slightly smaller (5¾–6 in.) than the House Sparrow. The crown, a small "mustache" at the side of the throat, a half-circle bib on the chest, and a broad tip band and the central feathers of the white tail are all black; the face, nape, lower breast, and flank are medium gray; the back, rump, and wing are buffy brown, with stripes on the back and with central areas of sooty brown on the wing feathers. A stripe just above the eye, the throat, and rest of the underparts are white. In winter the black feathers are hidden by brownish tips, which wear off by early spring. The hen is light buffy brown above and on the face, throat, breast, and flank and white below, with streaking of fuscous on the crown, nape, back, and rump. Her tail is fuscous except for the outer feathers, which are white with broad fuscous tips.

and face, and white below. The fine streaks on the side of the crown and face, streaks and stripes on the back, and rather profuse streaks on the breast, side of throat, and flank are all fuscous. The 3 larger spots on the breast show as a central ragged patch with a somewhat smaller patch on each side. In some varieties the stripe above the eye is whitish, as is most of the face. The largest variety, found on the Aleutian Is. of Alaska, has a medium gray cap, face, nape, and upper back. The forms in the arid Southwest are much paler-colored. There are 30 varieties recognized in U.S. and Canada alone, based on minor differences in color, size, and proportion.

Voice: Calls are a sibilant *sst* and a *tchenk* of alarm. In spring and early summer it seems to prefer singing to

The dusky-tipped bill is straw-yellow, the eye is dark brown, and the legs and feet are fuscous; as with all the longspurs, the nail of the fairly long hind toe is as long, or longer, than the toe. The immature birds resemble the hens but are browner.

Voice: The call is a low rattle. The song, sung while the bird drifts haphazardly back to earth on rigid, outstretched wings after a steep, spiralling ascent, is a loud, clear, throbbing warble.

Range and status: Breeds in the prairies of s.-c. Canada and n.-c. U.S. Winters from c. Ariz., Colo., Kans., and Okla. south to n.-c. Mexico and s. Tex. Common.

Habitat: Prairies and plains.

Seasonal movements: Moves north Mar.–early May and returns Sept.– Nov.

Biology: Nest: On the ground; made of grasses and lined with hair and feathers. Eggs: 3–5, usually 4; white or pale green, immaculate or spotted with dark browns. Incubation period and age at 1st flight unknown. Food: Seeds, mainly of grasses, and, in spring and summer, some insects.

Suggested reading: F. W. Mickey, "Breeding Habits of McCown's Longspur," *Auk,* vol. 60, pp. 181–209, 1943.

LAPLAND LONGSPUR (*Calcarius lapponicus*)

Appearance: Larger (6–7 in.) than the House Sparrow. A white streak starts just behind the eye and curves down along the side of the neck. The nape is brownish red. The breast, abdomen, flank, undertail feathers, and edges of the outer tail feathers are white. The rest of the head (including the throat), the upper breast, angular spots along the flank, and stripes on the back are black; the back, rump, wing, and tail are buffy brown (slightly more rufous on the wing and tail). In winter the black on the head is reduced to shadowy gray on the upper breast, side of the throat, and crown; underlying the blackish of the crown is a dull brownish red with a lighter medial streak; the nape is streaked with dusky, and the face is buffy brown; otherwise it is like the male in summer. The female resembles the winter male, but has more distinct patterns of color; in winter she is a somewhat duller version of the male at that season. The immature birds resemble the females. The bill is flesh-colored; the eye is dark brown; and the legs and feet, including the long hind toe with the very long nail, are blackish.

Voice: Calls are a clear, piping *teeleu,* a low *tutu-tuk,* or a *ticky-tick,* this last followed during migration with a melodious, whistled *ticky-tik-teeu.* The song is a cadenzalike outburst of rather sweet, lively notes, as *teetooree-teetooree-tr-reeoo.*

Range and status: Breeds on tundra and areas of arctic-stunted trees of Scandinavia, ne. Europe, n. Asia, w. and n. Alaska, n. Canada (including Arctic Archi-

pelago), and e. and w. Greenland. Winters south to s.-c. Europe, c. Asia, and Japan; and in America from s. Canada to ne. Calif., n. Ariz., n. N.Mex., ne. Tex., s. La., W.Va., and n. Va. Casually farther south. Has straggled to Bermuda and Iceland. Fairly common to locally common; irregular in U.S.

Habitat: Tundra and open areas of Arctic with scattering of dwarf trees and shrubs; in nonbreeding seasons open fields and prairies.

Seasonal movements: Arrives in s. Canada and U.S. in Oct. and departs by early May.

Biology: Nest: Made of grasses, sometimes mosses, and lined with feathers and hair; built on the ground or on hummock of grasses or mosses in shelter of some higher vegetation. Eggs: 5–7, usually 6; pale greenish gray or greenish brown, heavily spotted and blotched with darker browns. Incubation period unknown; 14 days in Eurasia, with the male assisting part of the time. Age at 1st flight unknown. Food: Almost entirely seeds in winter, spring, and fall; in summer they undoubtedly consume insects to some extent.

Suggested reading: G. M. Sutton and D. F. Parmelee, "Summer Activities of the Lapland Longspur on Baffin Island," *Wils. Bull.,* vol. 67, pp. 110–127, 1955.

SMITH'S LONGSPUR (*Calcarius pictus*)

Appearance: About the size (5¾–6¼ in.) of the House Sparrow. Cap and face are pied black-and-white; outer feathers of black tail are white; and there is a patch of white with black spots on the shoulder of the wing. The rump and wing are dull tawny, with darker central areas on the feathers; and the rest of the plumage is pale tawny, with streaks and stripes of black on the back. In winter the black and white of the head are replaced with

Lapland Longspur

Smith's Longspur builds its nest in a sheltered hollow on windswept tundra.

pale tawny, the crown and face are finely streaked with blackish, and there are some fine streaks of blackish on the flank and side of the breast. The female and immature birds resemble the winter male but are grayer. The bill is light flesh, the eye is dark brown, and the legs and feet are dusky brown.

Voice: A ticking in flight. The song mixes this watch-like ticking with a melodious, warblerlike song ending in a vigorous *wee-chew*.

Range and status: Breeds from ne. Alaska, n. Yuk., and n. Mack. south to s. Keewatin, n. Man., and nw. Ont. Winters from Kans. and Iowa to Okla., c. Tex., and nw. La. It has straggled to B.C., Ohio, and S.C. Rather rare; may be locally common.

Habitat: Tundra; in nonbreeding seasons, prairies and other open areas.

Seasonal movements: Found in U.S. from Oct.–Mar.

Biology: Nest: Made of grasses and lined with plant down and feathers; built on the ground in a hole dug by the birds, in a natural hollow, or on a hummock of mosses. Eggs: 4–6; smoke-gray, spotted and scrawled with browns. Incubation period and age at 1st flight unknown. Food: Seeds and some insects.

CHESTNUT-COLLARED LONGSPUR (*Calcarius ornatus*)

Appearance: About the size (5½–6½ in.) of the House Sparrow. The cap, a streak starting just behind the eye and curving back under the face, the central tail feathers and tips of the outer tail feathers, and the underparts are black. The nape is brownish red; the dusky brown feathers of the wing are rather broadly edged with pale tawny; the back and rump are striped tawny and black; and a stripe just above the eye, a small spot at the back of the head, all but the tips of the outer tail feathers, and a broad throat patch are white. There is usually a patch of buffy yellow under the eye. In the winter the black of the head and underparts and the brownish red of the nape are obscured by buffy brown tips on the feathers. The female has a white throat and breast; her tail is patterned like the male's but is white and dark gray; and the rest of her plumage is buffy brown streaked with darker browns, especially on the crown and back. The immature birds resemble the hen, but are grayer. The bill is flesh-colored, the eye is dark brown, and the legs and feet are blackish.

Voice: Calls are a low *zhi-zhiv* and, during flight, a pleasant but short and high-pitched twitter. The song is less twittering but weak and fluttery, somewhat like the song of the Western Meadowlark, and sung during flight.

Range and status: Breeds from s. Alta., s. Sask., and s. Man. south to ne. Colo., n.-c. Nebr., and sw. Minn. Winters from n. Ariz., c. N.Mex., ne. Colo., and c. Kans. south to n.-c. Mexico, s. Tex., and n. La.; casually farther south in e. Mexico. It has straggled to B.C., Calif., and the Atlantic Coast from N.B. to Md. Rather rare to locally common.

Habitat: Prairies, plains, and large fields.

Seasonal movements: Moves north mid-Feb.–Apr. and returns mid-Aug.–Nov.

Biology: Nest: A hollow dug in the ground by the birds in shelter of grasses or low bushes; nest cup made of grasses lined with finer grasses and/or hair. Eggs: 3–6, usually 4; white, pale pink, pale green, or pale buff, spotted with dark browns. Incubation: Said to be 10 days. Age at 1st flight unknown. Food: Weed seeds, grass seeds, and insects; in the summer more than 80% insects.

Suggested reading: R. D. Harris, "The Chestnut-collared Longspur in Manitoba," *Wils. Bull.*, vol. 56, pp. 105–115, 1944.

SNOW BUNTING (*Plectrophenax nivalis*)

Appearance: Larger (6–7¼ in.) than the House Sparrow. Plumage is white except for the back, the shoulder of the wing, larger flight feathers of the wing, the central tail feathers, and the tips of the outer tail feathers, which are black. The bill, legs, and feet are black, and the eye is dark brown. The hen is similar, but with pale gray on the throat, side of the neck, crown, and cheek; the cheek and crown are spotted with blackish and pale tawny; and the back and shoulder of the wing are tawny, with blackish spots. The male in winter acquires a spotty tawny cap, some tawny on the lower back, and pale tawny spotting on the breast. The hen in winter becomes more tawny about the head, nape, cheek, and side of breast, and the proximal ⅔ of the tail is tawny. The immature birds resemble the female. In winter the bills are dusky-tipped buffy yellow. There is

In winter, flocks of Snow Buntings wander far south of their arctic breeding range.

considerable variation in pattern through the winter; almost never, s. of Canada, is the full adult male breeding plumage seen.

Voice: The common call is a rippling twitter *tirrir-rirrip;* also a loud high *tweet* and a querulous, bottle-whistle *tooooo.* The song, delivered from a rock perch or on the wing, is loud, rather short, and pleasant but variable. A common song might be phrased as *tippy, tippy, tippy, tarry-wi-me.*

Range and status: Breeds farther north than any other perching bird, in the arctic coastal tundra from Greenland and the Canadian and Eurasian Arctic Archipelagos to the n. continental shores south to the Aleutian Is., s. Lab., Iceland, possibly n. Scotland, Norway, and the Kamchatka Peninsula of e. Siberia. This is the harbinger of spring of the Eskimos, Laplanders, and n. Siberian tribes. Winters south to n.-c. Europe, n.-c. Asia, n. Japan, Ore., Utah, Colo., Kans., Ind., and Ga.; casually to Bermuda and n. Africa. In America it is very rare north of the coast of w.-c. Alaska and s. Canada during winter.

Habitat: Tundra; during nonbreeding seasons, prairies, meadows, open areas, and seashores.

Seasonal movements: Present in s. Canada and U.S. from Oct.–Apr.

Biology: Nest: Made of grasses, weed stems, and mosses and lined with finer material, hair, fur, and many feathers; built on the ground, usually hidden by large stones, in rock crevices, or by mosses and grasses. Eggs: 4–8, usually 5–6; white, pale green, or pale blue, spotted and scrawled with dark browns. Incubation: 12–14 days, by female only; sometimes 2 broods each year. Age at 1st flight: 10–12 days. Food: Almost entirely seeds; some insects and other small invertebrates, such as sand fleas along beaches.

Suggested reading: N. Tinbergen, "The Behavior of the Snow Bunting in Spring," *Trans. Linn. Soc. N.Y.,* vol. 5, pp. 1–95, 1939. D. Nethersole-Thompson, *The Snow Bunting,* Oliver and Boyd, Edinburgh and London, 1966.

McKAY'S BUNTING (*Plectrophenax hyperboreus*)

Appearance: Larger (ca. 7 in.) than the House Sparrow. Plumage is all white, except for the black tips to the flight feathers of the wing and the tips of the central tail feathers. The female is gray where the male is black and has traces of smoke-gray on the nape, back, side of the head, and side of the breast. In winter the head, back, and breast are spotted with cinnamon. The bill, legs, and feet are black (in winter the bill becomes dark-tipped buffy yellow), and the eye is brown.

Voice: Short, weak warbles and twittering calls.

Range and status: Breeds on Hall and St. Matthew Is. off w. Alaska. In winter found on the coast of w. Alaska and on Nunivak I.; casual in the Pribilof Is. Rather rare.

Habitat: Tundra and arctic shores.

Seasonal movements: No schedule known.

Biology: Very similar to that of the Snow Bunting.

RUSTIC BUNTING (*Emberiza rustica*)

A small (ca. 5 in.) sparrow breeding in n. Eurasia and wintering south to s. Europe and s.-c. Asia. Light tawny above, with spotting of fuscous on the back, and darker brown on wing and tail; crown and face are black, with a white stripe just above the eye. White below, with light tawny on flank and breast. The black on the head of the female (and of the male in winter) is replaced with fuscous; in winter the hen is streaked with brown below. It has strayed once to the Aleutian Is. of Alaska.

ILLUSTRATION CREDITS

All drawings by Albert Earl Gilbert
Frontispiece: Burdette E. White

1 Frank Wilson from National Audubon Society
2 Michael Wotton (*top*)
 R. D. Muir (*bottom*)
4 Allan D. Cruickshank from National Audubon Society
7 Allan D. Cruickshank from National Audubon Society
8 Helen Cruickshank from National Audubon Society
9 Olin Sewall Pettingill, Jr., from National Audubon Society
10 Karl W. Kenyon from National Audubon Society (*top*)
 Alfred M. Bailey from National Audubon Society (*bottom*)
12 Eric Hosking
13 John Warham
14 H. I. Fisher from National Audubon Society
15 Thase Daniel
16 J. B. Nelson
18 Eric Hosking
19 John Warham
21 John Warham
22 Robert C. Hermes
23 Lewis Wayne Walker
24 Howard H. Cleaves
25 Fred LaTour
27 Allan D. Cruickshank from National Audubon Society
28 Grant Heilman
29 Bailey and Niedrach from National Audubon Society
30 Robert C. Hermes
32 Howard H. Cleaves
34 Allan D. Cruickshank from National Audubon Society
35 Karl W. Kenyon
39 Harry Engels
40 John H. Gerard
41 Jack Dermid
42 Allan D. Cruickshank from National Audubon Society
43 Lewis Wayne Walker
44 Allan D. Cruickshank from National Audubon Society
46 R. D. Muir
47 Dade W. Thornton
48 Allan D. Cruickshank from National Audubon Society
49 Thase Daniel
50 Winston Nanan
51 Allan D. Cruickshank from National Audubon Society
53 Allan D. Cruickshank from National Audubon Society
56 Larry West from Full Moon Studio
57 Les Line from National Audubon Society
58 R. D. Muir
60 Eugene Kridler, U.S. Bureau of Sport Fisheries and Wildlife
62 Alvin Staffan from National Audubon Society (*top*)
 David Mohrhardt (*bottom*)
63 William J. Bolte
65 Joe Van Wormer from National Audubon Society
66 David B. Marshall, U.S. Bureau of Sport Fisheries and Wildlife (*top*)
 Alvin Staffan from National Audubon Society (*bottom*)
67 Alfred M. Bailey
68 Allan D. Cruickshank from National Audubon Society
70 Alfred M. Bailey
71 Eric Hosking
73 Alfred M. Bailey from National Audubon Society
74 Norman R. Lightfoot
75 Jack Dermid (*top*)
 Karl H. Maslowski from Photo Researchers (*bottom*)

76 Allan D. Cruickshank from National Audubon Society
78 Paul A. Johnsgard from National Audubon Society
79 R. D. Muir
82 Michael Wotton
83 Thase Daniel
84 Thase Daniel
85 Richard Fyfe
86 Paul A. Johnsgard from National Audubon Society
87 Allan D. Cruickshank from National Audubon Society
88 Eric Hosking
89 Eric Hosking
90 Hugh M. Halliday
91 John Borneman from National Audubon Society
95 G. Ronald Austing from Photo Researchers (*top*)
 Allan D. Cruickshank from National Audubon Society (*bottom*)
96 G. Ronald Austing from National Audubon Society
97 R. D. Muir
99 G. Ronald Austing
100 R. D. Muir
102 Hugh M. Halliday
103 G. Ronald Austing
104 G. Ronald Austing
105 G. Ronald Austing
106 R. D. Muir
107 Howard H. Cleaves
111 G. Ronald Austing from National Audubon Society
112 Alvah W. Sanborn
114 Hugh M. Halliday
115 John Trott
116 Harry Engels
117 G. Ronald Austing
118 John H. Gerard
120 R. D. Muir
121 Alfred M. Bailey
123 R. D. Muir (*top*)
 Hugh M. Halliday (*bottom*)
124 Dan Sudia from Photo Researchers
125 Alfred M. Bailey
126 Thase Daniel (*top*)
 Allan D. Cruickshank from National Audubon Society (*bottom*)
128 Frank Stevens from National Audubon Society
129 Leonard Lee Rue III
130 Arthur W. Ambler from National Audubon Society
131 Robert McLeod from Photo Researchers
132 Grant Haist
134 Fred Lahrman from National Audubon Society
135 Michael Wotton
136 Allan D. Cruickshank from National Audubon Society
138 Olin Sewall Pettingill, Jr., from National Audubon Society
139 G. Ronald Austing from National Audubon Society (*top*)
 William J. Bolte (*bottom*)
140 Alfred M. Bailey from National Audubon Society
141 Samuel A. Grimes from National Audubon Society
142 R. Van Nostrand from National Audubon Society (*top*)
 Allan D. Cruickshank from National Audubon Society (*bottom*)
143 R. D. Muir
144 Arthur W. Ambler from National Audubon Society
145 Lewis Wayne Walker
147 Eric Hosking
148 R. D. Muir
150 Eric Hosking

506

332 Lawrence R. Owen
335 Frank A. Tinker
336 John H. Gerard from National Audubon Society
338 G. Ronald Austing
339 John H. Gerard (*top*)
     Allan D. Cruickshank from National Audubon Society
     (*bottom*)
341 Pat Witherspoon from National Audubon Society
342 Allan D. Cruickshank from National Audubon Society
343 G. Ronald Austing from National Audubon Society
344 Donald S. Heintzelman from National Audubon Society
345 Allan D. Cruickshank from National Audubon Society
346 Allan D. Cruickshank from National Audubon Society
347 Allan D. Cruickshank from National Audubon Society
348 Bailey and Niedrach from National Audubon Society
350 H. D. Wheeler from National Audubon Society
351 Jack Dermid from National Audubon Society (*top*)
     Hugh M. Halliday (*bottom*)
353 Allan D. Cruickshank from National Audubon Society
354 Allan D. Cruickshank from National Audubon Society
355 B. Brower Hall
356 W. V. Crich
357 Hugh M. Halliday
358 Eric Hosking
362 G. Ronald Austing
363 Pat Witherspoon from National Audubon Society
364 David B. Marshall, U.S. Bureau of Sport Fisheries and Wildlife
368 Allan D. Cruickshank from National Audubon Society
369 G. Ronald Austing
370 G. Ronald Austing
373 Hugh M. Halliday
375 W. V. Crich
376 Christina Loke from Photo Researchers
382 G. Ronald Austing
383 Allan D. Cruickshank from National Audubon Society
384 Allan D. Cruickshank from National Audubon Society
385 Karl H. Maslowski from National Audubon Society
386 Allan D. Cruickshank from National Audubon Society
389 Hal Harrison (*top*)
     Fred Lahrman (*bottom*)
390 W. V. Crich
393 David B. Marshall, U.S. Bureau of Sport Fisheries and Wildlife
395 Michael Ord from Photo Researchers
397 Arthur W. Ambler from National Audubon Society
398 Ralph E. Lawrence from National Audubon Society
399 Hal Harrison
400 Hal Harrison from National Audubon Society
401 John M. Stemen from National Audubon Society
403 Thase Daniel
404 Hal Harrison
405 Eliot Porter from National Audubon Society
406 Jack Dermid
407 G. Ronald Austing
408 Allan D. Cruickshank from National Audubon Society
410 Hal Harrison
411 Hal Harrison (*top*)
     Allan D. Cruickshank from National Audubon Society
     (*bottom*)
412 Lawrence R. Owen
414 Allan D. Cruickshank from National Audubon Society
416 Allan D. Cruickshank from National Audubon Society
417 Hal Harrison (*top*)
     L. H. Walkinshaw from National Audubon Society (*bottom*)
418 Hal Harrison from National Audubon Society
419 Larry West from Full Moon Studio
421 Jack Dermid

422 Hal Harrison from National Audubon Society
423 Thase Daniel
424 Thase Daniel
425 G. Ronald Austing
426 Hal Harrison
427 Hal Harrison
429 G. Ronald Austing
430 Hal Harrison from National Audubon Society
431 Hugh M. Halliday
432 Gaston LePage
433 John H. Gerard from National Audubon Society
435 G. Ronald Austing
436 Hugh M. Halliday
438 Hugh M. Halliday
439 G. Ronald Austing
440 G. Ronald Austing
441 B. Max Thompson
443 Jerry Focht from National Audubon Society
445 Allan D. Cruickshank from National Audubon Society
446 Allan D. Cruickshank from National Audubon Society
447 John H. Gerard
450 Hal Harrison
451 Hal Harrison
453 Russ Kinne from Photo Researchers (*top*)
     G. Ronald Austing (*bottom*)
454 Evan J. Davis
455 John H. Gerard
456 B. Max Thompson
457 Dale A. Zimmerman (*top*)
     Lawrence R. Owen (*bottom*)
458 B. Brower Hall
459 Jack Dermid (*top*)
     Pat Witherspoon (*bottom*)
460 Thase Daniel
461 Paul Schwartz from Photo Researchers
462 Thase Daniel from National Audubon Society
463 Allan D. Cruickshank from National Audubon Society
464 Thase Daniel
465 Allan D. Cruickshank from National Audubon Society
466 Pat Witherspoon
469 Gaston LePage
470 Dale A. Zimmerman
471 Therese Austing
472 Hugh M. Halliday from National Audubon Society
474 Thase Daniel
475 Thase Daniel
477 Pat Witherspoon
478 Hugh M. Halliday
481 G. Ronald Austing
483 H. D. Wheeler
485 Hiram L. Parent
487 G. Ronald Austing from National Audubon Society
488 B. Max Thompson
489 Allan D. Cruickshank from National Audubon Society
490 Jack Dermid
491 G. Ronald Austing
492 Richard Fyfe (*top*)
     W. V. Crich (*bottom*)
493 Samuel A. Grimes from National Audubon Society
494 John H. Gerard from National Audubon Society
496 Gaston LePage
497 Lawrence R. Owen
498 G. Ronald Austing
499 John H. Gerard (*top*)
     Alfred M. Bailey (*bottom*)
500 Hal Harrison from National Audubon Society
501 Robert C. Hermes
503 R. D. Muir
504 Charlie Ott

INDEX

Page numbers in **boldface** type indicate reference to illustrations.